P9-DIH-093

The Etiology of Schizophrenia

THE

Etiology of Schizophrenia

Don D. Jackson, M.D., Editor

Publishers   Basic Books, Inc.   New York

The editor of and contributors to *The Etiology of Schizophrenia* extend grateful thanks to the following publishers for permission to quote from the indicated materials:

The American Journal of Human Genetics: H. J. Muller, Progress and prospects in human genetics, Vol. 1, 1949.
The American Journal of Psychiatry: P. Bailey, A chemical approach to the problem of mental disease, Vol. 113, 1956; R. W. Gerard, The biological roots of psychiatry, Vol. 112, 1955.
W. W. Norton & Company: F. J. Kallmann, *Heredity in Health and Mental Disorder,* 1953.

Fifth Printing

© 1960 by Basic Books, Inc.
Library of Congress Catalog Card Number: 60–8232
Manufactured in the United States of America
Designed by Jerome Kuhl

Acknowledgments

I would like to acknowledge most gratefully my debt to the authors, for their cooperation, and to my assistant, Mrs. Charlotte Olmsted, without whose help this volume would still be a clutter of typewritten pages. I would like also to express my thanks to the library staff of the Palo Alto Medical Research Foundation for their help.

Finally, I cannot pass up an opportunity to acknowledge my debt to certain teachers and colleagues who have stimulated and encouraged my own interest in the study of schizophrenia. Especially I must mention Harry Stack Sullivan, Frieda Fromm-Reichmann, Jacob Kasanin, Robert A. Cohen, Lewis Hill, Charles Aring, Alfred Stanton, David Rioch, Gregory Bateson, Harold Searles, and John Fearing.

Contents

Introduction   3
    Don D. Jackson, M.D.

PART I GENETICS

1. Genetical Aspects of Schizophrenic Psychoses   23
    Jan A. Böök, Ph.D., M.D.
2. A Critique of the Literature on the Genetics of Schizophrenia   37
    Don D. Jackson, M.D.

PART II BIOCHEMISTRY

3. A Chemical Approach to the Problem of Mental Disease   91
    L. G. Abood, Ph.D.
4. Recent Biochemical Theories of Schizophrenia   120
    Seymour S. Kety, M.D.
5. A Biochemical Hypothesis on the Etiology of Schizophrenia   146
    Robert G. Heath, M.D.

PART III PHYSIOLOGY

6. A Study of the Influence of Schizophrenic Serum on the Behavior
   of the Spider: Zilla-x-notata   159
    Nicholas A. Bercel, M.D.
7. The Possible Relationship of Prenatal Environment to
   Schizophrenia   175
    L. W. Sontag, M.D.

PART IV PSYCHOLOGY

8. Some Psychological Studies of Schizophrenics   191
    C. L. Winder, Ph.D.
9. Anxiety, Perception, and Schizophrenia   248
    Paul McReynolds, Ph.D.

PART V   SOCIOLOGY

10. Social Relations and Schizophrenia: A Research Report and
a Perspective   295
    John A. Clausen, Ph.D., and Melvin L. Kohn, Ph.D.

PART VI   FAMILY DYNAMICS

11. Schizophrenia, Human Integration, and the Role of the Family   323
    Theodore Lidz, M.D., and Stephen Fleck, M.D.
12. A Family Concept of Schizophrenia   346
    Murray Bowen, M.D.
13. The "Double-Bind" Hypothesis of Schizophrenia and Three-Party
Interaction   373
    John H. Weakland
14. A Clinical Study of Childhood Schizophrenia   389
    Maleta J. Boatman, M.D., and S. A. Szurek, M.D.

    Name Index   441
    Subject Index   447

The Etiology of Schizophrenia

Don D. Jackson

Just a little over one hundred years ago, Morel coined the term "dementia praecox" to describe certain cases of insanity. It seems fitting to celebrate this centennial by reviewing some of the ideas that have been held about this disorder and by making an attempt to relate them to current opinion in the field.

At present, schizophrenia is one of our major medical problems. This is not only because of its incidence (estimated at from one to three per cent of the population) and its chronicity (keeping one quarter of the hospital beds in the country occupied), or because of the fact that its major incidence is during the most productive periods of life, roughly between the ages of 15 and 44. It is also because medicine has made progress against many other major disorders, thus allowing schizophrenia to loom larger by contrast. Perhaps also increasing acceptance of democratic ideas makes mental illness more an object of concern, especially in view of the fact that it often results in the individual's loss of his freedom. Still, public interest in mental illness is not widespread—a fact attested by the considerable discrepancy in funds allotted for work on schizophrenia as compared with more attractive medical disorders. The public's reluctance to face mental illness places a special burden on investigators in this field, and attempts to change prevailing attitudes, as in the open-door hospital idea, incur further public resistance. Thus it is likely that ideas held about schizophrenia—even by scientists— continue to reflect the old horror of mental illness as well as the feelings of despair aroused by the size of the problem.

3

Since 1940, roughly 500 papers have appeared in the medical literature on the etiology of schizophrenia. A much greater number has appeared on other aspects of the problem, such as therapy and problems of administration. These papers disagree widely with one another and reflect the fact that schizophrenia is a singularly difficult disorder to investigate. A comparison with papers published 30 years ago reveals less change than might be expected; although formerly the biochemical approach was stressed much more than the environmental, the range of viewpoints is wide both then and now.

Information theory, games theory, and the study of small group processes, all present interesting possibilities for bridging the gap between "brain" and "mind"—yet most papers on the etiology of schizophrenia continue to dichotomize. Although the most ardent biochemist agrees that there are psychological consequences from the processes he describes and the most convinced psychologist is prepared to admit the biochemical nature of the intermediate processes involved, yet they are scarcely able to communicate their findings to one another, let alone relate them in any meaningful fashion.

So wide are the divergences that it is difficult and confusing to attempt to find any consistent patterns in research. From the organic point of view, one may say that the history of the study of schizophrenia mirrors very faithfully the major trends in general medicine during the past 50 years. When research into organic causes brought such spectacular results in other areas, it was very natural that it should be attempted in this one. The very labeling of schizophrenia as a "disease" makes an assumption that it is analogous to "diseases" and therefore amenable to a physiological explanation. Thus Mott's early findings of atrophy of sexual glands and his and Alzheimer's study of nerve cells of the cortex with supposed nuclear swelling, shrinkage of cell body, increased lipoid, and general gliosis (1) have continued to attract attention despite the careful work of Dunlap (2) and others who conclude that schizophrenia is lacking in any fundamental or constant alteration of nerve cells and that such alterations as are found are reaction to various bodily conditions plus post-mortem and technical changes.

Interest in anatomy has also been reflected in the attempts to link schizophrenia with body type. The current view appears to be that thickness and thinness, tallness and shortness are all found in the schizophrenic population and that the more sophisticated methods of somatotyping are unwieldy from a statistical point of view. The linking of body type with that protean concept "schizoid personality" has not enjoyed much popularity in recent times.

Physiology has been represented in the study of schizophrenia most spectacularly by the work of Gjessing in his studies on periodic catatonia (3, 4). Other workers, however, have found a nitrogen phase exactly the reverse of that reported by Gjessing; and Hardwick and Stokes in 1941 (5) observed that swings in nitrogen balance were related to the state of general nutrition and could be avoided by improved nutrition without effect on the rhythm of mental illness. Indeed, some investigators report their difficulty in finding cases of periodic catatonia; and, except for Stokes and his co-workers, little has appeared recently on this fascinating concept. Selye's theories (6) and renewed interest in the adrenal glands spurred ideas of physiological adaption, stress, and schizophrenia, but this interest appears to have waned in the last few years. The unfolding secrets of the adrenocortex have no immediate application in psychiatry, as Cleghorn, Branch, Bliss, Holland, McDonald, and others have demonstrated. More recently, there has been much excitement and equally much controversy over such topics as serotonin, adrenochrome, ceruloplasmin, and taraxein.

It is interesting in view of the current murky condition of the etiology of schizophrenia to note hysteria's role in history (for we still have much to learn from some of the inglorious chapters of past psychiatric efforts). In the first place, hysteria has been like schizophrenia in being assigned multiple, shifting causes over the years, and these "causations" have had regional popularity. Secondly, the history of hysteria has been full of recommendations for therapy and reports of cures; and, as in schizophrenia, reports of cures have led to a reinforcement of the theory of causation, which led to further therapy, and so on. The unfortunate labeling of the syndrome (from the Greek "hysteron" meaning uterus) probably had its influence, and there is an analogous situation in the term "dementia praecox."

Perhaps the most important reason for noting the history of hysteria in relation to schizophrenia is that the disorder underwent a change in form and frequency once its essential cause was understood, and part of the reason for this remarkable change lay in the attitude of the medical profession. Nowhere more than in the works of Charcot is it apparent that many a hysteric was shaped by the institution he was housed in and the physician who treated him. Over and over again it has been necessary to learn the lesson that the observer influences the observed, and it is clear from papers comparing the effects of LSD with schizophrenia that the lesson will have to be learned once more. If LSD is viewed as an interesting chemical, perhaps closely linked to the etiologic agent of schizophrenia, patients are reported as confused, anxious, and hallucinating. If LSD is viewed as a vehicle for enriching the commonplace and touching one's untapped potential, the experience may be quite pleasant and nonhallucinatory. In some clinical laboratories, anxiety and somatic manifestations are emphasized; in some religious settings, the experience with LSD is described as uniformly pleasant. In the field of mental health, we have not only to reckon with the natural effect of the observers' own bias but we also have to deal with a second variable: the effect of this bias on the patient.

DISEASE OR DISORDER?

It has already been pointed out that the mere labeling of an entity can carry various implications as to modes of investigation and that the conception of schizophrenia as a "disease" has favored the physiological approach. This conceptualization arose quite naturally in Bleuler's time, when the psychiatrist had custodial care of the patient by day, and by night studied brain sections under the microscope and wrote up descriptions of his case.

Although Freud's discoveries might have influenced this situation, they had very little effect on ideas about schizophrenia, partly because Freud and his immediate followers were not much interested in psychoses, and partly because Kraepelin, the leading authority, had little use for psychoanalytical theories. As a matter of fact, he once stated, "As I am accustomed to walk on the sure foundation of direct experience, my philistine conscience of natural science stumbles at every step on objections, considerations, and doubts over which the lightly soaring power of Freud's disciples carries them without difficulty" (7). Actually, there was no difference of opinion between Freud and Kraepelin about the etiology of schizophrenia even though Freud's theories set the stage for present-day psychological concepts. Although Zilboorg, Federn, and others contributed some psychoanalytic understanding of schizophrenic behavior during the 1920's, it was not until the 1940's that the problem received intense interest, sparked by Sullivan, Fromm-Reichmann, Fairbairn, and others.

At the time of the definition of "dementia praecox" in the late 1800's, medicine and European culture in general were intensely interested in theories of social degeneracy, based on notions of "protoplasmic inferiority." This is not surprising when one recalls that this society was one of rather rigid class structure, theoretically based on hereditary lines, and was at the peak of the illusion of the "innate superiority" of the "white races." The anthropometric studies of Lombroso were based on the theory that the more a man resembled an ape, the more he thought like one, and the less soul he had. Although his notions did not long survive in quite so crude a form, they were the prototypes of Kretschmer's and, later, Sheldon's work on body types and mental illness. Both lines of thought are very old ones, based on the reasoning that there must be some correlation between outward form and inward nature. It is a region full of folklore and self-fulfilling prophecy —if red-headed people are not more hot-tempered to start with, they may soon become so if everyone treats them as if they were.

Concurrent with the study of dementia praecox, genetic and family studies, especially in Germany, Italy, and England, established beyond the shadow of a doubt that criminality ran like a taint through some families. These investigations and the study of mental deficiency, combined with fixed notions of genetic heredity which ignored social heredity, caused the whole subject to become of concern to the eugenicists. Naturally, the enactment of sterilization laws fortified beliefs about the organicity of dementia praecox, since obviously those who enacted these laws were convinced of the genetic basis.

The strides being made in the rest of medicine by Virchowian pathology stimulated psychiatrists to find the tissue basis of the "genetically induced degeneracy." Unfortunately, the schizophrenic's ability to develop tuberculosis and various other problems, many of them incidental to institutionalization, became a source of "proof" of protoplasmic inferiority. Some investigators found a death rate of nearly 80% from tuberculosis among schizophrenic patients. It took many years before this appalling correlation was related to epidemiological factors; however, at least one present-day geneticist still insists on a genetic linkage between tuberculosis and schizophrenia (8), although the evidence against this appears to be overwhelming (9) and the rate may be as high among other chronic, institutionalized patients, as, for example, drug addicts.

The temptation to link the "phthisic constitution" (tall, lean, hollow-chested) with the leptosomic build attributed to the schizoid individual is obvious in the work of many early investigators and even some at present. In 1941 an apparently little noticed paper demonstrated that weight and schizophrenia were both matters of how many years residence in an asylum the patient had had.

One event that probably had a strong influence in supporting the idea of schizophrenia as a "disease" was the discovery that general paralysis of the insane was caused by the spirochete of syphilis, and that a specific therapy could be developed which was effective in treating this disorder. Paretics could be sorted out from the general mass of the "insane" and treated; and, naturally, such an event spurred efforts for similar discoveries in other types of mental illness. Although it was later demonstrated by several investigators that the *form* of the behavioral disorder in paresis related to the premorbid personality, the general stream of medical thought had swept by and on to attempts to discover the organic basis for other serious personality disorders. Attempts to discover spirochetes in schizophrenia continue to the present, despite repeated failures. There is also a "spread effect" noticeable in analogizing between paresis and schizophrenia in that papers attributing schizophrenia to various micro-organisms appeared after the apparent stimulus of the discovery of the cause of paresis. The notion that syphilis in the parents could be passed on to the child as a predisposition to schizophrenia or other mental disorders was widely held, as is evident in Freud's writings. It represents a curious blend of genetics and microbiology and is held by several European investigators generally.

The idea of schizophrenia as a disease, especially as a degenerative cerebral process, has been considered questionable by some authorities for at least a hundred years. For example, the great English psychiatrist Maudsley stated:

> There are commonly many partial causes of disease, some predisposing, some exciting, and the bodily derangements which so commonly exist in cases of insanity cannot always be regarded in the light of a cause; it often partakes much of the character of an effect. The physical acts on the mental and the mental back again on the physical and vice versa—cause and effect acting and reacting and mutually aggravating one another. The old rule "The cause having ceased, the effect ceases" is false as often as it is true; the effect often continues after a cause has ceased and thus abiding becomes in its turn a cause.

A contemporary of Maudsley, Clouston, stated: (10) "It seems to me unphilosophical to say that 'mind' cannot rank as a causative factor; it seems contrary to plain clinical fact. To set aside the mental treatment of insanity would be to deprive ourselves of our chief therapeutic resource in many cases." One presumes he is talking of a treatment involving *communicating* a new and more rewarding attitude and behavioral pattern to the patient.

If we consider schizophrenia as a disease, it has several unique features. For one thing, the more florid the symptoms and signs, the better the prognosis. A number of genetic studies (quoted in Chapter 3) also show that the more heavily loaded the patient's genealogy is for schizophrenia, the more atypical the form and the better the patient's chances for recovery. This finding is compatible with theories of social heredity but does seem unusual compared to other medical diseases of hereditary origin. Again, the incidence of the disorder is unlike that of other hereditary diseases which are of the order of 1:10,000.

Another peculiar feature, making schizophrenia unlike any other disease of which we have knowledge, is the effect of therapy. Improvement due to electroshock or insulin therapy may be permanent. For example, schizophrenics who have maintained their sanity five years after electroshock therapy are reported to have as good a chance as the ordinary population of staying out of a mental hospital. Is it likely that EST has remedied a metabolic defect? This would be very unlike the effects of using insulin for diabetes or adrenal extracts for Addison's Disease. Lauretta Bender (11) followed her cases of hospitalized schizophrenic children through adolescence into adulthood; two thirds of them had improved. Although the author regards the disorder as organic and utilizes electroshock therapy, she does not make it clear how such progressive recoveries fit into the ordinary framework of disease.

The concept of schizophrenia as a disease also leads to unwarranted analogies with states brought about in sensory deprivation experiments, by toxic substances, and in model psychoses. Whereas these experiments can provide interesting comparisons with schizophrenia, they do not produce schizophrenia. The symptoms produced by these experiments are far more comparable to those produced by alcohol, anxiety, or various other factors in an individual—given the proper context. They show little in common with either the schizoid personality (basic to many theories of schizophrenia) or with that most chronic and progressive form of schizophrenia, the simple type.

Another puzzling feature of schizophrenia is that the chronic paranoid, who has nearly as bad a prognosis as the simplex patient, shows the least variation from the norm in physiological terms, weight, intactness of intelligence, dilapidation of habit patterns, etc. Thus, if one considers schizophrenia as a disease, it remains a paradox that the cases least amenable to treatment have the least resemblance to experimentally produced analogies and may demonstrate little in the way of toxic changes. Because most authorities agree that simple schizophrenia is not related to an onset caused by stress and because environmental factors appear to play no significant role, one would expect the constitutional factors to be higher in this form. Yet

most genetic investigators (see Chapter 3) make no claims of a relationship between the amount of family history of schizophrenia and the form or
severity of the illness of offspring.

DIAGNOSIS AND DATA

The concept of schizophrenia as a disease rather than as a group of disorders or as an end state delimited by the capacity of the brain and the shaping of culture, has influenced the majority of investigators. Thus, because
most medical diseases have a single etiological agent, this majority has approached schizophrenia in a reductionist frame of mind, looking for *a* rejecting mother or *a* specific toxin. The human being is relegated to the role of
host—much as he is when his lungs harbor pneumonia—and all his supra-
organic complexities are ignored. This reductionist, oversimplification tendency leads one to look for the "key to schizophrenia"; and premature claims
that it has been found undoubtedly result in the abandonment of promising
leads simply because they were not all inclusive.

Anyone familiar with the biological and psychological literature on
schizophrenia can recognize that the scattering of positive findings is frequent enough in both areas to make it unlikely that they are erroneous.
Whether such experimental results are primary or secondary to the etiology
(or etiologies) of schizophrenia is beside the point at this time. There is a
crying need for descriptive data in the form of positive laboratory or clinical
findings, even if such findings are the result and not the cause, and even if
they encompass only a small percentage of the entire schizophrenic group.

The investigator of schizophrenia is very apt to have had medical training or to work under the direction of a physician. This fact also introduces
certain biases which have changed but little in the last thirty years. One
such bias is the continued use of Kraepelin's categories despite repeated
demonstrations that they have little practical utility and probably hamper
our ability to conceptualize. Kraepelin's nosology presented a real advance
60 years ago, but present knowledge reveals that his categories of schizophrenia have no genetic or physiological basis and are inadequate as social
descriptions. Yet thousands of residents in psychiatry are at this very moment filling out an uninspired initial history form and carefully endeavoring
to place a round patient in a square diagnostic category.

Even granting the necessity of diagnostic categories for actuarial purposes and transmission of information there is little reason for confidence
in our present system. As Hoch has pointed out (12), Georgia is the only

state which consistently diagnoses more manic-depressives than schizophrenics on first admissions and discrepancies between various states may be as high as 30 to 60 per cent. Furthermore, Penrose has demonstrated that the chances of being labeled schizophrenic increase in proportion to the length of hospital stay, regardless of initial diagnosis (13). The term "schizophrenic" in medical circles carries almost as much of a ring of authenticity as "diabetic" or "tubercular." Yet it is actually nearly as much a fiction as that lovely legal appellation a "reasonable man." Even an objective, consistent observer is dealing with a subject who varies greatly from day to day and who, because of diet, exercise, and attitude, cannot easily be compared to the hypothetical "normal." As Dr. Kety reveals in his chapter, most recent biochemical claims have been demonstrated to result from such artifacts—even including the amount of coffee drunk.

Diagnosis is no mere plaything of state hospital psychiatrists. Almost every paper describing an investigation into the etiology of schizophrenia starts out with "X number of schizophrenics," rarely described except for that loose and varying label. Even if patients are limited to one or another Kraepelinean category, there is little reason to assume that the comparability with another investigator's series has improved to a significant degree. It would appear from the few papers dealing with the reliability of diagnosis that variation between even experienced clinicians is so great that comparisons between groups used by different investigators are subject to large error. In one study, three psychiatrists agreed in only 20 per cent of their cases and had a majority agreement in only 48 per cent (14). Another study revealed that the widest disagreement occurred among the most experienced clinicians (15).

In view of this variation which exists between judgments of schizophrenia *vs.* psychoneurosis, and between types of schizophrenia, it is difficult to justify or take seriously some of the precise statements that occur in the literature, especially the small percentage differences that are reported in the families of schizophrenics linking their blood tie with their chances of developing ("inheriting") schizophrenia. Either these are based on the investigator's own diagnosis (with the possibilities of creeping bias), or they are based on state hospital admissions with no attempt to compare the very varied criteria of diagnosis (16).

Hoskins has warned against "further pursuit of that will-o'-the-wisp, that semiprojective, synthetic artifact, the patient as a whole," in schizophrenia research (17). Still, it may be doubted whether this "will-o'-the-wisp" is much more arbitrary and artificial than abstracting aspects of a number of patients without regard to the context. When it is remembered that schizophrenia research may be divided between investigators with backgrounds in such varied fields as clinical symptomatology, psychodynamics, psychoanalysis, learning theory, personality theory, perception theory, group dynamics, sociology, cultural anthropology, and all of the biological sciences including biochemistry, genetics, neurophysiology, neuroanatomy, and psychological testing, the practical impossibility of any one investigator's having a wide enough background to "see the patient as a whole" provides the limitation.

Still another factor complicates research in schizophrenia: patients do improve, and the investigator's medical orientation, his desire to cure his patients, may mislead him. Many a cycle of belief about schizophrenia has been characterized by the empirical use of an agent, response of the patient (usually 60 per cent improved), and research into the mechanism of action of the agent. More than 50 etiological claims have been made in the course of such cycles, and many thousands of hours of patient research have followed. Among the more obvious examples are the introduction of thyroid by a Scottish psychiatrist and the study of this organ as an etiological factor or the empirical use of insulin shock therapy, followed by years of intensive research on the carbohydrate metabolism in schizophrenia. Perhaps one day we shall be able to isolate a specific percentage of improvement attributable merely to medical benevolence and the interest shown in the patient.

And then, investigators in this field, it must be admitted, show an all-too-human inclination to remain biased in favor of their own special theories. There are some who are unable to attribute sufficient power to interpersonal relations to be able to conceive even theoretically that some schizophrenia might have a psychological basis. So too are there those who find it impossible to imagine a physiological base.

Obviously, if schizophrenia represents a group of disorders (and this would appear to be the most reasonable assumption on the information we have at present), then it is important that the investigator should be able to remember that theoretically many possible etiological agents exist and that it is quite possible in any given case there might be a complicated combination of such agents. Unfortunately most of us are not gifted with the broad view, and cultural factors appear to play a significant role in what views we have. A certain acquaintance with centers doing research in schizophrenia in many localities impressed me with the differences between European and particularly Scandinavian emphasis on organic factors and the psychological orientation of many American centers.

First, there are those who see schizophrenia as a strictly organic disease with its own periodicity. Causative factors include constitution, heredity, bacteria, parasites, glandular malfunctioning, etc.

Second, there are those who view schizophrenia as primarily an organic disorder which cripples the individual's attempt to deal with ordinary life stresses. In short, his biological vulnerability is too great to be compatible with life and the world.

Third, there are those who see the schizophrenics as individuals biologically incapable of coping with major environmental stresses. Major stresses may include such things as adolescence, marriage, parenthood, or it may be assumed that the schizophrenic encounters unusual stresses because of his particular environment.

Fourth, there is a group who view schizophrenia much like a psychosomatic disorder in which major stresses produce internal changes which in turn bring about further changes, lower adaptive levels, etc.

Fifth, there is a group of investigators who see the schizophrenic as a regressed individual who withdraws before an onslaught of severe psychic trauma inflicted at a very early age and revivified by developmental environmental factors.

Six, there are investigators who view schizophrenia as a subtly occurring maladaptation which in some sense is appropriate to the covert operations of the family group.

Seventh, there could be a group, but as far as I know it has no adherents, who would view schizophrenia as essentially a psychogenic disorder but who would see the various forms of its expression—catatonia, paranoia, etc.—as hereditarily determined.

POSSIBILITIES FOR THE FUTURE

The most pressing problem appears to be the development of new and more useful diagnostic categories and a conceptual scheme that will enable us to think of all the multiple factors involved, from social through psychological to biochemical, in a single framework that will accommodate all the factual findings and enable us to relate them to one another. It may well turn out that there is a continuum from normal to neurotic to schizophrenic, but that within this continuum are clusters of disorders some of which can be labeled schizophrenic. These clusters, although part of a continuum, may be sufficiently distinct to be virtually qualitatively different from one another. It is my notion that when these clusters of disorders are viewed they will consist of an admixture of what might be called process features and reactive features as well as constitutional and psychogenic features. That is, biological and psychological factors operating over different time periods will produce different subgroups even if the factors are similar. To give a crude example, an individual with an I.Q. of 80 from birth is in quite a different position vis-à-vis himself and all those others than an individual whose I.Q. drops to 80 when he is 20 years of age—and this difference holds even if it were eventually established that I.Q. depends completely on the number of twists in the D.N.A. molecule. Thus, there is not only the possibility of multiple causation in schizophrenia but also that a similar cause acting over a long or short period of time will produce a different schizophrenia.

If we can divorce ourselves from a Kraepelinean focus on symptoms there are certain assumptions that appear to be worth considering and that seem to have scattered investigations to support them:

(1) Schizophrenia consists of a number of etiological causes leading, according to the principle of equifinality, to a similar end state.

The differences between these severally caused schizophrenias tend to be covered up and disguised by such factors as the ubiquitous biological adaptive functions in man and the human response to experiences such as institutionalization.

(2) Some schizophrenias get well faster than others, and such cases often show more florid initial symptoms and have been subjected to more recent severe stress—either psychological or physiological—than the group with a poorer prognosis. There are, however, some apparently florid cases which deteriorate rapidly into an incurable state. Whether such cases are the result of a weak constitution or are individuals who have been struggling against overwhelming odds for years is not known.

(3) In most investigations of a chronic hospital population, certain schizophrenics will show marked physiological abnormalities. Whether these findings are cause or effect is unimportant compared to the fact that such cases are lost by averaging them in with other patients. The same is probably true of most other approaches, including psychological studies.

(4) Social factors (age, race, religion, economic status, education, etc.) are so important in shaping the form and course of schizophrenia that no etiological study can ignore these variables, especially since they include the investigator's relation to the patient.

Assuming that the investigator accepts the presence of environmental factors in all cases (such as the reaction to being institutionalized), we then are left with two large variables: (1) time; (2) time acting on an X factor or factors. For purposes of this discussion, the experimenter can be left out since this will also fit into these two dimensions, as far as the effect on the patient goes, and his bias will exist whatever diagnostic scale is used. Also methodological procedures can be built into experiments to check on the investigator; for example, Maas (18) has shown that the longer the investigator took to get a systolic reading the more favorable the results with the Mecholyl test.

The time factor can be construed as a continuum from progressive to reactive, and the X factor as a continuum from organic to purely psychological causation. These factors might represent a graph and clusters of patients compared with each other. It must be understood that this is a functional and not an etiological scheme, because the "organic" end of the scale can represent patients with changes secondary to their schizophrenia or patients who have a contributing dysfunction that is not strictly etiological, as M. Bleuler demonstrated in the relationship of goiter to the onset of schizophrenia.

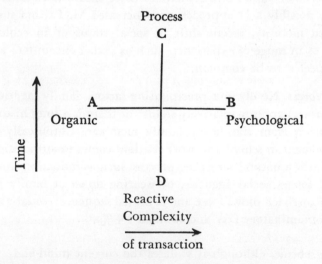

A patient who fell in the AC quadrant would represent quite a different sort of schizophrenia than an individual in the BD quadrant. Examples of the ordering of data to place individuals on the graph would be:

> *Organic:* History of schizophrenia in collateral or direct lines, abnormal EEG, leptosomic body build, endocrine disorders, lowered reactivity of central nervous system as measured by reac-

tion to ACTH, glucose tolerance, resistance of insulin, lowered skin temperature, 17 ketosteroid excretion, delayed time sense, flicker fusion, increased protein in CSF, organic findings on Rorschach, etc., relatively low I.Q.

Psychological: No evidence of chronic or primary biological abnormalities, although some physiological disturbance may be expected on the basis of severe emotional disturbance. Evidence of precipitating factors, psychological disturbances in family, and history of childhood and adolescence compatible with development of "weak ego." Psychological tests including Rorschach reveal evidence of potentialities overcome by conflict. I.Q. apt to be normal to superior.

Reactive: Acute onset with florid psychotic symptoms, evidence of fear and anxiety and ability to bring family or authorities' attention to these difficulties. Rorschach would indicate increased color values and sometimes color shock, normal W and F+%, possibly a D approach and increased M. Factors such as upward mobility, recent shift in social status or in ecological niche or in range of experiences such as sexual encounters would be expected to be common.

Process: No obvious precipitating factors, family (at least on the surface) appears relatively stable; or there is a long history of separation from significant family members. Chronically poor achievement in school and work. Patient comes to authorities' attention by a natural screening process, such as induction into the armed forces, social agencies, or wearing down of family members. Rorschach shows loose and confused sequence, confabulatory and contaminatory DW and lowered F+%.

Such a scheme, although it violates the current mind-body union emphasis, might have some usefulness in attempting to denote groups of schizophrenics. It deliberately cuts across the lines of the Kraepelinean categories of schizophrenia, which do not sufficiently take into account social and ethnic factors, the effects of institutionalization, and the shifts that occur with time from one nosological group to another.

There are current attempts to broaden the Kraepelinean categories; for example, the committee on nomenclature of the American Psychiatric Association lists in addition to the four classical types a chronic and acute undifferentiated form, a schizo-affective form, a childhood type, and schizophrenic reaction, residual type. These categories are deliberately loose, and attempts to define very specific forms have met with mixed reception. Included in these attempts would be the "acute periodic catatonia" of Gjessing, "Oneirophrenia" of Meduna and McCullough, "pseudoneurotic schizophrenia" of Hoch and Polatin, and the ambulatory schizophrenia of Zilboorg. These nosological labels do not appear to be enjoying much popularity currently. However, the concept of reactive and process schizophrenia as described by Winder and Cantor (see Chapter 8), and the well-defined nosological category of "paraphrenia," used extensively by English psychiatrists, seem to offer promise, although neither of these designations implies an etiology. Both of these concepts relate primarily to time. Paraphrenia, for example, is found in a group of older patients who gradually have become more socially isolated.

The problem of diagnosis obviously underlies the whole frustrating story of research in schizophrenia. Langfeldt, who has long concerned himself with prognosis in schizophrenia, attended an afternoon session of an American Psychiatric Association meeting in 1953 devoted to psychotherapy of schizophrenia. He remarked that the claims of improvement with psychotherapy he heard that afternoon, indicated that schizophrenia in Sweden and the United States were very different disorders.

But if we consider using a classificatory system involving time and a substratum on which time acts, then the symptoms presented by a given patient would not be the means of forming nosological classes. Instead, they would have to be related to the process-reactive, organic-psychological continua. There is reason to believe that psychological tests, perhaps especially psychophysiological measurements like flicker-fusion, offer promise in rating patients as to "fixedness" of reaction and as to prepsychotic potential (constitution?). However, there is a possibility of linking findings from learning and communication theories in such a fashion that the clinician can think about schizophrenic symptoms in a uniform way, whether he is studying them from social or biochemical viewpoints. The basic premise of such a system is that schizophrenics, whatever their basic pathology, are more human than otherwise and will communicate with the investigator if only by silence.

This type of diagnostic system we might label an "interactional diagnosis." For one thing, communication theory can be described in terms of neuronal circuits, synaptic facility and the like, and can also be thought of in terms of learning experience. An appropriate blend of information and learning theory would satisfy most of the present-day concepts about schizophrenia regardless of whether they are organic or psychogenic. Thus it is possible to imagine (like the computer model of the brain) that the manner in which information is utilized by the individual will depend on intactness and adaptability of his equipment, and that his output will be a combination of the kind of information fed him and the way his brain utilizes it.

If Tom persistently calls a *cat* a *hat,* and also calls a *cow* a *how,* we suspect a defect in his speech mechanism somewhere along the line and investigate accordingly.

If, however, he calls a *cat* a *rat* and exhibits no other confusion between *c*'s and *r*'s, we assume he is confusing the objects of reference in the real world. This does not necessarily imply Tom has something wrong with his brain; he may have been trained to call *cats rats.* If we are able to win his confidence enough to induce him to change the labels, there may be no change in his perceptions whatsoever, but he is able to communicate his perceptions in an acceptable form.

It is quite possible that his perceptions are such that to him cats and rats are indistinguishable. If we give him a drug and he is able to relinquish his old "false" labeling system and substitute a more socially acceptable and discriminating one, we must discover whether the drug affected his perceptions, the circuits and synapses within his brain which enabled him to verbalize these perceptions, or whether his general attitude changed so that he no longer found satisfaction in a defiantly individual view of things and was more ready to conform to social norms.

If Tom does not mislabel a cat but reacts to it in a strikingly unusual fashion, such as trying to kill every cat he meets or running to the nearest bed and hiding under it, such reactions will soon cause him trouble in a world full of cat fanciers. Here again, it may be misperception: the cat is confused with an actually threatening or hostile figure. Or it may be simply another case of miseducation. That is, either the apparatus for perceiving the cat is out of order, or the cat has become a symbol in itself, standing for a wide variety of feared and hated figures in Tom's private world.

Modifications of the machine (substrati) and of the input are occupying the attention of an increasing number of investigators. It is possible to vary one with a substance like LSD, and the other by brainwashing techniques. The range from "observing the output with a nonintact computer" to "varying the input in an intact computer" corresponds to the "organic" and "psychological" dimensions in the diagnostic system suggested above. A communication framework encompasses neuroanatomical findings and the data of psychoneurology.

Thus, it would seem that detailed study of schizophrenics in terms of learning theories might have much to offer whether one emphasizes taraxein or tension, adrenochrome or the folks at home. Sophisticated animal experiments in which learning experiences are related to breeding, hormone injections, and variable weaning times illustrate the possibilities of this framework; and because communication is learned, the two systems may be blended.

These overly simplified remarks are made not in the belief that they constitute more than the barest suggestion of a systematic approach but that they will indicate that anatomical, physiological, and learning experiences can be thought about within the same framework. Until such a system exists, all of us concerned with the tremendous problem that is schizophrenia must be aware of the research that is in progress. In this volume, the reader will find varying points of view along the bio-social continuum of etiology. These chapters may be regarded as a cross section of actual field work: much of the material is fresh, some of it original, and all stems from actual work with schizophrenics. Hopefully, this book, if it does nothing else, will serve to highlight some of the difficulties encountered in this field.

References

1.   F. W. MOTT, Studies in pathology and dementia praecox, *Proc. Roy. Soc. Med.*, *13*: 25, 1920.
2.   C. B. DUNLAP, Dementia praecox: some preliminary observations on brains from carefully selected cases, and a consideration of certain sources of error, *Am. J. Psychiat.*, *3*: 403, 1924.
3.   R. GJESSING, Disturbances of somatic function in catatonia with a periodic course and their compensation, *J. Ment. Sc.*, *84*: 608, 1938.
4.   J. CAMMERMEYER and R. GJESSING, Fatal myocardial embolism in periodic catatonia with fatty liver, *Acta med. scandinav.*, *139*: 358, 1951.
5.   S. W. HARDWICK and A. B. STOKES, Metabolic investigations in periodic catatonia, *Proc. Roy. Soc. Med.*, *34*: 733, 1941.
6.   H. SELYE, Stress and general adaptation syndrome, *Brit. M. J.*, *1*: 1383, 1950.
7.   E. KRAEPELIN, *Dementia Praecox* (tr. Barclay, R. M.), London: Livingstone, 1918.
8.   F. J. KALLMANN, *Genetics of Schizophrenia*, Locust Valley, N. Y.: Augustin, 1938.
9.   J. KATZ, S. KUNOFSKY, and B. Z. LOCKE, Tuberculosis in schizophrenia as compared with other types of mental disease, *Psychiatric Quart.*, July, 1957.
10.   A. LEWIS, Henry Maudsley; his work and influence, *J. Ment. Sc.*, *97*: 359, 1951.
11.   LAURETTA BENDER, "The Development of a Schizophrenic Child," in Caplan, G. (Ed.), *Emotional Problems of Early Childhood*, New York: Basic Books, 1955.
12.   P. HOCH, The etiology of epidemiology of schizophrenia, *Am. J. Pub. Health*, *17*: 1071, 1957.
13.   L. S. PENROSE, Propagation of the unfit, *Lancet*, *2*: 425, 1950.
14.   ARNOFF, Some factors influencing the unreliability of clinical judgments, *J. Clin. Psychol.*, *10*: 272, 1954.

15.   P. ASH, The reliability of psychiatric diagnosis, *J. Abnorm. & Social Psychol.*, *44*: 272, 1949.

16.   ILSA VEITH, On hysterial and hypochondriacal afflictions, *Bull. Hist. Med.*, *30*: 233, 1956.

17.   R. G. HOSKINS, *The Biology of Schizophrenia,* New York: Norton, 1946.

18.   H. S. MAAS, E. VARON, and D. A. ROSENTHAL, A technique for studying the social behavior of schizophrenics, *J. Abnorm. & Social Psychol.*, *46*: 119, 1951.

PART I

Genetics

1. GENETICAL ASPECTS OF SCHIZOPHRENIC PSYCHOSES

Jan A. Böök

Mental disease is recognized as one of the major public-health problems of our time. Some of the conditions creating the problem are undoubtedly associated with changes of cultural patterns or with the development of new environmental settings likely to create particular stress situations. Others, apparently, depend more on the large number of biological evolutionary forces which operate in human populations. Although in the first case mental breakdown may occur in any individual if the impact of environmental forces is strong enough, in the latter case specific vulnerabilities appear unevenly distributed.

Among mental diseases the schizophrenic psychoses are the chief causes of prolonged and serious disability. Although they rarely kill, they are significantly destructive by claiming their victims among people of the best working ages. In many parts of the world more than half of the beds in mental hospitals are occupied by schizophrenic patients.

It is important to realize that we have no proof that schizophrenia is a disease entity which has a single cause. Rather, there are reasons to believe that we are dealing with a mental syndrome which may be caused by a variety of different etiologies. I prefer, therefore, to use the expression "schizophrenic psychoses" instead of simply "schizophrenia."

Jan A. Böök, Ph.D., M.D., formerly director of the medical genetics research institute, University of Lund, is Professor of Medical Genetics at the University of Uppsala.

GENETICS IN MEDICAL RESEARCH

The interest in heredity of mental illness goes back to pre-Mendelian times. In the nineteenth century this heredity was thought of as a kind of degeneration that was passed on from generation to generation in certain families, particularly in conjunction with inbreeding. In spite of the fact that the development of medical genetics since the beginning of this century has brought a clear understanding of the principles of heredity and of what is inherited, pieces of old superstition have been difficult to abolish. One reason is that genetics has been misused or outlawed in certain political contexts; another that genetically determined characters, especially in the mental field, have been subjected to assessments of value. The latter idea led to the eugenic movements early in this century.

All this nonsense is still close enough in time to make even some scientists emotional rather than rational toward genetics. Obviously, genetics is neither a religion nor a special school of thought. It is a fact of life and the fundamental basis of modern biology. Therefore, it must take its proper place in medical research. To those who recognize mental disease as a problem of human biology, genetical inquiries are meaningful and important; to those who are believers in mental processes unassociated with biochemical or structural changes, genetics will appear pointless.

It may be useful to outline very briefly the main objects of genetical research in clinical medicine.

Identification of Genetical Diseases   Special methods for family and twin research have been developed by which the causes of individual variations can be grouped in environmental and genetical components. The genetical components may be polygenic, *i.e.*, due to many genes which combine freely and give continuous distributions (*e.g.*, stature or intelligence). More commonly, in clinical contexts the genetical components consist of major (single) gene differences which give uneven distributions. Then the point is that only those individuals who possess certain specific genes will develop the corresponding specific disease, provided proper environmental stimuli are present. Conversely, individuals free of these genes will, even when the same stimuli are present, not get ill. Genetical diseases are those for which specific genes can be shown to be the primary cause. All of them are, of course, more or less modified by the environment. This environmental modification may even, as in the case of schizophrenia, sometimes lead to total suppression. On the other hand, when the disease develops, fundamental specificity is retained.

Genetical Epidemiology   Whereas the disease-producing agent is the

altered (mutated) gene, the human germ cell is the vector. The mechanism of transmission is explained by gene distribution during meiosis and gene recombinations during fertilization (*i.e.*, the Mendelian laws of heredity). Gene mutations are transmitted from parents to children only. According to the type of genes involved (homo- or heterozygous expression) or their location (*e.g.*, in the sex chromosomes) different types of inheritance can be demonstrated. It is the task of family investigations to deal with such problems.

In a wider sense, genetical epidemiology deals with the behavior of gene mutations in larger groups of individuals, *i.e.*, whole populations, and with their consequences for public health. By and large, the prevalence of genetical diseases is determined by such factors as the frequency of new mutations, selective fertility of affected individuals, selective migrations, and chance fluctuations due to small family and population size (*i.e.*, genetical drift).

Mutation   Genetical diseases are primarily due to altered "normal" genes, so-called gene mutations. Such mutations may occur for as yet unknown reasons (spontaneous mutations) or may be caused by chemical or physical agents (induced mutations). Most widely known are the mutations caused by ionizing radiations. The fact that mutations represent random changes in genotypes which have been through long periods of selection and adaptation explains why the vast majority of them are nonadaptive (*i.e.*, harmful or pathological). Investigations on the origin and fate of mutations in human populations are also essential for an understanding of the epidemiology of genetical diseases.

Phenogenetics   The final main object of medical genetics is to study the effect of specific gene mutations on the individuals who carry them in all their cells. As the gene action is of biochemical nature and in most cases very likely consists in the synthesis of enzymes systems, all genetical diseases are primarily metabolic defects.

However, the pathway from these original intracellular metabolic defects to the symptoms and signs that can be observed by the clinician, and sometimes only with elaborate scientific techniques, is generally enormous. At present, this field of biochemical genetics is largely a *terra incognita* which invites fruitful exploration. In principle, metabolic defects should lend themselves to corrective measures, *e.g.*, by supplying the specific lack artificially. Consequently, phenogenetical research is of great importance for the therapy of genetical diseases.

EPIDEMIOLOGY OF SCHIZOPHRENIC PSYCHOSES

When discussing the epidemiology of schizophrenic psychoses it is important to inquire to what extent agreement exists between different investigators as to the delimitation of the schizophrenic syndrome. At present, diagnoses are based exclusively on psychological symptoms. Consequently, the field is open to a variety of subjective interpretations, more or less colored by the investigator's own ideas with respect to etiology. However, it is interesting to note that, at a 1957 conference on schizophrenia at the WHO in Geneva that brought together psychiatrists from all parts of the world, fair agreement could be reached as to certain prominent criteria of the disease. Pending more accurate and objective diagnostic standards, differences in the classification of mainly borderline cases are recognized. Caution must be exerted in the interpretation of differences in incidence between different populations unless it is specifically stated that identical diagnostic principles have been used.

Although the clinical picture may be modified by the cultural background, schizophrenic psychoses have been found in all kinds of human populations that have been thoroughly investigated, irrespective of whether they enjoy a high technical culture or not, e.g., Bantus in Africa (1), Chinese on Formosa (2), the people of Thailand (3).

Schizophrenic psychoses occur in all social strata. There is, however, some evidence which suggests a statistical association between social disorganization and schizophrenic reactions. Hare (4) and Carstairs et al. (5) have shown that more hospital patients with this disease came from slums and lower social strata. Pasamanick et al. (6) also found an association between psychoses and low economic status. Other investigators (7, 8) failed to show such uneven distributions. The precise significance of these findings (9) has not yet been worked out. Further studies are necessary to make possible an analysis of the complex interactions of cause and effect and of selective factors in different communities.

The epidemiological studies were initiated by genetically orientated psychiatrists in Germany early in this century. Since then, a number of Scandinavian geneticists and psychiatrists have made significant contributions (10). Recently the interest in this field has spread to people more exclusively interested in the social and psychiatric aspects of the disease (11, 12, 13).

For genetical purposes, it is convenient to compare the morbid risks calculated in different surveys. These figures express the total risk of becoming manifestly ill for all individuals who survive the period during which

the disease may appear, roughly from 15 to 45 years of age. In a large number of surveys, relatively small differences have been found, the average morbid risk being about one per cent (see Table 1.1). A notable exception is

TABLE 1.1

General morbid risk of schizophrenia as reported in studies of different types.

DATA ASCERTAINED BY	CORRECTED POPULATION (WEINBERG'S ABRIDGED METHOD)	SCHIZO-PHRENIA. MORBID RISK. PER CENT.	TYPE OF POPULATION
Genealogic random test method. Several authors. Data compiled by Fremming (1947) (14)	6,709	0.72 ± 0.10	Average, mostly German populations
Census method.			
Brugger, 1931 (15)	18,312[1]	0.38 ± 0.05	Thuringia, Germany
Brugger, 1933 b (16)	2,894[2]	0.41 ± 0.12	Allgäu, Germany
Brugger, 1938 (17)	1,643[2]	0.36 ± 0.15	Rosenheim, Germany
Schade, 1950 (18)	1,929[4]	0.52 ± 0.16	Schwalm, Germany
Strömgren, 1938 (19)	429[1]	0.47 ± 0.33	Rø, Bornholm
Strömgren, 1938 (19)	19,045[3]	0.65 ± 0.05[5]	Bornholm, Denmark
Sjögren, 1948 (20)	4,800[1]	0.83 ± 0.13	West-Swedish island
Sjögren, 1935 (21)	4,390[2]	0.68 ± 0.12	Two North-Swedish
	3,440[4, 6]	0.87 ± 0.16	isolates
Kaila, 1942 (22)	194,000[1]	0.91 ± 0.02[7]	Finland
Böök, 1953 (23)	3,467[4]	2.39 ± 0.26	North-Swedish
	2,912[3]	2.85 ± 0.31	isolate
Essen-Möller, 1956 (8)	1,515[2]	1.12 ± 0.27	South Swedish rural
Birth register test. Fremming, 1947 (14)	3,777[4]	0.90 ± 0.15	Bornholm, Denmark

The following risk periods were used: [1] 20–40. [2] 15–40. [3] 20–45. [4] 15–45. For comparisons these differences are not important. [5] With correction for excess mortality. [6] Recalculated by the writer. Sjögren had no actual age distribution of this population but computed it according to the average Swedish rural population. As shown in this paper, the population of North Sweden differs somewhat insofar as the younger age groups are larger. This calculation was based on the assumption of the same age distribution as persisted in the investigation area in 1935 which probably gives a more correct morbid risk. [7] Does not include recovered cases. If these are taken into account, the morbid risk might be estimated at 1.15–1.20 per cent (Kaila [1942]).

the figure of about 3 per cent found by Böök (23) in a North-Swedish community.

Differences in the morbid risk between different populations can at present hardly be explained as due chiefly to environmental variations. On the other hand, in view of the accumulated evidence that individual genetical differences are of major importance for this disease, the known distributions could be adequately explained in the ordinary terms of population genetics. Consequently any epidemiology of schizophrenic psychoses which disregards population genetics might disregard essential features of this illness.

GENETICAL EVIDENCE

Evidence for a genetical etiology has been accumulated in a very large number of adequate family and twin studies. As the results are very consistent, there is no need to repeat individual details here. In short, the morbid risk figures are for siblings 7–15 per cent, for children 7–16 per cent, and for parents 5–10 per cent. The figures for siblings and children are not significantly different if one compares families with one or no affected parent. Families with two affected parents have recently been studied by Elsässer (24), who calculated a risk of about 40 per cent for the children of such couples.

It is important to note that the risk of other psychoses is not significantly increased for the relatives of schizophrenic patients.

Attempts to show, by means of genetical-statistical methods, a significant genetical heterogeneity in terms of the common subgroups (i.e., simplex, hebephrenic, catatonic, and paranoid forms) have so far been unsuccessful, possibly due to small numbers when the data are broken down.

Statistical associations between symptomatic groups among siblings have been reported by Schulz (25, 26), Bleuler (27), and Slater (28). A striking symptomatic similarity was also found among the schizophrenics of my own North-Swedish investigation (23). This study was in fact planned to insure a genetically more homogeneous body of material than the samples surveyed earlier. At present, no definite conclusions can be drawn on the basis of these findings because such associations might as well be due to regional or familial environmental influences. Also, I think it would be hazardous to try to make genotypical divisions on the basis of highly peripheral psychological criteria.

Extensive twin studies by Kallmann (29, 30, 31) and Slater (32) have shown a concordance rate of 76 to 91 per cent for monozygotic and 10–17 per cent for dizygotic twins. In conjunction with the analysis of possible environmental specific causation, these results leave no reasonable doubt that the genotype is of primary importance for the development of schizophrenic psychoses.

Taken all together, the family and twin data accumulated over a period of more than forty years are consistent enough to provide a sound basis for the genetical theory of schizophrenia. The implication of this theory does not today go further than to say that unevenly distributed individual genetical differences are of decisive importance for *most* schizophrenic syndromes. It does not necessarily imply that all such syndromes have a genetical origin nor that those that have belong to one and the same genetical entity. Certainly it does not imply that genetics is the complete answer to this illness. It is important to realize, however, that so far genetics has provided the only well-founded biological starting point for further inquiries.

MODE OF INHERITANCE

It is a common misunderstanding that genetical research has failed because no agreement has been reached as to the Mendelian mechanism of inheritance. In fact, detailed agreement cannot be reached until there is greater agreement and precision in diagnosis. I do not feel that psychological diagnosis will ever be suitable for the rigid statistical analysis necessary to make a decision on gene recombinations. However, the most likely explanation of present data would be that the schizophrenic psychoses are basically caused by major gene differences which express themselves regularly in homozygotes (*i.e.*, in a recessive manner) and occasionally in heterozygotes (*i.e.*, in a dominant manner). A simple recessive type of inheritance is ruled out by the fact that the corrected risk figures for families of actual schizophrenics do not differ to a significant degree between parents (33), siblings, and children with one or no affected parent. Recently Slater (34) has come to the same conclusion.

This explanation has to include the assumption of what is commonly called a "reduced penetrance," at least in the heterozygotes—*i.e.*, the presence of a genetic factor that for one reason or another does not actually and visibly affect the person carrying it. The concept of penetrance in human genetics has often been ridiculed. It has been argued that by applying the proper penetrance a reasonable fit can be obtained with an optional Mendelian ratio. This is, of course, to a certain extent true, as it is also true of any senseless use of a statistical concept which was designed to describe a phenomenon but not to explain it.

It should be fully realized that penetrance is an operational and statistical concept and that its nominal value is a function of diagnostic precision. Also, the effect of practically all pathological human genes are subject to considerable modifications or suppressions as an effect of other genes and environmental or cultural factors.

The concordance rates for monozygotic twins may be used to calculate a penetrance which, however, has another meaning than that based on family data. When a series of schizophrenic twins are collected the investigator, naturally, is anxious that his *propositi* (*i.e.*, the original cases selected for investigation) should raise as little doubt as possible regarding the diagnosis. So he selects typical—often severe—cases. These cases, on the present genetical hypothesis, may be assumed to belong to special entities with high penetrance or possess genetical modifiers to the same effect. Probably they are a mixture of both. As the monozygotic twin siblings carry identical genes, the concordance rate and the derived penetrance will be higher than that calculated from family data. There are also a number of environmental mechanisms that work in the direction of increasing the concordance for monozygotic twins, particularly when mental traits are considered. Consequently the high concordance rates for schizophrenic psychoses in monozygotic twins cannot be used as an argument against the tentative explanations given above.

The argument whether one pair of genes or more are involved remains an open question. The point is that the distribution of schizophrenic individuals among the relatives of the *propositi* can hardly be explained otherwise than by postulating a major gene difference. The clearcut difference between psychotic and nonpsychotic siblings in the absence of specific environmental causation is in favor of this interpretation. At any rate, the present data do not justify a hypothesis of polygenic inheritance in the strict sense.

Much has been written about the etiological importance of mental trauma. Although there is no reason to deny that such a causation may exist in a limited number of cases, few data have been reported that are suitable for tests by which the value of beliefs may be ascertained. Recently Prout and White (35) have reported a psychological study of 90 siblings of 60 schizophrenic patients. They found that mental trauma was no more common in the patients as compared to their siblings, but the patients reacted differently to such traumata. The hypothesis of parental deprivation as a causative factor was not substantiated. These authors conclude that the theory of trauma in producing schizophrenic syndromes appears very questionable.

It is very unlikely that the high morbid risk of 3 per cent in the North-Swedish area (23) is associated with local environmental factors as no risk increase was found for the different categories of relatives of the *propositi*. The findings are best explained as an effect of selective immigration, genetical drift, or both.

As in other genetical diseases it is obvious that schizophrenic psychoses are not thought to be caused exclusively by major gene differences, but that the effect of these genes is modified by other genes and, of course, by thus far unspecified environmental factors. The important conclusion that I think is fully justified is that major gene differences are the basic prerequisite for the initiation of a chain of events which may result in a psychosis. Unless this specific genetical prerequisite exists, the illness will not occur, provided we are not dealing with a supposedly rare nongenetical schizophrenic syndrome.

Such a working hypothesis will give a firm biological basis for further research. With the traditional genetical statistical methods applied to the psychopathological traits we have probably already extracted all useful information. The next step should be to concentrate on approaches which appear suitable on studying somatical and biochemical effects of the major gene differences.

Whatever may be the final answer to the problem of genetical factors in schizophrenic psychoses there remains no doubt that psychological and social studies are as important as genetical ones. It seems clear that all genetical studies carried out so far have been more or less deficient in special techniques of environmental and interpersonal analysis. In a corresponding way most environmental, and especially psychological studies, have been deficient in statistical techniques and understanding of human biology. Instead of continuing a rather infertile argument it is time to exchange techniques and join forces. Schizophrenic psychoses display such immense mental health problems that at this juncture a call for more multidisciplinary approaches seems appropriate.

BIOCHEMISTRY AND GENETICS

Although it is certainly premature to talk about biochemical genetics of schizophrenic psychoses, it seems pertinent to discuss some of the highlights of biochemical approaches during recent years. The increasing number of biological investigations of mental disease have been stimulated mainly by the genetical work. Schizophrenic patients have been attacked with a battery of laboratory tests, often with more imagination and enthusiasm than skill and criticism. Nevertheless, this is considerably better than armchair philosophies.

The grand total of routine laboratory tests on schizophrenic patients is simply the establishment of a wider range of variation as compared to nonschizophrenic or normal individuals. A number of authors have tried to measure the toxicity of serum, urine, and spinal fluid from schizophrenics, using rabbits (36), rats (37), tadpoles (38, 39), yeast cells (40), or tissue cultures (41, 42) as test objects. The results are controversial. Interesting but so far inconclusive findings have been made in the fields of endocrine dysfunction (43, 44), aromatic metabolism (45, 46, 47), phosphorus metabolism (48, 49), adenine metabolism (50), and adrenocortical function (51). Insofar as positive findings have been made in these and other biochemical studies, schizophrenics have been reported to differ significantly as a group from normal control groups.

Adrenaline has been studied in schizophrenics for more than 30 years. Recently Leach and Heath (52) have shown that adrenaline oxidation is accelerated by fresh serum from schizophrenic patients and that this may be due to an increase of the enzyme ceruloplasmin. Elevated ceruloplasmin has also been reported by Akerfeldt (53) but is not characteristic of schizophrenics alone (54, 55), and its precise significance is doubtful (56, 57). It is therefore thought that the oxidation of adrenaline is qualitatively different in schizophrenics. A protein fraction called taraxein, possibly related to ceruloplasmin, has been isolated from the serum of schizophrenics. This fraction injected into voluntary humans gave rise to psychotic symptoms (58). The present working hypothesis is that some schizophrenic psychoses may be caused by a genetically determined defect in those enzyme systems which maintain homeostasis by the breakdown of substances produced during stress. It remains to be seen if this applies to adrenaline metabolism. So far the results are only suggestive.

Recently serotonin has been studied in relation to schizophrenic psychoses on the basis that LSD is an antimetabolite to this hormone and that reserpine liberates intracellular serotonin in brain tissue (59, 60). Serotonin itself does not produce psychotic symptoms when injected intravenously as it is incapable of passing through the blood-brain barrier. However, certain derivatives of it, such as bufotenine, n, n-dimethyltryptamine and n, n-diethyltryptamine, cause psychoticlike symptoms in humans. Investigations of this type have been made mainly by biochemists and pharmacologists. Psychiatrists have remained critical mainly because experimental LSD-psychoses differ greatly from schizophrenic states and the therapeutic value of reserpine in schizophrenic psychoses is doubtful. Nevertheless these new approaches should in a modest way be regarded as promising for the future. A number of potent substances have been found which are capable of producing profound mental changes when present in very minute quantities. As seen from this necessarily sketchy review from the vast research fields which are related to the genetics of schizophrenic psychoses, we are still very far from anything like a good lead to the core of the problems. I should like to end with some critical remarks and some thoughts on future research.

Most authors still give the impression that they anticipate schizophrenia as an entity. When no consistent characteristics are found in a group of patients the problem is dismissed and a new line taken up. It should be worthwhile to study more closely the extreme variates and then not only the patients themselves but above all their relatives. More serious is the fact that biochemical investigations have often been carried out on patients who were not only poorly classified but also in lack of proper nutritional control. It should be fairly obvious that the emotional stress which characterizes many schizophrenic patients may cause a variety of metabolic changes which have nothing to do with the etiology. Much more caution is needed in providing a more stable nutritional and emotional state before the biochemical studies are carried out. At least, comparable nutritional and emotional states should be thoroughly studied in nonschizophrenic individuals.

More collaboration is needed between biochemists, psychiatrists, and geneticists. We are still waiting for the extension of the biochemical investigations to monozygotic twins with only one schizophrenic partner. Etiologically important metabolic changes may be less obscured in a predisposed individual before the actual onset of the disease.

Because the various metabolic abnormalities which may be found in the blood, urine, or spinal fluid are extremely difficult to evaluate in terms of etiological significance, we are trying another approach. It seems likely that the pathology of many, perhaps all, genetical diseases is so generalized as to go down to the nuclear level. On this working hypothesis it should be worth while to study the metabolism of different types of cells from schizophrenics in cell cultures.

References

1.   A. MOFFSON, Schizophrenia in male Bantu admissions to Weskoppies hospital, *South African M. J., 28:* 662–666, 1954.

2.   TSUNG-YI LIN, A study of the incidence of mental disorder in Chinese and other cultures, *Psychiatry, 16:* 313–336, 1953.

3.   R. PRASOP, *Studies of Mental Illness in Thailand,* Bangkok: Phyathai, 1957.

4.   E. H. HARE, Mental illness and social class in Bristol, *Brit. J. Social Med., 9:* 191–195, 1955.

5.   G. M. CARSTAIRS et al., Changing population of mental hospitals, Brit. J. Social Med., 9: 187–190, 1955.

6.   B. PASAMANICK et al., Mental disease prevalence in an urban population, Pub. Health Rep., 72: 574–576, 1957.

7.   J. A. CLAUSEN and M. L. KOHN, Schizophrenia and the social structure of a small city, Pub. Health Rep., 72: 578–580, 1957.

8.   E. ESSEN-MÖLLER, Individual traits and morbidity in a Swedish rural population, Acta psychiat., Kbh. Supp. 100, 1956.

9.   A. HARRIS et al., Schizophrenia; a prognostic and social study, Brit. J. Social Med., 10: 107–114, 1956.

10.   T. LARSSON and T. SJÖGREN, A methodological, psychiatric and statistical study of a large Swedish rural population, Acta psychiat., Kbh. Supp. 89, 1954.

11.   J. W. EATON and R. J. WEIL, Culture and Mental Disorder, Glencoe, Ill.: Free Press, 1955.

12.   W. MAYER-GROSS, Mental health survey in a rural area, Eugenics Rev., 40: 140–148, 1948.

13.   J. BREMER, A social psychiatric investigation of a small community in northern Norway, Acta psychiat., Kbh. Supp. 62, 1951.

14.   K. FREMMING, Sygdomsrisikoen for Sindslidelser (Morbid Risk of Mental Diseases and Other Mental Abnormalities in an Average Danish Population), Copenhagen: Munksgaard, 1947.

15.   C. BRUGGER, Versuch einer Geisteskrankenzählung in Thüringen, Ztschr. f. d. ges. Neurol. & Psychiat., 133: 352–390, 1931.

16.   C. BRUGGER, Psychiatrische Ergebnisse einer medizinischen, anthropologischen und soziologischen Bevölkerungsuntersuchung, Ztschr. f. d. ges. Neurol. & Psychiat., 146: 189–207, 1933.

17.   C. BRUGGER, Psychiatrische Bestandesaufnahme im Gebiet eines medizinisch-anthropologischen Zensus in der Nähe von Rosenheim, Ztschr. f. d. ges. Neurol. & Psychiat., 156: 189–207, 1938.

18.   H. SCHADE, Ergebnisse einer Bevölkerungsuntersuchung in der Schwalm, Abh. math.-nat. Kl. Akad. Wiss. Mainz., 16: 419–491, 1950.

19.   E. STRÖMGREN, Beiträge zur psychiatrischen Erblehre, Acta psychiat., Kbh. Supp. 19, 1938.

20.   T. SJÖGREN, Genetic, statistical and psychiatric investigations of a West Swedish population, Acta psychiat., Kbh. Supp. 52, 1948.

21.   T. SJÖGREN, Investigations of the heredity of psychoses and mental deficiency in two North Swedish parishes, Ann. Eugenics, 6: 253–318, 1935.

22.   M. KAILA, Ueber die Durchschnittshäufigkeit der Geisteskrankheiten und des Schwachsinns in Finnland, Acta psychiat., Kbh., 17: 47–67, 1942.

23.   J. A. BÖÖK, A genetic and neuropsychiatric investigation of a North Swedish population, with special regard to schizophrenia and mental deficiency, Acta genet., 4: 1–100, 133–139, 345–414, 1953.

24.   G. ELSÄSSER, Die Nachkommen geisteskranker Elternpaare, Stuttgart: Thieme Verlag, 1952.

25.   B. SCHULZ, Zur Erbpathologie der Schizophrenie, Ztschr. f. d. ges. Neurol. & Psychiat., 143: 175–293, 1932.

26.   B. SCHULZ, Versuch einer genealogisch-statistischen Ueberprüfung eines Schiz-

ophreniematerials auf biologische Einheitlichkeit, *Ztschr. f. d. ges. Neurol. & Psychiat., 151*: 145–170, 1934.

27.   M. BLEULER, *Krankheitsverlauf, Persönlichkeit und Verwandtschaft Schizophrener und ihre gegenseitigen Beziehungen,* Leipzig: 1940.

28.   E. SLATER, Genetical causes of schizophrenic symptoms, *Monatsschr. Psychiat. u. Neurol., 113*: 50–58, 1947.

29.   F. J. KALLMANN, The genetic theory of schizophrenia. An analysis of 691 twin index families, *Am. J. Psychiat., 103*: 309–322, 1946.

30.   F. J. KALLMANN, *The Genetics of Psychoses, Congress Internat. Psychiat., Paris 1950.* VI. *Psychiatrie Sociale,* Paris: Hermann, 1950.

31.   F. J. KALLMANN, *Heredity in Health and Mental Disorder,* New York: Norton, 1953.

32.   E. SLATER, *Psychotic and Neurotic Illnesses in Twins,* Med. Res. Council, Special Report Series No. 278, London: H. M. Stationery Office, 1953.

33.   E. ESSEN-MÖLLER, The calculation of morbid risk in parents of index cases, as applied to a family sample of schizophrenics, *Acta genet., 5*: 334–342, 1955.

34.   E. SLATER, The monogenic theory of schizophrenia, *Acta genet., 8*: 50–56, 1958.

35.   C. T. PROUT and M. A. WHITE, The schizophrenic's sibling, *J. Nerv. & Ment. Dis., 123*: 162–170, 1956.

36.   B. MINZ and E. J. WALASZEK, Sur la présence de substances biologiquement actives dans le sérum de schizophrènes, *C. Rend. Acad. Sc., 244*: 1974–1976, 1957.

37.   A. K. SHAPIRO, An attempt to demonstrate a catatonigenic agent in cerebrospinal fluid of catatonic schizophrenic patients, *J. Nerv. & Ment. Dis., 123*: 65–71, 1956.

38.   R. FISCHER, Stress and toxicity of serum, *Science, 118*: 409–420, 1953.

39.   C. R. EDISEN, Studies of the toxicity of schizophrenic blood serum, *Dis. Nerv. System, 17*: 77–80, 1956.

40.   H. P. RIEDER, Biologische Toxizitätsbestimmung in pathologischen Körperflüssigkeiten. I. Versuche mit Nativflüssigkeiten von Geistesund Nervenkranken, *Confinia neurol., 14*: 65–87, 1952.

41.   S. FEDOROFF, Toxicity of schizophrenics' blood serum in tissue culture, *J. Lab. & Clin. Med., 48*: 55–62, 1956.

42.   S. FEDOROFF and A. HOFFER, Toxicity of blood serum from schizophrenic and non-schizophrenic subjects, *J. Nerv. & Ment. Dis., 124*: 396–398, 1956.

43.   M. BLEULER et al., Untersuchungen aus dem Grenzgebiet zwischen Psychopathologie und Endokrinologie, *Arch. Psychiat., 180*: 271–528, 1948.

44.   G. LANGFELDT, *The Endocrine Glands in Dementia Praecox,* Bergen, 1926.

45.   P. L. MCGEER et al., Aromatic excretory pattern of schizophrenics, *Science, 123*: 1029–1030, 1956.

46.   P. L. MCGEER et al., Relation of aromatic amino acids to excretory pattern of schizophrenics, *Science, 123*: 1078–1080, 1956.

47.   P. L. MC GEER et al., Aromatic metabolism in schizophrenia, *J. Nerv. & Ment. Dis., 125*: 166–175, 1957.

48.   I. BOSZORMENYI-NAGY and F. J. GERTY, Difference between the phosphorus metabolism of erythrocytes of normals and of patients suffering from schizophrenia, *J. Nerv. & Ment. Dis., 121*: 53–59, 1955.

49.   I. BOSZORMENYI-NAGY et al., Correlation between an anomaly of the intracellular metabolism of adenosine nucleotides and schizophrenia, J. Nerv. & Ment. Dis., 124: 413–416, 1956.

50.   K. KISHIMOTO et al., Biochemical genetics of schizophrenia, report II, Ann. Rep. Environment Med., Nagoya Univ., 1955: 65–69, 1955.

51.   H. HOAGLAND et al., Adrenocortical function and urinary phosphate excretion; comparison in schizophrenia and in lysergic acid diethylamide-induced psychotic episodes in normal persons, A.M.A. Arch. Neurol. & Psychiat., 73: 100–109, 1955.

52.   B. E. LEACH and R. G. HEATH, The in vitro oxidation of epinephrine in plasma, A.M.A. Arch. Neurol. & Psychiat., 76: 444–450, 1956.

53.   S. AKERFELDT, Oxidation of N, N-Dimethyl-p-phenylenediamine by serum from patients with mental disease, Science, 125: 117–119, 1957.

54.   I. H. SCHEINBERG et al., Concentration of ceruloplasmin in plasma of schizophrenic patients, Science, 126: 925–926, 1957.

55.   L. G. ABOOD et al., Comparative study of blood ceruloplasmin in schizophrenia and other disorders, A.M.A. Arch. Neurol. & Psychiat., 77: 643–645, 1957.

56.   M. H. APRISON and A. L. DREW, n, n-Dimethyl-p-phenylenediamine oxidation by serum from schizophrenic children, Science, 127: 758, 1958.

57.   M. OZEK, Untersuchungen ueber den Kupferstoffwechsel im schizophrenen Formenkreis, Arch. Psychiat., 195: 408–423, 1957.

58.   R. G. HEATH et al., Effect on behavior in humans with the administration of taraxein, Am. J. Psychiat., 114: 14–24, 1957.

59.   J. H. GADDUM, Antagonism between lysergic acid diethylamide and 5-hydroxyltryptamine, J. Physiol., 121: 15 P, 1953.

60.   D. W. WOOLEY, in Hoagland, H. (Ed.), Hormones, Brain Function, and Behavior, New York: Acad. Press, 1957.

2. A CRITIQUE OF THE LITERATURE ON THE GENETICS OF SCHIZOPHRENIA

Don D. Jackson

It is essential in any appraisal of our present knowledge of schizophrenia to consider genetic findings carefully, because in the controversy about etiology, they represent one of the main bases for the organic position. Dr. Böök has reviewed the topic from the point of view of the medical geneticist; this chapter approaches the question from the psychodynamically oriented side.

Much material has been collected by investigators who postulated a major role for genetic factors, and, in their opinion, the data confirm their hypothesis. But one may ask two questions: Are the facts as recorded subject to an alternative explanation? Are the studies sound with regard to method, especially in matters of diagnosis and statistical assumptions?

It may be said at the outset that the genetics of schizophrenia is a topic that arouses strong feelings and firm convictions. Although a few individuals, like M. Bleuler and Kanner, have cautioned against the blanket assumption of a genetic etiology, most writers seem to accept genetic findings, especially as they appear in the work of Kallmann. Recent reviews by Shea (1), Cade (2), and Balfour Sclare (3), for example, assume that a genetic basis has been established beyond question. One of the recent reviews of biochemical research (4) quotes Kallmann's statistics and concludes: "Despite the fact that some twin members were reared apart from infancy, the expectation was of the same magnitude. This clearly demonstrates, and such results have been

Don D. Jackson, M.D., Head, Department of Psychiatry, Palo Alto Medical Clinic, California, is a psychoanalyst and clinician. He is Director of the Mental Research Institute of the Palo Alto Medical Research Foundation.

37

confirmed by others, that there exists a predisposing factor in the face of life's stresses making for vulnerability leading to the development of schizophrenia." Linus Pauling (5) says, "I am sure that most mental disease is chemical in origin and that the chemical abnormality involved is usually the result of abnormality in the genetic constitution of the individual." A well-known British psychiatrist, discussing biochemical concepts of schizophrenia (6), writes: "The evidence for a genetic cause of schizophrenia is now generally agreed to be overwhelming, although the exact details may not yet be known. Kallmann (1953) has accumulated a large body of evidence favouring the hypothesis that single-factor inheritance of the recessive type is the genetic cause of schizophrenia."

These statements embody two assumptions that seem particularly common but that have, to my knowledge, no established foundation in fact: (1) that individuals have been exposed to stress or psychogenic trauma similar to that experienced by schizophrenics without developing schizophrenia; (2) that many cases exist of identical twins who have been reared from infancy or early childhood in separate and distinct environments and yet have both developed schizophrenia.

As to the first point, until there exists a valid theory of psychogenic causation for schizophrenia, we cannot state what constitutes psychic trauma for the schizophrenic-to-be. Assuredly it is nothing so obvious as beatings, rape, poverty, or the overgeneralized notion of rejection. The chapters in this volume by Lidz, Bowen, and Weakland offer points of view about the complicated family situation in which schizophrenia may arise. On the other hand, the more biologically oriented investigators take a simpler view of what constitutes trauma. For example, Kallmann states (7):

> From this lonely corner of the psychiatric orb no reason can be seen for placing all varieties of psychopathology in a mysteriously protean category of nonspecific species vulnerability. This is done *when disturbed interpersonal relationships are considered the cause rather than the consequence of severe maladjustment* [italics mine], or when all forms of mental illness are ascribed to cultural pressures, postnatal maternal imperfections or other universal shortcomings of human status. Indeed only human beings can respond with a true psychosis to unfavorable environmental circumstances yet there is abundant evidence to show that not all of them will. Certain persons seem capable of adapting themselves to any combination of distressing circumstances without developing progressive psychosis. The long list of such definable

frustrations include the physical hardships of starvation, complete exhaustion and prolonged malignant disease as well as extreme emotional stress and many behavioral inadequacies of the parents. Some of these adaptable persons come from family units or cultural areas which produce a true psychosis in another member of their group. . . . Actually there are some people in the normal population that seem to be capable of adapting themselves to pronounced life stresses without noticeable impairment of their *genetically controlled* [italics mine] ability to maintain a state of physical health and emotional equilibrium.

These statements strike at the heart of the recondite nature-nurture problem. If we assume that people who break down have poor genes and people who stay healthy have good genes, we have created two useless categories, because we have done no more than repeat the statement that some break down and some do not, and conjecture that they must be born that way.

There is first the problem of what is psychogenic trauma (8) and secondly there is the inescapable fact that in mental illness the thing being studied is produced in and by the population being studied by other than genetic means alone. Even supporters of a genetic basis for schizophrenia acknowledge the importance of an environmental precipitation. And many acknowledge the difficulty in separating social and biological factors.

Again, with regard to the all important concept of trauma, there is in human mental illness a time factor that probably will be revealed only by longitudinal studies. This time factor probably creates "genetic biasing" in which the attributes of a child inimical to his particular family role can be negatively selected against, increasing their importance over a period of time. For example, if a passive child were born to a mother who required constant reassurance about her mothering abilities, it would not only result in an unhappy relationship, but the increasing frustrations and failures over the years would require an increasing bias against the child to keep him the responsible party. If father is remiss in his role as well, there will be a great temptation for him to form an alliance with mother against the child's "lack of affection." The child will become increasingly affectionless and substantiate the parental view.

It would be misleading to imply we know nothing about psychogenic trauma, because, given sufficient information, psychodynamically oriented judges would agree, within limits, on a given case. But the fact remains that "sufficient information" is usually lacking in hospital charts, which, together with word of mouth reports on dead relatives, comprise a significant part of the data of most genetic studies. Ernst (9) in a study of 50 schizophrenic women found eight who, according to hospital histories, came from unstressful environments. He personally visited their homes and found the family relationships very abnormal.

With insufficient information and inadequate knowledge about what constitutes psychogenic trauma for the schizophrenic, estimates of the relative effects of heredity are bound to be controversial, if not premature. Galton in 1883 hoped that the nature-nurture problem might be immeasurably clarified by the means of twin studies. In the field of schizophrenia, such studies have been undertaken by Kallmann, Slater, Essen-Möller, Rosanoff, and Luxenberger. There exists such a mixture of fact and fiction in regard to these studies that I propose to review the entire literature following a discussion of some general problems in the study of the genetics of schizophrenia. Meanwhile, let it be said here regarding twins who are alleged to have been reared apart and who both developed schizophrenia, that an exhaustive search of American and European literature of the past forty years has uncovered only two such cases.

Although these two cases, considering the incidence of schizophrenia, could have occurred on a chance basis, they have been frequently referred to in the literature and will therefore be considered in detail. Evidently the rumor that there are many such cases extant stems from passing remarks like Hoagland's (4) and from the fact that Kallmann in his 1946 paper (10) designated a category among identical twins of "separated" and "non-separated." However, his terms refer only to *separation five years prior to the psychosis*. Because his age group ranged from 15 to 44 years, and because his average age is stated to be 33 years (p. 317), it is obvious that the twins were not apart during their formative years. Indeed, most remained together well past the usual age for marriage; and even this late in life separation resulted in a significant decrease in concordance for schizophrenia. Gedda (11) in his extensive review of the literature on twins mistakenly includes the cases of Richmond (12) and Ley (13) as examples of twins reared apart. Evidently this error arose because Richmond stressed how different his twins' environments were despite their being reared together, and Ley's case was simply a translated report of Craike and Slater's twins (14)—one of the two cases reported in the medical literature.

THE PROBLEM

The bias with which an investigation is launched can give it a direction that only overwhelming evidence acting over a prolonged period of time can alter. With this in mind, let us consider the history of genetic studies of schizophrenia and then the evidence on which they are based.

Before genetic studies were made, psychiatric opinion, influenced especially by German psychiatry, was that schizophrenia was an inherited disorder resulting in degeneration of the cortical cells. Through the 1920's and 1930's the majority of genetical studies were done by German investigators, and since 1938 the major effort has been that of Kallmann, an American who emigrated from Germany after working with the eminent early authority, Rudin. In the last fifteen years there have been surprisingly few genetic studies of schizophrenia other than Kallmann's massive contributions. Scandinavian studies have been made which provide much important material, but these have been concerned more with the basic problems of the incidence of schizophrenia in the population than with the examination of expectancy rates in families. Slater, an English psychiatrist, and Essen-Möller, a Scandinavian, have both contributed twin studies which are occasionally referred to and which will be discussed in detail hereafter, but Kallmann is the single major source referred to by most authors writing on schizophrenia, including modern textbook writers.

A truly Mendelian approach cannot be carried out with humans as it can with plants and animals. First, we have no pure stocks to begin with, we cannot demonstrate the 72 ratio, and we do not breed brother and sister. Secondly, human environments do not remain constant as required in Mendelian studies. (Dr. Böök stresses this point in his contribution.) Penrose, the medical geneticist (15), has stated that little practical help can be expected from genetical prognosis in relation to common diseases, *i.e.*, those with an incidence of one per 100 or greater. He specifically mentions schizophrenia, remarking that a careful history of the variability of clinical type, onset, age, and incidence immediately rules out all simple genetical explanations. He feels that population surveys are most needed in this disorder. Established hereditary disorders, in which genetic studies have been invaluable, are generally disorders having an incidence of one to 10,000 or less. Common disorders like tuberculosis, leprosy, mental defect, or criminality were once regarded as hereditarily caused but are now considered not to be so, or the role assigned to hereditary susceptibility is a small one (16, 17).

It is instructive to note in this connection that German psychiatrists did their early studies on the basis of a "taint" or "degeneracy" theory that vaguely linked mental defect, epilepsy, alcoholism, criminality, and insanity as the result of "poor heredity"; this theory was supplemented by Lombroso's anthropological measurements of criminals and was followed by Kretschmer's studies of body type and mental illness. There is no doubt that the culture of the time, including as it did fixed ideas about good and evil and hierarchical social classes without much mobility, rendered such ideas acceptable. Today Kallmann seems to stand virtually alone in claiming that there is a mesodermal resistance to the expression of the schizophrenic genotype in the athletic habitus and a relation between body weight and resistance to schizophrenia (18, 19). Other observers, such as Bleuler (17) and Rees (20), have stressed the common experience of examining short, tall, thin, and fat schizophrenics; and Slater (21) found no confirmation in his twin series for the larger twin being the least sick. As a matter of fact, Kallmann himself has published a report of twins with Morgnani's Syndrome (22) who demonstrate that his rule is not, as he has stated, invariable.

As Western culture, led by England and the United States, became more lower-class conscious, genetic studies broadened and socio-economic factors were assigned a predominant role in the causation of, for example, tuberculosis, leprosy, and criminality. It was discovered that some cases of feeblemindedness might not be a fixed condition but a combination of neglect and illiteracy and that class resentment and lack of jobs had much to do with the crime rate. Schizophrenia now stands virtually alone as a common disorder considered in terms of Mendelian genetics.

Bleuler (17, 23) appears to be the only psychodynamically oriented investigator who has studied the genetics of adult schizophrenia; and, as far as I know, he first raised the issue of whether identical twins did not have a unique environment and hence could not be compared to fraternal twins on a genetic basis alone. Nearly all other investigators appear to have been German trained and thus might represent similar biases. This is conceivably an important consideration because the study of mental deficiency reveals that a few investigators, uninfluenced by popular medical opinion, can revolutionize a strongly held theory. Mental defect makes a useful analogy to schizophrenia because initially, apart from a rough quantitative classification, all types of mental defect were lumped together and attributed to "poor heredity." Kanner (24) demonstrates the trend by reporting the following figures on the assumed relationship of heredity to mental defects: 1914, 77 per cent; 1920, 90 per cent; 1929, 80 per cent; 1934, 29 per cent. Fixed notions of heredity can be as comforting but unproductive as the Mohammedan view of "Fate" since they absolve one from seeking proximate causes. Some present-day geneticists are well aware of this danger (15, 25, 26). In examining the evidence on the genetics of schizophrenia it is therefore important to keep two factors constantly in mind: the ideas about the genetic basis of mental disorders have not been without a cultural component; and some disorders have been labeled hereditary because their etiology was not understood.

There are a number of questions about the hereditary nature of schizophrenia which careful study of the data obtained from the literature still leaves unanswered. The following are considered serious theoretical and methodological obstacles for the genetic study of schizophrenia.

1. The psychiatric disorders that have an agreed upon hereditary basis also reveal evidence of phenotypical defects, for example, Huntington's chorea and phenylpyruvic amentia; and such disorders are rare, generally are on the order of one to 10,000. No phenotypical defect has been found associated with schizophrenia, and it is a common disorder. An incidence of one per cent is used in most genetic studies, but this percentage does not include the possibility that there may be many more such cases that have not been hospitalized. Böök, in his large survey of northern Swedish parishes, found an expectancy rate of 3 per cent. Although one cannot analogize between figures for Sweden and other countries, it does seem that population surveys often find a higher incidence of schizophrenia than the one per cent usually used (see Chapter 1).

2. Not only is the diagnosis of schizophrenia a matter of psychiatric taste, but the chances that any individual case will be diagnosed as schizophrenic increase with each year that the patient remains in a mental hospital. Penrose (27) found that in England 33 per cent of first admissions were diagnosed as "schizophrenia" and 17 per cent "manic-depressive disorder." After 20 years, the diagnosis of schizophrenia in these cases had risen to 69.8 per cent and the diagnosis of "manic-depressive" had gone down to 7.4 per cent. Hoch (28) quotes the following statistics in order to demonstrate that psychiatric diagnosis on admission to a state hospital varies with the locality. Since diagnosis is essential to the validity of genetic studies, such variation could be an important sampling factor.

DATE	LOCALITY	SCHIZOPHRENIA	MANIC-DEPRESSIVE
1926	California	20.8%	23.2%
1926	New York	26.7%	13 %
1930	California	21.7%	12 %
1930	New York	25.2%	8 %
1934	Mississippi	21 %	20.7%
1935	Mississippi	21 %	4.6%

The diagnosis of schizophrenia cannot be made by such objective tests as finding sugar in the urine and there is reason to be skeptical of otherwise convincing statistics. This is particularly true when one considers that leading geneticists—*e.g.*, Luxenberger, Essen-Möller, and Slater—are so convinced of the genetic nature of schizophrenia that they quite frankly use a family history of schizophrenia as an aid in diagnosis. This may or may not be justified, but it is questionably scientific to use the material thus arrived at as "proof" of genetic origin.

Further, even unquestionably "physical" diseases may run in families without necessarily having a genetic basis. Beriberi tends to do so; what is "inherited" is the pattern of preference for vitamin-poor foods which the children pick up from their parents and in turn pass on to their children.

There have been no "blind" diagnoses used in genetic studies; and especially if one is diagnosing the co-twin of a schizophrenic index case, the pull toward "schizophrenia" may be very great indeed. Slater in his study (21, p. 55) candidly states: "To reach this figure of 76 per cent [corrected morbidity rate] we have included among the concordant pairs a number in whom the diagnosis of schizophrenia is not established." He then discusses seven of the 28 uniovular pairs and concludes: "But it would seem captious to exclude them as in every case schizophrenia is more probable than normality or any other diagnosis." The range between schizophrenia and normality is a vast one, and one would think Slater would be more puzzled over the diagnosis of "schizophrenia" or "borderline case." Because a number of investigators favor the theory of "schizoid personality" as the precursor of schizophrenia, they sometimes fuse psychotic and nonpsychotic cases under the term "schizophrenia."

The problem of nosology in this field is complicated by the assumed relationship between schizoid personality and schizophrenia. Many investigators assume "schizoid personality" to be the genotype and "schizophrenia" to be the phenotypical expression of this anatomical or metabolic defect. However, other authorities seem to view schizophrenia as the genotype and schizoid personality as a lesser expression of this genetic defect. The fact that no invariable relationship exists between schizoid and schizophrenia and that the diagnosis "schizoid personality" is vague and all encompassing further complicate the issues. Kretschmer (30) describes the schizoid personality as unsociable, silent, retiring, serious, solitary; or timid, shy, fragile, sensitive, nervous, unstable, and bookish; or amiable, good-natured, kind, quiet, dull, or stupid. With three such broad categories, the genetic diagnostician is given a large latitude in ascribing a schizoid basis for schizophrenia. Estimates of schizoid personality in the ordinary population vary within such large limits as to be meaningless. Kallmann is the only author who finds no normal twins among the identical twin groups and the only one who finds no crossovers with affective disorders. Slater also remarks on this and on his own inability to confirm this finding (21).

Morris (29) has thrown doubt on the schizoid-schizophrenia hypothesis by his follow-up study twenty years later of children diagnosed in an out-patient clinic. Those who became schizophrenic had been more frequently diagnosed as extroverts; this was probably a chance happening, but certainly no positive correlation of introversion and schizophrenia was shown. Johansen (31) estimated that 21.1 ± 4.8 per cent of her schizophrenic group could be judged to have had schizoid personalities and figures this is within the range of some population estimates. Birren in a study of 38 children who later became psychotic (32) noted that 75 per cent came from homes where there was severe friction and that many of his cases responded to the home situation with rebellion rather than increased apathy and withdrawal. These cases had a later age of onset for their psychoses. Frazee's study (33) of 23 boys who later became schizophrenic reveals that only half had symptoms characteristic of the schizoid personality. Only two had been diagnosed "schizoid" when seen in a child clinic.

Leonhard, Rennie, Schulz, and Bleuler have all described cyclic schizophrenia in families with varying personality disorders and have found no relation between the severity of schizophrenia and the incidence in the family genealogy. An especially interesting finding in this regard is Leonhard's description of "reactive, atypical" schizophrenia with a good prognosis and an affective prepsychotic personality occurring in patients whose families displayed a number of cases of schizophrenia (34, 35, 36, 37).

Rudin, one of the original psychiatric geneticists, studied 735 individuals who had a schizophrenic sibling. He found 58 had one schizophrenic parent and 130 had parents with other psychoses. Of the descendents for two generations of 20 schizophrenic patients, only three developed schizophrenic psychoses while a number had other mental disorders. Bleuler in 1930 reported on eight schizophrenics without schizophrenia in their family history. Their prepsychotic personality was not schizoid, and seven out of the eight had very unfavorable prognoses—the eighth having become psychotic too recently to judge (38).

Penrose (39) studied all known cases of mental illness occurring in at least two family members in an Ontario hospital over an 18-year period. He reports that schizophrenia and affective disorders occurred in pairs of relatives. Of 5456 pairs of relatives only 8.7 per cent were fathers compared to 24.5 per cent mothers; 30.7 per cent were otherwise related. Fathers admitted before the age of 35 had a higher percentage of schizophrenia than depressions, and the exact opposite was true for mothers. Correlations were made for first-admission age and were found closest for like sexed siblings and then mothers and sons. Penrose's data are difficult to account for on a strictly genetic basis and demonstrate the interweaving of schizophrenic and affective disorders. Another study of multiple psychoses in the same family was made by Zehnder (40) in Switzerland; she studied only siblings and her figures on like-sexed pairs are very similar to Penrose's. (These findings regarding like-sexed siblings are interesting and will be discussed later.)

Planansky (25) makes the interesting suggestion that if the schizoid personality is the genotypical representation of schizophrenia then the study of hospitalized schizophrenics is merely an expedient. He feels that the question of "schizoid personality" should be studied in families without an index case of schizophrenia.

3. The genetic mode of transmission of schizophrenia has not been determined. The majority of older authorities regarded schizophrenia as a dominant disorder, but recently recessivity has more adherents (41). It has been claimed to be a recessive disorder with a single-factor inheritance and variable penetrance (7), although most genetic authorities seem to dispute this claim (41). The following evidence is against recessivity, let alone a single-factor, or even double-factor, inheritance.

In recessive disorders, affected persons generally have unaffected parents and inheritance is through collateral lines. Any sibling of an affected index case has a 25 per cent chance of being affected, and the parents are likely to be related if the disease is rare. Schizophrenia, if recessive, should have a higher incidence rate in the siblings of the index case than in his children. Actually, the reverse is true; e.g., Kallmann finds an expectancy rate of 16.4 per cent in the children and 11.5 per cent in the siblings. He also finds 68 per cent expectancy for the children of two schizophrenic parents, whereas Rudin found 52 per cent, Schulz 38 per cent, and Elsässer 39 per cent. Obviously these figures should be a good deal higher to argue for simple recessivity. Moreover, Kallmann's findings of an expectancy rate of 85 per cent for monozygotic twins are difficult to reconcile with the 68 per cent, for according to the laws of recessive inheritance both should be 100 per cent. The proponents of a recessive mode of inheritance get around these figures by citing estimates of variable penetrance. The geneticist Neel (42) has referred to this practice as a convenient way to juggle figures.

A final argument offered to establish a recessive mode of inheritance is the incidence of consanguinity. This runs as high as 18 per cent in phenylpyruvic amentia and 23 to 38 per cent in the Laurence Moon Biedl syndrome, established recessive disorders. Kallmann found no increased consanguinity in his large Berlin study, but reported a 5 per cent incidence in his 1953 report. This would not appear to be a significant finding since his figures from the two studies are astonishingly identical. (See Table 2.1.)

TABLE 2.1

Expectancy figures reported by Kallmann

	1938 (BERLIN)	1941 (NEW YORK)	1946 (NEW YORK)	1950 (NEW YORK)	1954 (NEW YORK)
Index Cases	1,047	? (50+) twins	691	953	? 953
Samples (Blood relatives and Probands)	13,851	?	5,776	5,804	?
	SCHIZ.	SCHIZ.	SCHIZ.	SCHIZ.	SCHIZ.
Parents	9.3	10.3	9.2	9.3	9.2–10.3
Siblings	11.5	11.5	14.3	14.2	11.5–14.3
Children					
One S Parent	16.4	16.4	16.4	16.4	16.4
Two S Parents	68.1	68.1	68.1	68.1	68.1
Twin Studies					
Dizygotic			14.7	14.5	12.5
Same sex			17.7		
Opp. sex			11.5		
Monozygotic			85.8	86.2	86.2
Not separated			91.5		
Separated			77.6		

Slater reported a 5 per cent consanguinity rate at the First International Congress of Genetics in 1956, whereas Odegaard and Herloggen at the same meeting reported no increase. Böök found no increase on the basis of his large population survey in Sweden. Hanhart (43) found no increased incidence of schizophrenia in an area with a high percentage of consanguinous marriages.

The lack of agreement on the mode of transmission of schizophrenia is not, of course, in itself an argument pro or con the hereditary basis of the disorder. It is raised here only to indicate that geneticists themselves have many unsolved problems in establishing the hereditary nature of schizophrenia.

4. There has been established no relation between hereditary taint, type of schizophrenia, age at onset, and outcome. Masterson studied 153 patients with adolescent schizophrenia, of whom 67 per cent had a poor

outcome. Among the factors not related to poor outcome was family history
(44). Kanner, in a careful study of the relatives of 100 schizophrenic children
(45), found no hereditary trends or increase in the incidence of schizophrenia
in antecedents or collaterals; a total of 973 relatives and 131 siblings were
seen. Schulz (46) and Leonhard (47) studied typical and atypical cases of
schizophrenia and found that parents of the typical cases had one per cent
incidence of schizophrenia and parents of the atypical 6 per cent. The type
of schizophrenia and family genetic history were not related. Leonhard, in
another study (34) concluded that there was little relation between the diagnosis of an index case and the kind of illness in the family, and cited the
crossing over of affective and schizophrenic disorders. Lundby (48) studied a
group of Norwegian seamen with a high incidence of schizophrenia. Their
families, probably by chance, had a lower incidence of schizophrenia than
the average Norwegian population. Johansen (31), in a very complete study
of 138 male schizophrenics, found no difference in age at onset or symptoms in patients with a positive family history and those without. Canavan
and Clark studied 381 children, one of whose parents had been diagnosed as
schizophrenic. They felt 86 deviated emotionally or socially and compared
them to 500 children of nonpsychotic parents. In this group, by chance, there
were 145 children who deviated (49).

Alanen discovered no relation between the psychosis of the parent and
that of the child except in the type of case described by M. Bleuler (37) in
which there is a family resemblance of symptoms that is probably the result
of "learning." Alanen found that there were more psychotic mothers in the
benign group of patients than in the malignant. This has been reported previously (49). Alanen's reluctance to dismiss hereditary factors render his findings all the more impressive. The reader is urged to consult his monograph.

It can be argued, of course, that it is not surprising that the schizophrenia picture varies with the environment of the individual and the
precipitating causes. Such an argument, though in itself perfectly valid, is at
odds with another genetic argument; namely, the striking closeness of onset
and of symptoms in identical twins is evidence for their genetic similarity
(50).

5. There is no evidence for a hereditary basis for nosological classifications of schizophrenia or for connecting these classifications with inherited
constitutional defects. Probably one of the major handicaps to the genetic
study of schizophrenia is the problem of diagnosis mentioned above. Not
only do psychiatric fashions and length of residence in the hospital influence diagnosis, but every sample must be adjusted for age, sex, socio-economic level, and ethnic group if it is to be meaningful. This is not done

in the usual study. The devising of mathematical formulae to take into account age and mortality variations has been only partially successful and some authorities have questioned the rationale for their use. A formula, like that devised by Weinberg, may increase the concordance rate in twins by 15 to 20 per cent over the raw data.

"Sample" not only applies to a representative distribution; it also applies to the relationship between the special environment and the type of psychiatric diagnosis most likely to be made in that environment. Thus Henderson and Gillespie (51), in the most recent edition of their textbook, eliminate paranoid disorders from schizophrenic reaction types. Yet Kolle (52) has shown that the relatives of "paranoids" have the same incidence of various types of schizophrenia as other nosological categories. Roth (41) points out that paraphrenia is not a genetic category because its greatest frequency is among aged spinsters who are slightly deaf and live alone. One author describes five cases of "religious insanity" of a very similar nature occurring in Catholic women living in Egypt. All cases had florid paranoid psychoses, and all made good recoveries (53). The striking study of Eaton and Weil (54) among the Hutterites, in which they found almost no schizophrenia and a relatively large number of affective psychoses, does not lend itself to simple genetic explanations. Opler's work in demonstrating that Irish and Italian young men have a different nosological form to their schizophrenic breakdowns is also pertinent (55). Roumajon has pointed out (56), on the basis of his work in Indo-China with varied political, social, racial, and economic backgrounds, that certain mental aberrations are peculiar to certain cultures. He reported on nine cases chosen from a two-year period and gave evidence that some of the Manus, Dobus, and Kirdis, people who would have been considered abnormal by Western standards, were functioning members of their cultures. He noted the inadequacy of the Kraepelinian terminology when cultural differences are involved.

It would seem that large genetical studies, except when done on a population survey basis as in the Scandinavian work, run the risk of including nuclei, or groups of cases, which obscure the genetic effect because other factors (*e.g.*, social) are of crucial importance. This problem appears in Kallmann's work. For example, in comparing the paranoid group with his catatonic and hebephrenic cases (57), he attributed to the paranoid a less strong hereditary factor because their children had one half the expectancy rate of becoming schizophrenic of the "nuclear group." However, the paranoid patients were much older at the time of hospitalization, and this age factor could have increased the family stability and their children's security. This possibility is revealed by Johansen's findings of a significant difference be-

tween the age of onset of schizophrenia and the fact of the patient's coming from a broken home (31).

The male-female difference in age at hospital admission is considerable
and must be taken into account when studying what happens to the children. In Kallmann's American studies there is a 20 per cent excess of females,
and Slater finds 159 females to 76 males in his study of families of twin
index cases. Penrose's figures have already been mentioned (39), and they
correspond to Zehnder's study of multiple psychoses in the same family. Her
ratio of female to male in such multiple cases was 63 to 26, and 84 per cent
of pairs of siblings admitted to the hospital were female. Because over-all
figures for hospital admissions reveal the incidence of schizophrenia is nearly
50–50 for males and females, these various groupings of related cases point
to a social rather than a genetic explanation. Among the fathers of Johansen's 138 carefully studied patients there were no schizophrenics.

Alanen, in a recent study of the parents of schizophrenic patients based
on 156 Finnish cases, reports that of 152 mothers and 146 fathers (these
numbers being those parents available for examination) 17 mothers and
seven fathers had had psychotic diagnoses. Six mothers and two fathers had
developed chronic schizophrenia and four mothers had had schizophrenic
episodes with complete remission. Not only is the percentage of schizophrenic parents small; it again shows an interesting sex difference, ten
mothers and two fathers, a statistically significant difference.

The different incidence of schizophrenia between parents has been reported by investigators other than Johansen and Alanen (*e.g.*, Pollack and
Malzberg [58] and M. Bleuler [37]) and is difficult to explain on genetic
grounds.* Unfortunately, such large studies as Kallmann's give an over-all
figure for parents and do not give a breakdown for fathers and mothers.
Alanen in 1956 and again in 1948, points out that the psychiatric diagnoses
of the fathers are very varied compared to the mothers. He states that this
difference could be due to a mother-child relationship that ends in schizophrenia. In this connection, it is interesting that the fathers of schizophrenics
have been found in several studies to be more difficult to type than the
mothers (59, 60, 61).

In the attempt to relate schizophrenia to other disease, there are also
many statistical pitfalls. Because Kallmann was studying a chronic, poor,
state-hospital population he found a high incidence of tuberculosis and
concluded:

* Dr. Josephine Hilgard has preliminary figures from a large study at Agnew State
Hospital which indicate the incidence of alcoholism in the fathers of index cases
equals the psychoses in mothers. (Personal communication.)

SCHOOL OF PSYCHIATRIC NURSING
JACKSONVILLE STATE HOSPITAL
JACKSONVILLE, ILLINOIS

This statistical result is so conclusive that it excludes all possibility of coincidence and can only be interpreted as a genuine gene coupling of the tendency to schizophrenia and the heredito-constitutional susceptibility to tuberculosis infections. It also indicates an identical pattern of hereditary transmission for these two predispositions and confirms the assumption that schizophrenia and tuberculosis represent recessive traits.

No one questions that someone who actually contracted tuberculosis was susceptible to it, but environmental conditions are of such importance that the negative—that someone who did not contract it was necessarily resistant —can hardly be said to be true. Attempts based on this older concept of "constitutional weakness" to link schizophrenia with various other disorders have not been successful elsewhere. Alstroem (62), in an extensive study of the incidence of tuberculosis in mental hospitals, found that statistical methods had much to do with the linkage of tuberculosis with schizophrenia. When data were adjusted for age and other pertinent factors, other psychotics had as high or higher rates of incidence. Johansen (31) also found no increase in incidence of tuberculosis in her schizophrenic series. These are recent studies; however, M. Bleuler and his colleagues had already thrown doubt on any constitutional connection between tuberculosis and schizophrenia.

Mott's work (63) on degeneration of the sexual organs and brain cells has been refuted by several investigators (51). The attempt to connect schizophrenia with a particular body build looked promising; many investigators have found no such correlation. Lubin (64) and others (65) have reported an inability to utilize Sheldon's classification [statistically]. Alstroem (62) gives the results of an investigation of weight changes in 1600 psychotic patients. Apart from the catatonics, who showed some extremes in fluctuations, the schizophrenics did not differ from the rest of the hospital population. This would not be in accord with the theory that weight bears a specific relationship to resistance to schizophrenia.

An evaluation of expectancy figures. Table 2.1 demonstrates that the various factors considered in the preceding paragraphs may play a part in the expectancy rates arrived at. In this table it can be noted that Kallmann's expectancy figures vary slightly or not at all whatever the sample. Whether the study is done in Berlin by examining the hospital charts of patients who had been hospitalized between 1893 and 1902, or whether it is done in America on live subjects hospitalized up to fifty years later, the figures remain the same. In one sample (1938) no increased consanguinity is found, and in another (1950) 5 per cent is reported. In 1946, 4394 relatives (of whom 284 were marriage partners) were examined; and in 1950, 280 twin pairs had been added and only 28 more relatives. In addition, in 1946 the proportion of fraternal to identical twins fits the general population ratio, but by 1950 the identical-twin sample had increased 112 and the fraternal twins only 168. That is, the ratio of fraternal to identical had dropped from the expected 3:1 to less than 2:1. In the 1946 report there are 134 half sibs and 2741 siblings, whereas in the large 1952 article (50) 109 half sibs and 2461 siblings are listed despite the increase in the identical twin sample. Kallmann mentions in a 1949 paper (66), which is an amplification of his 1946 report, that of the 691 twin index pairs 211 had family histories negative for schizophrenia and 102 histories provided data insufficient for any conclusion. In subsequent papers on his increased twin sample, no proportions are given for history or for insufficient data. Furthermore, Kallmann does not mention how he has handled these negative cases, and, because they constitute nearly one half of his sample (45 per cent), this is vital information. Obviously families with negative histories cannot be averaged with positive ones or the concept of genealogy loses its meaning. Evidently Kallmann is so convinced of the hereditary nature of schizophrenia that the presence of it in both of a pair of identical twins suggests no other hypothesis. This attitude is surprising in view of an earlier statement of his (67) that if no hereditary predisposition is found "we must exclude these cases as 'genuine' schizophrenias and *differentiate them as schizoform psychoses of exogenous origin*" [italics mine].

The author regards the cases with a negative family history as no evidence against a genetic theory for he states: "Of 211 twin index pairs without schizophrenia in their known ancestry twelve sets (5.7 per cent) originated from consanguinous matings." Not only have higher consanguinity rates been reported for certain populations without an increase in schizophrenia, but Slater has thrown doubt on their per cent meaning by mathematical examination.

Kallmann's expectancy figures are based on the abridged Weinberg method. Slater, in discussing the concordance rate in his identical-twin series, states that his 68 per cent uncorrected concordance would be increased to 94.9 per cent by the abridged Weinberg method. He states (21, p. 54): "Such a figure has little meaning." It is possible that the use of this formula accounts for Kallmann's consistently higher figures than other observers. (See Table 2.2.)

Another item in Kallmann's 1949 report is that 1926 of 5776 subjects

TABLE 2.2

Typical expectancy figures from other
investigators compared with Kallmann's

INVESTIGATOR	PER CENT IN SIBLINGS * (1 SCHIZ. PARENT)	PER CENT IN PARENTS	NO. OF CHILDREN IN FAMILIES
Kallmann	14.0	9.30	4.10
Others:	5.6	4.00	6.30
	5.3	2.50–4.00	6.88
	5.1	1.85	6.50
	5.0	1.75	7.33
	4.5 (6.4 with doubtfuls)	1.25–2.25	4.50
		0.9 (5.5 with doubtfuls)	4.6
	3.3 (4.1 with doubtfuls)	2.6 ± 1.8 —mothers 0.00—fathers	5.9

* Per cent of children schizophrenic with two schizophrenic parents: Kallmann 68.1,
Rudin 53, Schulz 38, Elsässer 39.

examined were already dead. It would seem important to know how data
were obtained about these dead cases and what criteria were used to diagnose
schizophrenia and the high percentage of schizoid. In later reports, when the
twin sample had nearly doubled, the number of relatives interviewed had
not increased to any extent so that the dead sample remains relatively large
and, surprisingly, the per cent figures remain the same as in earlier reports
(Table 2.1).

Kallmann has backed up his morbidity figures with some very striking
findings about the difference in "resistance" to schizophrenia between identical and fraternal twins and has linked this resistance to "mesodermal elements." This could be a very convincing section of his genetic argument
except for the following reasons: his method of arriving at the conclusion;
the fact that he held such an opinion prior to his genetic studies; and the
fact that the same opinion influenced him to conclude that schizophrenia
and tuberculosis were gene linked (1938)—an opinion he has not entirely
relinquished (1953) despite overwhelming evidence to the contrary.

In the early 1930's, a drug called Sulfoan together with Sanovitan and
Phlogetan was enjoying a cure rate of 60 per cent on schizophrenics (68).

Kallmann (69) confirmed these good results and attributed them to a tonic sulfur effect which counteracted a metabolic dysfunction connected especially with the asthenic habitus. He has continued to emphasize metabolic dysfunction and mesodermal weakness despite the lack of evidence. This emphasis takes an extreme form when he points out a five-pound difference between a mentally ill twin and her better adjusted sister.

The "mesodermal-resistance" theory is illustrated by the following quotation:

> In the monozygotic group five out of 100 co-twins of schizophrenic cases show a tendency to favorable resistance and none showed a very favorable resistance if their twin partners are insufficiently resistant. In the dizygotic group, however, favorable resistance is seen in 72 out of 100 co-twins of insufficiently resistant index cases and very favorable resistance in about 30. This finding indicates constitutional resistance to the main genotype of schizophrenia is determined by a genetic mechanism which is probably nonspecific and certainly multi-factoral. Taking into account the results of biometric investigations, there is reason to believe that this constitutional mechanism is a graded character and somehow correlated with the morphological development of mesodermal elements (66, p. 76).

This is a restatement of the 1932 and 1938 theories that could be derived from the author's figures only by strong conviction and not by calculation. Apart from the question of how the 100 twins were selected (an important item) his chart (p. 74) shows that nine pairs of identical twins are listed as "dissimilar" because one has deteriorating and the other nondeteriorating schizophrenia, whereas 54 pairs of identical twins are listed as "similar" even though one twin has nondeteriorating schizophrenia and the other twin has no schizophrenia. In the totals of this chart, "no schizophrenia" to "extremely deteriorating schizophrenia" is given as 0:174—the last figure representing the total sample of identical pairs. By so classifying the co-twins without schizophrenia, the author finds that identical twins have a similar to dissimilar resistance of 3:55 (nine out of 174), whereas dizygotic twins have a 3:1 ratio for dissimilarity. However, in arriving at the 3:1 ratio for fraternals (actually 371:146), the author has included fraternals with "no schizophrenia" as dissimilar, although this was not done with the identical twins. Thus the statement that "similar behavior to schizophrenia is about 18 times more frequent than dissimilar behavior in monozygotic twins although dissimilarity predominates in dizygotic twin partners" is based on a selective and unjustified statistical procedure. In addition, all the above considerations of genetic constitutional factors are made without reference to the fact that 45 per cent of the twin pairs are without positive family histories. Positive and negative family histories are treated alike, as are cases of "no schizophrenia" and "nondeteriorating schizophrenia" when they occur in identical twins. Kallmann is not the only investigator (cases, ref. 11) who is guilty of automatically regarding concordant schizophrenia in twins as proof of heredity despite a negative family history. Almost every case report on twins in the literature which cites a negative family history makes a genetic assumption. (Gralnick noted a similar tendency in relation to *folie à deux* [70].)

In studying Table 2.2 it should be remembered that all these studies used a figure of .85 or one per cent for the incidence of schizophrenia. Therefore any incidence above this figure in the families is evidence for a consanguinous sharing of the tendency to schizophrenia. Böök in his large population survey found an incidence of 3 per cent. When this figure is compared to the most recent study of the families of male schizophrenics (31), in which the morbidity rate for fathers was zero, for mothers 2.6 ± 1.8 per cent, and for siblings 3.8 ± 0.9 per cent; or with Alanen's findings (49), the evidence is not striking.

Table 2.2 also lists the probability of schizophrenia when both parents are schizophrenic. Such figures fail to take into account such factors as broken homes and would be more meaningful if comparisons were made between variables. Pollack *et al.* (58) report that 38 per cent of their sample of 175 schizophrenic patients came from broken homes. Lidz and Lidz (71) reported that 40 per cent of 50 patients who became schizophrenic before the age of 21 came from broken homes. These figures contrast with estimates of 11 to 15 per cent broken homes in the United States, and these estimates include Negro and other population groups in which desertion and divorce tend to be high. Barry, in two studies (72, 73), has reported that of 549 patients with psychoses who were admitted between 16 and 25 years of age, 15.7 per cent had lost their mothers before the age of 12 in contrast to a 5.3 per cent estimate for the general population. It appears to be of critical importance whether the mother was lost before or after the child was eight years old. Such data are ignored in the oversimplified methods of most genetic studies.

Apart from the fact that genetic studies may be dealing, to some extent, with problems in family structure, there is a mounting and impressive literature on sociological factors in schizophrenia which can no longer be ignored by those doing genetic studies. The inclusion of various socio-economic and ethnic groups in a genetic sample is apt to obscure important subgroups which have a very high or a very low incidence of schizophrenia. For example, Cade did a study (74) in an attempt to test Hollingshead and Redlich's findings. He showed that there was an increased incidence of schizophrenia according to population density, and found no evidence of downward drift. However, his most important contribution was in the breakdown of his sample where it was revealed that male immigrants, who comprised 7.8 per cent of the population, had 27.6 per cent of the schizophrenia, and female immigrants, only 5.3 per cent of the population, had an incidence of 11.3 per cent.

It was mentioned earlier that consanguinity estimates in schizophrenics' families varied. Hanhart (43) studied the same Swiss population at 20-year intervals. This was an unusual group because there was an 11.5 per cent incidence of first-cousin marriages and a 32 per cent incidence of second-cousin marriages. Again, the importance of studying subgroups rather than large samples is demonstrated in the fact that the incidence of schizophrenia was within the normal population estimates and had actually decreased since his previous study. The author attributes the decrease to "natural eugenics"; in any case, if schizophrenia is a recessive disorder one would expect it to have a higher incidence in such a population.

Perhaps the most important aspect of the obscuring of social factors in genetic studies is that psychodynamic theories of the schizophrenic family favor a recessive social heredity. In the articles in this volume by Lidz, Bowen, and Weakland, the parents are not obviously schizophrenic, and it is postulated that the child's being psychotic may play an important part in the parent's mental economy. Hill's three-generation theory of schizophrenia (75) and the work of Mendell and Fisher (76) also favor a social heredity that would be transmitted in the same manner as postulated for a recessive gene. This theory is further supported by a three-generation study of the families of schizophrenics by Sivadon (77). The geneticist H. J. Muller (78) has stated:

> It is germane in this connection to remind ourselves that the brain is an organ constructed for the achievement of maximum plasticity in response, and that its reactions are therefore influenced in a far more thoroughgoing way by environmental differences than are those of any other organ. When it is recalled, in addition, that a vast store of environmental influences is handed down in families, and in whole groups, through unconscious as

well as overt tradition and through the transmission of the material means of existence, and further that all of these factors are themselves subject to the most profound and marked continuing differences it is seen how ultra cautious the investigator must be before ascribing any apparently inherited behavioral characteristics to the genes.

Neel, another geneticist, makes a relevant point when he remarks (42): "All of these facts [the complexities of the genealogical approach] so reduced the usefulness of the method that one is forced to conclude that for some time to come it will only be in the exceptional pedigree, where three or more generations can be studied and there is no close linkage that the fact of linkage will be of value to the prediction of which individuals in a population may be expected to develop disease due to an autosomal gene."

These words of caution apply particularly to using genealogies in the study of schizophrenia. Rudin reported 60 per cent more depressive disorder among the parents of his schizophrenic index cases (79). Schulz (80) found that of 38 marriages between manic depressives only 28 per cent occurred in the offspring and 12 per cent of them were diagnosed schizophrenic. Elsässer (81) reported that 19 per cent of 33 children both of whose parents were schizophrenic were mentally healthy and not schizoid. In addition to evidence of crossover are the data of investigators like Pasamanick (82) that race and socio-economic position are crucial, nongenetic, factors in psychiatric disorders. For example, without his data one might assume that the high incidence of mental defect in Negro families was on a hereditary basis.

TWIN STUDIES

Because in the controversy over the etiology of schizophrenia, so much reliance has been placed on the evidence from twin studies it is perhaps worthwhile to discuss the matter more thoroughly. The natural occurrence of monozygotic twins, the only human beings whose genotypical constitution is essentially the same, has a fascination and appeal to many others besides scientists. The notion of an identical twin responding out of biological sympathy to his other half and developing a similar disease of psychosis, even though he be many hundred miles distant, is a fascinating one, and it is not surprising that fantasy has outstripped fact in this area. One of the earliest studies, that of Tietze (83), pointed out that concordance in identical twins is such a striking occurrence that it is bound to be brought to someone's attention and perhaps overvalued and that only a careful study of other cases in which it did not occur would enable us to eliminate coincidence. Reports of discordant identical twins are strikingly absent in medical (including psychiatric) literature.

Because of the importance and interest of study in this area, and because the comparison of identical with fraternal twins has been offered as the most convincing evidence in favor of a purely biological or genetic theory of schizophrenia, I would like to review the English, German, French, Spanish, and Italian literature of the last forty years and a portion of the Scandinavian sources. I would like to give particular attention to the only two cases I have been able to find in the medical literature of identical twins reared apart from the formative years who are both diagnosed as schizophrenic, one pair reported by Kallmann from his earlier German studies (7), one by Slater in England (14).

It is not surprising that few such cases exist. Twin births occur only once in every eighty-five births, and only a third of these are monozygotic, the overwhelming majority of whom are reared together. Indeed, Newman *et al.* (84), combing the entire United States, were able to uncover only 19 pairs of twins reared apart; none of these twins happened to be schizophrenic. The paucity of twins reared apart is understandable on a chance basis, yet medical opinion appears to accept the existence of a number of such cases, perhaps because Kallmann created the classes of "separated" and "nonseparated" twins in his 1946 study (see Table 2.3).

I would also like to discuss the fairly frequent occurrence of simultaneous (or nearly simultaneous) schizophrenia in same-sexed fraternal twins, especially sisters, and the higher incidence of this phenomenon in sisters who are not twins, compared to other sibs. The classical *folie-à-deux* situation is especially worthy of attention because it does not lend itself to simple genetic explanations, and yet the form of the psychosis resembles that usually reported in identical twins.

Extensive Twin Studies in the Literature   Apart from scattered mention of pairs of psychotic twins, such as that reported by Rush during the Revolutionary War, and the cases written up by Moreau de Tours in 1859, Trousseau in 1873, and Dalton in 1876, it is only in modern times that twin studies have been treated in any systematic way. Earlier studies suffered from an inability to differentiate between monozygotic and dizygotic twins, and sampling problems were not sufficiently appreciated.

The first extensive study of a large group of schizophrenic twins is that of Luxenberger (85). Out of 25,000 patients examined, he found 350 who were of twin birth, a frequency slightly under the expectancy rate for the general population. Eighty-one of these pairs had at least one member diagnosed as schizophrenic. He was forced to eliminate 23 pairs as uncertain as to zygosity. Because 21 out of these 23 were discordant for schizophrenia, it may well be that this affected his final figures. For the remaining cases, he found a 65 per cent concordancy. Luxenberger was aware of the possibility of sampling difficulties; and, though strongly in favor of a genetic basis for schizophrenia, he was impressed by the admixture of schizophrenia with other mental illnesses and by the fact that his concordant twins tended to have a close time relationship in the onset of their psychoses. He remarks, in passing, that only in identical twins did one see this phenomenon.

Rosanoff (86) and, later, Rosanoff, Handy, *et al.* (87) collected a group of twins with many disorders including schizophrenia. They were primarily interested in discrepancies between fraternal and identical twins and did not study families. Again, there is impressive candor regarding sampling difficulties.

The next considerable study was Essen-Möller's (88); he undertook an extensive study of twins in Swedish hospitals. By sifting the reports of 10,000 patients, he found 179 who were of twin birth (a frequency of 1:48, approximately the same as in the general population). Eighty-five pairs were excluded because they were of unlike sex, and twenty-three were excluded because one member was dead, and two others were excluded for other reasons. His study consisted, therefore, of 21 identical and 48 fraternal, psychotic, index cases and their same-sexed co-twins. There were seven schizophrenic index cases among the identical group, and Kallmann gives a 71.4 per cent concordancy rate for this study (7). In four of these cases, however, the twin partner had never been hospitalized, in two the psychosis of the twin was of relatively brief duration and termed "induced" by Essen-Möller, and in only one were both about equally ill. Among the fraternal twins there were five pairs concordant for schizophrenia, and the author notes with surprise that when concordancy occurs in nonidentical pairs it is of higher degree than in identical pairs, both in its form and in its development. While this is not explicable on genetic grounds, it lends itself to a psychodynamic explanation: namely, psychotic identification is bound to be stronger, or more forced, in a pair who are not actually identical. Essen-Möller's own summaries of these cases are well worth reading for the light they shed on the problems inherent in such studies.

Kallmann in America has published two very extensive studies, in 1946 (10) and in 1952 (50). The figures from these studies have been reviewed in the preceding section, because they constitute his most important data on the incidence of schizophrenia in families as well as in twins.

Gedda (11) in Italy published an extensive review of all the literature to date (1951) on schizophrenia in twins but did not include any original material.

In 1953, Slater and Shield in England (21) published a study on psychotic and neurotic illnesses in twins. The study includes 41 identical and 115 fraternal schizophrenic index cases and their co-twins.

There are also approximately 60 individual reports in the literature of schizophrenia in twins. Most of these reports are of concordant cases, and despite great variation in the data presented the majority have features in common and will be discussed later.

Although a summary (Table 2.3) of the figures presented by the more

TABLE 2.3

Expectancy of schizophrenia in co-twins of schizophrenics

	YEAR	NO. OF PAIRS DZ	MZ	TOTAL INDEX	PER CENT MZ TO DZ	INCIDENCE OF S DZ	MZ
Luxenberger	1930	60	21	81	35.0	3.3	66.6
Rosanoff	1934	101	41	142	40.6	10.0	67.0
Essen-Möller	1941	24	7	31	29.2	16.7	71.0
Slater	1951	115	41	156	35.6	14.0	76.0
Kallmann	1946	517	174	691	33.7	14.5	77.6S* 91.5NS* 85.6
Kallmann	1952	685	268	953	39.1	14.5	85.6 (av.)

* Separated.

important available twin studies is impressive (even discounting discrepancies between observers), and although the comparison of identical twins of similar genotype with nonidentical twins whose genetic structure is no more similar than ordinary siblings has all the earmarks of a controlled experiment in the separation of environment from heredity, methodological criticisms have been made (15, 17, 89). Moreover, the ordinary comparison of fraternal to identical twins does not reveal the very striking finding that same-sexed fraternal twins, especially sisters, have a much higher concordancy rate than ordinary sibs. Unfortunately some studies have not broken their fraternal cases down as to sex, but where this has been done the concordance for like-sexed fraternal twins can be demonstrated to range from 17.6 per cent to 56 per cent in contrast to opposite sexed twins whose concordance ranges from 5 to 11.5 per cent. I will go into this question of same sexed and opposite sexed twins in some detail because, surprisingly, it has not been dealt with by those doing twin studies even though *a series like Slater's reveals that 11 of 13 concordant fraternal pairs are same-sexed.*

Reservations about Twin Studies   Genetic authorities themselves have a number of reservations about twin studies in general that are, I think, worth mentioning here. For example, Price (91), Neel and Schull (89), and others have cautioned that monozygotic twins do not merely share genetic structure; they share the same maternal circulation. This factor of their intra-uterine environment is most strikingly revealed in the work of Penrose, Benda (92), and others on Mongolism. Although an exceedingly high concordance for Mongolism in identical twins as compared to nonidentical twins has been reported, the establishment of the relation between maternal age and Mongolism has pointed to intrauterine development as the critical factor. Benda has since studied the specific placental defects involved (93, 94). Pasamanick's many studies will be cited further on. In short, both the incidence of twinning and of mental defect in Negroes is significantly higher than in whites and can be shown to be related to socio-economic factors.

Both Luxenburger and Rosanoff felt they had not escaped sampling difficulties in their twin studies, and Slater freely expresses his doubts also. This problem is further discussed by Price (95). Rosanoff made the specific point that when identical twins were concordant, they were so much easier to locate that he felt his sample was undoubtedly biased. He deliberately used the term "probably monozygotic" because of the difficulty in ascertaining zygosity. Only Kallmann has maintained his belief in the randomness of his sample, and yet this can be shown to be an incorrect assumption. Apart from the possible deficiencies of the modified Weinberg formula which Kallmann uses for expectancy rates, and the inclusion of 103 twin index cases who already had a hospitalized schizophrenic twin (10), a comparison of Kallmann's sample of 691 cases in 1946 with the 953 twin pairs gathered by 1950 reveals that in four years the identical twins had increased from 174 to 278 pairs, whereas the fraternal had increased only from 517 to 685. This is a much higher proportion of identical twins than is found in the normal population. One explanation for this disproportion might be that the period covered is a relatively short one (four years) so that most of the additions to the already surveyed hospital population of New York State would be new admissions. Since many observers have testified to the frequent and striking concordance in time of onset of psychosis in identical twins, and since by the terms of the experiment cases more than five years apart in time could not be added, there would be a natural tendency to collect more concordant identical pairs. Another factor difficult to judge as to importance is that concurrence of onset means a much greater burden for the family, and of course, a greater likelihood that both identical twins will be hospitalized. Rosanoff stated that if he found a pair of concordant identical twins they were usually in the same hospital (86).

Another obvious possibility is that outlying hospitals in the New York system, knowing of Kallmann's interest, would alert him to concordant pairs. This is a natural hazard of studying anything as spectacular as concordant identical twins. Neel and Schull (89) remark that there undoubtedly is preferential reporting of concordant identical twins and discuss other sampling problems, including the determination of zygosity and the tendency for twins to occur in certain families and in relation to maternal age.

Essen-Möller's study (88) also reveals that concordant figures on identical twins must be treated with caution. Of the few who had psychoses, only one of the identical twin partners had more than a transitory psychosis. If such cases are listed as schizophrenic along with cases who develop a chronic deteriorating form of the disease, there appears to be a more impressive concordance than in fact exists. This same study reveals the problem in diagnosis created by examining identical twins. The observer may see them as alike to such an extent that his definition of schizophrenia becomes overly loose. Evidently Kallmann reported Essen-Möller's concordance as 71.4 per cent on the basis of the author's statements regarding "similar character" rather than an actual occurrence of what most psychiatrists would agree was "schizophrenia." This tendency to see identical twins as alike may account for Kallmann's lumping of twins with "nondeteriorating schizophrenia" and "no schizophrenia" into the "similar" category. It should also be noted that Slater diagnoses one of his twins reared apart as schizophrenic, whereas paranoid character might be the more usual diagnosis of an English psychiatrist (21).

Because identical twins look alike, tend to have a similar prepsychotic personality (not entirely on genetic grounds), attract great interest if they are concordant, and are likely to be found in the same hospital within six months to a year of each other, they tend to blind the genetically oriented with the splendor of their sameness. Consider, for example, the statement by Kallmann in his recent article (1958 [96]): "Consistent similarity in the composition of these personality components is not observed in the absence of genotypical identicalness. Two-egg twins of the same sex tend to differ as much in their personalities as any siblings reared together or apart. It is only in one-egg twins that even pronounced differences in life experiences, however adverse, are not potent enough to erase basic similarities in appearance and general personality traits." Later in the same article he cites Kranz and

Lange's figures as evidence for an inherited aspect to criminality and notes they vary from 14 per cent in opposite sexed pairs, to 54 per cent in same sexed pairs, to 66 per cent in identical twins. The author then states: "Therefore the trend toward criminal behaviour in two-egg pairs may stem largely from the effect of unfavorable environmental influences." Clearly, this is a double standard: if identical twins are concordant it is heredity; and if fraternal twins are concordant, it is environment. The untenability of this position is revealed when the author notes that criminality may be caused in many cases by constitutional factors, but discordance may occur even in one-egg pairs if one twin manages to keep within the bounds of the law. Evidently, one is hereditarily outside the law, but environmentally within it.

Thus, aside from the questions of sampling, of diagnosis, and of statistical methods there remains the question of how the data are to be interpreted.

In this connection, it is important to establish, first, the position of those who see the results of twin studies as evidence for a genetic basis for schizophrenia. Slater (90), in answering Bleuler's criticism that the early environment of identical twins differed from the normal population and from nonidentical twins, stated his position as follows:

(1) It is not true that in infancy uniovular twins are more alike than binovular.

(2) There is no evidence that mothers differ significantly in their emotional attitudes to twins of the same sex.

(3) There is no evidence that differences in early emotional environment are related to later psychotic illness.

(4) The argument is dictated by emotional bias.

He then states his conviction that psychological environment of infancy and early childhood could not lead "to an endogenous psychosis such as schizophrenia." Slater does not, however, entirely neglect an environmental role in the etiology of schizophrenia; he points to discordance among identical twins as proof of the importance of interpersonal processes. His argument is one of emphasis only, and yet it deserves an answer because the relationship of the roles assigned to heredity and environment in the psychiatric field is still a crucial problem with practical and theoretical consequences.

(1) Uniovular twins are no more alike in infancy than binovular twins. Slater's own case histories frequently mention the confusion that the mother and others felt over which twin was which, and a number of cases in the literature contain statements by the patient about his own confusion over identity. For example, Laignel's (97) case reveals one twin (the sicker) refer-

ring to herself as "we" while the other is still able to say "I" and "my sister."

An examination of at least 100 photographs of twins from the literature (see especially Kallmann [17]) reveals a striking difference between the photographs of identical and nonidentical twins. Fraternal twins may be dressed differently even in infancy, whereas identical twins are regularly dressed alike through adolescence and many times into adulthood and even old age, thus emphasizing the already existing likeness.

Slater evidently refers to "infancy" because some psychodynamic theories have emphasized early trauma in schizophrenia. Identical twins are apparently very close at least through adolescence, and this closeness may be a more crucial factor than their infancy period. Wilson (98) sent questionnaires to 70 monozygotic and 69 like-sexed dizygotic and 55 unlike-sexed dizygotic high school students. Forty-three per cent of the identical twins and 26 per cent of the like-sexed fraternal twins had never been separated for a day; and 76 per cent of the identicals and 52 per cent of the fraternals had the same friends. The identicals and like-sexed fraternals showed similar preferences for foods, activities, and studies in about the same proportion as for friends.

Von Bracken (99) and Newman *et al.* (100) have both shown in studies of apparently normal twins that one twin becomes the "outside representative" as von Bracken labels him. He takes the initiative for both in regard to the outside world. This is interesting in view of the tendency of identical twins to have a *folie à deux* type of psychosis as the majority of cases cited in the literature indicate. It is not clear what Slater means when he states that monovular twins are not "more alike in infancy than binovular," but there is evidence to indicate that monovulars share a unique emotional relationship based on alikeness.

(2) There is no evidence that mothers differ significantly in their emotional attitude toward twins of the same sex. If one broadens this question into "Is there a relationship between same-sexedness and concordance for schizophrenia in twins?" then there is striking evidence from the twin studies already cited. Such a relationship has not been described previously, to my knowledge, and is mainly present in sister fraternals. Obviously, such a finding depends on a number of variables, but the mother's attitude is probably one.

Obviously same-sexed and different-sexed fraternal twins have the genotypical relationship of ordinary siblings. Therefore, because it is not claimed that schizophrenia is a sex-linked disorder, one would not expect a difference in concordance for schizophrenia on a hereditary basis. On the other hand, if the hypothesis is correct that identical twins are more concordant for schizophrenia because of their "twinness," one would expect a higher incidence of concordance for schizophrenia in same-sexed fraternal twins because they are more alike from an identity standpoint than different-sexed fraternal twins. For a number of reasons to be mentioned, it also seems likely that female twins would be "closer" on the whole than male twins. Slater (21) mentions that 11 out of 13 of his concordant fraternal pairs were same-sexed females, the other two were same-sexed males and were only possible, not probable, schizophrenics. He states: "We can only note this fact as a medical curiosity and cannot offer an explanation." Rosanoff (86) showed similar findings. Only one pair of 11 opposite-sexed twins were concordant, whereas seven out of twelve same-sexed were. He noted a concordance rate of 56 per cent for like-sexed fraternals, and four female fraternal pairs to one male with similar types of illness. He stated that of the discordant identical twins 47.5 per cent were male, whereas only 18.2 per cent of the females were discordant. Kallmann does not give a sex breakdown, but in his 1946 report (10) he does give figures for same-sexed and opposite-sexed pairs from which one can compute that the ratio is 17.6 to 11.5—a significant difference. Table 2.4 reports the studies where data were available on same-sexedness.

(3) There is no evidence that differences in early emotional environ-

TABLE 2.4

Nongenetic concordances

Same Sexed DZ Twins:
Lange—Criminality   MZ 66 DZ 54 (same sex) 14 (opposite sex)
Rosanoff—Schizophrenia MZ 86 DZ 56 (same sex) 21 (opposite sex)
Slater—9 out of 11 female DZ, 2 male (only possible schizophrenics)
Essen-Möller—of 5 concordant DZ, 4 are F
Kallmann   85.6   17.6 (same sex; female-male not given)
                           To 11.5 opposite sex

Family Groupings:
Zehnder: 84 per cent of pairs   *Sisters* (11F to 2M within 5 years)
           were female   (14F to 2M within 10 years)
Penrose: *Pairs of relatives, frequency:*   *Of total samples:*
               Sister–Sister   8.7% Fathers
               Brother–Brother   24.5% Mothers
               Mother–Daughter   30.0% Relatives
Folie à deux: Sisters—4.5 to 1 over other relatives
         Mother–Daughter—16 times greater than Father–Daughter
         Mother–Son   — 8 "   "   " Father–Son

ment are related to later psychotic illness. For the evidence on this question, I would refer the reader to other papers in this volume, as it is too large a question to be gone into here. It may be sufficient here to note that this is merely an argument in the negative and that no proof is offered that they are *not* related. Slater is correct, in my opinion, in taking issue with the over-stressed concept of infantile trauma, but overemphasis does not leave only genetic causation.

(4) The argument is dictated by emotional bias. This, being an argument *ad hominem,* is very difficult to answer on a rational basis. A review of the literature reveals that neither the heredicist nor the psychodynamicist has reason to be proud of his objectivity.

Ego Fusion and Ego Fission   The literature of fiction is rich with stories of the unique relationship of identical twins. *The Corsican Brothers* is perhaps the most exaggerated tale of ego fusion, whereas *The Years Are Even* is a psychologically sensitive novel about the damage to each twin that alikeness can bring. Edgar Allan Poe paints the horror of "which one is me?" in his story "William Wilson."

There have been a few scientific psychological studies, perhaps the most important being Dorothy Burlingham's book *Twins* (101), in which she describes in detail the unusual psychological circumstances of twins and their attitude to one another. She says: "Identical twins when they grow up often fail to develop into separate human entities. It remains a matter of conjecture whether this is due to the twinship itself or to the attitude of the mother who in their infancy could not tell them apart; who was driven by an inner urge to give them the same opportunities and experiences thus treating them as one being and not two."

If, then, we leave for a time the position of the heredicist and consider some of the factors we have been discussing from the point of view of the psychodynamicist—particularly the family-oriented psychodynamicist—it would appear that, in the family situation that has been described as psychogenetically important to the development of schizophrenia, the mother would have an especially difficult time with identical twins (see Chapters 11–13). In addition, the family environment might drive the twins into a close, yet mutually hostile and dependent, situation. The identity problem of the schizophrenic, most often stressed by psychodynamically oriented writers, could find no better nidus than in the intertwining of twin identities, in the ego fusion that in one sense doubles the ego (because the other is felt as part of the self) and in another sense halves it (because the self is felt as part of the other).

If the psychodynamic thesis is correct, if ego fusion in a particular family environment can be expected to lead to joint madness, then a plausible hypothesis—contrary to the genetical hypothesis—would be that, according to the degree of likeness in siblings, we will find an increased concordance for schizophrenia, without concern for genetic similarity.

In support of this psychodynamic hypothesis, it can be said that fraternal twins have a greater concordance for schizophrenia than ordinary siblings in all reported studies and like-sexed fraternal twins largely account for this difference. Moreover, like-sexed female fraternal twins have a significant and usually markedly increased concordance over like-sexed males. According to Zehnder's figures (40) and Penrose's (39), nontwin sisters are much more concordant in timing of onset of psychosis and in symptoms than are brothers or brother-sister mixed pairs. These sisters also make up the predominant number of pairs. Zehnder studied all of the siblings admitted to a Swiss hospital over a 20-year period. There were 38 family groupings, 28 being sibling pairs, five being three sibs, and five being four sibs. The total ratio of female to male was 63 to 26. However, of her pairs of sibs 84 per cent were female. The males came from the multiple sib families. Eleven pairs of sisters had their psychoses within five years of one another (the author divided the 20 years into five-year periods), whereas two brother pairs were in this category and no mixed sibs. Fourteen pairs of sisters had psychoses within ten years and only two brother pairs.

The heavy incidence of female pairs would point to there being a "closeness" in sisters, especially fraternal twin sisters, which might be accounted for, in part, by some of the following facts. Culturally, girls are more restricted in activities outside the home than are boys. This was especially true in the years nearer the Victorian era, the time at which the patients in these various studies were going through childhood and adolescence, and the situation still obtains in poorer families, who constitute a significant per cent of the patient population reported on. Under these conditions the boys probably work away from home, whereas the girls help around the house or work as domestic servants, with little opportunity for social contacts.

Close ties between sisters do not carry the opprobrium that they might with brothers. "Sissy" and "homosexual" implications would be more likely to attach to brothers than to sisters in our culture, especially in terms of kissing, hugging, handholding, and so on.

Sisters might be more restricted in their opportunities to marry because it is not culturally permissible for them to seek out the opposite sex. Indeed, a close yet jealous relationship between sisters might well be a factor in discouraging possible suitors. Sisters even more than brothers may experience considerable guilt and fear about establishing sexual relationships, and in turn would be driven back to each other as an outlet for feelings they dare not acknowledge. In this connection it is interesting to note that Kallmann reports a 20 per cent excess of females in his twin studies (67), Slater has 22 female pairs out of 28 concordant cases (21), and Essen-Möller 17 female and nine male concordant pairs (88). In Slater's total twin series, female index cases outnumber male 2:1. In 115 fraternal and 41 identical pairs, there are 103 female pairs. Of the 41 concordant pairs, 31 are female.

These observations on sex differences in fraternal twins, or in siblings, when added to the difference in concordance for like-sexed fraternals over opposite-sexed, and for fraternal twins over siblings, appear to me to be significant. They achieve further importance when one notes that *folie à deux* is four times more common in women than in men and most frequently in sister pairs. Because *folie à deux* and the psychoses of twins have a number of factors in common, this topic is worth considering further.

Folie à Deux   Many of the case studies in the literature of twins concordant for schizophrenia use the term "folie à deux" in the title. As a matter of fact, some of the earliest reports in the literature use terms like "twin madness," "la folie gemellaire," and "Zwillenschriften," implying a unique clinical entity.

If twinness in itself is an important contributor to the high concordance rate in identical twins, then one might expect clinical resemblances between their psychoses and *folie à deux*. The following important similarities can be noted.

The most consistent finding in *folie à deux*, according to Gralnick (70), is a long-standing association between the pair, usually accompanied by a reciprocal isolation. Deutsch (102), Fenichel (103), Burlingham (101), and Cronin (104) have stated that there is an unconscious sharing, not merely a living together. Compare this fact with the fact that every twin report I have discussed mentions the strength of attachment between the pair, either in positive terms or in terms of mutual antagonism and jealousy. There are no indifferent cases. It is possible to make this statement on the basis of a review of 60 case reports in the literature. Despite the fact that the vast majority are not psychodynamically presented, the historical data and descriptions of delusions leave no doubt about existing, intense hostile-dependent attachment.

Important data on association are available from Kallmann's 1946 report (10). Fifty-two of his identical twins separated at least five years prior to the onset of a psychosis in one of them; 115 did not. The "separated" group had an adjusted concordance of 77.6 per cent while the "nonseparated" group had a concordance of 91.5 per cent. This difference is very significant when it is realized that the average age was 33 years. A separation even past the formative years was apparently very effective in reducing the concordance rate. From another point of view, it is remarkable that so large a number were living together at so late an age. I have already mentioned Wilson's study, which revealed that 43 per cent of his identical group (college level) had not been separated for a day (98). Luxenberger (85) and Stolze (105) though genetically oriented imply that the close association of twins produces a unique psychosis.

Psychosis by association apparently requires the nidus of social isolation for its hatching. Not only have sociological studies pointed to the importance of social isolation for schizophrenia in general (see Chapter 10) but case histories of twins who are concordant for schizophrenia are rife with allusions to seclusiveness, religiosity, morality, and lack of sophistication. These characteristics increase the separation of the twin pair from the rest of the world and foster a joint ego fusion. Identification has been stressed in *folie à deux* by Gralnick (70), Brill (106), Deutsch (102) and Oberndorf (107). The attempt of one to be like the other is not dissimilar to the ego fusion of some twins.

As has been pointed out, one of the striking agreements between schizophrenia in twins and *folie à deux* is the high incidence in females. *Folie à deux* is four times as common in sisters as brothers, and mother-daughter combinations outnumber mother-son two to one. These combinations are, respectively, 16 and eight times more common than father-daughter and father-son combinations. In answer to the argument that these cases could all, by chance, have a hereditary basis, it is important to note that husband and wife combinations are next after sister-sister and mother-daughter. Furthermore, a number of *folie à deux* reports mention family histories negative for schizophrenia as do a number of twin reports. Gralnick says of this point (70): "The frequency with which *folie à deux* occurs within families . . . does not necessarily prove that heredity is important. It is only within the family unit, as we know it, that all or most of the factors and mechanisms that have been cited can operate."

In addition, it should perhaps be pointed out that in both *folie à deux* and the ego fusion of twins there are obvious homosexual fears and jealousies. Even in the twin reports that give almost no psychodynamic material, homosexual problems are evident in the content of delusions and hallucinations. Two cases of concordant male twins, for example, mention the fear of choking on a banana, and two cases of female twins cite the fear of being

poisoned by semen. (Lidz's report on a pair of identical twins concordant
for schizophrenia, one of the few that is psychodynamically oriented, is, unfortunately, unpublished.)

Although female cases are much more common, it is interesting to note
that more recognition has been given to the homosexual element in male
pairs, probably because of some of the cultural factors mentioned earlier and
because the sexual element in the relationship of such sisters most often
takes the form of mutual jealousy and strong rejection of any association
with any man by either of them.

I have compared the usual form of schizophrenia reported in concordant identical twins with *folie à deux* because of the interesting sex ratio, the
concurrence of onset, and the "induced" quality of the psychosis of the fol-
lower twin. These common factors, plus the number of non-blood-related
cases of *folie à deux,* would seem to render unlikely the validity of a hereditary argument. So also as separation is reportedly therapeutic for pairs with
folie à deux it is apparently therapeutic for identical twins reared in a sick
environment, a fact that again argues against a primarily hereditary basis
for either. For, in the relatively few cases reported of identical twins discordant for schizophrenia, the common denominator appears to be separation. In some cases the twins were geographically separated; in others, physical illness or handicap acted as a "separating" factor. Luxenberger (85)
emphasized this "separation protection" but on other grounds. In studying
a group of discordant female identical twins, he remarked that those who
became wives and mothers did not develop schizophrenia. He, therefore,
stressed the importance of "sexual equilibrium" or metabolism as an anti-
schizophrenic factor. However, the fact that the abandoned twin became
schizophrenic may have been due to psychological rather than endocrino-
logical factors, just as her co-twin's ability to break away may have been
evidence of superior mental health.

For a very different view of the psychoses of twins and *folie à deux* the
reader should consult Kallmann's paper on the subject (108). It was written
shortly after his first large twin series was reported to the American Psychiatric Association and may have served as a rebuttal to questions raised at the
meeting about the unique environment of identical twins. The author states:
"The result [of sociogenic theories] has been almost superstitious belief in a
mysterious phenomenon that produces mental disease through personal contact. In this rather nebulous manner *folie à deux* has been stretched into a
convenient cover for investigators who continue to be opposed to the principle of human heredity in any form."

Apart from the strongly emotional tone of the whole paper, Kallmann is quite right to criticize the indiscriminate use of the term "folie à deux." However, the term connotes more than psychoses occurring in two family members, as his examples would indicate. The literature of *folie à deux* describes the presence of *shared delusions,* a strong interaction of symptoms, and a mutual affective element that makes the whole greater than its parts. Since a similarity of symptoms has not been found to have a genetic basis in any study I have reviewed, and since such similarity can be demonstrated in groups (54, 55) or in non-blood-related pairs (70) there is reason to question Kallmann's strong stand against an environmental interpretation of *folie à deux.*

One final aspect of the question of the importance of association in the psychoses of identical twins should be noted. Oggioni has stated that the similarity of symptoms in identical twins depends to some extent on how long the twins have been ill (110). He cites several pairs discordant as to symptoms who became concordant after hospitalization. This fact can be noted in several case reports (111, 112), although it is not specifically commented upon. Kallmann (108) has used concordance as to form of schizophrenia in identical twins as an important argument for genetic causation. But, because no relation between form of schizophrenia and genetic structure has been established despite intense study by Leonhard, Kleist, Schulz, Bleuler and others, it is worth raising the question whether association does not play as large a part as genetic inheritance in the sameness of symptoms of identical twins. Several case reports describe sisters or dizygotic twins with strikingly similar clinical features (113, 114).

Cases from the Literature   There are some 60 case reports of schizophrenia in identical twins in the literature. Few of these contain any psychodynamic material. Exceptions are the cases reported by Kasanin (115), Oatman (116), Adler and Magruder (117), and Lidz (118), and only Lidz's paper constituted a detailed psychodynamic study. Much material of this nature can, however, be gleaned from other papers, and it is noteworthy that in a number of them the family history, both antecedent and collateral, is negative for schizophrenia, yet the concordance in itself is held as proof of genetic origin. This is especially striking in Slater's case (14), because he is reporting on twin sisters reared apart who are both alleged to have developed schizophrenia, and the case is presented as a crucial one for the genetic theory.

The case reports can be grouped into two general classes: the first is that in which one twin is reported as schizophrenic, the other as normal, neurotic, or (in at least four cases) manic-depressive. When the information is available, it is apparent that the discordant twins have had very different environmental circumstances. Kihn (111) mentions several cases where one identical twin is schizophrenic and the other manic-depressive. He states his agreement with Luxenberger that the outcome of the psychosis in twins can be varied according to their external circumstances. This is in marked contrast to Kallmann, who has stressed that crossovers between schizophrenic and affective disorders do not occur when proper diagnostic criteria are used. As recently as 1958 (96), Kallmann has stated that manic-depressive psychoses and schizophrenia do not occur in one-egg pairs. Interestingly, Slater chides his colleagues for disregarding Kallmann's statement and insisting there are crossovers between the two disorders; yet Slater is one of those who has reported an identical pair with both disorders (119).

In the second general class the twins are concordant for schizophrenia and developed their psychoses on the same day or within weeks of each other and either share a typical *folie à deux* situation or mimic each other in a fashion that Stolze (105) declares is only found in identical twins. He feels the symptomatology differs from ordinary schizophrenia and reports an illustrative case. However, there are several reports in the literature even more striking than Stolze's (117, 120, 121); and Siemens (122) reported that three of six identical twins had simultaneous onset.

Among the cases describing discordant twins, Wigers' (123), which I have already mentioned, is well worth careful study by any investigator of the nature-nurture problem. Although one twin became definitely schizophrenic while the other continued to function adequately, the material presented, particularly a long letter from the nonschizophrenic twin to his brother's doctor, appears to present a typical disturbed twin relationship. The brothers had been reared in a home environment described as good, and the only possible schizophrenic in the family history is a grandmother's brother, hospitalized with the diagnosis of dementia. It is particularly interesting to note that the schizophrenic twin is sent away from home by the family as punishment for sexual activity engaged in by both brothers, whereas the other twin remains at home. Evidently some difference in family role had already been present, with one twin in the more fortunate position. The few reports in the literature on discordant twins reveal that the schizophrenic twin has increasingly unsuccessful relationships for a variety of reasons. It would seem that doing less well than one's twin is much more intolerable than if an ordinary sibling were involved.

Among the reports of cases in the second category—concordant twins—a revealing and typical one is that reported by Oatman (116) of Negro male identical twins who developed schizophrenia simultaneously upon their being drafted and reporting to an army camp. At least five years prior to this, it had been noted by high-school friends that they communicated by hand signals and spoke of telepathic powers. This case is similar to Rubin's (121) and shares several features with other reports of male identical twins who became concordant for schizophrenia: (1) There was an attempt to separate which failed. (2) There are homosexual fears and homosexual content to delusions. (3) The twins, once psychotic, cling to each other and can only be separated by force, and any difference in their symptomatology blends together as the hospital stay continues. This situation was reported as early as 1859 by Moreau de Tours. Many reports note the isolation of the twins from other hospital patients; and to judge from the cases reported, separating them has not been the usual practice.

Wigers' case suggests that there may be only a difference in degree from the concordant situation. Whether by family attitude or by chance, separation appears to play a prominent role in the cases reported as discordant (115, 123, 124).

A fascinating and consistent finding in these case histories is that the first-born twin is apt to be the leader in a *folie à deux* situation. In Wynne's (125) report on a detailed study of identical female quadruplets who became schizophrenic all were born within 17 minutes, yet the first born remained the responsible "eldest" and the last born became the "baby." This study is one of the most interesting documents available on the nature-nurture situation. In *folie à deux,* the "leader" is more often the older sibling, and in opposite-sexed twins the sister is more often the leader (*e.g.,* see Slater's figures).

The problem of sharing and yet not being able to share or to separate is rampant in the case reports of identical twins with schizophrenia. This is more than a problem of twins being alike in infancy. It often continues into maturity. The sharing of the mother seems to be an especially thorny problem, as does the already mentioned identity difficulty and the homosexual implications in sharing each other. In this connection, Kallmann's figures on male homosexuality in twins are instructive; he found a concordance rate of 100 per cent for homosexuality in monozygotic twins, and 42 per cent for dizygotic. Although Kallmann (7) and Shea (1) have used this high concordance as evidence of the biological inheritance of homosexuality, this study has not been confirmed, does not include female twins, and identical twins discordant for homosexuality have been reported (126). In the 40 male cases studied by Kallmann, there is asserted to have been no intrapair sex play, which seems a remarkable finding in view of the ordinary situation between male siblings. It is possible that homosexual activity with outsiders is a defense against fusion with the co-twins.

A report which has features of both *folie à deux* and "twin psychosis"—
with more shared symptomatology rather than one twin's being active and the
other passive—is recorded by Adler and Magruder (117). Twenty-six-year-old
identical twin sisters show an important togetherness—or ego fusion as I
have called it—which lasted despite their marriages. One failed in the sixth
grade, and the other left school rather than be separated. At 17, both married farmers—alcoholics and poor providers—but continued to spend most
of their time at their father's house. After one twin had moved away and
returned without her husband, the other forced her husband out. But after
he returned for an evening's visit, the sisters became convinced that their
father was dead and one developed the delusion that the visiting husband
had tried to poison her twin, a delusion that the twin accepted—whereupon
the wife denied it. But after their discharge from the hospital, both maintained the charge, apparently convinced others of the truth of it, and continued to live together having thus excluded the interloping husband.

Solomon and Bliss (120) reported on the nearly simultaneous onset of
schizophrenia in a pair of male, homosexual identical twins. A's illness developed over an affair with the wife of his best friend, and B broke down out
of concern for his brother. One can speculate on the possible relationship to
sharing the mother. There are several similar reports of the second twin's
becoming increasingly concerned over the first's illness and finally joining
him in a duet of unreality.

A common occurrence in case reports is the presence of a third party
who apparently threatens the twins' relationship. This is reported, *e.g.*, by
Cronin (104), Lidz (118), Adler and Magruder (117), Gardner and Stephens
(127) Murphy and Luidens (128), and Heuyer and Longuet (129).

Rather than involving a third party as the villain, the twins may accuse
each other of being the persecutor. (This is a noteworthy feature in the two
cases of identical twins reared apart, as we shall see.)

A case reported by Weatherly and Diabler (130) is perhaps most illustrative of the ambivalence of a disturbed twin relationship. Although the
authors emphasize genetic features, there is no family history of schizophrenia except for an elder sister with an uncertain diagnosis. There were 11
siblings, the twins being seventh born. The father is described as strict, the
mother as warm and interested in her children. She felt that "Tom is so
babyfied I think I have tied him too strongly to my apron strings." Although
Tom was the larger (and later the leader), even their mother had difficulty
in telling them apart. They were close until high-school age, when they
went to different schools. Three years later, both left school, perhaps because
of their father's death that year or their sister's hospitalization two years
earlier.

When he was nearly 20, Tom joined the army and was discharged two years later. Two years after that he joined the Marines and a year later John joined. John became "abruptly" psychotic a little over a year later. He heard voices, was fearful, and was hospitalized. Later Tom heard voices calling him queer and was hospitalized. After some therapy, both twins were discharged and returned home. Soon Tom was rehospitalized with homosexual fears, and John became abruptly psychotic as a result of visiting Tom in the hospital. He improved when placed in the same ward as his brother.

While Tom was on a trial visit home, John escaped and both lived at home for five months. John was returned to the hospital, again escaped and returned home, and the twins returned to the hospital together. They had become mutually antagonistic. When Tom was given another trial visit John eloped and returned home, where he made a serious suicide attempt. He was lobotomized, improved, and returned home, whereupon Tom became "tearful, anorexic and depressed," stating: "I didn't hurt anybody." This unique zigging and zagging is reported in other case histories and surely points to a psychodynamic interplay that is a feature of the psychoses of identical twins.

Another interesting report is that of Walther-Buel and Storch (132). They discuss a pair of identical twins concordant for schizophrenia and note that they came from such a traumatic background that it is difficult to conclude whether heredity or twinness played any part. This paper is an exception (especially in the European literature), because concordancy in identical twins most often leads to the unitary idea that heredity is the controlling factor even in the presence of a negative family history.

It is interesting to compare with these twin studies Murphy's report (131) of two girls, adopted into the same family, from different natural parents. The girls became schizophrenic within a few years of each other, and the study reads like some twin reports. The younger maintained her "baby" role during her psychosis, a reminder of the twin reports that indicate a splitting into the "younger" and the "older" twin or of *folie à deux* histories that demonstrate a "stronger" and a "weaker" partner.

Finally, I would like to refer the reader to Essen-Möller's own summaries (88) of his seven identical pairs. They are reported by Kallmann (7) as showing a 71 per cent concordance, but it should be remembered that this figure is not claimed by Essen-Möller and is apparently based on the listing of similar prepsychotic character traits in the twins, not on schizophrenic psychoses. The cases are, however, well worth examination.

There are, as I have already said, only two studies in the literature reporting cases of schizophrenia in identical twins reared apart from infancy, one by Kallmann (57) and one by Craike and Slater (14). Because such a tremendous amount of emphasis has been given to them, I would urge all interested in the etiology to read the reports for themselves. They are presented as crucial natural experiments in the nature-nurture field, as indeed they would be if others could be found to raise their occurrence above the level of chance and if the twins had demonstrably different environments. But only two cases are available, and neither seems to me to fit the criteria of "separate environment." (That separation can produce striking differences is indicated in the book on twins by Newman *et al.* (100), in which, *e.g.*, they report a 60 per cent role for environment in the determination of I.Q. The largest difference occurred in a pair of sisters, one of whom was poorly educated, whereas the other finished college. The first had an I.Q. of 92, the second, 116.)

The earlier of these two studies is Kallmann's and concerns the identical twins Kaete and Lisa. The family history shows alcoholism, eccentricity, and a mother of "limited mental endowment," who as a domestic servant impressed all her employers with her peculiar behavior, bore the twins illegitimately, was committed twice before she developed tuberculosis, deteriorated both mentally and physically, and died at the age of 42.

Shortly after birth each of the twins was adopted by a different maternal uncle. These uncles lived in different cities and were on very bad terms with one another, so that the twins saw each other only a few times and for very brief periods in their first decade, later more often. They apparently adopted the mutually hostile relationship of the maternal uncles, and singled each other out for attack. Although they did well at school and both advanced to the upper grades, their uncles independently reported them to be "difficult to teach, stubborn, callous and indifferent," and stated that both girls were always doing the opposite of what they were told. Kaete had measles at 10, but Lisa did not; otherwise, they developed similarly and both had their first menstruation at the age of 12, in the same month. They were both exactly the same size and had the same blue eyes and blond hair; they are described as strikingly pretty.

After they left school, Kaete was employed in a factory, while Lisa became a domestic servant. Kaete was seduced at the age of 15 and gave birth to a baby who was raised in an orphanage; so far the child has been normal. The delivery was uncomplicated, but a few days later Kaete became excited and perturbed and eventually lapsed into a catatonic stupor and was committed to Herzberg Hospital in 1928. Except for a brief improvement in 1930, when she was discharged under family care, her progress has been downhill. She was readmitted in June 1930.

Lisa, who had remained a virgin and continued in domestic service, also began to exhibit schizophrenic symptoms about the time Kaete was released from the hospital in February 1930. These took the form of slowly increasing helplessness and emotional indifference which increased to such a point that she was hospitalized in June 1930, the same time as Kaete. However, she has never been quite as ill as Kaete; they are at present both patients in the same hospital.

In commenting on this case, Kallmann states that because the twins were exposed to utterly different conditions of life the environment could not have played a part in the development of the psychosis. "More pertinent evidence than is offered here for the hereditary conditioning of schizophrenia will not be forthcoming" and again "This case proves almost as accurately as if it had been a set experiment that definite somatogenic factors must count as dispositional determinants in the manifestation of a hereditary predisposition to schizophrenia." Kaete's pregnancy produced, according to the author, "a premature revolution of the internal secretory system especially affecting the sex glands—however, Lisa who remained a virgin matured gradually and achieved womanhood by regular degrees." It is difficult to reconcile the author's stressing somatic factors with the fact that Lisa was hospitalized only 15 months after her sister.

As to the relationship between the twins that might have led to *folie à deux* symptoms, Kallmann states: "It is therefore not surprising that, in the course of their subsequent psychoses, the two girls were emotionally so completely alienated that finally they had no affective contact whatsoever, but even singled each other out for mutually malicious attacks." This argues a much narrower definition of affect than most modern writers would allow, because the twins were obviously very far from indifferent to one another.

Kallmann also emphasizes the separation in space and argues a different environment. But since the adopting fathers were mutually hostile brothers and made extremely similar reports on the twin's development, and since the work of each twin (factory work, domestic service) argues a homogenous social background, one wonders if the difference could have been so great as is reported.

The second of these two important cases—reported by Craike and Slater (14)—concerns female twins reared apart from their ninth month, in which their mother died. The father remarried, and Florence was adopted by an unmarried maternal aunt. Edith stayed with her father, who became an alcoholic and who mistreated her. When she was eight, he struck her with a razor, whereupon she was put into a children's home where she stayed until she was 19. Although it is alleged that there was no contact between the twins until they were 24, Edith, when living with her father, certainly knew of Florence's existence, for she declared that Florence made trouble for her by telling her father that Edith said he was a drunkard. It may be important in view of their subsequent mutual antagonism and jealousy that they knew thus early of each other, for despite a lack of direct contact they could hardly have helped wondering who was getting the better breaks.

Edith went to work as a domestic servant and apparently gave satisfaction, as she held one job for eleven years; she lost this job at the age of 48. She was said to be pleasant and capable but felt that visitors to the home accused her of wrongdoing. She went to a glass factory, where she is reported to have been a superior worker, but from time to time would contact her supervisor to find out if she was causing any trouble among the other workers by her presence. The authors state that, when she was interviewed, "Edith was inclined to be suspicious and reserved but there were no characteristic schizophrenic symptoms."

Although the authors say that Florence had a happy time with her aunt, she is reported during her childhood as being "nervous," afraid of the dark, backward in school, and suffering from numerous fainting attacks. She left school at 14, also to become a domestic; she stole from her employer and was placed in a convent for two years. It is stated that she was happy while there, despite being away from the aunt who was so good to her. At 18, she had an attack of "nervous debility" with abdominal pain, vomiting, and nervousness. She stayed with another aunt while recuperating; a fact that casts further doubt on the authors' attempt to picture Florence as having a loving home situation.

At the age of 24, having been left some money by an aunt, the girls are said to have had their first meeting. It was apparently rather stormy, as Edith claimed that Florence said she had paid Edith's fare to London and that therefore Edith was under obligation to her. Florence accused Edith of stealing money from her purse. Nevertheless, Florence noticed how much alike they were and wished to live with Edith, but Edith refused.

Florence returned to the home of the aunt with whom she had lived since infancy. The twins continued to see each other from time to time; they were both very religious and frequently went to church together. Both in later life became somewhat deaf and each accused the other of feigning deafness; this deafness may have played a part in their delusions, since each felt that other people were talking about her. If they did not see each other face to face for some time, each began to accuse the other of spying on her, visiting her place of work, or following her from across the street—in other words, of maintaining contact. However, they continued to function adequately until the aunt's death in 1944 at the age of 85. Florence then became very depressed, felt that people were saying she ought to get married, and began to hear a man's voice saying "horrible things." She was hospitalized in this year.

The authors comment: "These monozygotic twins were brought up along entirely different lines. Florence had a stable home with an affectionate maternal aunt and has lived with her all her life until a year ago when the aunt died in 1944 at the age of 85." But I should like to point out that Florence did poorly at school, Edith well, and both twins have the same genetic endowment for intelligence. Florence breaks down and is hospitalized; Edith lives alone and does well at her work; Florence is convicted of stealing and Edith is not. The authors naturally have stressed those aspects of the twins' lives that point to a different environment. They assume, moreover, that Florence's was much superior because, on the surface, she had more advantages. However, without information about what the spinster aunt was like and without knowledge of Florence's reaction to being the one sent from home—even though her father was a drunkard—it would be unwise to make value judgments about "good" and "bad" environments. Indeed, the authors' insistence that Florence's home was a stable and happy one is difficult to reconcile with her desire to live with Edith, the fact that as a domestic she lived away from this aunt, and the fact that after her first illness she went to another aunt to recuperate.

In summary, we can see the following resemblances in the history of these twins. They lost their mother and to all intents their father (and their elder brother ran away from home and died at 27). Both sisters are unmarried domestics, sexually guilty and preoccupied with sex. Both are religious and extremely competitive and suspicious of each other, apparently with good reason. They developed their paranoid symptoms almost immediately after meeting, and they continued contacts with each other which sustained the delusions. They fed on each other in such a way that neither broke down until Florence did so at 52, immediately following her aunt's death. Actually the description of Edith is not that of classical schizophrenia, and one wonders if she would have been diagnosed as such had her sister not been.

In these two cases, it is interesting to note the similarity of family pattern. In both families, not only between the twins but also among the older generation, there is a strong drive toward separation and mutual hostility and at the same time the maintenance of contact. It is possible to speculate on the part this attitude may have played in reinforcing the twins' feelings about each other.

As proof of a primarily genetic origin of schizophrenia, these two cases would be far more convincing if each twin did not play so prominent a role in the delusional system of the other and if the environments were more dissimilar. A still more convincing proof would exist if there were a number of twins reared apart who had different schizophrenic pictures and not the symptoms of twin psychosis so frequently described in the literature.

CONCLUSION

This review has been written in an attempt to raise questions rather than to answer them, and, in particular, to question the assumption that seems to be very widely made that there is overwhelming factual evidence for a strong genetic component in the etiology of schizophrenia. Although it seems likely that hereditary factors do play a part in at least some of the schizophrenias, it remains to be established in what forms, how vital is a hereditary "vulnerability," and what the phenotypical expression is of the genotypical defect. It seems to me that with the exception of the painstaking population studies carried out in the Scandinavian countries and some of the Swiss work genetic studies in mental illness have not been of the caliber of such investigations in certain other areas of medicine. As Neel and Schull have stated (26), "An objective evaluation of the contribution which twin studies have thus far made to human heredity is a matter of some complexity. That the studies have not made the contributions which Galton envisaged is certain. In part this is due to the fact that many such studies have been approached with more perseverance than perspicacity."

Statistical studies can impress the unwary with their "scientific," "impartial" look, but it must never be forgotten that however one juggles the figures with dazzling mathematical techniques, they can never be any more accurate than the original observations upon which they are based. And impressive-looking statistics have a way of haunting investigators for years; J. de Sauvage Nolting collected extremely impressive figures to show that the majority of schizophrenics were conceived in March (133). Although no other investigator has confirmed these figures independently, many have tried to explain them on one basis or another (134, 135).

For example, it is statistically curious that the most genetically loaded families produce the majority of patients with "atypical" or "schizophreniform" psychoses with relatively good prognoses. Genetically, this finding is contrary to that for other medical disorders. But from a psychological viewpoint, it is easy to conceive of openly disturbed families allowing the individual to become more floridly psychotic. The cases reported by Johnson and her co-workers (132) may be examples of such situations.

Although the statistics that have been gathered in twin studies are impressive, there are, as we have seen, reasons to suppose that they have been inadequately controlled for nongenetic factors. Possible environmental causes and particularly psychic identification have been ignored in favor of possible genetic causes.

But, however much the geneticists may ignore the cultural, they have been able by their figures to convince many people to such an extent that they have led to unwarranted confident genetic counseling and in some cases to sterilization laws. Genetic arguments in general have a way of attaching themselves to socio-political feelings, as Pastore has shown in his interesting book *The Nature-Nurture Controversy* (136). In the field of psychiatry, too, we might expect that attitudes toward genetics and the efficacy of psychological treatment would bear an inverse ratio—and a relationship to the cultural setting of the investigators involved.

I feel that a very fruitful way of dealing with the statistics of mental illness is to break down the mass groupings according to such categories as the sex of the patient, the difference, if any, as between fathers and mothers in incidence of schizophrenia, the age of the child at the time of the parent's illness, and constitutional factors that might have affected the patient. Allen (16) describes a study that illustrates the effectiveness of this type of design. Rather than grouping epileptics into the usual categories of *grand mal, petit mal,* and psychomotor, they were studied in terms of their families and found to consist of six groups, ranging from those with a large hereditary predisposition to those with no hereditary elements but with a large psychological component. Perhaps we have been too bound by Kraepelinian classification to envisage a fresh approach, but I have tried to indicate that the technique of merely nose counting is a wasted effort.

References

1.   J. E. SHEA, The human body and the human being, *A.M.A. Arch. Neurol. & Psychiat.,* 76: 513, 1956.

2.   J. F. J. CADE, Problem of schizophrenia; Beattie-Smith lectures, *M. J. Australia,* 2, August 25, 1951.

3.   A. BALFOUR SCLARE, The problem of schizophrenia, *Med. Illus., 10* (8): 532, 1956.

4.   H. HOAGLAND, Biochemical aspects of schizophrenia, *J. Nerv. & Ment. Dis., 126* (No. 3), 1958.

5.   L. PAULING, The molecular basis of genetics, *Am. J. Psychiat., 113:* 492, 1956.

6.   J. R. SMYTHIES, Biochemical concepts of schizophrenia, *The Lancet,* p. 308, August 9, 1958.

7.   F. J. KALLMANN, *Heredity in Health and Mental Disorder,* New York: Norton, 1953.

8.   D. D. JACKSON, A note on the importance of trauma in the genesis of schizophrenia, *Psychiatry, 20:* 181, 1957.

9.   K. ERNST, "Geordnete Familienverhältnisse" späterer Schizophrener im Lichte einer Nachuntersuchung, *Arch. Psychiat., 194:* 355, 1956.

10.　F. J. KALLMANN, Genetic theory: analysis of 691 twin index families, *Am. J. Psychiat., 103*: 309, 1946.

11.　L. GEDDA, *Studio di Gemelli,* Rome: Edizioni Orrizonte Medico, 1951.

12.　W. RICHMOND, The psychic resemblances in identical twins, *Philos. Tr. Roy. Soc. London, 5*: 208, 1916.

13.　A. LEY, *L'hérédité et le Milieu, Revue de Droit Pénal et de Criminologie,* Louvain, 1946–47, p. 65.

14.　W. H. CRAIKE and E. SLATER, Folie à deux in uniovular twins reared apart, *Brain, 68*: 213, 1945.

15.　L. S. PENROSE, Value of genetics in medicine, *Brit. M. J., 2*: 903, 1950.

16.　G. ALLEN, Patterns of discovery in the genetics of mental deficiency, *Am. J. Ment. Deficiency, 62* (No. 5), 1958.

17.　M. BLEULER, Research and changes in concepts in the study of schizophrenia, 1941–50, *Bull. Isaac Ray Med. Lib., 3* (Nos. 1 and 2), 1955.

18.　F. J. KALLMANN and D. REISNER, Twin studies on significance of genetic factors in tuberculosis, *Am. Rev. Tuberc., 47*: 549, 1943.

19.　P. H. HOCH, *Failures in Psychiatric Treatment,* New York: Grune, 1948.

20.　W. L. REES, "Physical Characteristics of the Schizophrenic Patient," in Richter, D. (Ed.), *Schizophrenia: Somatic Aspects,* New York: Macmillan, 1957.

21.　E. SLATER, *Psychotic and Neurotic Illnesses in Twins,* Med. Research Council, Special Report No. 278, London: H.M. Stationery Office, 1953.

22.　F. J. KALLMANN and B. M. ASCHNER, Concurrence of Morgnani's syndrome, schizophrenia and adenomatous goitre in monozygotic twins, *Acta genet. med. et gemel., 2*: 431, 1953.

23.　M. BLEULER, *Endokrinologische Psychiatrie,* Stuttgart: Thieme, 1954.

24.　L. KANNER, *Textbook of Child Psychiatry,* London: Thomas, 1948.

25.　K. PLANANSKY, Heredity in schizophrenia, *J. Nerv. & Ment. Dis., 122* (No. 2), 1955.

26.　J. V. NEEL and W. J. SCHULL, *Human Heredity,* Chicago: Univ. Chicago Press, 1954.

27.　L. S. PENROSE, Propagation of unfit, *Lancet, 2*: 425, 1950.

28.　P. HOCH, The etiology and epidemiology of schizophrenia, *Am. J. Pub. Health, 47*: 1071, 1957.

29.　D. P. MORRIS, E. SOROKER, and G. BURRUSS, Follow-up studies of shy, withdrawn children. Evaluation of later adjustment, *Am. J. Orthopsychiat. 24*: 143, 1954.

30.　E. KRETSCHMER, *Körperbau und Charakter,* Berlin: Springer, 1948.

31.　E. JOHANSEN, A study of schizophrenia in the male, *Acta psychiat. et neurol. scandinav.,* Suppl. 125, *33*, 1958.

32.　J. E. BIRREN, Psychological examination of children who later became psychotic, *J. Abnorm. & Social Psychol., 39*: 94, 1944.

33.　H. E. FRAZEE, Children who later became schizophrenic, *Smith College Studies in Social Work, 23*: 125, 1953.

34.　K. LEONHARD, Zur Unterteilung und Erbbiologie der Schizophrenien: die "typischen" Unterformen der Katatonie, *Allgemeine Ztschr. Psychiat., 122*: 39, 1943.

35.　T. A. C. RENNIE, Analysis of 100 cases of schizophrenia with recovery, *Arch. Neurol. & Psychiat., 46*: 574, 1941.

36.   B. SCHULZ, Kinder aus Ehen zwischen einem endogen oder reaktiv Geisteskranken und einem Querulanten, *Ztschr. Neurol., 171*: 57, 1941.

37.   M. BLEULER, *Krankheitsverlauf, Persönlichkeit und Verwandschaft Schizophrener und ihre gegenseitigen Beziehungen*, Leipzig: Thieme, 1941.

38.   M. BLEULER, *Vererbungsprobleme bei Schizophrenen, Ztschr. Neurol. u. Psychiat., 127*: 321, 1930.

39.   L. S. PENROSE, Survey of cases of familial mental illness, *Digest Neurol. & Psychiat. 13*: 644, 1945.

40.   M. ZEHNDER, Über Krankheitsbild und Krankheitsverlauf bei schizophrenen Geschwistern, *Monthly J. Psychiat. & Neurol., 103*: 231, 1940.

41.   M. ROTH, "Interaction of Genetic and Environmental Factors in the Causation of Schizophrenia," in Richter, D. (Ed.), *Schizophrenia: Somatic Aspects*, New York: Macmillan, 1957.

42.   J. V. NEEL, Detection of genetic carriers of hereditary disease, *Am. J. Human Genet., 1* (No. 1): 19, 1949.

43.   E. HANHART, Zur geographischen Verbreitung der Erbkrankheiten (Mutationen) mit besonderer Berücksichtigung, *Schweiz. med. Wchnschr., 71*: 861, 1941.

44.   J. F. MASTERSON, Prognosis in adolescent disorders, *Am. J. Psychiat., 114*: 1097, 1958.

45.   L. KANNER, To what extent is early infantile autism determined by constitutional inadequacies? *A Res. Nerv. & Ment. Dis. Proc., 33*: 378, 1954.

46.   B. SCHULZ, Kinder schizophrener Elternpaare, *Ztschr. Neurol. u. Psychiat., 168*: 332, 1940.

47.   K. LEONHARD, Fragen der Erbbegutachtung bei den atypischen Psychosen, *Allgemeine Ztschr. Psychiat., 112*: 391, 1939.

48.   P. LUNDBY, Incidence of schizophrenia in a group of Norwegian seamen, *Acta psychiat. et neurol., 30*: 217, 1955.

49.   Y. O. ALANEN, The mothers of schizophrenic patients, *Acta psychiat. et neurol. scandinav.*, Suppl. 124, *33*, 1958.

50.   F. J. KALLMANN, in *Biology of Mental Health and Diseases*, New York: Hoeber, 1952.

51.   D. HENDERSON and R. D. GILLESPIE, *A Textbook of Psychiatry*, New York: Oxford, 1956.

52.   K. KOLLE, Paranoische Haftreaktionen, *Allgemeine Ztschr. Psychiat., 124*: 327, 1949.

53.   B. LEWIN, Der Einfluss magischer und religiöser auf die Pathoplastik reaktiver und endogener geistiger Störungen in Ägypten, *Ztschr. Psychotherapie u. Med. Psychol., 6* (2): 60, 1956.

54.   J. W. EATON and R. S. WEIL, *Culture and Mental Disorders*, Glencoe, Ill.: Free Press, 1955.

55.   M. K. OPLER and D. J. SINGER, Ethnic differences in behavior and psychopathology. *Internat. J. Social Psychiat., 2* (No. 1): 11, 1956.

56.   Y. ROUMAJON, Le problème de l'identité des psychoses à travers les facteurs ethniques, *Evolution Psychiatrique, 3*: 635, 1956.

57.   F. J. KALLMANN, *Genetics of Schizophrenia*, Locust Valley, N.Y.: Augustin, 1938.

58.   H. M. POLLACK and B. MALZBERG, Hereditary and environmental factors in the causation of manic-depressive psychoses and dementia praecox, *Am. J. Psychiat.*, *96*: 1227, 1940.

59.   T. LIDZ, B. PARKER, and A. CORNELISON, The role of the father in the family environment of the schizophrenic patient, *Am. J. Psychiat.*, *113*: 126, 1956.

60.   D. D. JACKSON, J. BLOCK, *et al.*, Psychiatrists' conceptions of the schizophrenogenic parent, *A.M.A. Arch. Neurol. & Psychiat.*, *79*: 448, 1958.

61.   D. D. JACKSON *et al.*, Psychiatrist's conceptions of the schizophrenic patient, *Arch. Neur. & Psychiat.*, *79*: 448, 1958.

62.   C. H. ALSTROEM, C. GENTZ, and K. LINDBLOM, Uber die Lungentuberkulose der Geisteskranken, in besondere der Schizophrenen: ihre Entstehung, Häufigkeit und Bekämpfung, *Acta Tuberc. scandinav.*, Suppl. 9, p. 1, 1943.

63.   F. W. MOTT, *J. Ment. Sc.*, *68*: 333, 1922.

64.   A. LUBIN, A note on Sheldon's table of correlations between temperamental traits, *Brit. J. Psychol.*, Statistical Section 3, p. 186, 1950.

65.   C. J. ADCOCK, A factorial examination of Sheldon's types, *J. Pers.*, *16*: 312, 1948.

66.   F. J. KALLMANN, in Kluckhohn, C., and Murray, H. A. (Eds.), *Personality in Nature, Society, and Culture*, New York: Knopf, 1949.

67.   F. J. KALLMANN, Genetics in relation to mental disorders, *J. Ment. Sc.*, *94*: 250, 1948.

68.   G. BLÜME, Hysterische psychose und "schizophrener reaktionstypus," *Allgemeine Ztschr. Psychiat.*, *99*: 355, 1933.

69.   Discussion of sulphosin, in *Year Book of Psychiatry and Neurology*, 1932, p. 221.

70.   A. GRALNICK, Carrington family: psychiatric and social study illustrating psychosis of association or folie à deux, *Psychiatric Quart.*, *17*: 294, 1943.

71.   R. W. LIDZ and T. LIDZ, The family environment of schizophrenic patients, *Am. J. Psychiat.*, *106*: 332, 1949.

72.   H. BARRY, JR., A study of bereavements: an approach to problems of mental disease, *Am. J. Orthopsychiat.*, *9*: 355, 1939.

73.   H. BARRY, JR., Significance of maternal bereavement before the age of eight in psychiatric patients, *Arch. Neurol. & Psychiat.*, *62*: 630, 1949.

74.   J. F. CADE, The aetiology of schizophrenia, *Med. J. Australia*, 2 (4): 135, 1956.

75.   L. HILL, *Psychotherapeutic Intervention in Schizophrenia*, Chicago: Univ. Chicago Press, 1956.

76.   D. MENDELL and S. FISHER, A multi-generation approach to treatment of psychopathology, *J. Nerv. & Ment. Dis.*, *126* (No. 6): 523, 1958.

77.   P. SIVADON, "The Pathological Process in Disturbed Families," Address at the World Federation for Mental Health Meeting, Copenhagen, 1957.

78.   H. J. MULLER, Progress and prospects in human genetics, *Am. J. Human Genet.*, *1*: 1, 1949.

79.   E. RUDIN, "Vererbung und Enstehung geistiger Störungen, I. Zur Vererbung und Neuentstehung der Dementia Praecox," *Monographien aus dem Gesamtgebiete der Neurologie und Psychiatrie*, Vol. 12, Berlin: Springer, 1916.

80.   B. SCHULZ, Kinder schizophrener Elternpaare, *Ztschr. Neurol. u. Psychiat.*, *168*: 332, 1940.

81.   G. ELSÄSSER, *Die Nachkommen geisteskranker Elternpaare,* Stuttgart: Thieme, 1952.

82.   B. PASAMANICK, Race, complications of pregnancy and neuro-psychiatric disorder, *Social Problems, 3,* 1957.

83.   H. KIND, in Reiss, M. (ed.), *Psychoendocrinology,* Grune, 1958.

84.   H. H. NEWMAN *et al., Twins: A Study of Heredity and Environment,* Chicago: Univ. Chicago Press, 1937.

85.   H. LUXENBERGER, Untersuchung an schizophrenen Zwillingen und ihren Geschwistern zur Prüfung der Realität von Manifestationschwankungen, *Ztschr. Neurol. u. Psychiat., 154:* 351, 1936.

86.   A. J. ROSANOFF, Study of mental disorders in twins, *Eugenical News, 17:* 37–39, 1932.

87.   A. J. ROSANOFF *et al.,* Etiology of so-called schizophrenic psychoses, with special reference to their occurrence in twins, *Am. J. Psychiat., 91:* 247, 1934.

88.   E. ESSEN-MÖLLER, Psychiatrische Untersuchungen an einer Serie von Zwillingen, *Acta psychiat. et neurol.,* Suppl. 23, 1941.

89.   J. NEEL and W. J. SCHULL, *Human Heredity,* Chicago: Univ. Chicago Press, 1954.

90.   E. SLATER, Genetic investigations in twins, *J. Ment. Sc., 99:* 44, 1953.

91.   B. PRICE, *Towards Reducing Ambiguity in Twin Studies,* Proc., 8th International Congress of Genetics, Stockholm, 1948.

92.   C. E. BENDA, *Mongolism and Cretinism,* New York: Grune, 1946.

93.   C. E. BENDA, Mongolism and heredity, *J. Hered., 38:* 177, 1947.

94.   C. E. BENDA, in *Biology of Mental Health and Disease,* New York: Hoeber, 1952.

95.   B. PRICE, Primary biases in twin studies: a review of prenatal and natal difference-producing factors in monozygotic pairs, *Am. J. Human Genet., 2:* 293, 1950.

96.   F. J. KALLMANN, The use of genetics in psychiatry, *J. Ment. Sc., 104:* 542, 1958.

97.   LAIGNEL-LAVASTINE and BENDIT, Un cas de "délire à deux" chez deux soeurs jumelles, *Ann. Médicales et Psychologiq., 15:* 237, 1940.

98.   P. T. WILSON, Study of like-sexed twins' health and disease records, *Human Biol., 3:* 270, 1931.

99.   H. VON BRACKEN, Über die Sonderart der Subjektiven Welt von Zwillingen, *Arch. Psychol., 97:* 97, 1936.

100.   H. H. NEWMAN *et al., Twins: A Study of Heredity and Environment,* Chicago: Univ. Chicago Press, 1937.

101.   DOROTHY BURLINGHAM, *Twins: A Study of Three Pairs of Identical Twins,* New York: Internat. Univ. Press, 1953.

102.   H. DEUTSCH, Folie à deux, *Psychoanalyt. Quart., 7:* 307, 1938.

103.   O. FENICHEL, *The Psychoanalytic Theory of Neurosis,* New York: Norton, 1945.

104.   H. J. CRONIN, Analysis of neuroses of identical twins, *Psychoanalyt. Rev., 20:* 375, 1933.

105.   H. STOLZE, Schizophrenie bei eineiigen Zwillingen: ein kasuistischer Beitrag, *Ztschr. Neurol. u. Psychiat., 174:* 753, 1942.

106.   A. BRILL, The empathic index and personality, *Med. Rec., 97:* 131, 1920,

107.   C. OBERNDORF, Folie à deux, *Internat. J. Psycho-analysis, 15*: 14, 1934.

108.   F. J. KALLMANN and J. S. MICKEY, Concept of induced insanity in family units, *J. Nerv. & Ment. Dis., 104*: 303, 1946.

109.   A. T. KIBZEY, Folie à deux: case of familial psychosis, *Psychoanalyt. Quart., 22*: 718, 1948.

110.   G. OGGIONI, Contribute alla cognoscenza delle psicosi gemellari, *Rass. studi psichiat., 26*: 919, 1937.

111.   B. KIHN, "Schizophrenie," in *Handbuch der Erbkrankheit,* Leipzig: Thieme, 1940.

112.   J. CARRÈRE, "Des psychoses gémellaires," in *1st Congrès Latin d'Eugènique,* Paris: 1937.

113.   J. JACOBI, Eine gleichartig verlaufende schizophrene Psychose bei einem zweieiigen Zwillingspaar, *Ztschr. Neurol. u. Psychiat., 135*: 298, 1931.

114.   C. M. SCHICK, *Dementia Praecox in Fraternal Twins,* N.S. Veteran's Bureau Medical Bulletin, 7: 586, 1931.

115.   J. KASANIN, Case of schizophrenia in only one of identical twins, *Am. J. Psychiat., 91*: 751, 1934.

116.   J. G. OATMAN, Folie à deux: report of a case in identical twins, *Am. J. Psychiat., 98*: 842, 1942.

117.   A. ADLER and W. W. MAGRUDER, Folie à deux in identical twins treated with electroshock therapy, *J. Nerv. & Ment. Dis., 103*: 181, 1946.

118.   T. LIDZ, unpublished paper.

119.   E. SLATER, Genetical causes of schizophrenic symptoms, *Monatsschr. Psychiat. u. Neurol., 113*: 50, 1947.

120.   R. SOLOMON and E. L. BLISS, Simultaneous occurrence of schizophrenia in identical twins, *Am. J. Psychiat., 112* (11): 912, 1956.

121.   H. E. RUBIN, Identical twins with psychosis, *Kentucky Med. J., 42*: 115, 1944.

122.   H. W. SIEMENS, *Die Zwillingspathologie,* München, 1924.

123.   F. WIGERS, Ein eineiiges, bezüglich Schizophrenie diskordantes Zwillingspaar, *Acta psychiat. et Neurol., 9*: 541, 1934.

124.   S. ARIETI, Interpretation of divergent outcome of schizophrenia in identical twins, *Psychiatric Quart., 18*: 587, 1944.

125.   L. WYNNE, unpublished paper presented at the International Congress of Psychiatry, 1957.

126.   J. LANGE, Psychiatrische Zwillings-Probleme, *Ztschr. Neurol. u. Psychiat., 112*: 283, 1928.

127.   E. J. GARDNER and F. E. STEPHENS, Schizophrenia in monozygotic twins, *J. Hered., 40* (6): 165, 1949.

128.   T. W. MURPHY and H. LUIDENS, Insulin and metrazol therapy in identical twins, *Psychiatric Quart., 13*: 114, 1939.

129.   G. HEUYER and LONGUET, Psychose gémellaire, *Ann. méd. psychol., 94*: 220, 1936.

130.   J. WEATHERLY and H. L. DIABLER, Schizophrenia in identical twins one of whom was lobotomized, *J. Nerv. & Ment. Dis., 120*: 262, 1954.

131.   B. W. MURPHY, Genesis of schizoid personality, study of two cases developing schizophrenia, *Psychiatric Quart., 26*: 450, 1952.

132.   ADELAIDE JOHNSON, MARY GRIFFIN *et al.,* Studies in schizophrenia, *Psychiatry 19*: 143, 1956.

133.   w. j. j. DE SAUVAGE NOLTING, Further studies on correlation between schizophrenia and month of birth, *Nederl. tijdschr. geneesk., 95:* 3853–3864, 1951.
134.   w. j. PILE, Study on correlation between dementia praecox and month of birth, *Va. Med., 78:* 438, 1951.
135.   E. T. HOVERSON, Meteorological factors in mental disease, *Arch. Neurol. & Psychiat., 92:* 131, 1935.
136.   N. PASTORE, *The Nature-Nurture Controversy,* New York: Kings Crown Press, 1949.

PART II

Biochemistry

3. A CHEMICAL APPROACH TO THE PROBLEM OF MENTAL DISEASE

L. G. Abood

This chapter is not intended to be a comprehensive review of the biochemistry of schizophrenia; it is primarily a brief discussion of the recent biochemical trends which, in the opinion of the author, appear to offer promise in the direction of eventual understanding. Considerable emphasis has been placed on the possible role of neurohumoral amines in mental health and disease, not only because of their essential role in neural function but also because of their pharmacological and chemical relationship to the many psychotomimetic and psychopharmacological agents which have recently assumed importance. The constituents of any biological system, including the nervous system, are chemicals which are dynamically interrelated, so that any alteration in the system, however slight, must reflect itself at the molecular level. Ralph Gerard has beautifully expressed this thought: "No twisted thought without a twisted molecule . . . the body is materially different, now, and any therapy by administering words and starting auditory nerve impulses or administering chemicals that change nerve cell thresholds, acts by 'untwisting' some materials somewhere in the body . . ." (1).

The original work described was supported in part by the Mental Health Fund, State of Illinois, and in part by a Scottish Rite Mason's grant. The author is indebted to Dr. Francis J. Gerty for his careful examination of the manuscript and for his many invaluable comments.

L. G. Abood received his Ph.D. in pharmacology from the University of Chicago and became Associate Professor of Neurophysiology and Biochemistry at the University of Illinois College of Medicine, where he is now Director of the Research Laboratories, Department of Psychiatry.

The gap existing between molecular interactions and psychogenic phenomena is tremendous and, perhaps, unbridgeable. But, as Percival Bailey so aptly stated in his Academic Lecture: "The demonstration of a chemical factor in the causation of schizophrenia would not help us to understand the contents of schizophrenic delusions, just as the demonstration of the spirochaete in general paralysis did not help us to understand the contents of megalomanic delusions of the paretic: it would merely make them superfluous" (2).

ENZYMATIC CHANGES IN SCHIZOPHRENIA

Attempts to demonstrate enzymatic differences in the blood and brain of schizophrenics have been notoriously unsuccessful. The literature in this area has not been extensively reviewed and evaluated, largely because the results are predominantly negative or inconclusive. There are some suggestions that cholinesterase activity is elevated in the brain (3) and serum (4) (pseudocholinesterase) of schizophrenics. On the other hand, innumerable reports fail to note any changes in either pseudo or true cholinesterase in the erythrocytes, serum, and spinal fluid of psychotics (5, 6). A report that acid phosphatase activity was decreased in the brains of psychotics (7) was not corroborated (8). In some psychotics, carbonic anhydrase appeared to be diminished, although in a high percentage of cases the enzyme activity was essentially normal (9). The observations that the nucleoprotein content of ganglion cells was depleted in psychotic patients (10) are inconclusive in view of the variability and inconclusiveness of histopathological findings. (See ref. 10 for review.) An interesting report that the monoamine oxidase activity of the globus pallidus and putamen was elevated in schizophrenic brain has never been checked or extended (11).

With regard to enzyme studies on the human brain, the obvious difficulty is in the acquisition of fresh samples, a difficulty not necessarily overcome by the use of biopsy material obtained during brain surgery (12). Elegant ultramicrochemical techniques have recently been developed, permitting chemical and enzymatic analysis on a single neuron (13, 14); but until techniques for obtaining adequate biopsy material become available, the application of such techniques to the human brain is limited.

The observation that schizophrenics exhibit a significant tolerance to insulin (15) has stimulated investigations into the mechanism of action of this interesting biochemical phenomenon. Perhaps the most obvious explanation is that an "anti-insulin" or hyperglycemic factor is responsible; and the presence of abnormally high amounts of a "hyperglycemic" factor in the urine of schizophrenics has actually been reported (16, 17). Recently, in an attempt to determine whether any glycolytic enzyme in the human erythrocyte was particularly sensitive to insulin, Nagy and Gerty (18, 19) noted a disturbance in the intracellular phosphate metabolism of schizophrenics in the presence of insulin. When normal erythrocytes are preincubated with insulin in the presence of adenylic acid, hexose diphosphate, and pyruvate, adenosinetriphosphate (ATP) accumulates at a much slower rate than it does in the absence of insulin. In the case of red cells from schizophrenics, this suppression of ATP formation by insulin does not occur, suggesting an insensitivity to insulin of some system involving ATP. The enzymes involved in the conversion of hexosediphosphate to pyruvate are apparently normal in schizophrenics, and insulin could be acting on the phosphorylative transfers from 1, 3-diphosphoglycerate and/or phosphopyruvate to ADP to form ATP.

Another site of action concerns electron transfer from reduced coenzyme I, which is coupled to phosphorylation (20). Whatever the mechanism, it appears that the insulin-sensitive reaction involves cellular or structural integrity and does not directly involve particular enzymes (18). The tremendous doses of insulin tolerated by some acutely psychotic patients (3000 units) need explanation (110). Although the nature of the insulin effect is still obscure, the observed difference in schizophrenics offers an interesting challenge to biochemists in general.

For over a quarter of a century it has been known that severe mental disturbances accompany certain inborn metabolic disorders, such as phenylketonuria, methemoglobinemia, and porphyria (21). Phenylketonurics generally develop severe mental retardation; and, although some evidence points to the abnormality of phenylalanine metabolism as the cause of the mental disturbance (22), the problem is in need of considerably more exploration.

Lipidoses, or disturbances in lipid metabolism, are definitely related to the severe mental disturbances involved in certain neuropathies. There are three diseases of this type which have been studied, Tay-Sachs disease, Gargoylism, and Niemann-Pick's disease. (See refs. 23, 24 for discussion of these and other inborn metabolic disorders.) In all such conditions there is an abnormal intracellular or extracellular accumulation of lipids; and it has been reported that a particular substance, neuraminic acid (25), is an important constituent of both the intracellular and extracellular lipoid deposits. In the case of porphyria, which is characterized by an excessive excretion of uroporphyrin, psychoticlike behavior is frequently observed, which disappears as a result of a spontaneous correction in porphyrin metabolism (26, 27).

Many other such congenital disorders are associated with mental disturbances, such as Huntington's chorea, presenile psychoses, and progressive cortical atrophy. Knowledge concerning the etiology and treatment of all such disorders is extremely scarce. It is evident, however, that the disorders are usually genetically homozygous, involving certain enzyme and other chemical deficiencies, and often eventuate in a variety of mental aberrations. In other chapters of this volume, the question of schizophrenia itself is discussed in terms of a genetic disturbance that may very likely reflect itself in the biochemical constitution of the brain. Whatever the etiology of schizophrenia, it would appear that a thorough examination of the biochemical factors involved in such genetic disorders will be of importance in understanding mental disorders in general. It is noteworthy that the deep depressions have not been studied by biochemists in late years. Since the advent of shock treatment, unmodified examples are hard to find, and consequently well developed acute cases are rarely seen.

It has been known for a number of decades that certain vitamin deficiencies are responsible for a variety of mental aberrations, but none are specific for our present diagnostic criteria. In both thiamine (28) and niacin (29) deficiency, symptoms are first manifested in the nervous system; and, in severe conditions, full-blown psychotic episodes are not uncommon. The psychoses disappear after the appropriate vitamin is administered, if no irreversible damage to the central nervous system has occurred as a result of prolonged deficiency. Deficiencies of other B vitamins, such as riboflavin, will likewise eventuate in psychosis, although the primary effects occur in organs other than the brain. The primary consideration here is that all of the B vitamins are essential constituents of coenzymes involved in energetic pathways of cellular metabolism and that the nervous system is especially vulnerable to their lack. Korsakov's psychosis has a fairly typical symptomatic constellation of both physical and mental nature, which may be related biochemically as well. By the same token, such factors as anoxia and hypoglycemia may induce severe mental changes without affecting organs elsewhere in the body. (See ref. 30 for review.)

In recent years, attempts have been made to relate schizophrenia to endocrine dysfunction, particularly with regard to the adrenal cortex. With the elucidation of the role of the adrenal cortex in stress, it was tempting to speculate that, because schizophrenics were more susceptible to stressful stimuli, some malfunction in the hypophyseal-adrenocortical axis was involved. In the last decade, a considerable number of reports have appeared that suggest that the adrenal cortex of psychotics is significantly less responsive to exogenous ACTH (31) or to severe stresses such as electroshock and insulin hypoglycemia (32, 33). Because the indices used in the evaluation of adrenocortical response (such as eosinophilic levels, uric acid, potassium, and 17-ketosteroid excretion) are so nonspecific, the results of these studies have been difficult to evaluate. Attempts to corroborate these findings have, therefore, been discouraging (34, 35). The possibility that the debilitated state of the patients may be a factor in the decreased excretion of 17-ketosteroids has been proposed (36).

The observation that cortisone (37) and ACTH (38) can bring about such alterations in mental activity as euphoria, anxiety, and excitatory behavior would seem to lend support to the theory that a malfunction of the hypophyseal-adrenal axis is involved in certain types of mental disease. Psychotic patients, who are less responsive to stress as measured by biochemical indices, show only transient improvement when treated with cortisone or ACTH (39). The correlation of prognosis to electroshock therapy with the degree of responsiveness to ACTH (40) is interesting, although difficult to interpret. As in the case of hormonal therapy in general, the doses of ACTH and cortisone used to produce mental effects are large in comparison to endogenous supplies, so that such pharmacological effects may not be related to the actual physiological function of the hormones. Nonetheless, many hormonal imbalances such as thyrotoxicosis (41) and Cushing Syndrome (43) are accompanied by psychotic episodes.

Within recent years, a considerable amount of interest has developed with regard to ceruloplasmin, since it has been reported to be elevated in schizophrenia (42–46). Ceruloplasmin is a copper alpha-globulin having a molecular weight of 150,000. Most of the copper in the serum is bound as ceruloplasmin under normal conditions; but, in certain situations such as Wilson's disease, in which ceruloplasmin is extremely low, the copper is either free or bound to polypeptides and nonspecific proteins. The protein has been reported to be elevated during conditions of acute schizophrenia, as well as in pregnancy (47), malignant carcinoma (48), hypertension (49), and certain types of liver disease (42, 43). Over 60 per cent of the population of acute schizophrenics show an elevation of ceruloplasmin, up to 200 per cent above normal. In chronic schizophrenics, particularly those who have been institutionalized for prolonged periods, the ceruloplasmin level is almost normal. The level of this serum protein is of no value as a diagnostic tool, particularly because it is elevated in a large variety of pathological conditions. There is a correspondence here to insulin effect in acute sclerotic cases (50). It might help to concentrate work on ceruloplasmin-positive cases to discover other possible concomitant changes.

In a recent study, it has been shown that the ceruloplasmin level seems to be related to alterations in feeling state (51). Such potent hallucinogenic agents as N-methyl-3-piperidyl benzilate (to be discussed in detail later) will cause a 50–100 per cent elevation of ceruloplasmin only when hallucinatory episodes are produced. Subthreshold doses, although producing anticholinergic peripheral effects, have no effect on ceruloplasmin.

It would appear as if the production of ceruloplasmin was under the control of some central mechanism, presumably located in subcortical structures that are likewise involved in the hallucinogenic properties of the drug. Since N-methyl-3-piperidyl benzilate is presumed to act by virtue of its anticholinergic effect, and since acetylcholine is concentrated largely in the basal ganglia, particularly within the hypothalamus (52), it does not seem unlikely that the hallucinogenic effects are occurring within this general area. Heath and his co-workers (53) have reported that stimulation of the "septal region" results in a considerable elevation of the copper enzyme. On the basis of these studies, it would seem that ceruloplasmin levels can under some circumstances be correlated with acute psychogenic disturbances. The significance of a ceruloplasmin elevation during such acute disturbances in behavior is not clear at present, but all suggestions point to the possibility that it is a compensatory mechanism rather than a causative factor.

Since substances such as the catechol amines (e.g., adrenalin and dopamine) have been shown to rise during alterations in feeling state (54, 55), and since they are substrates of ceruloplasmin (56), it was thought that the rise in ceruloplasmin was related to the increase in catechol amines. Attempts to demonstrate a rise in ceruloplasmin after the infusion of adrenalin and serotonin have been unsuccessful; indeed, it appeared as if a slight decrease occurred (51). If there is some relationship between the serum catechol amines and ceruloplasmin, it would appear to be somehow linked to the psychogenic effects produced by, or coincident with, the catechol amines. There are a number of problems here of considerable interest from both a biochemical and a clinical point of view. Recent observations by Melander and his co-workers (58) that purified ceruloplasmin is beneficial in paranoid and catatonic schizophrenia are of considerable interest.

The recent work of Heath et al. (57) on the presence of taraxein in the serum of schizophrenics has aroused widespread interest. Because this work will be discussed by Heath in another chapter of this book, it will only be alluded to here. During isolation of taraxein from the serum of schizophrenics, it is difficult to separate the material from ceruloplasmin itself. Actually, the method of extraction is similar to the one employed by Holmberg and Laurell (59) for the isolation of ceruloplasmin. Although it is believed that the material is different from ceruloplasmin, it nonetheless appears to be a globulin-type protein. Further investigation into its nature and its relation to ceruloplasmin certainly appears warranted.

NEUROHUMORAL SUBSTANCES AND ANTAGONISTS

The mechanism of action of any pharmacological agent is intimately related to its chemical structure, so that merely through a consideration of the chemical constitution of an agent, one can predict its general pharmacodynamic action. With the introduction into biology of the concepts of neurohumoral transmission, considerable attention was devoted to the chemical structure of such endogenous neurotropic agents as adrenalin, acetylcholine, and serotonin with a view toward eventually elucidating their mechanism of action at a molecular level. As part of the program to study "structure-activity" relationships, the assistance of the organic chemist was enlisted in order to develop chemical analogues and antagonists.

In the course of evaluating such analogues and antagonists of intrinsic neurotropic principles, information was obtained on the biological response arising from an excess or deficiency of the neurohumoral factor in question. With regard to many neurohumoral agents, alterations in their concentration or efficacy within the central nervous system results in bizarre psychophysiological disturbances simulating certain symptoms characteristic of psychotics. Despite the fact that a chemical imbalance in no one neurohumoral factor results in a condition resembling the clinical picture, the psychophysiological effects resulting from a generalized imbalance of several such factors could conceivably simulate clinical psychoses. Although some effort will be made in this discussion to relate the symptoms of mental disease to the pharmacological effects of the various neurohumoral agents, the concept of a "model psychosis" induced by drugs or other means can, naturally, be regarded only as a model. Nonetheless, a model can yield a great deal of information about its prototype. (By way of example, the model of the nerve fiber as a simple electrical circuit [60, 61] or the central nervous system as an analogue or digital computer [62, 63, 64] has proven invaluable in our understanding of neural function.)

Although the hallucinogenic effects of mescaline have been known for centuries and have been described in great detail (65), in recent years considerably more attention has been devoted to LSD. Hoffman, the chemist who synthesized LSD (66), accidentally ingested a minute quantity of the substance and later experienced "an uninterrupted procession of fantastic pictures of extraordinary plasticity and with an intensive kaleidoscopic play of colors" (67). One of the particularly astounding properties of LSD is its extremely low effective dose, as little as 50 micrograms producing in human subjects psychotomimetic effects that last for over 5 hours. In comparison, ½ gram of mescaline is required to produce a comparable effect. Furthermore, less than 10 per cent of the effective dose of LSD reaches the brain (68). LSD is, unquestionably, one of the most potent biologically active substances known. Some endogenous factor, possibly even more potent, may be operating regularly in many cases of psychosis.

The effects of LSD appear to be due to its direct action on the autonomic nervous center, as well as on certain sensory and motor areas (69, 70). Psychoticlike symptoms are frequently very marked, consisting of alterations in emotional mood, perception, somatic and temporal sensation, and highlighted by vivid visual hallucinations. The psychotic episodes are sometimes associated with paranoid and hypochondriacal delusions, as well as with a sense of depersonalization and with difficulties in verbalization and reasoning. Autonomic disturbances include blood pressure and heart rate changes, pupillary dilatation, nausea, dizziness, and sweating. Despite the fact that the psychogenic experience induced by LSD does not involve a loss of contact with the immediate surroundings, it is, nonetheless, accompanied by profound alterations in orientation and psychic functions not unlike those in schizophrenia.

If one examines the pharmacological literature on neurotropic drugs, it becomes quite evident that there are endless numbers and varieties of drugs which can produce so-called "psychotomimetic" effects. For the purpose of discussion, these psychotomimetic effects are characterized by disorders of memory, orientation, and awareness, accompanied by distinct visual and auditory hallucinations. Among the agents which constantly produce such effects in a wide enough variety of patients are LSD, mescaline, adrenochrome, marijuana, cholinesterase inhibitors (diisopropylfluorophosphate [DFP], eserine), morphine derivatives, and atropinelike agents. Among this group, however, LSD and mescaline have received most attention, particularly because their so-called psychotomimetic effects overshadow other central and peripheral effects of the agents.

From a pharmacological point of view, one of the most interesting characteristics of LSD and mescaline is the structural similarity of the molecules to some of the known neurohumoral amines such as adrenalin and serotonin. (See Figure 1.) The similarity between LSD and serotonin is especially striking. Pharmacologically, LSD is an extremely potent blocking agent to the powerful contractile effect of serotonin on smooth muscle preparations (82). Recently, Hoffman (71) has succeeded in identifying the active principle in the hallucinogenic mushroom *Psilocybe Mexicana*. The material, a phos-

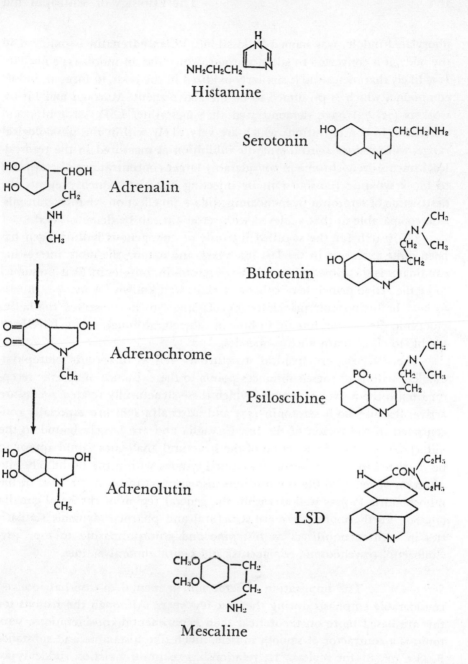

Histamine

Serotonin

Adrenalin

Bufotenin

Adrenochrome

Psiloscibine

Adrenolutin

LSD

Mescaline

FIGURE I

Chemical structure of a number of structurally related hallucinogenic drugs, showing relationship to adrenalin and serotonin.

phorylated indole, was named Psiloscibine. When adrenalin is oxidized in the body, it is converted to adrenochrome, which has an indole-type nucleus. It is likely that mescaline is similarly oxidized in the body to form an indole compound, which is presumed to be the active agent. Marrazzi and his co-workers (72, 73) have demonstrated that mescaline, LSD, serotonin, and adrenalin, in concentrations which are very likely within the physiological range, will produce central synaptic inhibition as measured in the transcallosal tract. Adrenochrome in considerably larger concentrations also appears to block synaptic transmission. By injecting marsalid, which prevents the destruction of serotonin by monoaminoxidase, an effect on synaptic transmission comparable to that achieved with serotonin can be demonstrated.

The search for the so-called intrinsic or endogenous hallucinogen has been quite extensive in the last few years, and among the more interesting candidates is the dimethyl derivative of serotonin, bufotenin. It is presumed to be the active principle of cohaba, a plant well known for many centuries to have hallucinogenic principles (75). Fabing (76) has observed the hallucinogenic effects of bufotenin in human subjects, although others have been unable to observe any such properties.

The similarity in chemical structure as well as in certain neurophysiological actions of these substances points to the existence of specific receptor sites in the nervous system at which these structurally related agents are active. Because both serotonin (77) and adrenalin (78) are especially concentrated in the region of the basal ganglia and are largely bound to the mitochondria, the site of action of the structural analogues would appear to be restricted to rather specific functional systems within the brain. The site of action of many of the tranquilizers also appears to be at the level of the mitochondria (79) as well as within the general region of the basal ganglia (79, 80). Furthermore, there are structural and pharmacodynamic similarities in such tranquilizers as reserpine and chlorpromazine to the "psychotogens" (psychotomimetic agents) and neurohumoral amines.

Serotonin   The implication of serotonin in mental disease has received considerable emphasis during the past few years. Although the reasons for this are based more on theoretical than experimental considerations, serotonin is a contractor of smooth muscle, much like histamine and substance P. (See ref. 81 for review.) Its relationship to brain function suddenly assumed importance after it had been shown that LSD (which, as previously mentioned, is structurally similar to serotonin) was, in addition to being an antagonist to LSD on smooth muscle (82), an extremely potent hallucinogen. There seems little doubt that the chemical similarity is responsible for the antagonistic relationship between LSD and serotonin on smooth muscle. Although it is still likely that some of the actions of LSD on the central nervous system are in some way related to serotonin, conclusive evidence is lacking for believing that serotonin is directly involved in the hallucinogenic effects of LSD.

Brom-LSD will penetrate the central nervous system as well as block the effects of serotonin on smooth muscle, yet it will not produce hallucinations (83). However, if administered before LSD, the bromine derivative will prevent hallucinations (70).

There is no reason to believe that because a pharmacological antagonism exists between LSD and serotonin the blockage of serotonin action in the brain is at the basis of mental disorders. There are those who have argued that mental aberrations result from a deficiency of serotonin in the brain (84, 85), although supportive evidence is lacking. Failure to find increased concentrations of indole acetic acid in the urine, the final metabolic product of serotonin, does not necessarily indicate any lack of disturbance in brain serotonin. Serotonin is evidently turning over rather rapidly in the brain, and the concentrations involved are rather small and are not, therefore, a reflection of serotonin activity. By the same token, the concentrations of acetylcholine in the brain in no way reflect the role of acetylcholine in brain functions.

Some supportive evidence for the role of serotonin in brain function stemmed from the observation that the administration of the precursor of serotonin, 5-hydroxytryptophane, resulted in disturbances of brain function (86). Similar results are obtained by the administration of marsalid, an inhibitor of monoamine oxidase (87). Intraventricular injections of serotonin, as has already been pointed out, will result in a sham rage (88). The observation that reserpine, a tranquilizing drug, causes a release of brain serotonin (85) is difficult to reconcile with the notion that a serotonin deficiency is involved in brain dysfunction. On the other hand, chlorpromazine, another tranquilizer, inhibits the formation of 5-hydroxyindole acetic acid from serotonin and presumably would have a serotonin-sparing action (89).

The possible role of serotonin as a chemical mediator in the brain has recently received a great deal of attention. As in the case of the other neurohumoral amines, serotonin does have a profound effect on smooth muscle and indeed, in the case of the heart of mollusks and crustaceans, may actually be a neurohumoral transmitter (81, 90). Evidence in support of its central mediator action is largely indirect. The first bit of evidence arose from the observation of Gaddum (82) that because LSD blocks the constrictive action of serotonin on smooth muscle, it may conceivably produce its hallucinatory

LINCOLN CHRISTIAN COLLEGE

action by virtue of a similar block of the serotonin in the brain. Brodie and associates (87) have attempted to explain the action of the tranquilizer reserpine by its ability to release serotonin from the brain as well as prevent its binding or fixation. As in the case of adrenalin, serotonin seems to be present in autonomic nervous centers, centers that influence temperature, blood pressure, wakefulness, and a host of other autonomic functions.

The work of Wooley and associates (91, 92) seems to link the role of serotonin to the oligodendroglia, presumably involved in the circulation of extravascular fluid throughout the brain and thereby indirectly regulating brain metabolism and function. Alterations in serotonin concentration might result in a cessation or disturbance in the pulsatory activity of the oligodendroglia and hence influence brain function. Geiger (93) has observed a pumping movement within human cerebral neurons grown in tissue culture and an aggregation in the cytoplasmic granules with less than 10^{-6} M serotonin. If serotonin should have such a function in the brain, it would not be surprising that many metabolic disturbances—for example, anoxia and starvation—are associated with such conditions as hallucinations and seizures. Here again, as with other neurohumoral substances, the localization of serotonin is quite specific, so that only certain types of oligodendroglia or other cells would seem to be involved. There is no anatomical evidence to suggest that the glia in such regions as the hypothalamus and the area postrema, where serotonin is richest, are different from those elsewhere in the brain.

Histamine   The role of histamine in the nervous system in general is rather obscure. Some have proposed that it is a chemical transmitter of monosynaptic reflexes (94). Others have suggested that it may be a peripheral mediator of pain, insofar as pain seems to be associated with both an injury to cells and a release of histamine (95). With regard to the central nervous system, however, the rather specific distribution of histamine (as in the case of adrenalin) seems to exclude its possible role as a neurohumoral transmitter. It is present in the brain in extremely low concentrations, except in the cerebellum and in some regions within the hypothalamus, and otherwise seems to be completely absent from most regions of the brain (96). High concentrations of histamine are associated with sympathetic postganglionic fibers, suggesting the presence of a "histaminergic" network in the sympathetic nervous system (97).

Neurohumoral properties have been attributed to other substances present in the brain, such as substance P (98) and adenosinetriphosphate (ATP) (99, 100) or a similar nucleotide. The problem of trying to establish a neurohumoral basis for central synaptic transmission is obviously a complex one. It is possible that there may be both an excitatory and an inhibitory substance, or even one that may be inhibitory in some regions and excitatory in others. The problems of central neurohumoral transmission have been extensively discussed elsewhere (101) and are beyond the scope of this discussion. There seems to be little question, however, that the heterocyclic amines do have a profound effect upon the central nervous system and that their role may not be that of a chemical transmitter but rather that of a metabolic or physiological regulator of central nervous system activity. Histamine, serotonin, and adrenalin will potentiate the response of the cat's superior cervical ganglion to submaximal preganglionic stimulation as well as to injections of acetylcholine and nicotine (102). If the blood supply of the preparation remains intact, then the effects of histamine, serotonin, and pilocarpine are mutually antagonistic. Trendelenburg (102) concluded from these observations that the superior cervical ganglion probably possessed specific receptors for histamine, serotonin, and adrenalin, in addition to acetylcholine. In this respect the ganglion resembles smooth muscle.

Acetylcholine   The effects of acetylcholine in the central nervous system are such as to leave little doubt that the substance plays a prominent role in nerve functions. Depending on the dosage, it can lead to both a stimulation and an inhibition of the respiratory center. It seems to influence most areas in the region of the autonomic nervous system, affecting such indices as blood pressure, heart rate, and gastrointestinal movements. Largely through the use of intraventricular injections, Feldberg and associates (101, 103) have demonstrated a dramatic series of events resulting from the injection of small amounts of acetylcholine. Cats exhibit a type of seizure, described as akinetic, characterized by retching, shrieking, and a slow loss of motor activity eventuating in hypnosis. Such drugs as DFP and eserine, which inhibit acetylcholinesterase, and hence increase the relative amount of acetylcholine, bring about dramatic central effects, highlighted by epileptiform seizures and other severe neurological disturbances (104, 105). As a result of studies on the distribution of choline acetylase (an enzyme which synthesizes acetylcholine), Feldberg (106) has come to the conclusion that there are functional units within the CNS which are essentially cholinergic (anterior horn cells; cranial motor nuclei; second sensory neurons and retina) and others which do not seem to involve acetylcholine as a mediator (optic tract; posterior roots; and spinal column).

Although there is evidence that acetylcholine does play a role as a chemical mediator in the central nervous system, there are unquestionably many areas which involve not acetylcholine but in all likelihood another type of mediator. Acetylcholine is richest in the basal ganglia, next in the cerebral gray matter, brain stem, and spinal gray matter, in the order indicated (52, 106). Such areas as the pyramidal tracts, dorsal columns, and cerebellum are almost devoid of acetylcholine. As in the case of the other neurohumoral amines, acetylcholine is especially concentrated in the region of the nervous system, regulating emotion and feeling as well as vegetative functions. The hypothalamus and its surrounding region appear to be considerably more sensitive to alterations in the concentration of acetylcholine than to other known neurohumoral amines (52).

An anticholinesterase agent, DFP, has been shown to benefit the mania of manic-depressive psychosis by virtue of its nicotinic stimulation of the CNS (107). Pfeiffer (108) has reported some improvement ("production of lucid intervals") in catatonic schizophrenics by the administration of "muscarinic" acetylcholinelike agents, such as arecoline and eserine. Methyl atropine was administered simultaneously, presumably to block the undesirable peripheral effects of the agents.

On the other hand, atropine, a cholinergic blocking agent, has long been known to produce hallucinations and delirium in normal human subjects (109, 110). Recently, in our laboratory, a number of synthetic cholinergic blocking agents have been found to possess striking psychotomimetic properties (51, 111). The agents were synthesized by Biel et al. (112); and originally they were developed as antispasmodic agents (113). Two of the agents most extensively studied have the following structures:

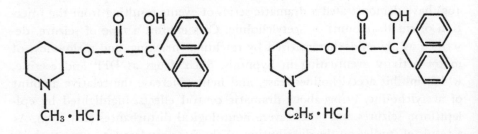

N-methyl-3-piperidyl benzilate   N-ethyl-3-piperidyl benzilate

Oral doses of 10 to 15 mg produced mild to severe visual and auditory hallucinations in normal human subjects which persisted for periods of from 1 to 3 hours. Among other psychotogenic effects were disorientation, paranoid and hypochondriacal delusions, difficulty in concentration and verbalization, extreme fear, and partial loss of contact. Such doses appeared to have only a slight effect on such peripheral cholinergic responses as salivation, pupillary dilatation, and heart rate. Frequently a single dose of these drugs was found to stimulate mildly depressed patients. In rats, both drugs, in doses of 10–20 mg/kg subcutaneously, produced marked hyperactivity accompanied by intermittent squeaking, paresthesia, and, presumably, fearfulness.

There appears little doubt that the piperidyl benzilates are acting by virtue of a cholinergic blocking effect upon the central nervous system. Even at concentrations exceeding 10^{-4} M, the piperidyl benzilates are inactive on numerous enzyme systems tested, including those involved in oxidative phosphorylation, acetylcholinesterase, amine oxidases, and phosphatases.

The psychotomimetic properties of these agents are in agreement with the concept that acetylcholine plays a significant role in mental health and disease. It would appear that psychogenic disturbances are generally associated with an impairment in the action of acetylcholine, either through an interference with its action or availability. The interesting suggestion has been offered that the psychotherapeutic action of reserpine is mediated through a cholinergic stimulating action of the alkaloid on the brain and that, in this respect, it resembles such agents as arecoline and eserine (114). The severe autonomic disturbances associated with such cholinergic agents as DFP and neostigmin are probably largely peripheral in origin, insofar as atropine will either prevent or reverse many of the effects. These few scattered observations with cholinergic and anticholinergic agents on psychogenic phenomena are significant enough to justify further exploration of the role of acetylcholine in mental disorders.

It would appear from the foregoing discussion that no one intrinsic metabolite or neurohumoral agent is outstanding in its relationship to the problem of psychoses. Instead, many substances of apparently different chemical structure and diverse pharmacological properties seem to play some kind of role. Attention has been confined to four such agents—acetylcholine, adrenalin, histamine, and serotonin—but only because more is known regarding their pharmacological properties. It is not inconceivable that the factors important in mental disease are only indirectly related to one or more of these substances, or that some hitherto undiscovered or lesser known agents, such as nucleotides or polypeptides, could be involved. In view of the supportive evidence, however, there seems to be little doubt that some, or perhaps all, of the neurohumoral agents discussed are in some way contributory to the problem. Perhaps the most formidable evidence for such an opinion is the striking similarity in chemical constitution between psychotomimetic agents (such as LSD) and some of the neurohumors or their derivatives and metabolites.

In considering whether the neurotropic agents being discussed act by virtue of their antagonism to the neurohumoral amines, the possibility remains that the mechanism is only an indirect or contingent one. The common denominator between the neurohumor and pharmacologic antagonist may be the receptor site within specific regions of the central nervous system. Each has a peculiar affinity for the receptor site by virtue of structural analogy, but the mechanism of action of each agent may be entirely unrelated. The essential relationship between the two analogues may lie in the equal accessibility of certain vital regions within the central nervous system. Such a substance as LSD or reserpine may, therefore, have an affinity for the same receptor sites as serotonin but, unlike serotonin, may be acting by virtue of its inhibitory effect on oxidative phosphorylation or some other vital enzyme system.

RELATIONSHIP OF METABOLITES TO PSYCHOSIS

Mental health or disease is a condition involving the total organism, but the nervous system is, nonetheless, the source of all mental or psychogenic phenomena. If a biochemical disturbance or toxic metabolite is responsible for mental aberrations, the disturbance should ultimately be reflected in the chemistry of the neuronal elements of the central nervous system. All normal brain function would be dependent on a precise balance of numerous chemical factors (*e.g.*, acetylcholine and adrenalin), many of which are extremely labile and turning over rapidly. Ordered or cyclical variations in the concentrations or availability of the neurohumors may be continually occurring during normal mental activity. Mental aberrations would presumably result when the chemical system is no longer stable or self-sustaining. Such an imbalance could result from numerous circumstances: (1) abnormal production or destruction of one or more of the neurohumors; (2) interference at the site of action by a chemical antagonist (antimetabolite); (3) a modification in the system normally responsive to the neurohumors.

The interesting observations of Eccles *et al.* (115, 116) that excitatory impulses to the neuron resulted in depolarization, whereas hyperpolarization is associated with inhibitory activity, led to the suggestion that both an inhibitory and excitatory chemical transmitter were involved. A number of neurohumoral substances including acetylcholine have been proposed as possible candidates for the neuron in the CNS, but none of the known ones seems very promising.

One of the chief problems involved in the hypothesis that a disturbance in the metabolism of neurohumoral amines results in mental dysfunction arises from the failure to demonstrate the role of the amines in the central nervous system. Perhaps the main reason for this difficulty is attributable to the extremely low concentration of these substances normally present in the brain, not to mention their localization in a few isolated regions of the brain.

The evidence in favor of adrenalin as a chemical mediator in the central nervous system is certainly less convincing. To begin with, it is distributed in very specific regions, particularly within the hypothalamus and areas of the fourth ventricle, and it appears to be completely absent from most other parts of the brain. Nevertheless, it is quite conceivable that adrenalin does have a function within the central nervous system, particularly in the hypothalamic region (101). In rather small quantities, both noradrenalin and adrenalin have been shown to produce cerebral synaptic inhibition in the transcallosal system (73). The intraventricular injection of adrenalin (20–80 μg) precipitates a condition resembling light nembutal anesthesia in the cat (117). Recently, many reports have appeared suggesting that conditions of anxiety result from the infusion of small amounts of adrenalin (118, 119). A study by Kosman and Gerard (120) on the effect of adrenalin on learned behavior in rats (conditioned emotional response) suggests that the generalized motor depression produced by adrenalin is largely peripheral in origin. Gerard (121) summarized the possible effects of adrenalin on behavior as follows:

It is tempting to think, then, that an unresolved and therefore stressful situation leads to neural activation of primitive brain stem structures, this to the liberation of sympathin type agents, and these, by a positive feedback upon the brain, to increased attention, alertness, and anxiety. It is not an unlikely extrapolation, that still larger doses or more active derivatives could stimulate still further and produce hallucinations, disorientation, and, in general, be psychotomimetic. An oversusceptibility of neurones might be an additional factor in the true psychoses. In fact, such considerations lead us back to a reconsideration of consciousness and memory, this time in terms of circuits and neural nets rather than of electrical and chemical fields.

Because of the similarity in chemical structure between adrenalin derivatives and certain hallucinogenic agents (*e.g.*, LSD and mescaline), some investigators have sought to relate directly this neurohumoral amine and its metabolic derivatives to mental disease. The possibility that adrenochrome and adrenolutin (122, 123), both oxidation products of adrenalin, may be endogenous hallucinogens has been mentioned previously.

In the conversion of adrenalin to adrenochrome, one could expect the formation of free radicals or intermediate quinones (124–128), the pathway for which is as follows:

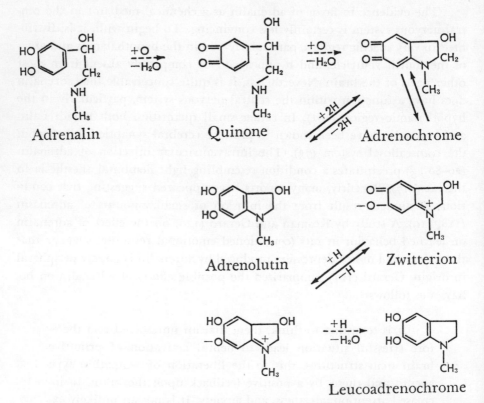

By the same token, the oxidation of all catechol amines would be expected to involve the formation of intermediate free radicals. Most of these free radicals and quinones are extremely reactive, so that it is not surprising that their presence in organisms escapes detection.

Both adrenochrome and adrenolutin are themselves extremely unstable and consequently have not been detected in the blood and urine, even in instances where adrenochrome was administered in fairly high concentrations (123). The instability of these adrenalin oxidation products (127) may explain their relatively high mortality dose (LD_{50} in rodents 5 mg/kg) (123). There is the further possibility that not adrenochrome or adrenolutin but rather intermediate free radicals and quinones are responsible for the biochemical and pharmacological effects of adrenalin oxidation. Indeed, from our own laboratory it has been shown that numerous unstable oxidation products of adrenalin and other naturally occurring catechol amines are capable of inhibiting oxidative phosphorylation of brain mitochondria at concentrations of 10^{-6} M (128).

Both adrenochrome and adrenolutin markedly interfere with mitotic activity and alter the morphology of mitochondria (129). Blood serum from schizophrenic and surgical patients was more toxic to strain L cells than that from healthy adults and nonschizophrenic mental patients (130).

The reactions of quinones in biological systems is only beginning to receive attention. Quinones are extremely powerful oxidizing agents capable of reacting with many components of the electron transport system in biological oxidation. They form additional compounds with free amino groups (131), sulfhydryl (132), and keto groups (133); and thus form numerous inactive enzyme systems. Quinones have long been known to substitute for endogenous components of biological oxidation and may actually play a physiological role in electron transport (134). Adrenochrome in concentrations of 10^{-7} M acts as an electron carrier in the enzymatic oxidation of malic and lactic acid (134); and, actually, it has been purported to have such a role in mammalian skeletal muscle, where it is normally present at 10^{-7} M concentration (135). The suggestion that the formation of quinones from adrenalin oxidation may be causing cerebral disturbances has been proposed by numerous investigators (122, 136).

Recently, a renewed and vigorous interest has developed in the abnormal urinary metabolites of psychotic patients. The rationale for this approach is obvious, since if a chemical or biochemical alteration should in some way be related to a disease, it should ultimately be reflected in the chemistry of the urine. There are in practice, however, many difficulties to such an approach. To begin with, urine contains hundreds of organic substances, many of them as yet unidentified. Many of these substances are present in such minute concentrations that they are undetectable by present chemical techniques of separation and identification. Another serious difficulty arises from the fact that many metabolites are extremely unstable and undergo changes within the urine, whether as a result of oxidation, polymerization, or interaction with other substances. An even more serious difficulty is that the composition of the urine is extremely variable and is profoundly influenced by such factors as nutrition, debilitation, and hormones. In spite of all such difficulties, the usefulness of this technique in the investigation of biochemical disorders is of considerable importance.

Numerous investigators have claimed to have found abnormal concentrations of indolic and aromatic compounds in the urine of schizophrenics. Since this report is not intended to be a comprehensive review, earlier studies of this nature will not be discussed except to make reference to the fact that in 1912 Ross (137) reported an increase in indoles in schizophrenics. Brief accounts of the evidence for and against abnormalities in the aromatic metabolism of schizophrenia are presented in reports by Buscaino (138) and McGeer et al. (139). Among the more significant positive findings are those of McGeer and his associates (140), who reported considerable increases in unidentified diazotizable aromatic compounds in schizophrenic urine. An earlier report by Sano (141) that indoles were increased in the urine of schizophrenics could not apparently be reconfirmed by this same investigator in a later study (142). A number of indolic compounds reacting with glyoxylic acid (e.g., tryptophane metabolites) were distinctly positive in up to 80 per cent of the urine from schizophrenics, while only 25 per cent of the nonschizophrenics were positive (143). Riegelhaupt (143) suggested that the "glyoxylic test" was of diagnostic value, despite the fact that less than 100 schizophrenics were studied and these without adequate controls and with no evaluation of their nutritional status. Chromatographic analysis of over 1,000 specimens of human urine has disclosed a marked increase in the excretion of indole acetic acid (IAA) and an ether-soluble indole, which yielded a blue-green product with Ehrlich's reagent (144). IAA increased from 0.1 in controls to as much as 8.0 mg/liter in urine from schizophrenics, as well as phenylketonurics and terminal cancer patients. The presence of a red pigment in urine specimens has been attributed to hydroxyindole acetic acid (HIAA) resulting from the oxidation of IAA by nitrates present (145). Other investigators have also reported a significant elevation of IAA and HIAA in schizophrenic urine (146). On the other hand, many have failed to detect noticeable differences in the excretion of IAA or HIAA between normals and schizophrenics (142, 147), and an actual decrease in hydroxylated indoles in schizophrenic urine has been reported (147).

A metabolic product of tryptophane metabolism, which has been variously characterized as oxindolealanine or β-hydroxy-pseudotryptophane (148), is believed by Sherwood (149) to have hallucinogenic properties. Even in the case of phenylketonuria, a condition characterized by extremely high excretion of phenylketo acids, the excretion pattern of the urine returns essentially to normal once phenylalanine is eliminated from the diet. The subject of abnormal excretion patterns in schizophrenia and any other

disease is a highly controversial and difficult one experimentally and therefore demands considerable caution. There is an endless variety of substances in the urine, and the techniques for separating and differentiating
them have only recently been made possible with the development of
chromatography. The failure to find abnormal concentrations of metabolic
products of the neurohumoral amines and other intrinsic humoral substances need not necessarily mean that disturbances in the formation and
detoxification of these substances may not exist somewhere within the body.
It is the concentration of a substance at its site in a given time that is critical
and not the over-all concentration reflected by its metabolic excretory product. Although an examination of the excretory pattern of aromatic and
indole substances may eventually prove fruitful in the understanding of
schizophrenia, the failure to observe differences does not necessarily mean
that important biochemical disturbances may not be involved.

From time to time, numerous reports have appeared suggesting that
substances within various body fluids of schizophrenics possess biological
activity lacking in normal subjects. Such materials have been found in the
spinal fluid of schizophrenics (150) and have been claimed to produce in-
flammatory changes in rabbit eyes and acute toxicity in mice, in addition to
causing histopathological changes. These observations, however, could not
be confirmed by others (151). The report that an extract from cerebral spinal
fluid of schizophrenic patients resulted in catatonic symptoms when injected
subcutaneously in rats (152) was likewise not confirmed (153). Numerous
other such reports have appeared, most of which have not been confirmed
by successive investigators. As with studies concerned with many other biochemical abnormalities presumed to exist in schizophrenics, these studies
lack adequate controls and have failed to take into account dietary factors
or the state of debilitation.

Before the last decade or so, the biochemical approach to the problem
of schizophrenia has been largely one of blind empiricism, lacking either in
sound concepts or in pragmatic generalizations. As a consequence, the
rather extensive accumulation of unrelated experimental observations on
schizophrenics has proven to be either of little consequence or largely discredited by subsequent investigators. A similar situation has existed with
respect to the treatment of schizophrenia, as evidenced by the application of
such techniques as electroshock, insulin-shock, and lobotomies. With the
tremendous strides being made in neurophysiology, neurochemistry, and
neuropharmacology, there is every reason to believe that the problem of
mental disease can eventually be defined and dealt with in terms of purely
biological concepts. The problem of the brain and its disorders must be

treated, as must any other biological phenomenon, dynamically, that is, as a process rather than a condition. The inherent difficulty in this approach will not be so much in methodology as it will be in the availability of human tissues, particularly brain, for proper biochemical or neurophysiological studies. With the refinement of instrumentation and the development of ultramichrochemical procedures, this obstacle may eventually be minimized. For the present, at least, the potentialities of studying "model psychoses" in animals with psychotogenic agents have only just begun to be explored— not to mention the application of such agents to studies on human beings. Despite all these considerations, the answer to the problem of psychoses may have to await the development of considerably more basic knowledge in the fields of neurochemistry and neurophysiology. It is, perhaps, toward this end that the majority of our efforts must continue to be directed.

References

1.   R. W. GERARD, unpublished talk, Committee on Mental Health, Washington, 1956.

2.   P. BAILEY, The great psychiatric revolution, *Am. J. Psychiat., 113*: 387, 1956.

3.   A. POPE, in *Biology of Mental Health and Disease,* New York: Hoeber, 1950.

4.   M. S. JONES and H. TOD, Effect of altering conditions of autonomic nervous system on choline esterase level in human blood serum, *J. Ment. Sc., 83*: 202, 1937.

5.   D. B. TOWER and D. MC EACHERN, Acetylcholine and neuronal activity; cholinesterase patterns and acetylcholine in cerebrospinal fluids of patients with craniocerebral trauma, *Canad. J. Res., 27*: 105, 1949.

6.   S. MUTRUX and B. GLASSON, Etude des cholinestérases du sang et du liquide céphalo-rachidien dans différents syndromes psychiatriques, *Monatssch. Psychiat. u. Neurol., 114*: 20, 1947.

7.   A. POPE, J. A. MEATH, W. F. COVENESS, H. E. LIVINGSTON, and R. H THOMPSON, Histochemical distribution of cholinesterase and acid phosphatase in prefrontal cortex of psychotic and nonpsychotic patients, *Tr. Am. Neurol. A., 74*: 147, 1949.

8.   A. WOLF and D. COWEN, in Mettler, F. A. (Ed.), *Pathology,* New York: Hoeber, 1949.

9.   W. M. ASHBY, "Enzymatic Changes in Mental Disease," in *Biology of Mental Health and Disease,* New York: Hoeber, 1950.

10.   A. WOLF and D. COWEN, "Histopathology of Schizophrenia and Other Diseases of Unknown Origin," in *Biology of Mental Health and Disease,* New York: Hoeber, 1950.

11.   H. BIRKHÄUSER, Cholinesterase und Mono-Aminoxydase im zentralen Nervensystem, *Schweiz. med. Wchnschr., 71*: 750, 1941.

12.   H. FREEMAN, J. M. LOONEY, R. HOSKINS, and C. G. DYER, Results of insulin and epinephrine tolerance tests in schizophrenic patients and in normal subjects, *Arch. Neurol. & Psychiat., 49*: 195, 1943.

13.   H. HYDEN, in Waelsch, H. (Ed.), *Biochemistry of the Developing Nervous System,* New York: Acad. Press, 1955.

14. O. H. LOWRY, N. R. ROBERTS, K. Y. LEINER, M. WU, L. FARR, and R. W. ALBERS, The quantitative histochemistry of brain: III. Ammon's horn, *J. Biol. Chem.*, *207*: 39, 1954.

15. L. J. MEDUNA, F. J. GERTY, and V. G. URSE, Biochemical disturbances in mental disorders; anti-insulin effect of blood in cases of schizophrenia, *Arch. Neurol. & Psychiat.*, *47*: 38, 1942.

16. L. J. MEDUNA, "Biochemical Disturbances in Mental Disorders: Anti-insulin Effect of Blood in Cases of Schizophrenia," in *Oneirophrenia: The Confusional State*, Urbana: Univ. Illinois Press, 1950.

17. M. S. MORGAN and F. J. PILGRIM, Concentration of hyperglycemic factor from urine of schizophrenics, *Proc. Soc. Exper. Biol. & Med.*, *79*: 106, 1952.

18. I. BOSZORMENYI-NAGY and F. J. GERTY, Differences between phosphorus metabolism of erythrocytes of normals and of patients suffering from schizophrenia, *J. Nerv. & Ment. Dis.*, *121*: 53, 1955.

19. I. BOSZORMENYI-NAGY and F. J. GERTY, Diagnostic aspects of study of intracellular phosphorylations in schizophrenia, *Am. J. Psychiat.*, *112*: 11, 1955.

20. M. FRIEDKIN and A. L. LEHNINGER, Oxidation-coupled incorporation of inorganic radiophosphate into phospholipide and nucleic acid in a cell-free system, *J. Biol. Chem.*, *177*: 775, 1949.

21. G. A. JERVIS, in *Biology of Mental Health and Disease*, New York: Hoeber, 1950.

22. G. A. JERVIS, Familial mental deficiency akin to amaurotic idiocy and gargoylism; apparently new type, *Arch. Neurol. & Psychiat.*, *47*: 943, 1942.

23. L. S. PENROSE, in Elliott, K. A. C., Quastel, J. H., and Page, I. H. (Eds.), *Neurochemistry*, Springfield: Thomas, 1955.

24. Symposium on inborn errors of metabolism, *Am. J. Med.*, 22 (No. 5), 1957.

25. E. KLENK, Neuraminsäure, das Spaltprodukt eines neuen gehirnlipoids, *Ztschr. f. Physiol. Chem.*, *268*: 50, 1941.

26. Q. H. GIBSON, Reduction of methaemoglobin in red blood cells and studies on cause of idiopathic methaemoglobin-aenemia, *Biochem. J.*, *42*: 13, 1948.

27. Q. H. GIBSON, D. C. HARRISON, and D. A. D. MONTGOMERY, Case of acute porphyria, *Brit. M. J.*, *1*: 275, 1950.

28. J. WALDENSTROM, Studien über Porphyrie, *Acta med. Scandinav.*, Suppl. 82, 1937.

29. T. D. SPIES, C. COOPER, and M. A. BLANKENHORN, Use of nicotinic acid in treatment of pellagra, *J.A.M.A.*, *110*: 622, 1938.

30. H. E. HIMWICH, *Brain Metabolism and Cerebral Disorder*, Baltimore: Williams & Wilkins, 1951.

31. H. HOAGLAND, G. PINCUS, F. ELMADJIAN, L. ROMANOFF, M. FREEMAN, J. BALLAN, A. BERKELEY, and J. CARLO, Study of adrenocortical physiology in normal and schizophrenic men, *Arch. Neurol. & Psychiat.*, *69*: 470, 1953.

32. G. PINCUS and H. HOAGLAND, Adrenal cortical responses to stress in normal men and in those with personality disorders, *Am. J. Psychiat.*, *106*: 641, 1950.

33. S. Y. TSAI, A. BENNETT, L. G. MAY, and G. L. GREGORY, Effect of insulin hypoglycemia on eosinophiles and lymphocytes of psychotics, *Proc. Soc. Exp. Biol. & Med.*, *74*: 792, 1950.

34. M. D. ALTSCHULE and B. H. PARKHURST, Effect of treatment on excretion of

17-Ketosteroids in patients with mental disease, *Arch. Neurol & Psychiat., 64*: 516, 1950.

35.   R. DICKES, G. H. FLAMM, W. BOWNAN, E. E. HOLLANDER, and H. A. POTTER, Studies in responsivity of the adrenal cortex in schizophrenia, *Am. J. Psychiat., 110*: 125, 1953.

36.   F. H. TYLER and M. D. ARMSTRONG, Diseases of the nervous system. Metabolic aspects of some neurological and muscular disorders, *Am. Rev. Med., 5*: 207, 1954.

37.   R. A. CLEGHORN, S. M. GRAHAM, M. SAFFRAN, and D. E. CAMERON, Study of effect of pituitary ACTH in depressed patients, *Canad. M. A. J., 63*: 329, 1950.

38.   H. HOAGLAND and G. PINCUS, *Proceedings of the First Clinical ACTH Conf.*, Philadelphia: Blakiston, 1950.

39.   E. F. GILDEA, E. RONZONE, and S. D. TRUFANT, in *Biology of Mental Health and Disease*, New York: Hoeber, 1950.

40.   H. HOAGLAND, E. CALLAWAY, F. ELMADJIAN, and G. PINCUS, Adrenal cortical responsivity of psychotic patients in relation to electroshock treatments, *Psychosom. Med., 12*: 73, 1950.

41.   E. HARSLOF, Case of myxedema dominated by mental symptoms, *Ugesk. laeger, 114*: 573, 1952.

42.   E. BLICKENSTORFER, Zum ätiologischen Problem der Psychosen vom akuten exogenen Reaktionstypus. Lysergsäure diathylamid, ein psychisch wirksamer toxischer Spurenstoff, *Arch. Psychiat., 188*: 226, 1952.

43.   S. AKERFELDT, Oxidation of N, N-Dimethyl-*p*-phenylene-diamine by serum from patients with mental disease, *Science, 125*: 117, 1957.

44.   M. ÖZEK, Untersuchungen über den Kupferstoffwechsel im schizophrenen Formenkreis (Research on copper metabolism in several forms of schizophrenia), *Arch. Psychiat., 195*: 408, 1957.

45.   B. E. LEACH, M. COHEN, R. G. HEATH, and S. MARTENS, Studies of the role of ceruloplasmin and albumin in adrenaline metabolism, *A.M.A. Arch. Neurol. & Psychiat., 76*: 635, 1956.

46.   L. G. ABOOD, F. A. GIBBS, and E. GIBBS, Comparative study of blood ceruloplasmin in schizophrenia and other disorders, *A.M.A. Arch. Neurol. & Psychiat., 77*: 643, 1957.

47.   J. FAY, G. E. CARTWRIGHT, and M. M. WINTROBE, Studies on free erythrocyte protoporphyrin, serum iron, serum iron-binding capacity and plasma copper during normal pregnancy, *J. Clin. Invest., 28*: 487, 1949.

48.   I. H. SCHEINBERG, in Korey, S. R., and Nurnberger, J. H. (Eds.), *Neurochemistry*, New York: Hoeber, 1956.

49.   A. OSTFELD, personal communication.

50.   L. MEDUNA and F. J. GERTY, personal communication.

51.   A. OSTFELD, L. G. ABOOD, and D. MARCUS, Studies with ceruloplasmin and a new hallucinogen, *A.M.A. Arch. Neurol. & Psychiat., 79*: 317, 1958.

52.   W. S. FELDBERG, Present views on mode of action of acetylcholine in central nervous system, *Physiol. Rev., 25*: 596, 1945.

53.   R. HEATH, personal communication.

54.   C. LANDIS and W. A. HUNT, Conscious correlates of galvanic skin response, *J. Exper. Psychol., 18*: 505, 1935.

55.   M. D. ALTSCHULE, Physiologic psychology of neurosis, *New England J. Med., 251*: 476, 1954.

56.   C. G. HOLMBERG and C. B. LAURELL, Ceruloplasmin as an enzyme, *Acta chem. scandinav.*, 5: 476, 1951.

57.   R. G. HEATH, S. MARTENS, B. E. LEACH, and M. COHEN, Effect on behavior in humans with the administration of taraxein, *Am. J. Psychiat.*, *114*: 14, 1957.

58.   B. MELANDER, S. MARTENS, S. VALLBO, *Third International Neurochem. Symposium*, Strasbourg, 1958.

59.   C. G. HOLMBERG and C. B. LAURELL, Investigations in serum copper. II. Isolation of the copper-containing protein, and a description of some of its properties, *Acta chem. scandinav.*, 2: 550, 1948.

60.   N. RASHEVSKY, *Mathematical Biology*, Chicago: Univ. Chicago Press, 1948.

61.   H. A. BLAIR, On the intensity-time relations for stimulation by electric currents, *J. Gen. Physiol.*, *15*: 709, 1932.

62.   W. S. MC CULLOCH and W. PITTS, *Bull. Math. Biophys.*, 5: 115, 1943.

63.   *Cybernetics*, Vols. I–IV, New York: Macy, 1955, 1956, 1957, 1958.

64.   W. ROSS ASHBY, *Design for a Brain*, New York: Wiley, 1952.

65.   H. KLÜVER, *Mescal*, London: Kegan Paul, 1928.

66.   A. STOLL and A. HOFFMAN, Ergot alkoids, *Z. physiol. chem.*, *251*: 155, 1938.

67.   A. STOLL, Lysergsäure-diäthlamid ein Phantastikum aus der Mutterkorngruppe, *Schweiz. Arch. Neurol. u. Psychiat.*, *60*: 279, 1947.

68.   U. LANZ, A. CERLETTI, and E. ROTHLIN, Distribution of lysergic acid diethylamide in the animal body, *Helvet. physiol. et pharmacol. acta*, *13*: 207, 1955.

69.   E. ROTHLIN, Pharmacology of natural and dihydrogenated alkaloids of ergot, *Bull. schweiz. Akad. med. Wissensch.*, 2: 249, 1947.

70.   E. ROTHLIN, Lysergic acid diethylamide and related substances, *Ann. New York Acad. Sc.*, *66*: 668, 1957.

71.   A. HOFFMAN, *First Neuropsychopharmacology Collegium*, Amsterdam: Elsevier, in press.

72.   A. S. MARRAZZI and E. R. HART, Relationship of hallucinogens to adrenergic cerebral neurohumors, *Science*, *121*: 365, 1956.

73.   A. S. MARRAZZI, The effects of certain drugs on cerebral synapses, *Ann. New York Acad. Sc.*, *66*: 496, 1957.

74.   M. I. GLUCKMAN, E. R. HART, and A. S. MARRAZZI, Cerebral synaptic inhibition by serotonin and iproniazid, *Science*, *126*: 448, 1957.

75.   H. OSMOND, in *Neuropharmacology, Transactions of the Second Conference*, New York: Macy, 1956.

76.   H. FABING, *Neuropharmacology, Transactions of the Second Conference*, New York: Macy, 1956.

77.   A. H. AMIN, T. B. C. CRAWFORD, and J. H. GADDUM, Distribution of substance P and 5-hydroxy-tryptamine in central nervous system of dog, *J. Physiol.*, *126*: 596, 1954.

78.   M. J. VOGT, Concentration of sympathin in different parts of central nervous system under normal conditions and after administration of drugs, *J. Physiol.*, *123*: 451, 1954.

79.   L. G. ABOOD and L. ROMANCHEK, The chemical constitution and biochemical effects of psychotherapeutic and structurally related agents, *Ann. New York Acad. Sc.*, *66*: 812, 1957.

80.   E. K. KILLAM, K. F. KILLAM, and T. SHAW, The effects of psychotherapeutic

compounds on central afferent and limbic pathways, *Ann. New York Acad. Sc.*, *66*: 784, 1957.

81. V. ERSPAMER, Pharmacology of indolealkylamines, *Pharmacol. Rev.*, *6*: 425, 1954.

82. J. H. GADDUM, Antagonism between lysergic acid diethylamide and 5-hydroxytryptamine, *J. Physiol.*, *121*: 15, 1953.

83. A. CERLETTI and E. ROTHLIN, Role of 5-hydroxytryptamine in mental diseases and its antagonism to lysergic acid derivatives, *Nature*, *176*: 785, 1955.

84. D. W. WOOLEY and E. SHAW, Some neurophysiological aspects of serotonin, *Brit. M. J.*, *2*: 122, 1954.

85. B. B. BRODIE, P. A. SHORE, and A. PLETSCHER, Serotonin releasing activity limited to rauwolfia alkaloids with tranquilizing action, *Science*, *123*: 992, 1956.

86. S. UDENFRIEND, H. WEISSBACH, and D. F. BOGDANSKI, Biochemical findings relating to the action of serotonin, *Ann. New York Acad. Sc.*, *66*: 602, 1957.

87. B. B. BRODIE, A. PLETSCHER, and P. A. SHORE, Serotonin as a mediator of reserpine action in brain, *J. Pharmacol. & Exper. Therap.*, *116*: 84, 1956.

88. J. H. GADDUM and M. VOGT, Some central actions of 5-hydroxytryptamine and various antagonists, *Brit. J. Pharmacol.*, *11*: 175, 1956.

89. I. SANO, personal communication.

90. J. WELSH, Serotonin as a possible neurohumoral agent: evidence obtained in lower animals, *Ann. New York Acad. Sc.*, *66*: 618, 1957.

91. H. BENITEZ, M. MURRAY, and D. W. WOOLEY, Effect of serotonin on oligodendroglia in tissue cultures, *Proc. Second Intern. Neuropathol. Congr. Excerpta Med.*, London, 1955.

92. D. W. WOOLEY and E. N. SHAW, Evidence for the participation of serotonin in mental processes, *Ann. New York Acad. Sc.*, *66*: 649, 1957.

93. R. GEIGER, Effect of lysergic acid diethylamide (LSD-25) and serotonin on adult cortical brain cells in tissue culture, *Fed. Proc.*, *16*: 44, 1957.

94. H. F. HAUSLER, On the central transmission of nervous impulses, *Abst. XIX Internat. Physiol. Congr.*, p. 443, 1953.

95. S. R. ROSENTHAL, Histamine as possible chemical mediator for cutaneous pain. Dual pain response to histamine, *Proc. Soc. Exper. Biol. & Med.*, *74*: 167, 1950.

96. H. KWIATKOWSKI, Histamine in nervous tissue, *J. Physiol.*, *102*: 32, 1943.

97. G. UNGAR, Démonstration de la mise en liberté de substances histaminiques. Transmission neuro-humorale histaminergique, *J. Physiol. Path. gén.*, *34*: 77, 1936.

98. B. PERNOW, Studies on substance P; purification, occurrence and biological actions, *Acta physiol. scandinav.*, *29*, Suppl. 105, 1953.

99. H. F. HELLAUER and K. UMRATH, Über die Aktionssubstanz der sensiblen nerven, *Arch. ges Physiol. 249*: 619, 1948.

100. F. A. HOLTON and P. HOLTON, The possibility that ATP is a transmitter at sensory nerve endings, *J. Physiol.*, *119*: 50, 1953.

101. W. S. FELDBERG, "Central and sensory transmission," in Symposium on Neurohumoral Transmission," *Pharmacol. Rev.*, *6*: 85, 1954.

102. U. TRENDELENBURG, Modification of transmission through superior cervical ganglion of cat, *J. Physiol.*, *132*: 529, 1956.

103. W. S. FELDBERG, J. A. B. GRAY, and W. L. M. PERRY, Effects of close arterial injections of acetylcholine on activity of cervical spinal cord of cat, *J. Physiol.*, *119*: 428, 1953.

104.   G. B. KOELLE, Chronic toxicity of di-isopropyl fluorophosphate (DFP) in dogs, monkeys and rats, *J. Pharmacol. & Exper. Therap.* 87: 435, 1946.

105.   A. SCHWEITZER, E. STEDMAN, and S. WRIGHT, Central action of anticholinesterases, *J. Physiol.*, 96: 302, 1939.

106.   W. FELDBERG and M. VOGT, Acetylcholine synthesis in different regions of central nervous system, *J. Physiol.*, 107: 372, 1948.

107.   D. W. ROWNTREE, S. NEVIN, and A. WILSON, Effects of diisopropylfluorophosphate in schizophrenia and manic depressive psychosis, *J. Neurol. Neurosurg. & Psychiat.*, 13: 47, 1950.

108.   C. C. PFEIFFER and E. H. JENNEY, The inhibition of the conditioned response and the counteraction of schizophrenia by muscarinic stimulation of the brain, *Ann. New York Acad. Sc.*, 66: 753, 1957.

109.   J. P. QUIGLEY, Mental disturbances from atropine or novatropine given to subjects under the influence of insulin, *J.A.M.A.*, 109: 1363, 1937.

110.   F. J. GERTY, personal communication.

111.   L. G. ABOOD, A. OSTFELD, and J. BIEL, A new group of psychotomimetic agents, *Proc. Soc. Exp. Biol. & Med.*, 97: 483, 1958.

112.   J. H. BIEL, E. P. SPRENGLER, H. A. LEISER, J. HORNER, A. DRUKKER, and H. L. FRIEDMAN, Antispasmodics. II. Derivatives of N-Substituted-3-piperidols, *J. Am. Chem. Soc.*, 77: 2250, 1955.

113.   P. L. EWING, L. D. SEAGER, G. KELLER, and D. DODSON, Cardiovascular effects of some 3-piperidyl diphenylacetate derivatives, *J. Pharmacol. & Exper. Therap.*, 110: 17, 1954.

114.   C. C. PFEIFFER and E. H. JENNEY, A component of pharmacological action which inhibits the conditioned response and counteracts schizophrenia, *Abst. XX Internat. Physiol. Congr.*, 1956.

115.   J. C. ECCLES, The electrophysiological properties of the motorneurone, *Cold Spring Harbor Symp.*, 18: 175, 1952.

116.   L. G. BROCK, J. S. COOMBS, and J. C. ECCLES, Recording of potentials from motoneurons with intracellular electrode, *J. Physiol.*, 117: 431, 1952.

117.   W. S. FELDBERG and S. L. SHERWOOD, Injections of drugs into lateral ventricle of cat, *J. Physiol.*, 123: 148, 1954.

118.   C. LANDIS and W. A. HUNT, Conscious correlates of galvanic skin response, *J. Exp. Psychol.*, 18: 505, 1935.

119.   H. BASOWITZ et al., Anxiety and performance changes with a minimal dose of epinephrine, *A.M.A. Arch. Neurol. & Psychiat.*, 76: 98, 1956.

120.   M. E. KOSMAN and R. W. GERARD, Effect of adrenaline on conditioned avoidence response, *J. Cell. & Comp. Physiol.*, 48: 506, 1955.

121.   R. W. GERARD, The biological roots of psychiatry, *Am. J. Psychiat.*, 112: 81, 1955.

122.   A. HOFFER, H. OSMOND, and J. SMYTHIES, Schizophrenia: new approach; result of year's research, *J. Ment. Sc.*, 100: 29, 1954.

123.   A. HOFFER, Epinephrine derivatives as potential schizophrenic factors, *Quart. Rev. Psychiat. Neurol.*, 18: 27, 1957.

124.   A. M. UTEVSKIY, New Facts on biochemistry of vascular tonos, *Adv. Med. Biol.*, 18: 45, 1944.

125.   G. B. WEST, Oxidation of adrenaline in alkaline solution, *Brit. J. Pharm.*, 2: 121, 1947.

126.   G. N. COHEN, Existence and composition of an adrenalin-molybdic acid complex, *Bull. Soc. chim. biol.*, 27: 237, 1945.

127.   Z. M. BACQ, Metabolism of adrenaline, *J. Pharmacol. & Exper. Therap.*, 95: 1, 1949.

128.   L. G. ABOOD, Some chemical concepts of mental disease, *A. Res. Nerv. & Ment. Dis.*, 37: 384, 1959.

129.   W. B. BULLOUGH, Stress and epidermal mitotic activity; effects of adrenal hormones, *J. Endocrin.*, 8: 265, 1952.

130.   S. FEDOROFF, Toxicity of schizophrenia blood in tissue culture, *Anat. Rec.*, *121*: 394, 1955.

131.   R. H. HACKMAN and A. R. TODD, Some observations on the reaction of catechol derivatives with amines and amino acids in presence of oxidizing agents, *Biochem. J.*, *55*: 631, 1953.

132.   J. M. SNELL and A. WEISSBERGER, The reaction of thiol compounds with quinones, *J. Am. Chem. Soc.*, *61*: 450, 1939.

133.   C. KRUEGER, The effect of β-Keto acids on the action of Tyrosinase, *Arch. Biochem.*, *56*: 394, 1955.

134.   D. E. GREEN and D. RICHTER, Adrenaline and adrenochrome, *Biochem. J.*, *31*: 596, 1937.

135.   J. WAJZER, Synthèse du glycogène en présence d'adrénochrome, *Bull. Soc. chim. biol.*, 29: 237, 1947.

136.   M. D. ALTSCHULE, Physiologic psychology of neurosis, *New England J. Med.*, 251: 476, 1954.

137.   E. L. ROSS, A preliminary note on the excretion of indolacetic acid urine, *Arch. Int. Med.*, *12*, 1912.

138.   V. M. BUSCAINO, "Discussions on Schizophrenia," *Proc. 1st Internat. Cong. of Neuropath.*, Rome, 1952.

139.   P. L. MC GEER, E. G. MC GEER, and W. C. GIBSON, Aromatic excretory pattern of schizophrenics, *Science, 123*: 1029, 1956.

140.   P. L. MC GEER, F. E. MC NAIR, E. G. MC GEER, and W. C. GIBSON, Aromatic metabolism in schizophrenia, *J. Nerv. & Ment. Dis.*, *125*: 1, 1957.

141.   Y. TAKAHASHI, An enzymological study on brain tissue of schizophrenic patients, *Folia Psychiat. neur. Jap.*, 8: 214, 1954.

142.   I. SANO, On 5-hydroxyindoleacetic acid excretion in urine of schizophrenics, *Schweiz. med. Wchnschr.*, 87: 214, 1957.

143.   L. M. RIEGELHAUPT, Investigations on the glyoxylic acid reactions on schizophrenic urine, *J. Nerv. & Ment. Dis.*, *123*: 383, 1956.

144.   W. L. SHERWOOD, unpublished conference on Biochemistry of Mental Illness, University of British Columbia, 1957.

145.   W. M. HOUFF, The nature of an oxidation product of 3-indoleacetic acid, *J. Am. Chem. Soc.*, *76*: 5654, 1954.

146.   H. HOAGLAND, in *Neuropharmacology, Transactions of the Fourth Conference*, New York: Macy, 1959, p. 106.

147.   C. E. DAGLIESH et al., Intermediary metabolism of tryptophane, *Nature, 168*: 20, 1957.

148.   C. E. DAGLIESH, Biological degradation of tryptophane, *Quart. Rev.* (London), 5: 227, 1951.

149.   w. k. sherwood, Paper presented before British Columbia Academy of Science, March, 1957.

150.   e. gamper and a. kral, Zur empirischen Erbprognose der psychopathie (Untersuchungen an Kindern von psychopathen), *Ztschr. Neurol. u. Psychiat., 159*: 609, 1937.

151.   p. j. reiter, Untersuchungen zur Beleuchtung der Intoxikationstheorie bei der dementia praecox mit besonderes Berücksichtigung der versuche mit totaltransfusionen, *Ztschr. Neurol. u. Psychiat., 160*: 598, 1938.

152.   a. le grand and p. arnee, *Ann. Med. Psychol., 97*: 306, 1939.

153.   a. k. shapiro, An attempt to demonstrate a catatonigenic agent in cerebrospinal fluid of catatonic schizophrenic patients, *J. Nerv. & Ment. Dis., 123*: 65, 1956.

4. RECENT BIOCHEMICAL THEORIES OF SCHIZOPHRENIA*

Seymour S. Kety

The concept of a chemical etiology in schizophrenia is not new. The Hippocratic school attributed certain mental aberrations to changes in the composition of the blood, but it was Thudichum (1), the founder of modern neurochemistry, who in 1884 expressed the concept most cogently:

> Many forms of insanity are unquestionably the external manifestations of the effects upon the brain substance of poisons fermented within the body, just as mental aberrations accompanying chronic alcoholic intoxication are the accumulated effects of a relatively simple poison fermented out of the body. These poisons we shall, I have no doubt, be able to isolate after we know the normal chemistry to its uttermost detail. And then will come in their turn the crowning discoveries to which our efforts must ultimately be directed, namely, the discoveries of the antidotes to the poisons and to the fermenting causes and processes which produce them.

In these few words were anticipated and encompassed most of the current chemical formulations regarding schizophrenia.

It may be of value to pause in the midst of the present era of psycho-

Seymour S. Kety, M.D. is Chief of the Laboratory of Clinical Science, National Institute of Mental Health.

* An adaptation of this chapter has appeared in *Science, 129*: 1529, 1959.

chemical activity to ask how far we have advanced along the course plotted by Thudichum. Have we merely substituted "enzymes" for "ferments" and the names of specific agents for "poisons" without altering the completely theoretical nature of the concept? Or, on the other hand, are there some well-substantiated findings to support the prevalent belief that this old and stubborn disorder, which has resisted all previous attempts to expose its etiology, is about to yield its secrets to the biochemist?

An examination of the experience of another and older discipline may be of help in the design, interpretation, and evaluation of biochemical studies. The pathological concepts of schizophrenia have been well reviewed recently (2, 3, 4). Prompted by the definite histological changes in the cerebral cortex described by Alzheimer and confirmed by a number of others, an early enthusiasm developed which penetrated into the thinking of Kraepelin and Bleuler. This was followed by a period of questioning and the design and execution of more critically controlled studies leading to the present consensus that a pathological lesion characteristic of schizophrenia or any of its subgroups remains to be demonstrated.

Earlier biochemical theories and findings related to schizophrenia have been reviewed by a number of authors, of which those by McFarland and Goldstein (5), Kcup (6), and Richter (7) may be mentioned. Horwitt (8) and others (9, 10, 11) have pointed out some of the difficulties of crucial research in this area. It is the purpose of this review to describe the biochemical trends in schizophrenia research of the past few years, to discuss current theories, and to examine the evidence that has been used to support them.

SOURCES OF ERROR

Because of the chronicity of the disease, the prolonged periods of institutionalization associated with its management, and the comparatively few objective criteria available for its diagnosis and the evaluation of its progress, schizophrenia presents to the investigator a large number of variables and sources of error which he must recognize and attempt to control before he can attribute to any of his findings a primary or characteristic significance.

Despite the phenomenological similarities which permitted the concept of schizophrenia to emerge as a fairly well-defined symptom-complex, there is little evidence that all of its forms have a common etiology or pathogenesis. The likelihood that one is dealing with a number of different disorders with a common symptomatology must be recognized and included in one's experimental design (10, 12, 13). Errors involved in sampling from heterogeneous populations may help to explain the high frequency with which findings of one group fail to be confirmed by another. Recognition of the probability that any sample of schizophrenics is a heterogeneous one should seem to emphasize the importance of analyzing data not only for mean values but also for significant deviations of individual values from the group. The biochemical characteristics of phenylketonuria would hardly have been detected in an average value for phenylalanine blood levels in a large group of mentally retarded patients.

Most biochemical research in schizophrenia has been carried out in patients with a long history of hospitalization in institutions where overcrowding is difficult to avoid and hygienic standards cannot always be maintained. It is easy to imagine the spread of chronic infections, especially of the digestive tract, among such patients. The presence of amebiasis in a majority of patients at one large institution has been reported (14), and one wonders how often this condition or a former infectious hepatitis has accounted for the various disturbances in hepatic function found in schizophrenia. Even in the absence of previous or current infection, the development of a characteristic pattern of intestinal flora in a population of schizophrenic patients living together for long periods and fed from the same kitchen is a possibility which cannot be dismissed in interpreting what appear to be deviant metabolic pathways.

The variety and quality of the diet of the institutionalized schizophrenic are rarely comparable to those of the nonhospitalized normal control. Whatever homeostatic function the process of free dietary selection may serve is often lost between the rigors of the kitchen or the budget and the overriding emotional or obsessive features of the disease. In the case of the "acute" schizophrenic, the weeks and months of emotional turmoil which precede the recognition and diagnosis of the disease are hardly conducive to a normal dietary intake. Kelsey, Gullock, and Kelsey (15) confirmed certain abnormalities in thyroid function previously reported in schizophrenia and showed that in their patients they resulted from a dietary deficiency of iodine, correctable by the introduction of iodized salt into the hospital diet. It is not surprising that a dietary vitamin deficiency has been found to explain at least two of the biochemical abnormalities recently attributed to schizophrenia (11, 16, 17, 18). It is more surprising that the vitamins and other dietary constituents, whose role in metabolism has become so clearly established, should so often be relegated to a position of unimportance in the intermediary metabolism of schizophrenics. Horwitt (19) has found signs of liver dysfunction during ingestion of a diet containing borderline levels of protein, while nonspecific vitamin therapy accompanied by a high protein and carbohydrate diet has been reported to reverse the impairment of hepatic function in schizophrenic patients (20).

Another incidental feature of the schizophrenic which sets him apart from the normal control is the long list of therapies to which he may have been exposed. Hypnotic and ataractic drugs and their metabolic products or effects produce changes that have sometimes been attributed to the disease. Less obvious is the possibility of residual electrophysiological or biochemical changes resulting from repeated electroshock or insulin comas.

Emotional stress is known to cause profound changes in man, in adrenocortical and thyroid function (21), in the excretion of epinephrine and norepinephrine (22) and of water, electrolytes, or creatinine (23, 24), to mention only a few recently reported findings. Schizophrenic illness is often characterized by marked emotional disturbance even in what is called the basal state and by frequently exaggerated anxiety in response to routine and research procedures. The disturbances in behavior and activity which mark the schizophrenic process would also be expected to cause deviations from the normal in many biochemical and metabolic measures: in urine volume and concentration, in energy and nitrogen metabolism, in the size and function of numerous organic systems. The physiological and biochemical changes that are secondary to the psychological and behavioral state of the patient are of interest in themselves as part of a total understanding of the schizophrenic process; it is important, however, not to attribute to them a primary or etiological role.

An additional source of error that must be recognized is one which is common to all of science and which it is the very purpose of scientific method, tradition, and training to minimize—the subjective bias. There are reasons why this bias should operate to a greater extent in this field than in many others. Not only is the motivation heightened by the tragedy of this problem and the social implications of findings that may contribute to its solution, but the measurements themselves, especially of the changes in mental state or behavior, are so highly subjective, the symptoms so variable and responsive to nonspecific factors in the milieu, that only the most scrupulous attention to controlled design will permit the conclusion that a drug, or a diet, or a protein fraction of the blood, or an extract of the brain is capable of causing or ameliorating some of the manifestations of the disease. This is not to suggest that the results of purely chemical determinations are immune to subjective bias, and the same vigilance is required to prevent the hypothesis from contaminating the data. In a field with as many variables as this one, it is difficult to avoid the subconscious tendency to reject for good reason data that weaken an hypothesis while accepting uncritically those data which strengthen it. Carefully controlled and "double blind" experimental designs, which are becoming more widely utilized, can help to minimize this bias.

Obvious as many of these sources of error are, it is expensive and difficult, if not impossible, to prevent some of them from affecting results, especially in the preliminary testing of interesting hypotheses. It is in the interpretation of these results, however, and in the formulating of conclusions that the investigator has the opportunity and indeed the responsibility to recognize and evaluate his uncontrolled variables rather than to ignore them, for no one knows better than the investigator himself the possible source of error in his particular experiment. There are enough unknowns in our guessing game with nature to make it unnecessary to indulge in such a sport with one another.

The Schizophrenia Program of the Laboratory of Clinical Science   Since 1956, the Laboratory of Clinical Science has been developing and pursuing a program of biological research in schizophrenia designed to minimize many of these sources of error while increasing the opportunity for true biological characteristics, if they exist, to be detected. One of the wards houses a group of approximately 14 clearly diagnosed schizophrenic patients, representative of as many clinical subgroups as possible. They are chosen from a patient population of 14,000 with an attempt to minimize the non-disease variables of age, sex, race, and physical illness and, on the basis of careful family surveys, to maximize the likelihood of including within the group whatever genetic subgroups of the disease may exist (12). They are maintained for an indefinite period of time on a good diet and under excellent hygienic, nursing, medical, and psychiatric care. No specific therapy is employed or even necessary and drugs or dietary changes are introduced only for research purposes and for short periods of time. The other ward houses a comparable number of normal controls, who volunteer to remain for protracted periods of time, exposed to the same diet and in a reasonably similar milieu. We recognize, of course, that only a few of the variables are thus controlled and any positive difference which emerges in this preliminary experiment between some or all of the schizophrenics and the normal population will have to be subjected to much more rigorous examination before its significance can be evaluated. This has rarely been necessary since our schizophrenic patients show so little abnormality in the biological studies that have thus far been completed.

OXYGEN, CARBOHYDRATE, AND ENERGETICS

A decrease in basal metabolism was found in schizophrenia by earlier workers, although more recent work has not confirmed this (7). Theories attributing the disease to disturbances in the fundamental mechanisms of energy supply or conversion in the brain have enjoyed some popularity, but on the basis of such extremely inadequate evidence as spectroscopic oximetry of the ear lobe or nail bed (25). Our finding of a normal rate of cerebral circulation and oxygen consumption in schizophrenic patients (26) was confirmed by Wilson, Schieve, and Scheinberg (27) and more recently in our laboratory by Sokoloff and associates (28), who also found a normal rate of cerebral glucose consumption in this condition. These studies make it appear unlikely that the moderate decrease in these functions reported by Gordan and associates (29), but only in their patients with long-standing disease, is fundamental to the disease process. These studies do not, of course, rule out a highly localized change in energy metabolism somewhere in the brain, but cogent evidence for such a hypothesis has yet to be presented.

Richter (7) has pointed out the uncontrolled factors in earlier work which implicated a defect in carbohydrate metabolism as a characteristic of the schizophrenic disease process. An abnormal glucose tolerance in conjunction with considerable other evidence of hepatic dysfunction (30) or evidence of a retarded metabolism of lactate by the schizophrenic (31) does not completely exclude incidental hepatic disease or nutritional deficiencies as possible sources of error. Horwitt and associates (32) were able to demonstrate and correct similar abnormalities by altering the dietary intake of the B group of vitamins.

Evidence for higher than normal anti-insulin or hyperglycemic activity in the blood or urine of a significant segment of schizophrenic patients was reported in 1942 by Meduna, Gerty, and Urse (33) and as recently as 1958 by Moya and associates (34). Some progress has been made in concentrating or characterizing such factors in normal urine (35) as well as in that from schizophrenics (36). Harris (37) has thrown some doubt on the importance of such anti-insulin mechanisms in the pathogenesis of schizophrenia, and it is hoped that further investigation may clarify the nature of the substance or substances involved and their relevance to schizophrenia.

Defects in oxidative phosphorylation have been thought to occur in this disease. Reports of alterations in the phosphorus metabolism of the erythrocyte (38, 39) await further definition and independent confirmation.

Two recent reports of a more normal pattern of carbohydrate metabolism, as well as clinical improvement, following the infusion of glutathione (40, 41) in psychotic patients, some of whom were schizophrenic, are perhaps of interest. There is little verifiable evidence for a reduction in the blood glutathione index in schizophrenia (11); one group that has repeatedly postulated this reduction has done so on the basis of decreasingly convincing data (18, 42), while our laboratory has failed to find it at all (15), and a very recent report publishes identical figures for the schizophrenic and normal groups (43). Clinical and biochemical improvement in a variety of psychoses following glutathione infusion, even if it is accepted without the necessary controls, suggests at best that glutathione is of secondary and nonspecific import.

It is difficult to believe that a generalized defect in energy metabolism, a process so fundamental to every cell in the body, could be responsible for the highly specialized features of schizophrenia. It is perhaps for this reason that the center of interest today appears to have shifted to other, more specialized aspects of metabolism with more specific effects.

AMINO ACIDS AND AMINES

The well-controlled studies of the Gjessings (44, 45, 46) on nitrogen metabolism in periodic catatonia have aroused considerable interest in the possible relationship of intermediary protein metabolism to a specific form of schizophrenia, although earlier workers had also postulated defects in amino acid metabolism in this disease (47). The hallucinogenic properties of some compounds related directly or indirectly to biological amines further stimulated this interest, and the techniques of paper chromatography offer new and almost unlimited opportunity for its pursuit.

The first group to report chromatographic studies of the urine of schizophrenic and control groups found certain differences in the amino acid pattern and, in addition, the presence of certain unidentified imidazoles in the urine of schizophrenics (48). Although a normal group of comparable age was used for comparison, there is no indication of the extent to which dietary and other variables were controlled, and the authors were properly cautious in their conclusions. In a more extensive series of studies, another group has reported a significantly higher than normal concentration of aromatic compounds in the urine of schizophrenic patients (49) and suggested certain qualitative differences in the excretion of such compounds (50). Others have reported the abnormal presence of unidentified amines (51) or indoles (52); and one group, the absence of a normally occurring indole (53) in the urine of schizophrenic patients. Not all of these studies appear to have controlled possible drug therapy, urinary volume, or concentration, and few have controlled the diet. There are numerous mechanisms whereby vitamin deficiencies may cause substantial changes in the complex patterns of the intermediary metabolism of amino acids. In addition, the large number of aromatic compounds in the urine that have recently been shown to be of dietary origin (54, 55, 56, 57, 58) suggest the need for considerably more caution than has usually been employed with regard to this variable.

Another point which has not been emphasized sufficiently is that chromatographic procedures make possible the simultaneous determination of scores of known and unknown substances, thus requiring statistical analyses somewhat different from those that were developed for the testing of single, well-defined hypotheses. It is merely a restatement of statistical theory to say that in an analysis for 100 different compounds simultaneously in two samples of the *same* population, five would be expected to show a difference significant at the 0.05 level of confidence. It is interesting to note that a more recent study was able to demonstrate considerably fewer differences between the urines of normal and schizophrenic populations and drew very limited and guarded conclusions (59).

In our own laboratory, Mann and LaBrosse (60) undertook a search for urinary phenolic acids in terms of quantity excreted rather than concentration and discovered four compounds significantly higher in the urine from the schizophrenics than in that from the normals. These compounds were found to be known metabolites of substances in coffee. The presence of these four compounds in the urine was, in fact, better correlated with the ingestion of this beverage than with schizophrenia.

That disordered amino acid metabolism is a fundamental component of some forms of schizophrenia remains an attractive though fairly general hypothesis. The chromatographic search for supportive evidence is interesting and valuable, and the preliminary indications of differences certainly provocative. Proof that any of these differences are characteristic of even a segment of the disease rather than artifactual or incidental has not yet been obtained.

THE EPINEPHRINE HYPOTHESIS

The theory that relates the pathogenesis of schizophrenia to faulty metabolism of epinephrine (61, 62, 63, 64) is imaginative, ingenious, and plausible. It postulates that the symptoms of this disease are caused by the action of abnormal, hallucinogenic derivatives of epinephrine, presumably adrenochrome or adrenolutin. By including the concept of a possible genetic enzymatic defect with another factor—epinephrine release—which may be activated by stressful life situations (22), such a theory encompasses the evidence for sociological as well as constitutional factors in the etiology of the schizophrenias.

The possibility that some of the oxidation products of epinephrine are psychotomimetic received support from anecdotal reports of psychological disturbances associated with the therapeutic use of the compound, especially when it was discolored (61), and from some early experiments in which the administration of adrenochrome or adrenolutin in appreciable dosage was followed by certain unusual mental manifestations (64). A number of investigators failed to demonstrate any hallucinogenic properties in adrenochrome (65), and the original authors were not always able to confirm their earlier results.

Meanwhile, reports were emerging from the group at Tulane University, suggesting a gross disturbance in epinephrine metabolism in schizophrenic patients. Five years previously, Holmberg and Laurell (66) had demonstrated a more rapid oxidation of epinephrine *in vitro* in the presence of pregnancy serum than with serum from the umbilical cord and had suggested that this was due to higher concentrations of ceruloplasmin in the former. There had also been a few reports of an increase of this protein in the blood of schizophrenics. Leach and Heath (67) reported a striking acceleration in the *in vitro* oxidation of epinephrine in the presence of plasma from schizophrenic patients as compared with normals; and shortly thereafter they implicated ceruloplasmin, or some variant of ceruloplasmin, as the oxidizing substance (68). Hoffer and Kenyon (69) promptly reported evidence that the substance formed from epinephrine by blood serum *in vitro* was adrenolutin and pointed out how this strengthened the epinephrine hypothesis.

All of the evidence does not, however, support the epinephrine theory. Despite considerable new information regarding the metabolism of epinephrine *in vivo* that has been acquired in this laboratory and elsewhere during the past few years, both in animals (70, 71) and in normal and schizophrenic man (72, 73), no evidence has been found for the oxidation of epinephrine via adrenochrome and adrenolutin in any of these populations. Although appreciable levels of adrenochrome have been reported to occur in the blood of normal subjects and to increase considerably following administration of lysergic acid diethylamide (74), Szara, Axelrod, and Perlin, using techniques of high sensitivity, have been unable to detect it in the blood of normals or of acute or chronic schizophrenic patients (75). Holland and his co-workers (76) found no differences between normals and schizophrenic patients in the rate of destruction of epinephrine. Finally, it has been shown, in our laboratory by McDonald (11) and by the Tulane group themselves (18), that the low level of ascorbic acid in the blood was an important and uncontrolled variable in the rapid *in vitro* oxidation of epinephrine by plasma from schizophrenic patients. The fact that McDonald has been able to produce wide fluctuations in the epinephrine oxidation phenomenon from normal to highly abnormal rates in both normals and schizophrenics merely by dietary alterations in blood ascorbic acid level without any effect on the mental processes of either group is quite convincing evidence of the dietary and secondary nature of the phenomenon.

It should be pointed out that none of this negative evidence invalidates the theory that some abnormal product of epinephrine metabolism produces the major symptoms of schizophrenia; it does, however, considerably weaken the evidence that has been used to support it. In addition, there is the bothersome observation of numerous workers (77–79) and of our own experience that the administration of epinephrine to schizophrenics, which, according to the theory, should aggravate the psychotic symptoms, is usually accompanied by considerably less mental disturbance than occurs in normal subjects. Quite recently a new report on inconstant psychotomimetic effects of epinephrine oxidation products in a small number of subjects has appeared (80), with evidence suggesting that the psychotoxic substance is neither adrenochrome nor adrenolutin, is active in microgram quantities, and is highly labile. This report, like the previous one which described the psychotomimetic effects of epinephrine products, is highly subjective and incompletely controlled. Even if these conclusions are accepted, the relevance of such hallucinogens or their presence in schizophrenia remains to be demonstrated.

CERULOPLASMIN AND TARAXEIN

The rise and fall of ceruloplasmin as a biochemical factor significantly related to schizophrenia is one of the briefest if not the most enlightening chapter in the history of biological psychiatry. The upsurge of interest can be ascribed to a report that a young Swedish biochemist had discovered a new test for schizophrenia. The test depended upon the oxidation of n, n-dimethyl-p-phenylenediamine by ceruloplasmin (81, 82). It is difficult to understand the exaggerated interest that this report aroused because Holmberg and Laurell (66) had demonstrated previously that ceruloplasmin was capable of oxidizing a number of substances, including phenylenediamine and epinephrine, and Leach and Heath (67) had already published a procedure based on epinephrine oxidation that was equally valid in distinguishing schizophrenics from normals and had identified the oxidizing substance as ceruloplasmin (68). All of these observations were compatible with earlier reports in the German literature (6) of increased serum copper in schizophrenia, the demonstration that practically all of the serum copper was in the form of ceruloplasmin, and the fact that this compound was elevated in blood during pregnancy and in a large number of diseases (83, 84). There had even been preliminary observations of an increase in blood ceruloplasmin in schizophrenia (84). Following the announcement of the Akerfeldt test, however, interest in copper and ceruloplasmin rose; and very soon a number of investigators reported this reaction or some modification of it to be positive in a high percentage of schizophrenics (82, 85), although its value as a diagnostic test was discredited because of the large number of diseases besides schizophrenia in which it was positive. Both Akerfeldt and Heath recognized that ascorbic acid could inhibit the oxidation of phenylenediamine and of epinephrine, respectively, but neither felt that this was crucial to either phenomenon because each had satisfied himself that the feeding of large doses of ascorbic acid to the patients had not influenced the respective reactions (82). In addition, the Abood (85) modification of the Akerfeldt procedure, which was unaffected by ascorbic acid, produced a positive reaction in two thirds of more than 250 schizophrenics examined.

In recent months the interest in ceruloplasmin has declined along with the blood levels reported. In May of 1957, McDonald (16) reported his findings on three groups of schizophrenics, one from the wards of the National Institute of Mental Health, where they had been maintained on a more than adequate diet, and two from state hospitals. He performed the Akerfeldt test and the Abood modification of it, as well as independent measurement of ascorbic acid and copper, on these groups and on three groups of controls. In none of the schizophrenic groups was there an increase in serum copper or other evidence of increased ceruloplasmin. The state hospital patients and one group of controls, however, showed low ascorbic acid levels and positive Akerfeldt tests. The Institute schizophrenic patients had normal levels of ascorbic acid and negative Akerfeldt tests. It was clear that a high ceruloplasmin was not characteristic of schizophrenia and that the positive Akerfeldt test, where it occurred, could be completely explained by a dietary insufficiency of ascorbic acid.

In the Tulane group, the mean values for serum copper in schizophrenia have decreased from a high of 216 μg/100 ml in 1956 (68) to 145 μg/100 ml at the end of 1957 (18), mean normal values remaining at 122 and 124 μg/100 ml during the same time. Other groups have found slight differences or no differences at all in ceruloplasmin or copper blood levels between schizophrenic and normal subjects (17, 86, 87, 88) and no support for the ability of the Akerfeldt reaction to distinguish between schizophrenic and nonschizophrenic patients (89). It is not clear why some schizophrenics apparently show an elevated blood ceruloplasmin level; among the possibilities are dietary factors, hepatic damage, chronic infection, or, as preliminary experiments appear to suggest (90), the tendency of excitement to raise the blood ceruloplasmin.

Quite early in their studies, the Tulane group recognized that the potent oxidant effects of the serum of schizophrenics on epinephrine *in vitro* could not be satisfactorily explained by the ceruloplasmin levels alone (68). Before they recognized the importance of ascorbic acid deficiency to this reaction (18), they had postulated in the blood of schizophrenics the presence of a qualitatively different form of ceruloplasmin (68), which they proceeded to isolate and test in monkey and man and to which they have given the name taraxein (from the Greek root "to be confused or disturbed"). They have reported that when certain batches of this material were tested in monkeys, marked behavioral and electroencephalographic changes occurred. When samples of these active batches were injected intravenously at a rapid rate into carefully selected prisoner volunteers, all of the subjects developed symptoms that have been described for schizophrenia, including disorganization and fragmentation of thought, autism, feelings of depersonalization, paranoid ideas, auditory hallucinations, and catatonic behavior (78, 91, 92).

The demonstration of toxic materials in the blood and body fluids of schizophrenic patients is not new. The voluminous and inconclusive work of earlier investigators has been well reviewed (6). Since that time, many new reports have appeared, although none have had extensive substantiation. One concerning the toxicity of serum and urine of schizophrenic patients on the larvae of *Xenopus levis* (93) was disputed by the laboratory in which the work was done (94). Edisen (95) was unable to demonstrate toxicity of such serum against the species of tadpole previously used or against other species and genera. A report that serum from schizophrenic patients is toxic to cells in tissue culture (96) lost some of its significance when one year later the same laboratory reported comparable toxicity in the sera of surgical patients (97). Reports that certain extracts of the urine of schizophrenic patients induce electroencephalographic and behavioral changes when injected in rats (98) or disturbances in web construction in spiders (99) have not yet received confirmation in the scientific literature. Such urine, however, has been reported to have no effect on the Siamese fighting fish, which is remarkably sensitive to certain hallucinogens (100). Contrary to earlier findings, a recent attempt to demonstrate behavioral changes in rats following the injection of cerebrospinal fluid from catatonic patients was unsuccessful (101). A highly significant decrease in rope-climbing speed in rats injected with sera from psychotic patients as opposed to that from nonpsychotic controls has been reported by Winter and Flataker (102). Their later findings (103) that the phenomenon occurs with sera of patients with a wide variety of mental disorders (including mental retardation and alcoholism) and that there is a considerable variation in this index between similar groups at different hospitals, coupled with the inability of at least one other investigator (104) to demonstrate this phenomenon in the small group of schizophrenic patients under investigation in this laboratory, suggest that the quite real and statistically significant phenomenon originally observed may be related to variables other than those specific for or fundamental to schizophrenia.

It has been reported that rabbits pretreated with serum from schizophrenics do not exhibit a pressor response following the local application of an epinephrine solution to the cerebral cortex (105). This procedure failed to differentiate between the sera of a small series of normals and schizophrenics on our wards.

The significance of all of these studies in animals, whether successful or unsuccessful in demonstrating a toxic factor in schizophrenia, is quite irrelevant to and considerably dwarfed by the implications of the taraxein studies. It is because of the tremendous implications which these results could have in the etiology and rational therapy of this important disorder that the reviewer must evaluate them with even more than the usual care.

In the first place, the important biochemical phenomena originally reported in schizophrenia—reduced blood glutathione and the rapid oxidation of epinephrine *in vitro,* which prompted the search for taraxein and directed its isolation toward the ceruloplasmin fraction of serum (68, 78, 92) —have since been brought into question by data from the same group, as well as by others, as being spurious or at least unrelated in any direct way to the schizophrenic process (11, 18, 43). This, in itself, does not preclude the possible validity of the taraxein phenomenon because bona fide discoveries have occasionally been made on the basis of erroneous leads; it does, however, reduce the probability of its occurrence from that involved in the logical interrelationship of sequential, proven steps to the extremely small chance of selecting this particular and heretofore unknown substance from the thousands of substances that occur in blood and that might have been chosen.

One attempt by Robins, Smith, and Lowe (106) to confirm the Tulane findings, using comparable numbers and types of subjects and at least as rigorous controls, was quite unsuccessful. In twenty subjects, who at different times received saline or extracts of blood from normal or schizophrenic donors prepared according to the method for preparing taraxein, there were only five instances of mental or behavioral disturbances resembling those in the original report on taraxein, and these disturbances occurred as often following the administration of saline or extracts of normal plasma as following taraxein. It is easy to dismiss these negative findings with taraxein on the basis of the difficulty of reproducing exactly the 29 steps described for its preparation; it is considerably more difficult to dismiss the observation that a few subjects who received only saline or normal blood extract developed psychic manifestations similar to those reported from taraxein.

During the preliminary investigations it was stated that taraxein was qualitatively different from ceruloplasmin (68), but the studies that were cited remain unpublished. A physicochemical or other objective characterization of taraxein would do much to dispel some of the confusion regarding its nature. Is it possible, for example, that taraxein is, in fact, ceruloplasmin, but derives its special properties from the psychosocial characteristics of the situation in which it has been tested? This question was raised in 1957 (107), and since then additional evidence has become available which tends to support the possibility. A detailed report from a psychoanalyst at Tulane concerning the experience of one of his patients who received taraxein (108) suggests the possibility of an unconscious bias capable of influencing the results. The subject, a psychiatric resident, knew before the injection that he was to get either saline or a potent sample of taraxein which had made a monkey catatonic for several hours. Immediately following the injection, he noted venous distension, tachycardia, a swollen feeling of the head, and flushing of the head and face, which, a footnote explains, was probably a reaction to the ammonium sulfate in the solution. Following these symptoms, which the subject could hardly have attributed to saline, there ensued a period of introspective cogitation with occasional mild mental disturbances, quite compatible with the anxiety of the situation, the preparation and cues that he had received, and his anticipation of marked psychotic reactions, without the necessity of invoking a chemical toxin at all. The changes were not qualitatively dissimilar to those which Robins and his associates had on a few occasions obtained with their control solutions (106). The report of the observer who injected the material was longer and more inferential regarding subjective feelings than the report of the subject himself. His summary of the subject's reactions as blocking of thought processes, autism, bodily estrangement, and suspiciousness seems incompletely supported by the subject's retrospective report.

The possibility, remote as it may be, that the reported effects of taraxein are the result of a combination of suggestion, nonspecific toxic reactions from ammonium sulfate or other contaminants, and reinforcement of these cues by the unconscious biases of subject and observer through the device of an unstructured interview is one which has not been ruled out. Hypotheses related to the mechanism of action of this material have moved from the area of abnormalities in the blood to abnormalities in the blood-brain barrier; but the question of whether it acts as a biological cause or mediator of some of the symptoms of schizophrenia is by no means resolved. This reviewer is aware of only one attempt on the part of an independent group (106) to confirm the original results in a controlled series of significant size, and this was unsuccessful.

SEROTONIN

Serotonin, an important derivative of tryptophan, was first shown to exist in the brain in high concentration by Amin, Crawford, and Gaddum (109). Interest in its possible function in the central nervous system—and in its relationship to schizophrenia—was inspired by the finding that certain hallucinogens, notably lysergic acid diethylamide, in extremely low concentration could block the effects of serotonin on smooth muscle. Thus, Wooley and Shaw in 1954 wrote:

> The demonstrated ability of such agents to antagonize the action of serotonin in smooth muscle and the finding of serotonin in the brain suggest that the mental changes caused by the drugs are the result of a serotonin-deficiency which they induce in the brain. If this be true, then the naturally occurring mental disorders—for example, schizophrenia—which are mimicked by these drugs, may be pictured as being the result of a cerebral serotonin deficiency arising from a metabolic failure . . . (110).

Simultaneously in England, Gaddum was speculating, ". . . it is possible that the HT [5-hydroxytryptamine or serotonin] in our brains plays an essential part in keeping us sane and that the effect of LSD is due to its inhibitory action on the HT in the brain" (111). Since 1954 these hypotheses have apparently been strengthened by additional evidence. The concentration of serotonin has been found to be considerably higher in the limbic system and other areas of the brain apparently associated with emotional states (112, 113). Bufotenine, or dimethyl serotonin, extracted from an hallucinogenic snuff of West Indian tribes, was found to have some properties similar to those of lysergic acid diethylamide (114, 115). A major discovery was the finding that the ataractic agent reserpine causes a profound and persistent fall in the level of brain serotonin (116), a process which more closely parallels the mental effects of reserpine than does its own concentration in the brain. By administration of its precursor, 5-hydroxytryptophan, the levels of serotonin can be markedly elevated in the brain, with behavioral effects described as resembling those of lysergic acid diethylamide (117), a finding quite at odds with the original hypotheses. On the other hand, administration of this precursor to mental patients, along with a benzyl analogue of serotonin to block the peripheral effects of the amine, has been reported in preliminary trials to suppress the disease (118). Meanwhile, the reviewer's confusion is compounded by the report that the benzyl analogue alone is an effective tranquilizing drug in chronically psychotic patients (119).

Still another bit of evidence supporting the hypotheses of a central function for serotonin was the accidental discovery of toxic psychoses in a certain fraction of tuberculous patients treated with iproniazid (120, 121), a finding that has led to the therapeutic use of this drug in psychic depression. Iproniazid is known to inhibit the action of monoamine oxidase, an enzyme that destroys serotonin, and has been shown to increase the levels of this amine in the brain (117).

There are certain inconsistencies in the data cited above to support the serotonin hypotheses that prevent any single theory from explaining all of the findings even though full use is made of the concept of "free" and "bound" forms or of the common pharmacological principle of stimulant and depressant effects from the same drug under different circumstances. Moreover, certain weaknesses have appeared in each of the main supports and should be noted.

Although the ability of the hallucinogen lysergic acid diethylamide to block effects of serotonin on smooth muscle prompted the development of the hypotheses relating serotonin to mental function or disease, a number of lysergic acid derivatives have since been studied, and the correlation between mental effects and antiserotonin activity in the series as a whole is quite poor (122). One of these compounds is 2-brom-LSD, which has 1.5 times the antiserotonin activity of LSD, and which can be demonstrated by this property in the brain after systemic administration, but which in doses more than 15 times as great produces none of the mental effects of LSD (122). A recent report that, at least in one preparation, lysergic acid diethylamide in low concentration behaves like serotonin rather than antagonizing it (123) may seem to reconcile some of the empirical inconsistencies in the field although it is quite at odds with the original hypotheses based on its antagonistic action.

In addition to serotonin, norepinephrine is also markedly reduced in the brain following reserpine (124, 125). In fact, the brain concentrations of these two amines follow each other so closely in their response to reserpine as to suggest some mechanism common to both and perhaps obtaining as well for other active amines in the brain. In one study, 3,4-dihydroxyphenyl-alanine, a precursor of norepinephrine, was capable of counteracting the behavioral effects of reserpine, whereas the precursor of serotonin was ineffective (126). Nor are the effects of iproniazid limited to brain serotonin; a comparable effect on norepinephrine has been reported (127), and it is possible that other amines or substances still to be discovered in the brain may be affected by what may be a nonspecific inhibitor of a relatively non-specific enzyme. Of great interest in this connection are recent studies of Olds and Olds (128), indicating a positive behavioral response for iproniazid injected into the hypothalamus but not for serotonin or norepinephrine.

Chlorpromazine, which has the same therapeutic efficacy as reserpine in disturbed behavior, is apparently able to achieve this action without any known effect on serotonin. In addition, the provocative observation that iproniazid, which elevates serotonin levels in the brain, can cause a toxic psychosis loses some of its impact when one realizes that isoniazid, which does not inhibit monoamine oxidase and can hardly raise the brain serotonin concentration, produces a similar psychosis (121, 129).

It seems reasonable that the serotonin as well as the norepinephrine in the brain have some important functions there, and the evidence in general supports this thesis even though it also suggests that their roles still remain to be defined.

If the picture of the role that serotonin plays in central-nervous function is blurred, the direct evidence to support the early speculations that it is involved in mental illness is meager and contradictory. From all of the evidence cited above, one could find a basis for predicting that in schizo-phrenia the serotonin levels in the brain, if they are altered at all, should be quite low or quite high. Results to confirm both predictions have been reported.

The urinary excretion of 5-hydroxyindole acetic acid has been used as an indicator of the portion of ingested tryptophan which is metabolized through serotonin to that end product. Although the excretion of 5-hy-droxyindole acetic acid is normal in schizophrenic patients under ordinary circumstances, Zeller and associates (130, 131) have reported a failure on the part of schizophrenics to increase their output of 5-hydroxyindole acetic acid after a tryptophan load, whereas nonpsychotic controls doubled it (132, 133). Banerjee and Agarwa, on the other hand, have reported exactly the opposite results; in their study it was the schizophrenics who doubled their output of the serotonin end product, whereas the output of the controls remained unchanged (134).

Kopin, of our laboratory, has had the opportunity to perform a similar study on schizophrenics and normal controls maintained on a good and reasonably controlled diet and in the absence of drugs. In each group there was a slightly greater than twofold increase in output of 5-hydroxyindole acetic acid following a tryptophan load and no significant deviation from this pattern by any single case (135).

That the heuristic speculations of Wooley and Shaw and of Gaddum have not yet been established does not mean that they are invalid. The widespread experimental activity which they stimulated has broadened and deepened our knowledge of the metabolism and pharmacology of serotonin and its effects on behavior and may lead the way to their definitive evaluation in normal and pathological states.

DISCUSSION

The chapters by Böök and Jackson reveal the many questions surrounding the genetics of schizophrenia; yet I find the evidence for a significant genetic factor in many or all schizophrenias to be compelling. Arguments which indicate that genetic factors do not operate alone but only in association with socioenvironmental ones do not counter the evidence for a genetic susceptibility in many forms of schizophrenia.

Such factors may operate through some ubiquitous enzyme system to effect changes in one or another metabolic pathway detectable by studies on blood or urine; although so far no such factor has been discovered, it may well be that continued search in this area will be rewarding. On the other hand, it may very well be that genetic factors operate through an enzyme system confined to the brain or localized areas within it. New hypotheses such as those of Elkes (136) could be helpful here. Gamma-amino-butyric acid seems as promising a substance for study in this area as the catechols or the indoles. Not only has it been isolated only from nervous tissues, and its metabolism there investigated in some detail (137, 138), but its neurophysiological properties appear to be better defined than are those of the other two groups (139, 140), in addition to which its inhibitory properties may have special relevance to diseases in which a failure in central inhibition seems to be involved.

Amphetamine possesses psychotomimetic properties which should not be overlooked (141), and its possible relationship to the naturally occurring catechol amines makes it at least as interesting a subject of study as LSD.

The possibility should not be overlooked that genetic factors in schizophrenia may operate to determine inappropriate interconnections or interaction between chemically normal components of the brain, in which case the physiological psychologist, the neurophysiologist, or the anatomist is likely to find meaningful answers long before the biochemist. It would take many biochemists a long time to find a noisy circuit in a radio receiver if they restricted themselves to chemical techniques.

But by no stretch of the analogy must the brain be thought of merely as an electronic computer. Biochemical events in the case of the brain supply the power for each of the components and probably operate to modulate the interactions in a manner which no electronic instrument can duplicate. Even if "the biochemical lesion" in schizophrenia does not exist or may not be discovered for many generations, present and future research in that area if it is critical as well as imaginative cannot help but lead to a better understanding of the nervous system and of behavior.

References

1.   J. W. L. THUDICHUM, *A Treatise on the Chemical Constitution of the Brain,* London: Balliere, Tindall & Cox, 1884.

2.   G. PETERS, "Dementia praecox," in Lubarsch, Henke, and Rössle (Eds.), *Handbuch der Speziellen Pathologischen Anatomie und Histologie,* Vol. 13, Part 4, Berlin: Springer-Verlag, 1956, pp. 1–52.

3.   G. B. DAVID, The Pathological Anatomy of the Schizophrenias, in *Schizophrenia: Somatic Aspects,* London: Pergamon, 1957, pp. 93–130.

4.   D. K. DASTUR, The pathology of schizophrenia, *A.M.A. Arch. Neurol. & Psychiat., 81:* 601–614, 1959.

5.   R. A. MC FARLAND and H. GOLDSTEIN, Biochemistry of dementia praecox; a review, *Am. J. Psychiat., 95:* 509, 1938.

6.   W. KEUP, Die "Biochemie der Schizophrenie," eine kritische stellungnahme, *Monatsschr. f. Psychiat. u. Neurol., 128:* 56, 1954.

7.   D. RICHTER, "Biochemical Aspects of Schizophrenia," in *Schizophrenia: Somatic Aspects,* London: Pergamon, 1957, pp. 53–75.

8.   M. K. HORWITT, Fact and artifact in the biology of schizophrenia, *Science, 124:* 429, 1956.

9.   S. S. KETY, The implications of psychopharmacology in the etiology and treatment of mental illness, *Ann. New York Acad Sc., 66:* 836, 1957.

10.   E. V. EVARTS, A discussion of research methods as applied to physiological studies of psychiatric patients, *Psychiatric Research Reports, 9:* 52, 1948.

11.   R. K. MC DONALD, Problems in biologic research in schizophrenia, *J. Chronic Dis., 8:* 366, 1958.

12.   S. PERLIN and A. R. LEE, Criteria for the selection of a small group of chronic

schizophrenic subjects for biological studies, *Am. J. Psychiat., 116*: 231–243, 1959.

13.   D. A. FREEDMAN, Various etiologies of the schizophrenic syndrome, *Dis. Nerv. System, 19*: 108, 1958.

14.   P. VESTERGAARD, M. T. ABBOTT, N. S. KLINE, and A. M. STANLEY, Endamoeba histolytica infections in patients on a psychiatric research ward, *J. Clin. & Exper. Psychopath., 19*: 44, 1958.

15.   F. O. KELSEY, A. H. GULLOCK, and F. E. KELSEY, Thyroid activity in hospitalized psychiatric patients, *A.M.A. Arch. Neurol. & Psychiat., 77*: 543, 1957.

16.   R. K. MC DONALD, Plasma ceruloplasmin and ascorbic acid levels in schizophrenia. Paper presented at Annual Meeting, Am. Psychiatric Assoc., Chicago, 1957.

17.   M. H. APRISON and H. J. GROSZ, Ascorbic acid level and lag time in oxidation of n, n-dimethyl-p-phenylenediamine, *A.M.A. Arch. Neurol. & Psychiat., 79*: 575, 1958.

18.   C. ANGEL, B. E. LEACH, S. MARTENS, M. COHEN, and R. G. HEATH, Serum oxidation tests in schizophrenic and normal subjects, *A.M.A. Arch. Neurol. & Psychiat., 78*: 500, 1957.

19.   M. K. HORWITT, "Report of Elgin Project No. 3 with Emphasis on Liver Dysfunction," *Nutrition Symposium Series No. 7*, New York: National Vitamin Foundation, 1953.

20.   R. FISCHER, F. GEORGI, R. WEBER, and R. M. PIAGET, Psychophysische Korrelationen, VII. Leberstütztherapie bei Schizophrenie, *Schweiz. med. Wchnschr., 80*: 129, 1950.

21.   F. BOARD, H. PERSKY, and D. A. HAMBURG, Psychological stress and endocrine functions, *Psychosom. Med., 18*: 324, 1956.

22.   F. ELMADJIAN, J. M. HOPE, and E. T. LAMSON, Excretion of epinephrine and norepinephrine in various emotional states, *J. Clin. Endocrinol., 17*: 608, 1957.

23.   W. W. SCHOTTSTAEDT, W. J. GRACE, and H. G. WOLFF, Life situations, behavior, attitudes, emotions, and renal excretions of fluid and electrolytes. II. Retention of water and sodium; diuresis of water, *J. Psychosom. Res., 1*: 147, 1956.

24.   W. W. SCHOTTSTAEDT, W. J. GRACE, and H. G. WOLFF, Life situations, behavior, attitudes, emotions, and renal excretion of fluid and electrolytes. V. Variations in excretion of endogenous creatinine, *J. Psychosom. Res., 1*: 292, 1956.

25.   J. W. LOVETT DOUST, Spectroscopic and photo-electric oximetry in schizophrenia and other psychiatric states, *J. Ment. Sc., 98*: 143, 1952.

26.   S. S. KETY, R. B. WOODFORD, M. H. HARMEL, F. A. FREYHAN, K. E. APPEL, and C. F. SCHMIDT, Cerebral blood flow and metabolism in schizophrenia, *Am. J. Psychiat., 104*: 765, 1948.

27.   W. P. WILSON, J. F. SCHIEVE, and P. SCHEINBERG, Effect of series of electroshock treatments on cerebral blood flow and metabolism, *A.M.A. Arch. Neurol. & Psychiat., 68*: 651, 1952.

28.   L. SOKOLOFF, S. PERLIN, C. KORNETSKY, and S. S. KETY, The effects of d-lysergic acid diethylamide in cerebral circulation and over-all metabolism, *Ann. New York Acad. Sc., 66*: 468, 1957.

29.   G. S. GORDAN, F. M. ESTESS, J. E. ADAMS, K. M. BOWMAN, and A. SIMON, Cerebral oxygen uptake in chronic schizophrenic reaction, *A.M.A. Arch. Neurol. & Psychiat., 73*: 544, 1955.

30.   V. LONGO, G. A. BUSCAINO, F. D'ANDREA, A. URAS, E. FERRARI, F. RINALDI, F. PASO-

LINI, and E. FAILLA, Prove combinate di funzionalita epatica negli schizofrenici e negli amenti, *Acta Neurol., 3:* 21, 1953.

31.   M. D. ALTSCHULE, D. H. HENNEMAN, P. D. HOLLIDAY, and R. M. GONCZ, Carbohydrate metabolism in brain disease. VI. Lactate metabolism after infusion of sodium d-lactate in manic-depressive and schizophrenic psychoses, *A.M.A. Arch. Int. Med., 98:* 35, 1956.

32.   M. K. HORWITT, E. LIEBERT, O. KREISLER, and P. WITTMAN, "Investigations of Human Requirements for B-complex Vitamins," *Bulletin National Research Council No. 116,* Washington: Nat. Acad. Sci., 1948.

33.   L. J. MEDUNA, F. J. GERTY, and V. G. URSE, Biochemical disturbances in mental disorders. I. Anti-insulin effect of blood in cases of schizophrenia, *Arch. Neurol. & Psychiat., 47:* 38, 1942.

34.   F. MOYA, J. DEWAR, M. MAC INTOSH, S. HIRSCH, and R. TOWNSEND, Hyperglycemic action and toxicity of the urine of schizophrenic patients, *Canad. J. Biochem. & Physiol., 36:* 505, 1958.

35.   F. MOYA, J. C. SZERB, and M. MAC INTOSH, Identification of a hyperglycemic factor in urine, *Canad. J. Biochem. & Physiol., 34:* 563, 1956.

36.   M. S. MORGAN and F. J. PILGRIM, Concentration of a hyperglycemic factor from urine of schizophrenics, *Proc. Soc. Exper. Biol. & Med., 79:* 106, 1952.

37.   M. M. HARRIS, Insulin sensitivity of patients with mental disease, *Arch. Neurol. & Psychiat., 48:* 761, 1942.

38.   I. BOSZORMENYI-NAGY, F. J. GERTY, and J. KUEBER, Correlation between an anomaly of the intracellular metabolism of adenosine nucleotides and schizophrenia, *J. Nerv. & Ment. Dis., 124:* 413, 1956.

39.   I. BOSZORMENYI-NAGY and F. J. GERTY, Difference between the phosphorus metabolism of erythrocytes of normals and of patients suffering from schizophrenia, *J. Nerv. & Ment. Dis., 121:* 53, 1955.

40.   M. D. ALTSCHULE, D. H. HENNEMAN, P. D. HOLLIDAY, and R. M. GONCZ, Carbohydrate metabolism in brain disease. VII. The effect of glutathione on carbohydrate intermediary metabolism in schizophrenic and manic-depressive psychoses, *A.M.A. Arch. Int. Med., 99:* 22, 1957.

41.   M. P. SURIKOV, G. K. USHAKOV, B. N. IL'INA, A. A. VERBLIUNSKAIA, and L. K. KHOKHLOV, Ob izpol'zovani gliutationa dlia lecheniia psikhicheski bol'nykh (Glutathione in the treatment of mental patients), *Zh. Nevropat., 57:* 237, 1957.

42.   S. MARTENS, B. E. LEACH, R. G. HEATH, and M. COHEN, Glutathione levels in mental and physical illness, *A.M.A. Arch. Neurol. & Psychiat., 76:* 630, 1956.

43.   A. J. BARAK, F. L. HUMOLLER, and J. D. STEVENS, Blood glutathione levels in the male schizophrenic patient, *A.M.A. Arch. Neurol. & Psychiat., 80:* 237, 1958.

44.   R. GJESSING, Disturbances of somatic functions in catatonia with a periodic course, and their compensation, *J. Ment. Sc., 84:* 608, 1938.

45.   R. GJESSING, Beiträge zur Kenntnis der Pathophysiologie periodisch katatoner Zustände, IV. Mitteilung, Versuch einer Ausgleichung der Funktionsstörungen, *Arch. f. Psychiat., 108:* 525, 1939

46.   R. GJESSING, A. BERNHARDSEN, and H. FRØSHAUG, Investigation of amino acids in a periodic catatonic patient, *J. Ment. Sc., 104:* 188, 1958.

47.   V. M. BUSCAINO, Pathogénèse et étiologie biologiques de la schizophrénie, *Acta Neurol., 13:* 1, 1958.

48.   H. K. YOUNG, H. K. BERRY, E. BEERSTECHER, and J. S. BERRY, "Metabolic Pat-

terns of Schizophrenic and Control Groups," *University of Texas Publication No. 5109*, 1951.

49. P. L. MC GEER, F. E. MC NAIR, E. G. MC GEER, and W. C. GIBSON, Aromatic metabolism in schizophrenia. I. Statistical evidence for aromaturia, *J. Nerv. & Ment. Dis., 125*: 166, 1957.

50. E. G. MC GEER, W. T. BROWN, and P. L. MC GEER, Aromatic metabolism in schizophrenia. II. Bidimensional urinary chromatograms, *J. Nerv. & Ment. Dis., 125*: 176, 1957.

51. F. GEORGI, C. C. HONEGGER, D. JORDAN, H. P. RIEDNER, and M. ROTTENBERG, Zur Physiologie und Pathophysiologie körpereigener Amine, *Klin. Wchnschr., 34*: 799, 1956.

52. L. M. RIEGELHAUPT, Investigations on the glyoxylic acid reactions on urine from schizophrenics and other psychotic patients, *J. Nerv. & Ment. Dis., 123*: 383, 1956.

53. E. J. CAFRUNY and E. F. DOMINO, Urinary excretion of some products of tryptophan metabolism in schizophrenic patients, *A.M.A. Arch. Neurol. & Psychiat., 79*: 336, 1958.

54. M. D. ARMSTRONG and K. N. F. SHAW, The occurrence of (-)-β-m-hydroxyphenylhydracrylic acid in human urine, *J. Biol. Chem., 225*: 269, 1956.

55. M. D. ARMSTRONG, K. N. F. SHAW, M. J. GORTATOWSKI, and H. SINGER, The indole acid of human urine, *J. Biol. Chem., 232*: 17, 1958.

56. M. D. ARMSTRONG, P. E. WALL, and V. J. PARKER, The excretion of m-hydroxyhippuric acid by humans, *J. Biol. Chem., 218*: 921, 1956.

57. A. N. BOOTH, O. H. EMERSON, F. T. JONES, and F. DEEDS, Urinary metabolites of caffeic and chlorogenic acids, *J. Biol. Chem., 229*: 51, 1957.

58. T. P. WAALKES, A. SJOERDSMA, C. R. CREVELING, H. WEISSBACH, and S. UDENFRIEND, Serotonin, norepinephrine, and related compounds in bananas, *Science, 127*: 648, 1958.

59. R. M. ACHESON, R. M. PAUL, and R. V. TOMLINSON, Some constituents of the urine of normal and schizophrenic individuals, *Canad. J. Biochem. Physiol., 36*: 295, 1958.

60. J. D. MANN and E. H. LABROSSE, The urinary excretion of phenolic acids by normal and schizophrenic males, *A.M.A. Arch. Gen. Psychiat., 1*: 547, 1959.

61. H. OSMOND, Inspiration and method in schizophrenia research, *Dis. Nerv. System, 16*: 101, 1955.

62. H. OSMOND and J. SMYTHIES, Schizophrenia: A new approach, *J. Ment. Sc., 98*: 309, 1952.

63. A. HOFFER, Epinephrine derivatives as potential schizophrenic factors, *J. Clin. & Exper. Psychopath., 18*: 27, 1957.

64. A. HOFFER, H. OSMOND, and J. SMYTHIES, Schizophrenia: A new approach. II. Result of a year's research, *J. Ment. Sc., 100*: 29, 1954.

65. K. RINKEL and H. C. SOLOMON, Chemical theories of psychosis, *J. Clin. & Exper. Psychopath., 18*: 323, 1957.

66. C. G. HOLMBERG and C. B. LAURELL, Oxidase reactions in human plasma caused by caeruloplasmin, *Scandinav. J. Clin. & Lab. Invest., 3*: 103, 1951.

67. B. E. LEACH and R. G. HEATH, The in vitro oxidation of epinephrine in plasma, *A.M.A. Arch. Neurol. & Psychiat., 76*: 444, 1956.

68. B. E. LEACH, M. COHEN, R. G. HEATH, and S. MARTENS, Studies of the role of

ceruloplasmin and albumin in adrenaline metabolism, *A.M.A. Arch. Neurol. & Psychiat.*, *76*: 635, 1956.

69.   A. HOFFER and M. KENYON, Conversion of adrenaline to adrenolutin in human blood serum, *A.M.A. Arch. Neurol. & Psychiat.*, *77*: 437, 1957.

70.   R. W. SCHAYER and R. L. SMILEY, The metabolism of epinephrine containing isotopic carbon, *J. Biol. Chem.*, *202*: 425, 1953.

71.   J. AXELROD, J. K. INSCOE, S. SENOH, and B. WIKTOP, O-methylation, the principal pathway for the metabolism of epinephrine and norepinephrine in the rat, *Biochim. et Biophys. acta*, *27*: 210, 1958.

72.   E. H. LABROSSE, J. AXELROD, and S. S. KETY, O-methylation, the principal route of metabolism of epinephrine in man, *Science*, *128*: 593, 1958.

73.   O. RESNICK, J. M. WOLFE, H. FREEMAN, and F. ELMADJIAN, Iproniazid treatment and metabolism of labeled epinephrine in schizophrenics, *Science*, *127*: 1116, 1958.

74.   A. HOFFER, Adrenochrome in blood plasma, *Am. J. Psychiat.*, *114*: 752, 1958.

75.   S. SZARA, J. AXELROD, and S. PERLIN, Is adrenochrome present in the blood? *Am. J. Psychiat.*, *115*: 162, 1958.

76.   B. HOLLAND, G. COHEN, M. GOLDENBERG, J. SHA, and L. LEIFER, Adrenaline and noradrenaline in urine and plasma of schizophrenics, *Fed. Proc.*, *17*: 378, 1958.

77.   E. LINDEMANN, The psychopathological effect of drugs affecting the vegetative system. I. Adrenalin, *Am. J. Psychiat.*, *91*: 983, 1935.

78.   R. G. HEATH, B. E. LEACH, L. W. BYERS, S. MARTENS, and C. A. FEIGLEY, Pharmacological and biological psychotherapy, *Am. J. Psychiat.*, *114*: 683, 1958.

79.   J. B. DYNES and H. TOD, The emotional and somatic response of schizophrenic patients and normal controls to adrenalin and doryl, *J. Neurol. & Psychiat.*, *3*: 1–8, 1940.

80.   G. TAUBMANN and H. JANTZ, Untersuchung über die Adrenochrom zugeschriebenen psychotoxischen Wirkungen, *Nervenarzt*, *28*: 485, 1957.

81.   S. AKERFELDT, Oxidation of n,n-dimethyl-p-phenylenediamine by serum from patients with mental disease, *Science*, *125*: 117, 1957.

82.   F. A. GIBBS (Ed.), *Blood Tests in Mental Illness*, Chicago: Brain Research Foundation, 1957.

83.   C. G. HOLMBERG and C. B. LAURELL, Investigations in serum copper. II. Isolation of the copper containing protein and a description of some of its properties, *Acta Chem. Scand.*, *2*: 550, 1948.

84.   H. MARKOWITZ, C. J. GUBLER, J. P. MAHONEY, G. E. CARTWRIGHT, and M. M. WINTROBE, Studies on copper metabolism. XIV. Copper, ceruloplasmin and oxidase activity in sera of normal human subjects, pregnant women, and patients with infection, hepatolenticular degeneration and the nephrotic syndrome, *J. Clin. Invest.*, *34*: 1498, 1955.

85.   L. G. ABOOD, F. A. GIBBS, and E. GIBBS, Comparative study of blood ceruloplasmin in schizophrenia and other disorders, *A.M.A. Arch. Neurol. & Psychiat.*, *17*: 643, 1957.

86.   I. H. SCHEINBERG, A. G. MORELL, R. S. HARRIS, and A. BERGER, Concentration of ceruloplasmin in plasma of schizophrenic patients, *Science*, *126*: 925, 1957.

87.   M. K. HORWITT, B. J. MEYER, A. C. MEYER, C. C. HARVEY, and D. HAFFRON, Serum copper and oxidase activity in schizophrenic patients, *A.M.A. Arch. Neurol. & Psychiat.*, *78*: 275, 1957.

88. C. E. FROHMAN, M. GOODMAN, E. D. LUBY, P. G. S. BECKETT, and R. SENF, Seroplasmin, transferrin, and tryptophan in schizophrenia, *A.M.A. Arch. Neurol. & Psychiat., 79*: 730, 1958.

89. M. H. APRISON and A. L. DREW, n,n-dimethyl-p-phenylenediamine oxidation by serum from schizophrenic children, *Science, 127*: 758, 1958.

90. A. M. OSTFELD, L. G. ABOOD, and D. A. MARCUS, Studies with ceruloplasmin and a new hallucinogen, *A.M.A. Arch. Neurol. & Psychiat., 79*: 317, 1958.

91. R. G. HEATH, S. MARTENS, B. E. LEACH, M. COHEN, and C. A. FEIGLEY, Behavioral changes in nonpsychotic volunteers following the administration of taraxein, the substance obtained from serum of schizophrenic patients, *Am. J. Psychiat., 114*: 917, 1958.

92. R. G. HEATH, S. MARTENS, B. E. LEACH, M. COHEN, and C. ANGEL, Effect on behavior in humans with the administration of taraxein, *Am. J. Psychiat., 114*: 14, 1957.

93. R. FISCHER, On the Toxicity of Schizophrenic Serum and Urine, Proc. 19th International Physiol. Congr., pp. 350–351, 1953.

94. F. GEORGI, H. P. RIEDER, and R. WEBER, Remarks on Fischer's article "Stress and the toxicity of schizophrenic serum," *Science, 120*: 504, 1954.

95. C. B. EDISEN, Studies of the toxicity of schizophrenic blood serum, *Dis. Nerv. System, 17*: 77, 1956.

96. S. FEDOROFF, Toxicity of schizophrenic blood serum in tissue culture, *Anat. Rec., 121*: 394, 1955 (Abstract).

97. S. FEDOROFF and A. HOFFER, Toxicity of blood serum from schizophrenic and nonschizophrenic subjects. *J. Nerv. & Ment. Dis., 124*: 396, 1956.

98. J. WADA, Behavioral and electroencephalographic changes induced by the injection of an extract of schizophrenic urine, *Proc. Soc. Biol. Psychiat.*, Twelfth Annual Convention, Atlantic City (Article 25), 1957.

99. H. P. RIEDER, Biologische Toxizitätsbestimmung pathologischer Körperflüssigkeiten. III. Prüfung von Urinextrakten Geisteskranker mit Hilfe des Spinnentestes, *Psychiat. Neurol., 134*: 378, 1957.

100. K. SMITH and A. C. MOODY, Schizophrenia and the Siamese fighting fish, *Dis. Nerv. System, 17*: 327, 1956.

101. A. K. SCHAPIRO, An attempt to demonstrate a catatonigenic agent in cerebrospinal fluid of catatonic schizophrenic patients, *J. Nerv. & Ment. Dis., 123*: 65, 1956.

102. C. A. WINTER and L. FLATAKER, Effects of blood plasma and extracts of urine from psychotic patients upon the performance of trained rats, *Proc. Soc. Biol. Psychiat.*, Twelfth Annual Convention, Atlantic City (Article 26), 1957.

103. C. A. WINTER and L. FLATAKER, Effect of blood plasma from psychotic patients upon performance of trained rats, *A.M.A. Arch. Neurol. & Psychiat., 80*: 441, 1958.

104. C. KORNETSKY, Personal communication.

105. B. MINZ and E. J. WALASZEK, Sur la présence de substances biologiquement actives dans le sérum de schizophrènes, *Compt. Rend. l'Acad. Sci., 244*: 1974, 1957.

106. E. ROBINS, K. SMITH, and I. P. LOWE, in *Neuropharmacology, Transactions of the Fourth Conference,* New York: Macy, 1959.

107. S. S. KETY, in *Neuropharmacology, Transactions of the Fourth Conference,* New York: Macy, 1959.

108. H. I. LIEF, The effects of taraxein on a patient in analysis, *A.M.A. Arch. Neurol. & Psychiat., 78*: 624, 1957.

109.   A. H. AMIN, T. B. B. CRAWFORD, and J. H. GADDUM, The distribution of substances P and 5-hydroxytryptamine in the central nervous system of the dog, *J. Physiol.*, *126*: 596, 1954.

110.   D. W. WOOLEY and E. SHAW, A biochemical and pharmacological suggestion about certain mental disorders, *Science*, *119*: 587, 1954.

111.   J. H. GADDUM, "Drugs Antagonistic to 5-hydroxytryptamine," in *Ciba Foundation Symposium on Hypertension*, Boston: Little, 1954.

112.   D. F. BOGDANSKI, H. WEISSBACH, and S. UDENFRIEND, The distribution of serotonin, 5-hydroxytryptophan decarboxylase, and monoamine oxidase in brain, *J. Neurochem.*, *1*: 272, 1957.

113.   M. K. PAASONEN, P. D. MC LEAN, and N. J. GIARMAN, 5-hydroxytryptamine (serotonin, enteramine) content of structures of the limbic system, *J. Neurochem.*, *1*: 326, 1957.

114.   E. V. EVARTS, Some effects of bufotenine and lysergic acid diethylamide on the monkey, *A.M.A. Arch. Neurol. & Psychiat.*, *75*: 49, 1956.

115.   H. D. FABING and J. R. HAWKINS, Intravenous bufotenine injection in the human being, *Science*, *123*: 886, 1956.

116.   P. A. SHORE, A. PLETSCHER, E. G. TOMICH, A. CARLSSON, R. KUNTZMAN, and B. B. BRODIE, Role of brain serotonin in reserpine action, *Ann. New York Acad. Sc.*, *66*: 609, 1957.

117.   S. UDENFRIEND, H. WEISSBACH, and D. F. BOGDANSKI, Biochemical findings relating to the action of serotonin. *Ann. New York Acad. Sc.*, *66*: 602, 1957.

118.   D. W. WOOLEY, Manipulation of cerebral serotonin and its relationship to mental disorders, *Science*, *125*: 752, 1957.

119.   L. H. RUDY, E. COSTA, F. RINALDI, and H. E. HIMWICH, Clinical evaluation of BAS (benzyl analog of serotonin): A tranquilizing drug, *J. Nerv. & Ment. Dis.*, *126*: 284, 1958.

120.   G. E. CRANE, Further studies on iproniazid phosphate, *J. Nerv. & Ment. Dis.*, *124*: 322, 1956.

121.   H. PLEASURE, Psychiatric and neurological side-effects of isoniazid and iproniazid, *A.M.A. Arch. Neurol. & Psychiat.*, *72*: 313, 1954.

122.   E. ROTHLIN, Lysergic acid diethylamide and related substances, *Ann. New York Acad. Sc.*, *66*: 668, 1957.

123.   J. H. WELSH and A. C. MC COY, Actions of d-lysergic acid diethylamide and its 2-bromo derivative on heart of venus mercenaria, *Science*, *125*: 348, 1957.

124.   M. HOLZBAUER and M. VOGT, Depression by reserpine of the noradrenaline concentration in the hypothalamus of the cat, *J. Neurochem.*, *1*: 8, 1956.

125.   M. VOGT, "Distribution of Adrenaline and Noradrenaline in the Central Nervous System and Its Modification by Drugs," in Richter, D. (Ed.), *Metabolism of the Nervous System*, London: Pergamon, 1957, pp. 553–565.

126.   A. CARLSSON, M. LINDQUIST, and T. MAGNUSSON, 3,4-dihydroxyphenylalanine and 5-hydroxytryptophan as reserpine antagonists, *Nature*, *180*: 1200, 1957.

127.   S. SPECTOR, D. PROCKOP, P. A. SHORE, and B. B. BRODIE, Effect of iproniazid on brain levels of norepinephrine and serotonin, *Science*, *127*: 704, 1958.

128.   J. OLDS and M. E. OLDS, Positive reinforcement produced by stimulating the hypothalamus with iproniazid and other compounds, *Science*, *127*: 1175, 1958.

129.   S. L. O. JACKSON, Psychosis due to isoniazid, *Brit. M. J.*, *2*: 743, 1957.

130.   G. A. BUSCAINO and L. STEFANACHI, Urinary excretion of 5-hydroxyindoleacetic acid in psychotic and normal subjects, *A.M.A. Arch. Neurol. & Psychiat., 80*: 78, 1958.

131.   A. FELDSTEIN, H. HOAGLAND, and H. FREEMAN, On the relationship of serotonin to schizophrenia, *Science, 128*: 358, 1958.

132.   E. A. ZELLER, J. BERNSOHN, W. M. INSKIP, and J. W. LAUER, On the effect of a monoamine oxidase inhibitor on the behavior and tryptophan metabolism of schizophrenic patients, *Naturwissenschaften, 44*: 427, 1957.

133.   J. W. LAUER, W. M. INSKIP, J. BERNSOHN, and E. A. ZELLER, Observations on schizophrenic patients after iproniazid and tryptophan, *A.M.A. Arch. Neurol. & Psychiat., 80*: 122, 1958.

134.   S. BANERJEE and P. S. AGARWA, Tryptophan-nicotinic acid metabolism in schizophrenia, *Proc. Soc. Exper. Biol. & Med., 97*: 657, 1958.

135.   I. KOPIN, The effect of tryptophan loading and excretion of 5-hydroxyindoleacetic acid in normal and schizophrenic subjects, *Science, 129*: 835, 1959.

136.   J. ELKES, "Effects of Psychotomimetic Drugs in Animals and Man," in *Neuropharmacology, Transactions of the Third Conference,* New York: Macy, 1956.

137.   E. ROBERTS and S. FRANKEL, Gamma-aminobutyric acid in brain, *J. Biol. Chem., 187*: 55, 1950.

138.   E. ROBERTS, M. ROTHSTEIN, and C. F. BAXTER, Some metabolic studies of gamma-aminobutyric acid, *Proc. Soc. Exper. Biol. & Med., 97*: 796, 1958.

139.   D. P. PURPURA, M. GIRARDO, and H. GRUNDFEST, Selective blockade of excitatory synapses in the cat brain by gamma-aminobutyric acid, *Science, 125*: 1200, 1957.

140.   K. IWAMA and H. H. JASPER, The action of gamma-aminobutyric acid upon cortical electrical activity in the cat, *J. Physiol., 138*: 365, 1957.

141.   P. H. CONNELL, *Amphetamine Psychosis,* Maudsley Monograph No. 5, London: Chapman & Hall, 1958.

5. A BIOCHEMICAL HYPOTHESIS ON THE ETIOLOGY OF SCHIZOPHRENIA

Robert G. Heath

Because the etiology of schizophrenia is not definitely known, a presentation of this type must be limited to outlining hypotheses. Our group has formulated a hypothesis based on data from our clinical studies as well as from our recent physiological and biochemical findings and the observations of others. We have attempted to consider psychodynamic factors within the framework of genetics, physiology, and chemistry. Ours is an operational concept within which we are collecting data. We assume that continuing modification of the hypothesis will come about as more data accumulate.

We consider schizophrenia to be a genetically determined metabolic disease, or, more specifically, a disease characterized by alterations in the metabolic pathway for the breakdown of certain (as yet unidentified) endogenously occurring compounds. Our current hypothesis, based on our most recent data, is that the genetic defect is manifest by the presence of a qualitatively different protein (taraxein) in the blood stream. A toxic compound formed as a result of the interfering presence of taraxein alters physiological activity in specific parts of the brain, with associated behavioral changes. From our data, we postulate that these changes develop because the protein substance impairs enzymatic activity in a pathway related (in an undetermined way, as yet) to the metabolism of amines. Our current studies suggest

Robert G. Heath, M.D., Professor and Chairman of the Department of Psychiatry and Neurology, Tulane University School of Medicine, is a member of both The Association of Psychoanalytic Medicine and the Society of Biological Psychiatry.

that histamine may be implicated, either directly or indirectly in the faulty metabolic process.

Clinical and laboratory findings suggest that, as in other metabolic diseases, a basic deficiency exists to varying degrees in different patients. If disease symptoms are related to amine metabolism, then stress and, particularly, stress associated with emergency emotions and the physiochemical counterparts should intensify symptoms. Thus, we believe that the psychodynamic factors play a secondary role in the production of the characteristic symptoms of the disease. Although, in our hypothesis, the fundamental defect is in enzymatic activity, it is our conception that amines, which are poured into the blood stream during stressful situations, are somehow implicated in the abnormal metabolic process. In our current hypothesis we assume that these fluctuations in levels of amines are responsible for the fluctuations in intensity of pathological symptoms in schizophrenic patients.

CLINICAL CONSIDERATIONS

In our formulation, the inborn metabolic defect is associated with life-long characteristic behavioral patterns. The symptoms are at the level of basic feelings of pain and pleasure. We assume that they are a consequence of the chemical aberration. These symptoms are not to be confused with the classical textbook description of schizophrenic symptomatology. The latter (*i.e.*, classical or overt symptoms) are secondary complications of the addition of stress to a defective system. Persons who display symptoms reflecting the defect in the pain-pleasure mechanism have been referred to as schizophrenic phenotypes. Rado (1), describing the patterns of behavior in this group, prefers to call them schizotypal adaptation. The schizotype is described as presenting two basic groups of symptoms, the result of his inherited defect: one, an integrative pleasure deficiency; two, the proprioceptive diathesis. In Rado's conceptualization, these defects underlie the symptoms that Bleuler (2) first characterized as "fundamental symptoms." Rado postulates that as a result of these defects a variety of rather consistent patterns of behavior are present in the schizophrenic. In our framework, overt clinical or secondary symptoms of schizophrenia can occur only in this group and generally appear with stress. Persons without the inherent defect do not develop classical, secondary schizophrenic symptoms even though subject to overwhelming stresses.

Thus, we consider that schizophrenic symptoms are a complication of a fundamental disease and are precipitated by psychological pressures in predisposed individuals only. Because of the nature of the schizotypal adaptation, the genesis of stress is quite different from that in persons not affected by this disorder. In fact, the schizotype often appears even better integrated in some situations (*e.g.*, combat—when the individual is able to identify with a group with high morale) that produce stress in others. Careful statistics show lessened incidence of decompensation in schizophrenics during periods of actual combat in some circumstances. This is understandable when considered in the light of Rado's observations of the basic manifestations of the disease. Because of the schizophrenic's incapability of integrating pleasure feelings and the associated proprioceptive diathesis, which makes him unable to feel just who he is and how he fits into the scheme of life about him, he is apt to function better when he is in a highly regimented setting. This is so particularly when he can identify with a military outfit of high morale in which codes of behavior are fairly well spelled out. In these simplified circumstances, the subject can function with relative ease, relying upon his intellect, which enables him to copy the behavior of his associates. There is no need to rely upon his feelings, which are defective, in meeting situations. Thus, he can feel secure and a part of things. He is not subject to the stress and panic that tend to develop in the schizotype when he feels he is beginning to lose contact with the world of reality. The development of stress and panic often precede and are related to the appearance of classical decompensating secondary symptoms of schizophrenia.

An understanding of these symptoms and an awareness that they represent a fundamental basic deficit is of considerable practical value, in our experience. Recognition of this type of disorder is a necessity for the proper planning of therapy because the therapist who fails to recognize these symptoms and evaluate their significance may undertake a type of psychotherapy that can result in dire consequences. In our outpatient clinics for intensive therapy, our primary consideration in evaluating new patients is to ascertain the presence or absence of the schizotypal adaptation. We have found that the symptoms which Rado describes are consistent indicators of the presence of the integrative defect. In a number of articles (1, 3), authors have elaborated on the mechanism of symptom formation, both the fundamental and accessory symptoms of Bleuler, and the relationship of these to the more basic manifestations cited above. I feel it is unnecessary here to go further into a description of symptomatology as it evolves from the basic manifestations in the schizophrenic patient. The point I wish to make is that it is of the utmost importance to recognize early the presence of the disease because the therapist who fails to do so may employ psychotherapeutic techniques that will increase the patient's disability rather than improve his social adaptation.

Our concept of the etiology and pathogenesis of schizophrenia obviously is not universally accepted. Many investigators into the nature of schizophrenia have, on the basis of available data, advanced hypotheses that are considerably different. Perhaps the most commonly advanced concept in psychiatric literature is one that considers the disease schizophrenia a complication of severe stresses resulting from impaired intrafamily relationships. Thus, the disease becomes closely related to neurosis. Disease symptoms are complications of faulty environmental circumstances. Anyone can be a potential victim of the disease. Within this concept, differences between schizophrenia and neurosis are quantitative.

Henceforth, I shall refer to this approach as "the environmental-social concept of etiology" and contrast this approach with our views concerning the nature of the observed pathological interrelationships in the families of schizophrenics. Also, because we interpret the schizophrenic's reaction to stress as essentially a manifestation secondary to a basic biological defect, we obviously consider the role of the psychological factors as secondary in importance. This is in contradistinction to the "environmental-social" theory, in which stress is considered as a primary etiological factor. I shall present our basis for this assumption in more detail.

RELATIONSHIPS BETWEEN INTRAFAMILY DYNAMICS AND THE DEVELOPMENT OF SCHIZOPHRENIA

Those who consider the cause of schizophrenia to be environmental and social state directly, or imply, that faulty interpersonal relationships between one or both parents and the young child are crucial etiological factors. Data gathered on the behavior of families of schizophrenic patients consistently reveal a higher incidence of interpersonal psychopathology in such homes than one finds in the homes of nonschizophrenic groups. These data are consistent and undeniable. Opinions differ, however, as to whether or not this unhealthy emotional relationship in the home is of primary etiological significance. Some authors (4, 5, 6, 7, 8, 9), in describing their findings in this area, state that it is not etiological, or else they tend to avoid the issue. Those authors (10, 11, 12, 13) who conclude or imply that the finding is of etiological significance often refer to the mother in such circumstances as a "schizophrenogenic mother." Others (14) make specific reference to a disturbance in the symbiotic mother-child relationship—usually when the child is approximately 18 months of age—as being of crucial etiological importance. There is also literature describing the pathological child-father relationship, and other articles cite both parents as etiological determinants of the disease process (15, 16, 17, 18).

In our concept, based on our clinical studies, we consider that the pathological family relationships seen frequently, although not always, in the families of schizophrenic patients are not determinants of schizophrenic behavior but rather are the result of a basic metabolic alteration in one or both parents—as well as in the child who has inherited the alteration from the afflicted parent or parents. It is our view, in keeping with Rado's hypothesis (1), that the mother, rather than being merely a schizophrenogenic mother, is schizophrenogenic in every aspect of her behavior. Assuming that schizophrenogenic means that she has a unique form of behavior in her relationship to the child ("unique" in that it causes a specific disease in the child), then, by the same token, she also is a schizophrenogenic wife, friend, sibling, and what not. Others with whom she has contact do not, however, become schizophrenic because they do not receive her genes. There is no substantial evidence to indicate that her interpersonal relationship *per se* with anyone can cause the disease schizophrenia. Findings in our Clinic suggest that the child's behavior is at least as important as the mother's in inducing pathological family relationships. The only solid evidence, based on Kallmann's (19) studies, is that the passing on of her defective genes seems to be the crucial factor. Similarly, the child, very early in his behavior, displays blunted emotional reactions or autistic thinking. Our findings suggest that these characteristics do not result from environmental influences but instead are manifestations of an impaired metabolic pathway resulting from biochemical aberrations of faulty genes.

STRESS IN THE SCHIZOPHRENIC: QUALITATIVE AND QUANTITATIVE CONSIDERATIONS

Stress, seemingly the important factor in the appearance of secondary symptoms, develops in a unique manner in the schizophrenic. Stress appears to be a reaction to features of his basic deficit and not the result of faulty learning processes as in the neurotic. This observation is best described by Rado (1) and supports the contention of the basic deficiency. Because of the schizophrenic's inability to integrate pleasure and his resulting deficient concept of self, he tends to copy the activities of others. Unquestionably, his psychodynamics, or learning experiences, play a role in this process as well as do external circumstances. These dynamic features, however, seem to be less important than the endogenous integrative defect which predisposes schizophrenics to stress and decompensating symptoms. My experience as a psychoanalyst and the experiences of colleagues and students at Tulane University have indicated, with virtual certainty, that the principal sources of stress in the schizophrenic are other than those in persons without the disease. Most psychiatrists and psychoanalysts, in describing the disease process, present their data as if schizophrenia were a more extensive form of neurosis. In our experience, this is not true. We believe that schizophrenia is an entirely different disease. In the neurotic and the normal individual, the psychiatric data suggest that inferior adaptive patterns in current behavior are related to past faulty learning experiences..As a result of faulty learning, the individual develops inappropriate fears. The behavioral patterns of the neurotic are inferior attempts to decrease the stress of his unrealistic emergencies.

In contrast, it is our experience that only a very small amount of stress is derived from the area of faulty learning in the schizophrenic. Of far greater intensity and therefore of more importance in the development of decompensating symptoms in the schizophrenic is stress resulting from the basic, deficient behavioral patterns described by Rado. Schizophrenic patients develop their most intense panics when they recognize that they do not "feel" as other persons do (a recognition derived from deficit in pleasure mechanism). They sense that they are different and lost, as if without a rudder. Their "proprioceptive defect" thereby contributes to this panic. They do not know who they are or where they fit in. Attempts at intellectual control (*e.g.*, copying others, play acting) suffice to hold together the milder schizophrenic, the one with less of the basic defect. These reparative attempts are usually inadequate, however, in patients with more serious deficits, particularly if they encounter realistic vicissitudes in life. To summarize this point, I believe that stress in the schizophrenic is derived from a set of factors different from those causing stress in the neurotic and normal individual. This is an important consideration in psychotherapy, *i.e.*, therapy through the influence of one individual on another, and one that should also be taken into account by biologists working in this area. This hypothesis considers two biological factors as crucial: (1) a fundamental inherited deficit; and (2) the stress factor. These factors are interrelated because increased stress results from the fundamental deficit, and stress in itself is important in precipitating or exaggerating the decompensating clinical symptomatology. The great majority of psychoanalytic theorists do not consider this.

BIOLOGICAL DATA

Because we assume an inborn endogenous defect, our hypothesis must, of necessity, provide methods for the collection of data in addition to clinical observation. Clinical data alone can lead us only into the old *cul-de-*

sac of the chicken and the egg. We have postulated that behavioral defects are due to an inborn error of metabolism. It then follows that this error should be associated with specific physiological and biochemical findings. I will review briefly some biological data which we believe give support to this concept.

We have reported physiological studies in schizophrenic patients in a number of articles (20, 21, 22, 23). Animal studies were reviewed and subsequent patient studies described. One finding of importance in developing the present thesis has been the consistent recording of an electrical abnormality through the septal region and the hippocampus when the patient is displaying psychotic behavior. Animals under the influence of psychotomimetic drugs have also shown somewhat similar alterations in depth recordings. The intensity of the abnormality has been proportionate to the degree of psychotic behavior. The electrical abnormality has not been present in a small series of humans who were not exhibiting psychotic behavior or in a large group of primates from whom we obtained depth recordings. This irregularity is not present in other parts of the brain from which we have recorded, including many other deep nuclear masses as well as the cortex. This electrical abnormality is not unique to schizophrenic behavior. An abnormality similar although not of identical character appears in conjunction with psychotic behavior of other types, *e.g.*, when induced by psychotomimetic drugs or during episodic behavioral disturbances in epilepsy. Altered recordings from the brains of patients with focal areas of cellular damage also are seen. Thus, all of our findings indicate that we have psychotic behavior when this region of the brain is disturbed, and it can be disturbed for a variety of reasons.

We have conducted a number of studies in an attempt to determine more specifically the nature of the endogenous inborn defect in schizophrenia which could account for this physiological disturbance and concomitant behavioral disorder. Considerable data have been accumulated which we believe provide provocative, although not definitive, leads as to the presence of a metabolic defect and the possible area of this defect. One provocative investigation concerns the isolation of taraxein (24, 25, 26, 27, 28). Several observations (29, 30, 31, 32) led us to suspect an irregularity in the oxidizing system for amines. While studying oxidizing enzymes, we isolated a qualitatively different substance, taraxein, from the serum of schizophrenic patients. When this substance is injected into nonpsychotic volunteers, it induces symptoms characteristic of schizophrenia. The clinical symptoms following taraxein administration are associated with electrical abnormalities in recordings from specific parts of the limbic system which we have obtained from schizophrenic patients. The finding was of importance because taraxein (which induced the behavioral and physiological changes) is an endogenous substance present in schizophrenics, but not in normals.

We have further explored the area of amine oxidation. The finding of Sulkowitch and Altschule (33) that schizophrenics eliminate considerably larger amounts of amine and related substances in the urine than normals seemed important in our conceptual framework. Specifically, the finding was impressive since our clinical observations suggested a deficiency in the schizophrenic's ability to manage stress. It has long been established that certain amines are released and metabolized during stressful periods (34). We have confirmed the finding of Sulkowitch and Altschule in our laboratories. With their method, the quantity of amines has been as much as 100 times higher in schizophrenics than in normals (25).

Throughout our early studies of epinephrine oxidation, we found evidence that *in vitro* the serum of acute schizophrenics often oxidized epinephrine more rapidly than did serum from normals (in the absence of systemic disease in both groups). Further studies showed that copper levels (principally, ceruloplasmin in serum) were largely responsible for this phenomenon. We also demonstrated that oxidation curves were altered by ascorbic acid and the enzyme activity of ceruloplasmin inhibited by albumin (32). Accordingly, we devised procedures that might shed light on the relationship of this enzyme system to stress; in particular, we have attempted to determine whether or not the response of this system is in any way different in schizophrenics and normals. We followed several procedures to explore this area. One has consisted of measuring copper levels in schizophrenic and normal control groups at varying periods from one to 24 hours after the subcutaneous administration of epinephrine. There were but minimal and inconsistent differences in the changes in ceruloplasmin following administration of hypodermic epinephrine to the two groups even though the normals exhibited a much more profound physiological and behavioral response. At present we believe that the ceruloplasmin-oxidation phenomena are a peripheral reflection of the difference in metabolic response in the two groups. Results are provocative, but the mechanism is obviously not this simple. Another procedure to test this system has consisted of administering ceruloplasmin to schizophrenics. When large amounts are given (quantity sufficient to double the serum-ceruloplasmin levels), the clinical response to the administration of epinephrine is changed markedly. The patients develop much more profound physiological changes, suggesting that they are metabolizing more epinephrine. They respond with greater increases in blood pressure and pulse rate to constant amounts of epinephrine (25).

To summarize very briefly our thinking regarding oxidation of epinephrine and the copper oxidizing enzymes, it would seem that in schizophrenics the system is somewhat different than it is in the normal controls. However, we do not consider this the fundamental factor in the disease schizophrenia.

SUMMARY

We have presented our concept of the etiology of schizophrenia. We consider the disease to be basically a genetically determined inborn error of metabolism. There are characteristic clinical symptoms, in the form of fundamental basic symptoms, associated with the disease. The schizophrenic, as a result of his behavioral patterns, can develop excessive stress. The hormones that he releases with stress are not properly metabolized because of the metabolic error. Thus far, the most specific biochemical correlation with schizophrenic behavior that we have found is a qualitatively different protein in the serum of schizophrenic patients. The administration of this substance to nonpsychotic volunteers is followed by the appearance of schizophrenic symptoms. This fraction is close to the plasma oxidase, ceruloplasmin, and frequently is found mixed with the ceruloplasmin fraction. Whether it is or is not responsible for suggested alterations in amine metabolism is not yet clear to us. It is very clear, however, that administration of taraxein is followed by physiological activity in specific parts of the limbic system of the brain—alterations of a type that we have been able to correlate with psychotic behavior. The manner in which taraxein affects brain activity is currently being investigated. We consider that the taraxein fraction may be a biochemical manifestation of a genetic defect present in the disease schizophrenia.

References

1. S. RADO, B. BUCHENHOLZ, H. DUNTON, S. H. KARLEN, and R. A. SENESCU, "Schizotypal Organization: Preliminary Report on a Clinical Study of Schizophrenia," in Rado, S., and Daniels, G. (Eds.), *Changing Concepts of Psychoanalytic Medicine,* New York: Grune, 1956, p. 225.

2. E. BLEULER, *Dementia Praecox or the Group of Schizophrenias,* New York: Internat. Univ. Press, 1950.

3. P. HOCH and P. POLATIN, Pseudoneurotic forms of schizophrenia, *Psychiatric Quart., 23:* 248, 1949.

4. C. T. PROUT and M. A. WHITE, The schizophrenic's sibling, *J. Nerv. & Ment. Dis., 123:* 162, 1956.

5. C. T. PROUT and M. A. WHITE, A controlled study of personality relationships in mothers of schizophrenic male patients, *Am. J. Psychiat., 107:* 251, 1950–51.

6. L. KANNER, Autistic disturbances of affective contact, *Nervous Child,* 2: 217, 1942–43.

7. L. KANNER, Problems of nosology and psychodynamics of early infantile autism, *Am. J. Orthopsychiat., 19*: 416, 1949.

8. J. E. OLTMAN, J. J. MC GARRY, and S. FRIEDMAN, Parental deprivation and the "broken home" in dementia praecox and other mental diseases, *Am. J. Psychiat., 108*: 685, 1952.

9. E. SLIMP, Life experiences of schizophrenic children, *Smith College Studies in Social Work, 21*: 103, 1950.

10. M. A. RIBBLE, *The Rights of Infants*, New York: Columbia, 1943.

11. J. L. DESPERT, Some considerations relating to the genesis of autistic behavior in children, *Am. J. Orthopsychiat., 21*: 335, 1951.

12. J. L. DESPERT, Schizophrenia in children, *Psychiatric Quart., 12*: 366, 1938.

13. T. TIETZE, A study of mothers of schizophrenic patients, *Psychiatry, 12*: 55, 1949.

14. P. H. STARR, Psychoses in children: their origin and structure, *Psychoanalyt. Quart., 23*: 544, 1954.

15. T. LIDZ, A. CORNELISON, S. FLECK, and D. TERRY, The intrafamilial environment of the schizophrenic patient: I. The father, *Psychiatry, 20*: 329, 1957.

16. T. LIDZ, S. FLECK, A. CORNELISON, and D. TERRY, The intrafamilial environment of the schizophrenic patient: IV. Parental personalities and family interaction, *Am. J. Orthopsychiat., 28*: 764, 1958.

17. T. LIDZ, B. PARKER, and A. CORNELISON, The role of the father in the family environment of the schizophrenic patient, *Am. J. Psychiat., 113*: 126, 1956–57.

18. T. LIDZ, Schizophrenia and the family, *Psychiatry, 21*: 21, 1958.

19. F. J. KALLMANN, *The Genetics of Schizophrenia*, New York: Augustin Press, 1938.

20. R. G. HEATH (Ed.), *Studies in Schizophrenia*, Cambridge: Harvard, 1954.

21. R. G. HEATH, Correlations between levels of psychological awareness and physiological activity in the central nervous system, *Psychosom. Med., 17*: 383, 1955.

22. R. G. HEATH, Correlation of electrical recordings from cortical and subcortical regions of the brain with abnormal behavior in human subjects, *Confinia Neurol., 18*: 305, 1958.

23. R. G. HEATH and W. A. MICKLE, Evaluation of seven years' experience with depth electrode studies in human patients. Presented at *Conference on Electrical Studies on the Unanesthetized Brain*, Georgetown University, 1957. In press.

24. R. G. HEATH, B. E. LEACH, S. MARTENS, M. COHEN, and C. A. FEIGLEY, "Metabolic Abnormalities in Schizophrenia," in Rinkel, M., and Denber, H. C. B. (Eds.), *Chemical Concepts of Psychosis*, New York: McDowell, Obolensky, 1958.

25. R. G. HEATH, B. E. LEACH, L. W. BYERS, S. MARTENS, and C. A. FEIGLEY, Pharmacological and biological psychotherapy, *Am. J. Psychiat., 114*: 683, 1958.

26. R. G. HEATH, S. MARTENS, B. E. LEACH, M. COHEN, and C. A. FEIGLEY, Behavioral changes in nonpsychotic volunteers following the administration of taraxein, the substance extracted from serum of schizophrenic patients, *Am. J. Psychiat., 114*: 917, 1958.

27. R. G. HEATH, in *Neuropharmacology, Transactions of the Fourth Conference*, New York: Macy, 1959.

28. R. G. HEATH, B. E. LEACH, and M. COHEN, "Relationships of Psychotic Behavior and Abnormal Substances in Serum," in *The Effect of Pharmacologic Agents on the Nervous System*, Proceedings of the Association for Research in Nervous and Mental Disease, Baltimore: Williams & Wilkins, 1959, Vol. 37, p. 397.

29.   B. E. LEACH, M. COHEN, R. G. HEATH, and S. MARTENS, Studies of the role of ceruloplasmin and albumin in adrenaline metabolism, *A.M.A. Arch. Neurol. & Psychiat.*, 76: 635, 1956.

30.   S. MARTENS, B. E. LEACH, R. G. HEATH, and M. COHEN, Glutathione levels in mental and physical illness, *A.M.A. Arch. Neurol. & Psychiat.*, 76: 630, 1956.

31.   B. E. LEACH and R. G. HEATH, The in vitro oxidation of epinephrine in plasma, *A.M.A. Arch. Neurol. & Psychiat.*, 76: 444, 1956.

32.   C. ANGEL, B. E. LEACH, S. MARTENS, M. COHEN, and R. G. HEATH, Serum oxidation tests in schizophrenic and normal subjects, *A.M.A. Arch. Neurol. & Psychiat.*, 78: 500, 1957.

33.   H. SULKOWITCH and M. D. ALTSCHULE, The excretion of urinary "epinephrines" in psychiatric disorders. To be published.

34.   WALTER B. CANNON, *Wisdom of the Body*, Norton: New York, 1939.

PART III

Physiology

6. A STUDY OF THE INFLUENCE OF SCHIZOPHRENIC SERUM ON THE BEHAVIOR OF THE SPIDER: ZILLA-X-NOTATA

Nicholas A. Bercel

In a concerted attack on the schizophrenias, biological theories are being increasingly tested *pari passu* with psychological ones. The mainstreams of current biological research are only a little over forty years old. The reproduction of schizophrenic target symptoms became possible as a result of (1) Pavlov's work on experimental anxiety states in animals through conditioned frustration; (2) the production of miniature rhinencephalic lesions based on the pioneering works of Papez, Bard, and Bucy-Kuever; and (3) the discovery of bulbocapnine, mescal, LSD-25, and a host of other psychotomimetic drugs. Thus, the clinical symptoms of schizophrenia are reproduced, studied, and influenced. Target symptoms in schizophrenia are, however, *secondary* reactions to a *basic* pathological process, and as such, even though phenomenologically the most evident, they do not allow for the solution of the riddle from an inside-outward direction. Every individual has his own style of reacting to the basic process; hence the baffling variety of schizophrenias with all their protean manifestations. Schizophrenia is considered to be a general distortion of behavior behind which one suspects all kinds of rapid, labile, elusive, and transient psychic processes—all parts of an abnormal way of experiencing existence.

The assistance of the Los Angeles Mental Health Association is hereby gratefully acknowledged.

Nicholas A. Bercel, M.D., is a member of the Department of Physiology, University of Southern California Medical School, and of the Attending Staff, Veterans Administration Hospital, Sawtelle.

Hence, it is believed that the more *general* approach of studying body chemistry might be the royal way to the core of the problem. Unfortunately, the psychotomimetic drugs that produce *general* distortion of behavior in men are poorly suited to animal experimentation. Even if they were not, however, the interpreter would be hampered unavoidably by the hazard and the bias of anthropomorphization, whether or not he belonged to a psychological sect.

During the past three decades, many attempts have been made to demonstrate the existence of toxic substances in the body fluids of schizophrenics, following up (after some delay) the autointoxication theory of Kraepelin and Jung's speculation about the toxin-x of the schizophrenic. Thus, a higher death rate was reported (1) among tadpoles when their water was contaminated with schizophrenic rather than normal serum. This same schizophrenic body fluid was found to inhibit the mitose rate in the shoots of the common lupine (2) and in cell cultures (3). The bile of catatonic schizophrenics appeared to be toxic to doves (4), and catatonic-like conditions were produced in monkeys when schizophrenic serum was injected into their ventricles (5). None of these experiments, however, was capable of assigning the position which has to be accorded to toxins in the etiology of schizophrenia.

Current theories on basic metabolic defects in schizophrenia, however attractive, remain unconvincing. Disturbances in the metabolisms of amino acids, of adrenalin, and of serotonin were assumed, tested, and disputed. An increase in blood ceruloplasmin in the schizophrenic (6) excited imagination for a while, until it was ascribed to deficiency in ascorbic acid (7). Yet, it is probably too early to discard these theories entirely, for the body fluids studied came from patients who were categorized into an obscure clinical plurality called schizophrenia. Thus, a currently uncontrollable variable was built into such research efforts from the start. So the search is still going on for the hypothetical, abnormal metabolite in the system of the schizophrenic.

Our medium under study was the serum of the schizophrenic, and the test animal was the orb-weaver spider Zilla-x-notata. In order to understand any deviation from normal behavior in an animal as far removed from the human as this spider, it is mandatory that the rather limited range of its daily behavior be described in detail with as many references as possible to the photographed web pattern.

First, some historical comments, in order to justify the selection of this spider as the test animal. In 1948, while studying the web-building mechanism of this orb-weaver, Peters of the University of Tübingen became impatient with the spider's nighttime web-building habits. He asked for some help from one of his collaborators, Dr. Peter N. Witt (8), who proceeded to administer a CNS stimulant to the spider in the hope that this would displace the web-building time to the more respectable hours of the day. The spider, however, failed to comply, but the drug produced marked changes in the web pattern. Witt then proceeded to use the spider for purposes of biological assay, thus demonstrating the pronounced reactivity of the animal to substances that influence CNS function.

Although the effect of stimulants and depressants on web formation eventually proved to be dramatic, easily identifiable, and reproducible, the changes produced by psychotomimetic drugs such as LSD-25 and mescaline appeared to be more subtle. It further appeared that, despite the marked similarity of the aforementioned two substances in their effect on the human, their influence on the Zilla's web pattern was opposite (though no less significant). The effect was limited to two parameters of web regularity. Thus, the standard deviation in the mean values of the distance between the spiral strands and of the angles of the radial sectors dropped significantly when lysergic acid in a certain dose was administered, whereas the change was in the opposite direction when the substance given was mescaline. In simple terms, therefore, LSD-25 made the web more regular, whereas mescaline made it more irregular. Eventually, psychotomimetic drugs such as adrenochrome were found which produced more profound and visible alterations in the web pattern; this, however, was not known to the author when he began to study the effect of schizophrenic blood on spider behavior in 1955.

Our immediate interest in this study was stimulated by some findings obtained in the course of administering LSD-25 to chronic schizophrenics, who (as also reported by others) exhibit a considerable resistance to such a drug. Sometimes from six to ten times the amount sufficient to induce a florid LSD state in the normal subject had to be given to the chronic schizophrenic before he showed or indicated the first sign of the LSD state. The resistance applied equally to autonomous nervous system changes which were observed and to the perceptual anomalies or delusions which the patient clearly recognized as alien to his usual mental trend. This apparent resistance raised a good deal of speculation centered on certain assumptions. The most prevalent assumption considered the possibility of the schizophrenic's possessing in his system an abnormal metabolite similar to LSD, connected somehow with his psychosis.

Proceeding from this assumption, it would have been best to administer extracts from the brain tissue of schizophrenics who were undergoing frontal lobotomy. These extracts, however, were next to impossible to obtain in numbers in 1955 and have become even less obtainable subsequently, because of the progressive abandonment of this type of surgery—not to mention the difficulty of obtaining normal extracts for use as controls. The next best substance would have been the spinal fluid, which is likewise hard to obtain in quantity and not at all obtainable from normal subjects for controls. Thus, the choice was narrowed down to urine or blood.

While the urine is easier to obtain and to concentrate and while most of the known psychotomimetic drugs are vegetable amines, it was thought that blood would be a better body fluid to use than a filtrate. Witt (9) was not able to demonstrate changes in the urine of patients suffering from acute delirium and from schizophrenia, but among the possible explanations for this failure, he considered the disadvantage that inactivated breakdown products of active substances are not detected in the urine.

Because we were looking for a hypothetical substance (which, if present, would probably be so only in small amounts), we decided not to add any preservatives or anticoagulants to the fresh blood drawn from the patient. It was the same attempt to avoid any addition of potential variables which made us take the blood at a time when drugs were not present in any concentration in the system. After the cell pack was eliminated by centrifugation, the blood was kept refrigerated until the time of administration. All substances studied, as well as the serum, were mixed with sugar to make them attractive to the spider.

The administration conformed to the technique recommended by Witt: the amputated, emptied, and dried abdomen of a fly served as the receptacle which, with some sugar smeared on the surface (10), was carefully deposited in the centrum of the web; when the spider was teased out via a tuning fork vibrating on the web (11), it immediately began to absorb the contents for the allowed time of thirty minutes; and then the receptacle was withdrawn to keep the spider from removing it into the grotto for subsequent (and uncontrollable) consumption. In the earlier part of our project, various substances were tried out, which, by and large, confirmed Witt's findings. If there were minor variations in our results as compared to his, we were inclined to ascribe them to our own lack of precision, for we made our mistakes in the process of gaining experience.

The Zilla-x-notata spider can be found in at least two places in the United States: under and around the Fisherman's Wharf of Monterey, California, and on the pier of Atlantic City, New Jersey. The eggs are hatched in California at the end of the year or in early January. Before the spider reaches an adult size (before which time the web size is inadequate for testing purposes), it has to go through three or four ecdyses (moltings), each of which takes about four days. Experiments generally can be started in the first half of March.

The immature spider is not capable of self-sustenance, and a natural selection takes place in accordance with the carnivorous ratio. Surviving spiders show an immature behavior characterized by unrestrained self-exposure, random nonfunctional web formation, absence of signal strand, and random selection of grotto site.

The presence of the signal strand is crucial in the adult, functional web, for this component of the web is the spider's chief sensory receptor. This strand is strong and tight and picks up vibration from a distance. Since it is surrounded by a free sector on each side and since the hungry spider rests its feet on it, this strand not only signals the approach of the fly but makes it easy for the spider to descend unimpeded by cross-strands on the prey with lightninglike speed. Absence of this strand deprives the web of its most important sensory outlet. The young spider, resting or moving about on its web in daylight, is vulnerable, because, other than hiding as the adults do most of the time, it has no means of warding off danger.

The fine architectural detail which serves the purpose of natural reinforcement and characterizes the adult web is missing in the web of the young. As time goes by, the spider spends less and less time on the web, begins to build a signal strand, and is ready, by withdrawing into a grotto, to use the web as its chief source of food provision. Unlike the immature spider, the adult always selects a high point for its grotto. As it dangles at the end of its own thread, it has to rely on gravity to enable it to bounce from one side to the other as it builds the frame strands.

The conditions under which spiders spin webs have been studied in great detail. Thus, it appears that hunger is the most potent source of motivation for web-building. Next in importance are variations in temperature and in lighting. However hungry the spider may be, if temperature is kept fixed, the frequency of web-building will decline markedly. The darkest point in the night and the lowest temperature are the signals to the spider of the time when the web will have to be built.

There are life periods when the spider will not spin, *e.g.*, at the height of molting. The last web before and the first web after molting are usually abnormal. With the hard skin gone, the spider is transparent and extremely vulnerable; accordingly, it goes into hiding and cannot be teased out of the grotto no matter what amount of food is offered to it. After mating (towards the end of the year), which marks the death of the male, the female stops web-building for several days, usually a week. After depositing the eggs, the female dies.

If a spider is saturated with food, drugs, or blood, its web-building drive is eliminated for several hours; consequently, in all our experiments, the spider was given the serum under study never less than five hours before the anticipated time of web-building. Actually, five to nine hours before that time is the best period for the study of any substance, for this schedule allows for the maximum effect of the serum and the greatest likelihood of web-building.

Unless it has to, the spider does not build an entirely new web. A fly in the web causes some damage, which the spider will first attempt to repair. Only when the web is so full of patches that it is no longer operational will the spider find it necessary to eat up the old web (to conserve the building material) and build anew.

Any untoward condition such as extreme heat or extreme dryness tends to cut down on web-building frequency. Thus, by keeping a record of such changes in the atmospheric conditions, it was possible to read off the daily logs the lasting changes caused by the substances under study.

The spider builds its web according to a fixed, structured system in which one phase begins only when the previous one is finished. If one were to destroy the strands built in the early phases, the spider would keep on methodically going through the subsequent phases of web-building, even though the end product would be nonoperational. The spider uses one gland for the frame and radial strands (thick and smooth) and another for the spiral strands (thin and sticky) and would not start using the second gland unless the radial strands were finished.

The automatic, slavish adherence to the phasic schedule is matched by the fixity of the proportions of the web, which hardly change from one day to another. The web is not built in absolutes; distances are picked by relativity. The chief engineering tools of the spider revolve around its proprioceptive sense; touch, tension, and the feeling of gravity determine the web pattern. The web with its hub and spokes appears like an extension of the body into space. As in the human, the spider's body scheme improves with age and is reflected by the web. There seems to be a Gestalt-process in operation here, and the output is predetermined by the input.

Mechanical interference with the aforementioned elements of proprioception may profoundly influence the web pattern. We have covered the wires upon which the wooden frames were suspended with mineral oil to keep the roving members of the spider colony at home. As long as the oil adhered to their feet, the spiders spun abnormal webs, especially in the fine detail. At another time, we covered the back of the spider with a drop of paint in an attempt to identify it, with the result that there was either a marked drop in its web-building frequency or the spider produced incomplete (though otherwise regular) webs. In this instance, the spider's drive was believed to have been reduced by the animal's feeling too "heavy." If one radial-strand thread is burned off in the course of the building process (12), the next strand will be placed at one half of the angle opening as contrasted with the control web.

If one frustrates the Zilla (by teasing it out with a tuning fork six or eight times without depositing any food in the catch area), the spider eventually withdraws into the grotto and fails to heed the signal at all. We also found to our surprise that a good many of these frustrated spiders never came out again and died—a fate recalling that of Liddell's sheep when they met an insoluble conflict in the course of conditioning. We should also mention the negative connotation attached to a frame or bag once it has been deserted by a spider. We tried thirty-eight times in a row to put a spider back into such a house; it would never stay. Our observations extended to all these elements of spider behavior, not all of which can be recorded in the photograph of the web.

These findings were matched against such controls as daily spider behavior uninfluenced by foreign substances, changes following the administration of serum from normal subjects, from patients afflicted with various, verified, organic diseases, and from patients in psychotic states other than schizophrenia.

METHOD

Only adult spiders were used that were adapted to the frame on the day of their capture in Monterey, California. Control pictures were taken before and after experiments to avoid confusion with changes induced by molting (ecdysis). Spiders not used for experiments were fed fruitflies and water. Temperature and light variations were kept natural, and no fumigation was used to make the strands more easily visible for purposes of photography. Blood from patients who had been free from drug influence for from eight to twenty-four hours (depending upon the drug) was centrifuged without the addition of anticoagulants and was kept refrigerated until the experiment. The serum was administered six to nine hours before the onset of web-building. The setting was artificial to the extent that the spiders were kept in the frame, that the food and liquid were supplied by us, and that the webs were removed after feeding each day.

Ecdysis was ushered in by abnormal webs that were either miniatures of the normal one or lacking in spiral strands. Less commonly, the web was more irregular, a condition that will be described in detail below. During molting, the spider kept to its grotto even when food was provided, and it showed no inclination to spin at all.

RESULTS

When the spider was not used for experiments and received the maintenance diet of fruitfly and water, the web-building frequency was 79 per cent. Webs were normal in 92 per cent of the cases and were abnormal (mostly minor) in 8 per cent. (See Table 6.1.) These episodic deviations from the normal could not be accounted for on the basis of changes in the physical environment, nor were they the consistent responses of any one member of the colony.

TABLE 6.1
Effects of serum on web

SUBSTANCE GIVEN	NUMBER OF BATCHES	WEB FREQUENCY	% OF WEBS NORMAL	% OF WEBS ABNORMAL	% OF WEBS "R" RESPONSE
Controls					
Fruitfly *	—	79	92	8	—
Normal Serum	17	70	83	11.6	5.4
Non-psychotic Serum	12	68	92.4	7.6	—
Schizophrenic					
Catatonic	27	59	23.3	10	66.7
Paranoid	13	65.5	76	12	12
Hebephrenic	6	60	90	10	—
Other					
Depressed	12	75	90	—	10
Cerebral Atrophy	3	71.5	90	10	—
LSD-25	16	74	92	2.4	5.5
Spiders					
Normal	9	74.7	85.3	14.7	—
Molting	11	49.5	21	9.7	69.3

* See Note at bottom of Table 6.3.

The abnormal webs found just before and after molting were not included in either category of this uninfluenced group, for we were dealing here with a physiological variation that would not fit into either column. Among these premolting webs, there were eighteen cases that exhibited a beginning effort to draw in the first strands, which usually had a "Y"-shape. After this start, however, these cases abandoned the whole web-building process, and the spiders withdrew into the grotto to undergo molting. Because of the importance of this rudimentary web in the experiments—where it occurred independently of molting—these responses will be designated, for the sake of economy as the "R" (for rudimentary) responses. And, because they were not expressions of physiological variation (although in a separate column), they have to be considered as definitely abnormal. Each test means an experiment with a different blood sample. The number of tests has to be multiplied by the census of the spider colony used for the experiment, which varied from eight to twenty-five spiders, with an average of eleven. In order to get an idea of the total number of webs which served as the basis for the percentages of the tables deduct the nonspinning spiders from the above total.

In a comparison of the results, the single outstanding deviation is the high rate of rudimentary webs ("R" response) when catatonic serum was used: 66.7 per cent. Several such rudimentary webs can be distinguished:

A. The initial pattern is normal, but it stops at the frame-building stage. (Fig. 1A)

B. The initial pattern is abnormal with a few, random, unusable frame strands. (Fig. 1B)

C. The same abnormal pattern with additional spiral strands. (Fig. 1C) This mixture of frame strands and spiral strands has never been seen in other experiments; therefore, if it is kept in mind that web-building is a structured enterprise, the mixture signifies confusion about the web-building phase. Normally, spiral strands are drawn in only when the frame fibers, the central catch area, and the radial strands are finished. After a pause, the spider switches to the gland used for the spirals and adheres strictly to this phasic order.

D. Finally, we found markedly irregular, nonfunctional webs (less common than the above), containing large lacunae and radial strands that did not pass through the middle. The whole web was pushed as though compressed to the side without system or structure. (Fig. 1D) These webs are not unlike those built under the influence of caffeine and adrenochrome.

Most of the experiments show a drop in web-building frequency, which is also the case when drugs are being tested. There is a suggestion, not evident in this table, that the size of the spider may have something to do with the incidence of normal webs when catatonic serum was used. Proportionately more normal webs were found in the second half of the year (when the spider increases in size) than in the first half. Because the amount of substance absorbed was about the same in each experiment, it might have been more diluted in the body fluid of the larger spider.

In the control groups, the proportionate representation of normal versus abnormal webs was close to that obtained when no serum was given. The only deviation was the 5.4 per cent "R" response in the normal blood category.

Normal webs were obtained in just about as high a percentage when the serum used was that of patients who had noncatatonic forms of schizophrenia, cyclothymic depression, or cerebral atrophy. In an effort to see whether the normal webs would increase in regularity, as is the case with LSD-25, the parameters of web regularity were compared and statistically evaluated. The results showed that about as many webs were more regular than less regular after the experiment. *It should be stressed, therefore, that with the exception of catatonic schizophrenic cases, serum from patients with other forms of schizophrenia does not produce abnormal webs in a percentage that is significantly different from the normal controls.*

As indicated above, some variations of this "R" response (notably the one shown on Fig. 1A) are indistinguishable from the rudimentary webs that spiders normally exhibit just before they go into molting. This type of web, coupled with the well-known reluctance of the spider in ecdysis to move or eat, could be considered as an expression of a form of periodic, natural, catatonialike state, occurring at time when the spider possesses only a transparent membrane as its covering and hence is vulnerable in the extreme. This similarity suggested a set of experiments in which molting spiders were fed to the spider colony. The webs thus obtained showed the "R" response in 69.3 per cent, and the frequency of web-building, too, was below the normal at 49.5 per cent.

Because the "R" response occurred—and not at the time of ecdysis—with paranoid schizophrenic serum (12 per cent), with cyclothymic depressed serum (10 per cent), and with the serum of normal subjects (5.4 per cent), it seems that this finding relates more to catatonia than to schizophrenia. As has been suspected for a long time on purely clinical grounds, a certain catatonic potential seems to exist in a variety of psychoses and in some presumably normal subjects. In fact, some psychotomimetic drugs like LSD-25 exceptionally bring out such a response in spiders that are not molting (5.5 per cent).

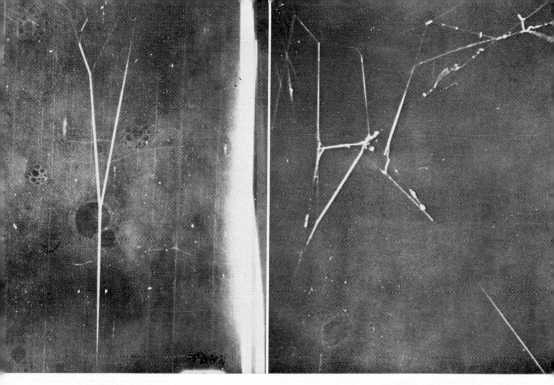

FIGURE 1A   FIGURE 1B

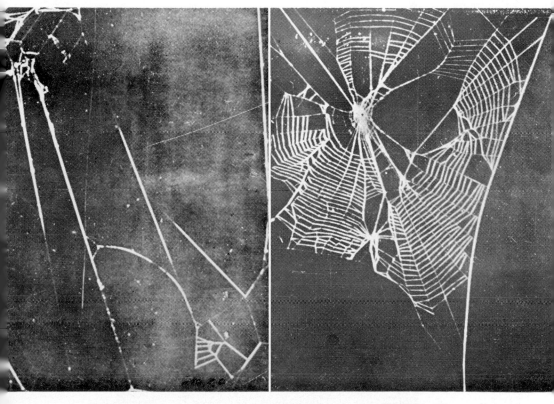

FIGURE 1C   FIGURE 1D

FIGURE 2

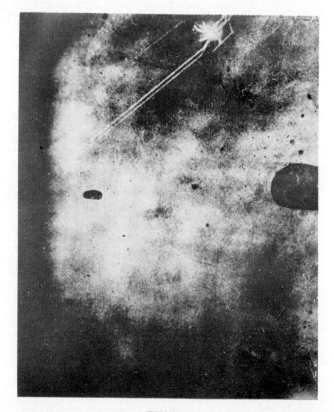

FIGURE 3

TABLE 6.2

Effects of serum on Zilla behavior

SUBSTANCE GIVEN	WEBS EXAMINED	NEW GROTTO	ABSENT SIGNAL STRAND	SELF-EXPOSURE	LASTING CHANGES
Controls					
Fruitfly	100	6	1	4	5
Normal Serum	100	2	—	2	6
Non-psychotic Serum	100	1	—	1	5
Schizophrenic					
Catatonic	100	13	7	9	15
Paranoid	100	3	—	2	8
Hebephrenic	50	—	—	—	1
Other					
Depressed	100	—	—	1	1
Cerebral Atrophy	30	—	—	—	—
LSD-25	100	5	—	6	3
Spiders					
Normal	50	2	—	—	3
Molting	50	3	2	7	10

Changes in behavior, some of which cannot be documented in the photograph (Table 6.2), were based on one week's observation following an experiment; and, in the case of controls given the usual fruitfly, a week was chosen when the spiders were not used in any experiments. The change in grotto and self-exposure often occurred when the web was otherwise normal. Obviously, webs without signal strands were placed in the abnormal category. The lasting changes consisted of continued absence of web-building (which in some cases ended in death) or any of the other changes in this table which occurred repeatedly during the week or for the first time on the day following the experiment. Care was taken in all these cases to exclude any change that was caused by molting.

In the catatonic group, the frequency with which new grottoes or take-off points were built was increased over the control (Fig. 2). In no other group did we see grottoes that were started on the vertical part of the frame, below the midline. There was also an increase in webs devoid of signal strands; this defect makes even a good web nonfunctional. Too, an increase in self-exposure was noted in this group. Adult spiders do not ordinarily rest during the day on the web. Yet, they were not only found to do just that, but they could be photographed without reaction to light, touch, or vibration; and they were even caught in the process of daytime web-building (Fig. 3), which Witt in all his experience has seen only once.

The statistical treatment of these values is summarized in Tables 6.3 and 6.4. They show clearly that the catatonic serum and molting spider taken together behave similarly in respect to their effect on web formation and spider behavior. Moreover, these tables show high statistical significance (an over-all Chi-Square value well beyond the .01 level of confidence) when contrasted with the controls or other psychotics.

The description of normal spider behavior demonstrates that we are dealing with a rigid, instinctive activity. While the change from the randomly woven, primitive web of the young spider to the architectural marvel that is the adult web appears to be impressive and while this evolution corresponds to a like change in behavior that appears to be goal-directed and geared for survival, there is no proof that this improvement is accomplished through learning from experience. Evolution climbs on the steps of maturation; therefore, the spider starts its life with its behavior "wired in the circuit." This fact is underlined by the demonstration that the spider, like a rigid automaton, continues to build webs even when the effort fails to achieve its biological meaning (the capacity to catch flies). Furthermore, the failure of one cue—e.g., lack of temperature, light variation—in the chain of signals that releases this innate behavior stops the web-building.

There is nothing to indicate that the spider is capable of learning after it reaches maturation. There may be some temporary adaptation for a few days, but not the plasticity that characterizes learning. Even this adaptation is in the nature of negative behavior, as, for example, the spider's reluctance to return to a frame once deserted or its aforementioned withdrawal into the grotto after having been teased out repeatedly with the tuning fork without the expected prey in the web.

Since the sensory-motor activity associated with web-building is the same regardless of the outcome, instinctive action cannot be equated with purposeful behavior. In fact, there was nothing that would indicate the existence of subjective experience in the spider.

Although the spider leaves a permanent, sensitive, reactile record that

TABLE 6.3

Effects of serum on web–numbers of spiders
Table for calculating chi square

SUBSTANCE GIVEN	NO. OF BATCHES	AVERAGE NO. OF SPIDERS PER BATCH	TOTAL NO. OF SPIDERS FOR THIS SUBSTANCE	WEBS NORMAL Observed vs. Expected Number		WEBS ABNORMAL Observed vs. Expected Number		"R" RESPONSES Observed vs. Expected Number		ABSENT WEBS Observed vs. Expected Number		CONTRIBUTION TO CHI SQUARE
				Obs.	Exp.	Obs.	Exp.	Obs.	Exp.	Obs.	Exp.	
Controls												
Fruitfly	—	(Note 1)	200	**146**	99.2	13	11.2	0	24.7	42	64.8	54
Normal Serum	17	11	185	107	91.8	15	10.4	7	22.9	56	60.0	16
Non-psychotic Serum	12	11	135	85	66.8	7	7.5	0	16.7	43	43.7	22
Schizophrenic												
Catatonic	27	11	300	*41*	148.7	18	16.9	**118**	37.1	*123*	97.3	**260**
Paranoid	13	11	140	70	69.5	11	7.8	11	17.3	48	45.4	3
Hebephrenic	6	11	67	36	33.3	4	3.8	0	8.2	27	21.7	10
Other												
Depressed	12	11	135	*91*	66.8	0	7.5	10	16.7	34	43.7	**21**
Cerebral Atrophy	3	12	35	23	17.3	2	2.0	0	4.3	10	11.4	6
LSD-25	16	11	172	**117**	85.4	3	9.6	7	21.2	45	55.7	28
Spiders												
Normal	9	10	91	58	45.2	10	5.1	0	11.2	23	29.5	**21**
Molting	11	11	125	*13*	62.0	6	7.1	*43*	15.5	63	40.5	**100**
TOTALS			1,585	786		89		196		514		540

Values that are exceptionally high are indicated in bold face.
Values that are somewhat high are indicated in italics.
A high "expected" value means the same thing as a *low observed* value.

NOTE 1: The number 200 is arbitrarily selected. It represents a random sub-sample: the much larger set of control experiments for which the percentage values in Table 6.1 apply.

TABLE 6.4

Effects of serum on Zilla behavior
Table for calculating chi square

SUBSTANCE GIVEN	NUMBER OF WEBS EXAMINED	WEBS SHOWING: NEW GROTTO SELF-EXPOSURE ABSENT SIG. STR.		DIRECTION OF DIFFERENCE	CONTRI-BUTION TO CHI SQUARE
		OBSERVED	EXPECTED		
Controls					
Fruitfly	100	11	9	+	½
Normal Serum	100	4	9	−	3
Non-psychotic Serum	100	2	9	−	5
Schizophrenic					
Catatonic	100	29	9	++	50
Paranoid	100	5	9	−	2
Hebephrenic	50	0	5	−	5½
Other					
Depressed and Cerebral Atrophy	130	1	12	−	10
LSD-25	100	11	9	+	½
Spiders					
Normal	50	2	5	−	2
Molting	50	12	5	++	11
TOTALS	880	77	81		90

Considering the table as a whole, we get an over-all chi-square value which is highly significant at well beyond the .01 level. Most of this significance comes from the Catatonic and Molting Spider rows. Considering these separately from the rest of the table, we find:

NOTE 1: The difference between the Catatonic and Molting Spiders is not statistically significant.

NOTE 2: The differences amongst the remaining rows excluding Catatonic and Molting Spiders still show some statistical significance; the high chi-square value is largely contributed by the heightened number of abnormal behaviors evidenced in the Fruitfly and LSD rows. (The rows where the spiders were not fed on blood.)

can be expressed in mathematical formulae and thus is useful in testing for the presence of abnormal substances in the body fluids of schizophrenics, the fact that the spider is hatched with its behavior "wired in" the gene and is not capable of learning imposes some sobering limitations on the interpretation of its behavior by human observers.

According to our results, only the blood taken from catatonic schizophrenics produced (in two thirds of the experiments) clearly identifiable alterations in the web pattern; and this response was not exclusively limited to this diagnostic category, as it appeared in a small percentage of experiments with paranoid, cyclothymic, and even normal blood. Because this rudimentary ("R") response was analogous with the web occasionally built by the spider ready to go into molting, whatever constituent of the human blood responsible for it may be identical with an element in the body fluid of the molting spider. The "R" response obtained with human blood did not, however, initiate molting. With catatonic schizophrenic serum, there also appeared to be a rise (though less impressive) in such anomalies as change in grotto, absence of signal strand, and self-exposure, all of which in adult spiders suggest a return to an immature level of behavior. These anomalies, were they to continue, would make it impossible for the spider to survive.

It may not be just a coincidence that the only form of schizophrenia expressed as a physical state and the first experimentally reproduced in animals was the one to produce behavioral changes in and outside of the web, presenting analogies at least suggestive of the human catatonic state. Inactivity, withdrawal, and retrogression reappear periodically in the uninfluenced spider as it goes into ecdysis, a state that is vulnerable in the extreme, and these defensive behavioral features assure its survival. Only future fractionation studies of the body fluid of the molting spider can reveal the presence of a substance responsible for these changes and answer the question of whether such a substance can be linked with human catatonia or catatonic potential.

In closing, it is thought best to give expression to a possibility. Since the majority of the catatonic patients were first admissions whose blood was taken usually right after admission (catatonics get to a doctor or hospital faster than other forms of schizophrenia), no special effort was made to make sure that these patients did not suffer from nutritional and vitamin deficiencies. However, if it can be confirmed that the marked, sudden weight loss at the onset of catatonia (nine pounds in twenty-four hours), described by Crammer (13) is the physical expression of the catatonic process rather than the result of mental symptoms (noneating), then it is possible that some abnormal metabolite as a catatonic by-product is the cause of the "R" response. In that event, however, it would be more difficult to bring this response into harmony with the normal molting response from which it cannot be differentiated in so many instances.

References

1.   E. W. LAZELL and L. H. PRINCE, A study of the causative factors of dementia praecox: the influence of the blood and serum on embryological cells; a preliminary communication, *U. S. Veterans Med. Bull.*, 5: 40–41, 1929.

2.   D. I. MACHT and M. B. MACHT, Phytotoxic reactions of some blood sera: with biometric analyses, *J. Lab. & Clin. Med.*, 26: 597–615, 1941.

3.   S. FEDOROFF, Toxicity of schizophrenics blood serum in tissue culture, *J. Lab. & Clin. Med.*, 48: 55–62, 1956.

4.   H. BARUK, Experimental catatonia and the problem of will and personality, *J. Nerv. & Ment. Dis.*, 110: 218–235, 1949.

5.   P. L. MC GEER, E. G. MC GEER, and J. E. BOULDING, Relation of aromatic amino acids to excretory pattern of schizophrenics, *Science, 123*: 1078–1080, 1956.

6.   S. AKERFELDT, Oxidation of n,n-dimethyl-p-phenylenediamine by serum from patients with mental disease, *Science, 125*: 117–119, 1957.

7.   K. R. MC DONALD, "Ceruloplasmin and Schizophrenia," in Rinkel, M. (Ed.), *Chemical Concepts of Psychosis,* New York: McDowell, Obolensky, 1958, pp. 230–236.

8.   P. N. WITT, *Die Wirkung von Substanzen auf den Netzbau der Spinne als biologischer Test,* Berlin: Springer Verlag, 1956.

9.   P. N. WITT, *Psychopathology. A Source Book,* Cambridge: Harvard, 1958.

10.   D. WOLFF and U. HEMPEL, Versuche über die Beeinflüssung des Netzbaues von Zilla-x-notata durch Pervitin, Scopolamin und Strychnin, *Z. vergl. Physiol., 33*: 497, 1951.

11.   C. V. BOYS, The influence of a tuning fork on the garden spider, *Nature, 23*: 149, 1880.

12.   M. KÖNIG, Beiträge zur Kenntnis des Netzbaues orbiteler Spinnen, *Z. Tierpsychol., 8*: 463, 1951.

13.   J. L. CRAMMER, Rapid weight changes in mental patients, *The Lancet,* 259–262, August 10, 1957.

7. THE POSSIBLE RELATIONSHIP OF PRENATAL ENVIRONMENT TO SCHIZOPHRENIA

L. W. Sontag

Whether schizophrenia be a metabolic disorder, the syndrome of bizarre psychological defenses, or the result of early life experiences, or whether it be a psychosomatic combination of the product of life experience and its subsequent modification of metabolic processes, we do not know. Regardless of exactly where the etiology lies, it seems to me very important to examine that period of life between conception and birth, during which environment may modify both metabolic function and behavior. This too often neglected period has, during the past few years, become increasingly recognized as a vital one in the determination of many aspects of life's behavior and function.

PRENATAL NUTRITION

Animal experimentation has contributed heavily to our growing respect for the importance of fetal environment as a determinant of fetal behavior and postnatal structure and function. Nutrition is one element of that environment. Hydrocephalus has been produced some time after birth in the offspring of rat mothers fed a diet containing all of the water-soluble vita-

L. W. Sontag, M.D., is Director of the Fels Research Institute for the Study of Human Development at Yellow Springs, Ohio, heading a program concerned with environmental, physiological, biochemical, and genetical correlates and determinants of behavior and of social and emotional adjustment.

mins except folic acid plus Vitamins A and D. The hydrocephalus developed not earlier than ten days of age (1). Although the percentage of hydrocephalus produced in these experiments was small, subsequent experiments in which a folic acid antagonist was added produced a greater percentage. Nelson and Wright (2) have produced multiple congenital abnormalities from transitory deficiencies of pteroylglutamic acid during gestation of the rats. The use of antimetabolites for such substances as Vitamin B^{12} has resulted in more precise methods of exploration of this field. Hale (3) was able to produce congenital blindness in pig fetuses by a gross deficiency of Vitamin A during pregnancy of mothers. Cleft palate appeared frequently in the offspring of his Vitamin-A-deficient pigs.

Maxwell (4) described fetal rickets among the offspring of Chinese mothers who suffered grave starvation during their period of gestation. During the depression of the 1930's, the author had the opportunity to examine X rays taken during the first three months of life, many of them at one month, of children whose families were destitute. More than half of these children showed X-ray evidences of rickets by the age of one month, although most of them were being breast fed. Normal expectation would not anticipate the appearance of rickets at one month, even though supplementary Vitamin D had not been provided. One must assume that the fetal storage of Vitamin D, plus perhaps Vitamin D in mother's milk, was so deficient as to permit the early development of this metabolic disease.

There are innumerable other experiments and observations in the literature on the effect of specific nutritional deficiency during pregnancy upon the structure of the newborn. Such deficiencies are, in the main, of an extreme nature—such as we would not anticipate as a common finding among human beings in our culture. Yet the studies are evidence of the importance of dietary intake as an environmental factor during the fetal period. It is not too farfetched to contemplate that lesser disturbances in fetal nutrition from failures in fetal or maternal metabolic processes might modify, perhaps permanently, patterns of function of brain cells, without affecting body structure.

ALTERED OXYGEN SUPPLY

There are a number of conditions, occurring accidentally or for reasons of bad health, which interfere with the oxygen supply to the fetus. Clinical evidence and experiments with laboratory animals would indicate that mentally defective offspring may result from such oxygen lack. Ingalls (5), using epidemiological methods, suggests hemorrhage and resultant threatened abortion as one cause of Mongolism. Schroder (6) reports severe bleeding in 17 of 99 women who gave birth to Mongoloid babies. This figure, 19 per cent, compares with 1 per cent of 248 mothers who gave birth to normal babies in the control series. Ingalls (7) also calls attention to congenital defects that he produced in experimental mice by subjecting the mothers to short periods of severe anoxia during critical periods of gestation. He suggests that we should be more concerned about the effects of altitude on available oxygen to the fetus. Pre-eclamptic toxemia of pregnancy is known to produce thrombosis of the part of the vascular system of the placenta that later becomes fibrosed. It is not unusual for a third or more of the placental tissue to be destroyed in a long-standing toxemia pregnancy. It is interesting to observe that there is an immediate change in the behavior of the fetus in such instances, in that its rate of movement of arms and legs increases many fold. Barcroft (8) has described irritation behavior in sheep fetuses when a similar period of oxygen deprivation is induced and when carbon dioxide exchange is interrupted. Preyer (9) reports similar activity in the human fetus in instances of severe hemorrhage. Premature separation of the placenta with its hemorrhage also produces increased activity. It must be presumed that such hemorrhages act adversely primarily because they reduce the placental area available for oxygen exchange. Windle (10) has demonstrated in cats that clamping the cord of fetuses for a very short period of time produces marked behavior changes in the offspring, including ataxia.

The changes that experimenters and clinicians have noted and described are fairly profound, but little is known about changes that might be produced by lesser degrees of oxygen deprivation. We do not know, for example, whether it is possible that the oxygen deprivation during a severe labor could result in a 10-point lowering of the Binet Test. Whether there actually is mild problem behavior or suboptimal growth progress in children born of mothers suffering from pre-eclamptic toxemia with its fibrosed placenta is not known. Whether the spasm of the arterioles and the altered pattern of capillary function that can be observed in the mother during pre-eclamptic toxemia also occur in the fetus and can alter the function of its central nervous system is not known. Whether the potential of the cells is so modified that later psychological defenses tend to take different forms or whether the psychosomatic pattern, the central nervous system's interrelationship with the metabolic functions of the various organs, is changed is a matter for speculation.

ENDOCRINE ASPECTS

The pancreases of fetuses of untreated diabetic mothers show as much as 24 times the insulin content of fetuses of nondiabetic mothers (11). There is a vastly increased number of islands of Langerhans in such fetal pancreases (12). Newborn mammary glands of both boys and girls are enlarged at birth and many secrete for a short period. Pseudohermaphrodism in lower animals can be produced if testosterone in large quantities is injected into the maternal host during pregnancy (13). Freemartins or sterile female hermaphrodites result when twin male and female calves occur in the gestation of cattle, presumably from the action of the male calf's sex hormones on the developing female. Sontag and Munson (14) have shown that large doses of Evans' growth hormone administered to pregnant rats result in fetuses that are larger than control fetuses. The newborn infants of diabetic mothers are usually much larger than average, presumably because of an increased level of blood sugar and perhaps other endocrine changes. Such infants tend to develop hypoglycemia after birth and have been known to go into hypoglycemic shock. It has been suggested that fetal goiter may result from pregnancies in which the mother has an inadequately functioning thyroid (15). Apparently the secretion of the fetal thyroid gland supplements maternal thyroid production (16). It has been demonstrated that administration of progestins to women during pregnancy often results in the birth of masculinized or pseudohermaphroditic female infants (17).

These observations lead to two conclusions: (a) The fetal-maternal endocrine system must be considered, at least in part, as a unit, and dysfunction of the maternal endocrine system disturbs the function and balance of the fetal system. (b) Maternal endocrine disturbances during pregnancy are capable of modifying the structure of the fetus as well as its behavior and physiology.

The formation of brain cells and the process of myelinization might well have their current and future function modified by disturbing endocrine changes during pregnancy. Schizophrenia is spoken of by some as a constitutional disease, and one of the determinants of constitution is the fetus's endocrinal environment.

THE PLACENTAL BARRIER

Substances pass or fail to pass the undamaged placental barrier depending upon the size of their molecules. Mepharsan, quinine, and sodium salicylate, when injected into pregnant experimental animals, produce hemorrhages in the labyrinth of the developing fetal auditory apparatus without producing damage in the mother (18). An increased incidence of congenital deafness has been reported in the offspring of mothers who, during the malarial season, were heavy users of quinine (19), a finding which has not been verified by others. Sulfonamides and antibiotics work by inhibiting one or more of the elements of the enzyme systems of bacteria. They are essentially enzyme poisons. Presumably, the side effects of headache and malaise that were experienced during the early years of the use of the sulfonamides were due to such enzyme interference in cells of the central nervous system. One may well ask whether it is possible for such drugs to have a different effect when present in heavy concentrations in the cellular fluids of *developing* brain cells. It is legitimate to wonder whether the potential of such cells may be modified by this early environmental factor. Such speculation need not, of course, involve the question of whether the cells become abnormal. It is enough to wonder whether they have undergone a modification of their initial potential. Sontag and Wallace (20) found that the smoking of cigarettes by mothers during the last three months of pregnancy produced an immediate increase in the fetal heart rate, comparable in magnitude to that produced in the heart rates of many adults when smoking cigarettes. The experimental results were published to prove that the products of the burning tobacco did enter the blood stream of the fetus. No claim was made that these products were harmful. Recently, however, a number of people have claimed that maternal cigarette smoking is harmful to the fetus; and, although there are no scientific publications to this effect as yet, it seems likely that they will appear in the not too distant future.

EXPERIMENTAL STUDIES

Two very readily available measures of fetal behavior are fetal heart rate and fetal activity. In the laboratory, changes in the pattern of such responses may be used as evidence of the perception of outside stimuli. If one places a small block of wood on the mother's abdomen in the neighborhood of the fetal head and strikes it with the vibrator of a doorbell, thus producing rather raucous noise of 120 vibrations per second, there will occur during the last three months of pregnancy a convulsive body movement on the part of the fetus. This movement is apparently a startle reflex and is accompanied by a pronounced increase in heart rate (21). This response emerges in the last three months of fetal life and, increasing in frequency and amount, is greatest just before birth.

In studying the heart-rate response to stimulation, we became interested in the question of the effect of *repetitive* stimulation and set up an experiment to investigate the matter. The essentials of our procedure were as follows: All records were made on the heart-rate recorder previously described (21). This recorder mechanically timed intervals of 10 heart beats as they were counted by an observer with a stethoscope. Such 10-beat samples were timed in rapid succession throughout a 14-minute period, the average

number of samples being about 10 per minute. The first 5 minutes gave a
control or prestimulation period. At the end of the fifth minute, vibratory
stimulation of 3-second duration was introduced. This stimulation was repeated at 1-minute intervals—5 times in all. The heart-rate record was continued throughout the stimulation period and for 5 minutes after the last
stimulus. Hence, 625 stimulations to the experimental fetus were given in
the course of 125 such 14-minute intervals. The three parts of such a record
will be referred to hereafter as the prestimulation period, the stimulation
period (including five repetitions of the stimulus), and the poststimulation
period. For the present report we have used only the first record of each
experimental day. All records conceivably influenced by such extraneous factors as fetal hiccoughs were excluded. Thus, we obtained 36 records, each
preceded by more than 12 hours without vibratory stimulation and uncomplicated by any other known influence on the fetal heart. These records
represent a fairly even sampling of the 9-week experimental period.

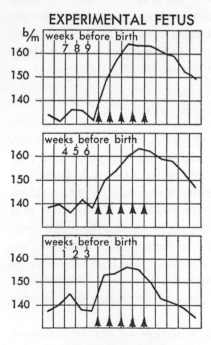

FIGURE 1

*Experimental fetus heart-rate re-
sponse to sound stimulation and
recovery during three, three-week
periods preceding birth.*

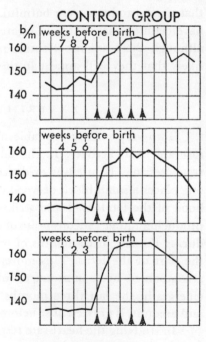

FIGURE 2

*Response and recovery of heart
rate to sound stimuli in three
periods in the control group.*

Figure 1 shows the "Average Record" of our experimental fetus for successive thirds of the 9-week experimental period. The earliest records at 7, 8, and 9 weeks before birth are shown at the top, whereas the records for the 3 weeks prior to birth are the lowest graph. Mean heart rate for each minute of the 14-minute record is shown. The arrows indicate vibratory stimulation. The most marked differences between the first and the last record are in the direction of: (a) decreased heart rate response during the stimulation period; (b) more complete return to prestimulation level during the poststimulation period; (c) recovery from acceleration even during the stimulation period.

As yet, we have made no attempt to determine the significance of these differences. The task of getting critical ratios is complicated by the fact that the levels we speak of are averages of averages of subaverages in that heart rate is counted in 10-beat samples. Because about five hundred separate ten-beat samples of heart rate contribute to each level, however, we can scarcely doubt that these are real changes.

There is an evident falling-off of this fetal heart-rate response under conditions of extensively repeated stimulation. Our knowledge of the maturation of the response, as reported elsewhere (21), would have led us to suspect the opposite outcome if repeated stimulation had no effect. Two questions immediately present themselves: (1) What further data beyond evidence from previous work do we have concerning this response at various age levels in nonstimulated subjects? (2) Was our subject a normal fetus at the beginning of the experiment, for whom the normal course of development of this response might have been predicted?

Concerning the first point, we have in the present study obtained records on 18 other fetal subjects from 1 to 15 times, usually at intervals of one week, a total of 51 records. These subjects may be considered relatively unstimulated as compared with the heavily stimulated fetus. Not one of them had as much stimulation altogether as the experimental fetus had during his first 3 experimental weeks. And they had, as a group, the mean of only 2 or 3 records of the experimental subject.

Their records, grouped according to age, give a picture of the change in response to be expected on the basis of maturation alone. Figure 2 gives curves for the unstimulated fetuses at the three age levels previously defined. At each level, subjects rather than records were weighted evenly. The data in the earliest weeks are inadequate, being based on only three records for three subjects as compared to fourteen records for nine subjects in the middle three weeks, and thirty-four records for sixteen subjects in the last three-week period. But the general picture is one of consistent increase with age in the magnitude and immediacy of the response without increase in amount of recovery.

These records are in accord with those of previous work. Taken together they provide convincing evidence that the decrease in response shown by the experimental fetus would not have been expected as a result of normal maturation.

As for the second question—was the experimental fetus a typical one from whom a typical development of response could have been expected— it would, of course, be unwarranted to generalize beyond this one case and to suggest what results might be expected from fetuses similarly treated. If this fetus was obviously exceptional in any respect other than change in heart beat, our interpretation of this change might be affected. In bodily activity during fetal life, this child fell within the normal range, somewhat below the mean. He was born from a week to ten days after the predicted delivery date, thus within the normal deviation. His length and weight were about average. He was described by the examining physician as normal in every respect, a mature or hypermature newborn. These facts give little clue to interpretation of the results. A real postmaturity of, say, two weeks, which would have made this fetus two weeks older at each level than the controls with whom he was compared, would not account for the fact that 6 weeks before the controls his response was as its peak and from that time on declined. Actually, in averaging the data for 3-week age periods, much of the dramatic course of change has been obscured.

Recovery for the experimental fetus is seen to become more and more complete through the experiment as the curve approximates the base line. In the later weeks the heart rate has returned to a normal rate by the end of the record, often reaching a level even lower than the one from which it started. The control group shows no such speeding up of recovery with age. Poststimulation rate remains well above prestimulation level in all age groups and is the highest just before birth.

In the control group, stimulation has its most pronounced and most prolonged effect on heart rate in the later weeks, whereas, in the extensively stimulated subject, the least pronounced and least prolonged effect occurs at this time.

The picture of more and more limited response is suggestive of persisting negative adaptation, or, in other words, fetal learning. In looking for flaws in the hypothesis, we considered, but found no evidence for, the possibility that a conditioned uterine contraction may have complicated the experiment. To find evidence for learning of some rudimentary sort in the present picture requires the following inferences: (a) At the outset of the experiment, response was normal for age. (b) A few repetitions of the stimulation induced a much exaggerated response. (c) Response fell off progressively as an effect of hundreds of repetitions of the situation.

The hypothesis of fetal learning meets the immediate facts but may be rash in the absence of more support from similar experimental work and related neurological evidence. Other interpretations may be offered, some of which have been indicated. Perhaps extensive animal work may confirm or contradict this single experiment. The experiment itself is presented in detail here, not because it offers an explanation for the etiology of schizophrenia, but because it offers further evidence of the importance of fetal environment as a determinant of behavior postnatally, perhaps, as well as prenatally.

MATERNAL EMOTIONS

The question of whether a mother's emotions during the period of gestation can modify either fetal behavior or the pattern of postnatal behavior is a fascinating one. Obviously, emotions do produce major changes in the function of glands and organs in laboratory animals and in man. Many of these changes are immediately expressed in changes in blood level of various substances. For example, blood-sugar level is raised markedly in most people during periods of excitement. The available insulin level in the blood is modified dramatically in excitement or fear. Epinephrine is liberated into the blood stream in states of fear and excitement. These are only a few of the many known changes in level of blood constituents during periods of emotional stress. Many humoral substances are of a molecular weight such that one would expect them to pass easily through the placental barrier. Those humoral agents of proper molecular size which normally stimulate glands and the nervous system, when increased in concentration, might well be suspected of producing similar stimulation of fetal nerve cells. The developmental stage of the fetus might alter the extent of such reactions.

We can then presume the possibility of a humoral mechanism linking the psychosomatics of mother's behavior and emotions and those of the fetus. And if it is possible to modify an individual's response to any environmental stimulus through previous psychoendocrine or psychochemical stimulation, then we might investigate the possibility of the production, through such chemical stimulation intrauterinely, of postnatal behavior resembling what we usually describe as anxious or neurotic. Such expectation is not basically dissimilar to our expectation that early childhood psychic trauma will modify an individual's behavior pattern and response to environmental stimuli at a later age. Such modification of later behavior and response as a result of early childhood experience may, in many instances, be considered as conditioning. There is no reason to rule out fetal conditioning as a determinant of postnatal behavior.

Actually, in our study here at the Fels Research Institute we have observed in human beings a number of instances where intense emotional experiences of the mother appear to modify early postnatal patterns of behavior as well as those of the prenatal state. The program of the Institute includes the study of some 300 children over their entire life span. These children are studied, not from birth, but from the fifth or sixth months of gestational life. A part of our records consists, therefore, of studies of fetal nutrition, activity of the fetus, heart rate, etc. at regularly determined intervals. As might be expected, there are in a group of this size a few individual women who experienced home situations, accidents, or other perceived threats, which evoked strong emotions during a part of their period of gestation. In our group there were five who had experiences ranging from having a husband killed at the seventh month of pregnancy to abandonment by a husband in eighth month of pregnancy. In each of the five instances, our fetal heart rate and fetal activity records before the occurrence of the disturbing situation, provided an excellent control for what happened after the incidents. In each instance the activity of the fetus increased by four- or fivefold, in one instance tenfold and the fetal heart rate increased by twenty or twenty-five beats per minute; and these phenomena persisted over a period of several weeks. It was of interest to note that a single, acute emotional peak produced fetal response that persisted for many hours after overt evidence of the mother's reaction had disappeared. This persistence of response to stimulation is akin to the ulcer patient's experiencing hypermotility and pain for eight or ten hours after a five minute explosion of anger. The number of infants was, of course, too small to produce a statistically significant research product, one that would indicate without doubt that their behavior was different at birth from the anticipated behavior of the group. Nevertheless, all five of them were hyperactive babies. Furthermore, in most instances, they had hyperactive gastrointestinal tracts with more bowel movements and greater intolerance of food and spitting up than were usual in the other infants being studied. They tended to be irritable and restless with more interruptions in their sleep and more crying.

Recently, William R. Thompson (22) has attempted to test in animals the hypothesis that neurosis may be produced in the offspring through excesses of maternal emotion during the period of gestation. He proceeded to create a situation which was known to arouse strong anxiety in female rats, an electric shock, and to provide them with a standard means of reducing this anxiety via an escape door. He then created these anxiety-arousing situations during pregnancy but blocked the usual means of escaping it. Thompson compared the behavioral characteristics of 30 control and 30 experimental offspring at the ages of 30 to 40 days and 130 to 140 days. He used the usual measures of emotionality: latency of activity in an open field situation and latency in leaving the cage and of reaching food at the end of an alley leading out from the cage. Latency was increased and amount of activity was decreased in the experimental animals. Efforts of the experimental animals to reach food were much delayed also. These factors were markedly different in the experimental animals and the controls. Furthermore, at 130 days, young adulthood in the rat, the evidences of anxiety were still apparent.

Thompson and Sontag (23) subjected gestating rats to audiogenic seizures from the fifth day to the eighteenth day of pregnancy. Performance of the offspring was observed in the water maze at 80 days of age. The offspring of the experimental group exhibited significantly slower water-maze learning than did the offspring of the control group. Their behavior strongly suggested that their slowness was the product of the higher anxiety level rather than some other limitation of ability to learn. Further experimental work is planned to delineate this point.

CONCLUSION

The various nutritional, endocrine, toxic, and emotional environments that I have discussed in this paper bear no known relationship to the etiology of schizophrenia. Yet if constitution turns out to be an important factor in the etiology of schizophrenia, involving alterations in vital metabolism, it is not unthinkable that such modifications of constitutional characteristics in the biochemical and physiological nature of brain cells may, in some instances, be influenced adversely by fetal environment, and that at a later date they may be responsible for grave behavioral deviation. We must recognize the importance of the patient's physiological constitution as a determinant of how he will react to an adverse environmental stress. We may speculate on whether the function of brain cells may be modified by fetal environment in such a way as to make an adult organism react differently, say, to an adverse parental relationship during childhood. Such a statement implies that constitution may be, and undoubtedly is, a product both of the genes an individual inherits and of the modification of the expression of these genes, in part by differences in fetal environment. It also implies that constitution is an essential determinant of how any human being reacts to a given social environment. While we may describe the kinds of early social-parental environment occurring often in the life of a schizophrenic patient, this description in no way explains the fact that for every such situation associated with a schizophrenic outcome, there appear to be many equally as unfavorable which produce no schizophrenia. It seems to me, therefore, that it is only rational to think of schizophrenia as a somatopsychic disease, one in which the cerebral physiology, determined and modified as it may be by genic inheritance, and by prenatal and postnatal environment, combines in a symbiotic reaction with a social-emotional environment, that is adverse, at least to that individual, to create psychological defense mechanisms that may be both physiologically and psychologically inappropriate and inadequate for the organism's protection.

References

1.   L. R. RICHARDSON and A. G. HOGAN, Diet of mother and hydrocephalus in infant rats, *J. Nutrition, 32*: 459, 1946.

2.   M. M. NELSON, H. V. WRIGHT, C. W. ASLING, and H. M. EVANS, Multiple congenital abnormalities resulting from transitory deficiencies in pteroylglutamic acid during gestation in the rat, *J. Nutrition, 56*: 349, 1955.

3.   F. HALE, Relation of vitamin A to anophthalmos in pigs, *Am. J. Ophth., 18*: 1087–1093, 1935.

4.   J. P. MAXWELL, C. H. HU, and H. M. TURNBULL, Foetal rickets, *J. Path. & Bact., 35*: 419, 1932.

5.   T. H. INGALLS, Etiology of mongolism, epidemiologic and teratologic implications, *Am. J. Dis. Child, 74*: 147–165, 1947.

6.   H. SCHRODER, Haben gynaekologische Erkrankungen eine Bedeutung fuer die genese des Mongolismus? *Ztschr. f. d. ges. Neurol. u. Psychiat., 163*: 390–396, 1938.

7.   T. H. INGALLS, F. J. CURLEY, and R. A. PRINDLE, Anoxia as a cause of fetal death and congenital defect in the mouse, *Am. J. Dis. Child, 80*: 34–45, 1950.

8.   J. BARCROFT, *The Brain and Its Environment*, New Haven: Yale University Press, 1938.

9.   W. PREYER, *Spezielle Physiologie des Embryo*, Leipzig: Grieben, 1885.

10.   W. F. WINDLE, Personal communication to the author.

11.   S. H. GRAY and L. C. FEEMSTER, Compensatory hypertrophy and hyperplasia of the islands of langerhans in pancreas of child born of diabetic mother, *Arch. Path. & Lab. Med., 1*: 348–355, 1926.

12.   K. A. HEIBERG, Das Inselgewebe bei einem neugeborenen Kinde einer Zuckerkranken Mutter, *Arch. path. Anat., 287*: 629, 1932–33.

13.   R. R. GREENE, M. W. BURRILL, and A. C. IVY, Experimental production of intersexuality in female rat, *Am. J. Obst. & Gynec., 36*: 1038–1046, 1938.

14.   L. W. SONTAG and P. L. MUNSON, The effect on the weight of the offspring of administration of Antuitrin G to the pregnant rat, *Am. J. Physiol., 108*: 593–598, June, 1934.

15.   W. B. PATTERSON, Congenital factors in thyroid disease, *West. J. Surg., 47*: 273–276, 1939.

16.   W. B. PATTERSON, H. F. HUNT, and R. E. NICODEMUS, Evidence that most thyroid disease is congenital, *West. J. Surg., 45*: 486–499, 1937.

17.   L. WILKINS, H. W. JONES, C. H. HOLMAN, and R. S. STEMPFEL, JR., Masculinization of the female fetus associated with administration of progestins during gestation, *J. Clin. Endocrinol., 18*: 559–588, 1958.

18.   H. P. MOSHER, Does animal experimentation show similar changes in ear of mother and fetus after ingestion of quinine by mother? *Laryngoscope, 48*: 361–395, 1938.

19.   H. M. TAYLOR, Prenatal medication as possible etiologic factor of deafness in newborn, *Arch. Otolaryn., 20*: 790–803, 1934.

20.   L. W. SONTAG and R. F. WALLACE, The effect of cigarette smoking during pregnancy upon the fetal heart rate, *Am. J. Obst. & Gynec., 29*: 77–82, 1935.

21.   L. W. SONTAG and T. W. RICHARDS, Studies in fetal behavior: I. fetal heart rate as a behavioral indicator, *Child Develpm. Monogr., 3* (4), 1938.

22.   WILLIAM R. THOMPSON, Influence of prenatal maternal anxiety on emotionality in young rats, *Science, 125*: 698–699, 1957.

23.   W. D. THOMPSON, JR. and L. W. SONTAG, Behavioral effects in the offspring of rats subjected to audiogenic seizure during the gestational period, *J. Comp. & Physiol. Psychol., 49*: 454–456, 1956.

PART IV

Psychology

8. SOME PSYCHOLOGICAL STUDIES
OF SCHIZOPHRENICS

C. L. Winder

In general, psychology is concerned with developing and verifying theories of behavior. The range of persuasions represented among psychologists who study schizophrenia is certainly wide. There are those who assume some organic, deteriorative process and for whom the research task seems to be the demonstration of behavioral similarities between organic patients and schizophrenics. Closely related are those who see schizophrenia as some complex of abnormal physiological processes and who work to show how the behavioral symptoms follow from the physiological disorder. At another extreme are those who conceptualize schizophrenia in terms of a depth, psychodynamic theory, whose primary interest is in techniques of intensive psychotherapy and intuitive formulations stimulated by observations from therapy sessions and performances on projective techniques. None of these is an adequate representative of contemporary psychology. But, it would not be accurate, either, to assume that classical behaviorism is more than one of several influences that have marked current psychology. Rather, some form of neobehaviorism seems to characterize the majority of psychologists who have shown research interest in schizophrenia.

We have said that psychology is concerned with the study of behavior. Behavior is not something to be explained in terms of the somehow more fundamental social matrix or physiological processes. Rather, behavior is to

C. L. Winder, Ph.D., Director, Psychological Clinic, Department of Psychology, Stanford University, is involved both in clinical work and in research.

be analyzed directly, although the analysis will often lead into a consideration of physiological and social factors. Characteristic of a great many contemporary American psychologists is the strategy of analyzing behavior in terms of some stimulus-response formulation. What intermediary processes should be assumed is debated with vigor and reason. Likewise, the optimum level of analysis of stimuli and responses is controversial, as is the proper conceptualization of motivation and learning. But, focusing on behavior, psychologists can make their debates meaningful.

Stimulus-response formulations have seemed to many observers to be far removed from psychodynamic theories and physiologically oriented analyses of the functioning of the organism. Quite the contrary. There is reason to believe that *rapprochements* from both directions are both appropriate and possible. Thus, psychoanalytic theory seems to bear important similarities to stimulus-response formulations in which drive concepts are basic (1), and certain psychoanalytic concepts contribute directly to experimental studies of behavior (2). Similarly, when motivational concepts are invoked, intensive analyses often lead into a liaison with physiology (3). Assuming that this line of reasoning is sound, psychologists who study schizophrenia in terms of the concepts and procedures of general psychology can expect to be able to link their work to some psychoanalytic formulations on the one hand and to physiological evidence on the other. Some studies of the latter variety are already in print, and the basis for the former step is being laid in research on personality development.

Much in this chapter reflects the work of psychologists who bring to research on schizophrenia a tradition of systematic study of defined aspects of behavior, often based on learning theory and psychodynamically flavored personality concepts. The strategy is to measure particular aspects of behavior and changes in behavior under controlled conditions using sufficient subjects to permit generalization of conclusions. The topics covered include psychomotor functioning, intellectual functioning, perception, thinking, learning, and characteristics of the primary family group.

Psychological research on dementia praecox and schizophrenic patient groups has a relatively long history. Bevan-Lewis (4) published data on reaction times of several diagnostic groups in 1899. An analysis of remembering was published in 1909 by Gatewood (5), and there followed other learning studies by Kent in 1911 (6), Boring in 1913 (7), and Hull in 1917 (8). Emotional reaction as measured physiologically was studied as early as 1909 by DeBruyn (9). The word-association technique of Jung was applied to schizophrenics by 1910 (see 10). A report on sensory threshold appeared in 1915 (11). Standardized intelligence tests were being employed by 1920 (*e.g.*, 12,

13). In 1924, Wentworth (14) drew attention to three groups of dementia praecox patients on the basis of Stanford-Binet test performance: (a) those who were uniformly poor, (b) those who were variable in terms of the range of items passed and failed, and (c) those who seemed uniformly efficient. Rorschach's work on the inkblot technique was published in 1921. In 1930, Moore (15) reported a factor analysis based on measures of emotional reactions, thinking, perception, memory, and ratings of psychiatric signs and symptoms. This was an effort to generate a set of dimensions for a more rational system of diagnosis. Personality inventories were applied in the study of schizophrenics in the 1920's and 1930's. In the early 1930's the Bender-Gestalt was published, and Hausmann (16) reported on goal setting following success and failure. Investigation of concept formation and thinking took on more definite form (see 17) in work by Vigotsky, Bolles, Goldstein, Cameron, Hunt, and others. Use of the Thematic Apperception Test in the study of schizophrenia became prevalent in the 1940's, particularly influenced by the work of Rapaport *et al.* (18). World War II brought a tremendous expansion of applied interest in diagnostic and treatment activities. There is a body of research concerned with assessment of psychiatric status and category and some reports of efforts to evaluate treatments. While these latter interests in diagnostic techniques and effects of treatment continue, there is a resurgence of research that deals with the more detailed study of particular aspects of behavior, in which the objective is more complete understanding of the functioning of schizophrenic patients. Certainly not all psychologists would agree that emphasis on the latter is optimal, many preferring emphasis on the superiority of studies of the "whole person."

REFINEMENT OF THE DEFINITION
OF SCHIZOPHRENIA

The present diagnosis of schizophrenia is based on an array of signs and symptoms. Although schizophrenics can be differentiated from the total group of hospital patients in a fairly reliable fashion (19), this is still only a global rating and subject to much variation and error, a rating which undoubtedly leads to much confusion in trying to integrate research results of different investigators. Classical Kraepelinian diagnosis of subtypes is not satisfactory (19) and forms a poor basis for research. But the clinical observation upon which it was based—that there are large differences between schizophrenic patients—still holds; and to abandon subtypes altogether seems too drastic a step. One promising alternative would seem to be to develop explicit techniques or procedures for measuring limited aspects of the syndrome. In line with this, Shakow (20) organized the observation clues commonly used in clinical judgments of deterioration and found substantial agreement between judges. Over a period of several years the correlation between ratings was .73 for a group of chronic patients. This is, of course, simply a more formalized way of expressing clinical observation, but the advantages of explicit definition and direct comparison of rating for reliability are obvious.

There are other techniques that endeavor to avoid both the retreat into the global classification "schizophrenia" and the retreat into consideration of such single aspects of the syndrome as deterioration. These consist of lists of signs and symptoms covering many aspects of the psychopathology of schizophrenic patients. Each item is the basis for a rating scale, and all patients are to be rated on each of these. Two such systems currently gaining some use in research are the Multidimensional Rating Scale for Psychiatric Patients (21) and the Hospital Adjustment Scale (22). Unfortunately, these scales do not apply to the nonhospitalized group, but some progress along these lines has been made (23, 24). These various techniques are designed to promote a more orderly, explicitly defined description of each case. Less salient symptoms are included, and overgeneralized psychiatric diagnoses are replaced by a description of behavior that can be observed in a specific time at a specific place. Amount of change can be systematically evaluated, and as overlap of nosological groups becomes evident, meaningless distinctions can be abandoned and a more useful classification of subtypes can gradually emerge.

A more technical and ambitious approach involves the use of factor analysis (25). Here, again, comprehensive description in terms of standard items is the first step. The correlations among all items or rating scales are determined and analyzed so as to yield information regarding descriptive variables, called factors, which form an efficient summary of the set of intercorrelations. However, it is well to remember that the results will be no more comprehensive than the basic information—i.e., the rating scales—and are no more than a focused view of this information.

In addition to the early study by Moore mentioned above, Degan (26), Wittenborn (27), Guertin (28), and Lorr, Jenkins, and O'Connor (29) report factor analytic studies of mental hospital patients, based on a series of brief sign-symptom rating scales which call for the information upon which clinical diagnoses are usually based. Results from the latter study are typical of those for schizophrenics.

According to this analysis, the defining descriptive variables of schizophrenia are withdrawal, conceptual disorganization, perceptual disorder, deviant motor behavior, paranoid projection, and grandiosity. (For the factor "withdrawal," there is an end point defined by indifference, taciturnity, seclusiveness, untidyness, and an unhappy appearance which contrasts with the other pole of constant busyness, talkativeness, and a neat, clean, cheerful appearance; this seems to be a bipolar factor and there is need for further refinement of it.) If these defining factors coincide with clinical definition, then the systematic rating items underlying them offer the desired explicit measure by which comprehensive, public diagnostic assessment can be made. Though this work is somewhat preliminary, it does serve to organize bits of information about psychopathology and to emphasize the need for detailed study in certain areas.

Extension of the method would probably lead to some realignment of the above factors and possibly to some added factors. For example, all the factors in the studies discussed above were based on more or less casual observation. None of them included results of psychological tests. If some of the recording systems which have been developed for analyzing interactions in small groups were used in gathering some of the basic data, definition of psychopathological variables would probably be sharpened. For example, an analysis of the social reinforcements given by schizophrenics might add significantly to the concept of withdrawal because it would seem plausible that paranoids would differ radically from some catatonic and hebephrenic patients.

Sharpening of the clinically derived definition of schizophrenia might do no more than reduce the likelihood of looking into blind alleys, in itself no trivial matter. But as the range of observations is widened to include results of procedures described elsewhere in this book and the resulting observations dealt with in a truly systematic way, it seems likely that a new definition of the schizophrenias which can be of real significance in guiding research will emerge.

INTELLECTUAL DEFICIT*

Many psychological studies have been done in an apparent effort to confirm or disconfirm dementia and deterioration in schizophrenia. Often this has implied an effort to assess the validity of some organic theory. A basic problem in this regard has often been ignored. Evidence from studies of

* The term deficit is used without any theoretical implications, simply to indicate performance below that expected in comparison to others or to a prior level of the same individual (17).

intelligence can lead only to highly inferential conclusions about the presence or absence of organic defects which would be better assessed at other levels of observation. The study of tasks requiring continuous work involving pre-scribed shifts in the basis of performance still seems to be a promising ap-proach which has not been fully exploited. Perhaps physiological assessments will replace behavioral or psychological tests. If more direct techniques for testing the organic hypotheses are devised and adopted, a very confused area of psychological research can be reorganized.

Most of these efforts to bolster the concept of organically based deteri-oration assume that schizophrenics function less effectively than at a previous time and that this deficiency is greater than would occur because of factors such as aging or motivation. Other efforts involve testing the proposition that schizophrenics and organics depart from normal in very similar ways. The implications are obscure unless differential predictions can be deduced that distinguish between organic deficits and such psychodynamic concepts as regression. Insofar as the organic positions might imply marked similarity between particular organic cases and schizophrenics, the propositions might be capable of disconfirmation. It is doubtful that propositions based on the regression concept could be disconfirmed on the basis of assessments of in-tellectual functioning of schizophrenics as compared with organics.

Organic theories strongly imply intellectual deficit among schizo-phrenics and the similarity of these patients to some organic cases. Psycho-dynamic, psychosocial, and developmental theories imply intellectual deficit under ordinary testing conditions, but do not seem to imply similarity of schizophrenics and organics. Despite the difficulties in drawing any infer-ences, it is clear that intellectual deficit among schizophrenics is expected, and empirical evidence on this point has been sought by many investigators. Demonstration of deficit would be best accomplished if current performance were contrasted with premorbid performance.

A very large number of people who served in the armed forces in World War II were given induction intelligence tests, and some of these people were later diagnosed as schizophrenics. Unfortunately, very little has been done with this store of data, but two studies give some information. Mason (30) contrasted 510 patients, of whom 368 were schizophrenics, with a large control group. Those who were later diagnosed paranoid and catatonic schizophrenics did not differ from normals on intelligence tests at induction, but those who became hebephrenic, simple, and "other" were lower than the controls. All patients—schizophrenics, alcoholics, neurotics, manic-de-pressives, and character disorders—taken together did not differ from the normals, manic-depressives being above controls on the average. Mason found that those who became schizophrenic soon after induction were not lower on the tests than were those who broke down later. In the absence of more information, one assumes that there were significant differences in induction intelligence which were somehow related to development of certain types of schizophrenia.

Using Army and Veterans Administration records, Miner and Anderson (31) present data on a mixed psychiatric group composed of neurotics and psychotics. In general, the results are that those who received psychiatric discharges were somewhat less well educated and scored lower on induction tests, and that neurotics did not differ from psychotics in either respect. The last point seems in doubt because the distribution of psychotics on intelligence might differ from that for neurotics if larger groups and a more sensitive statistical test were employed. Of particular interest is the finding that those psychiatric discharges who became the more chronic patients, in terms of needing one or more additional post-discharge hospitalizations, scored lower than the less chronic psychiatric group on the tests at time of induction. One could possibly interpret this as evidence that lower intelligence is instrumental in causing greater chronicity, possibly because of less adequate dealing with stress. As an attractive alternative, this could be taken as evidence of deficient intellectual development as part of the premorbid condition of these patients. The same view could be applied to Mason's data, and the assumption would be that deficient premorbid intellectual development is only one deficit of those who become the more severe cases.

Earlier studies that are most relevant are those of Kendig and Richmond (32), Roe and Shakow (33), and Shakow (20). In these, there were no premorbid tests available, and education was taken as an adequate estimate of intelligence. An analysis of educational levels by Shakow (20) is of some interest in itself. There were 723 schizophrenics who were admitted to Massachusetts state hospitals. Education-level percentages were: 66 grammar school, 29 high school, 6 college. Comparable general population data were: 65 grammar school, 25 high school, and 10 college. Possibly schizophrenia is slightly less likely among those of college potential, but it seems more plausible that a larger proportion of those of college potential who later became schizophrenic terminated their education prematurely at the high-school level. If education level were an adequate estimate of premorbid intelligence, these data would prompt serious consideration of some sampling biases in the above studies of World War II veterans. But, although the correlation between intelligence and education is of the order of .65 (*e.g.*, 34), there is a wide margin of error in predicting one from the other. It is unfortunate that more thorough analyses based on army and veterans administration files have not been made. Similarly, there are undoubtedly many cases admitted to civilian hospitals on whom records exist in school files.

With reservations dictated by the very limited information, one may conclude that late adolescent or young adult premorbid intelligence level is, on the average, normal among those who become paranoid and catatonic and is often below normal, in an unknown amount, among those who become hebephrenics. This would indicate that aspects of the processes that underlie some schizophrenias are apparent in terms of intellectual level during this premorbid period. In terms of psychodynamic theories, failure of ego development is suggested, rather than regression. For organic theories, the implication is that dementia or deterioration begins well before the time of overt psychotic symptoms and introduces the possibility that often there is no significant decrease in intellectual performance during a large part or even all of the psychotic period.

The conclusions drawn may be incorrect and further study may reveal that there is no significant deviation of premorbid intelligence in any of the groups of schizophrenics as contrasted with the general population. But if the premorbid intellectual deficit of some schizophrenics is confirmed there are immediate implications. First, study of intellectual characteristics earlier in the lives of these patients must be accomplished somehow. Retrospective study based on school records is one possibility. Selection of children and families in which close relatives have been or are schizophrenic would make longitudinal studies feasible (35). A second implication is that there may be very important differences among patients in the operation of the factors that are antecedent to the development of schizophrenia; hence, various schizophrenias may reflect varied etiological factors. Possibly making a distinction between two kinds of schizophrenia would result in more rapid progress in understanding etiology. In any event, this problem of premorbid intellectual efficiency and development is open for further study. Since longitudinal studies of the intellectual development of normals suggest the importance of interpersonal and adjustment factors (36), the investigation of the potency of these factors in intellectual development of schizophrenics is mandatory.

The Period of Psychosis   One would prefer to have the matter of premorbid intellectual characteristics settled before making an analysis of intellectual deficit during psychosis. But this latter topic has received much more research attention.

Roe and Shakow (33) and Kendig and Richmond (32) have provided two major studies. In both, the long obsolete 1916 Stanford-Binet was the measuring instrument. Even in these relatively superior studies, age, education, sex, and socio-economic variables were only moderately well controlled. Roe and Shakow were able to use a fairly adequate normal control group for which the mean mental age was 164 months * as compared with the mean of their lumped group of schizophrenic patients, which was 141 months. Kendig and Richmond found a mean of 143 months for their sample of white schizophrenic patients, a figure similar to that reported in previous studies. It can be concluded, therefore, that, as a group, schizophrenics hospitalized in large public hospitals show a general intellectual deficit. Since deficit is found, can the amount be estimated? Hunt and Cofer (17) in 1944 estimated that among the total group of schizophrenics the average impairment is 20 months of mental age. From several studies employing the Wechsler tests, the results are indicative of an average deficit of 10 I.Q. points.

What are the findings regarding subtypes of schizophrenics? In both the Roe and Shakow and the Kendig and Richmond studies, the intellectual level for each of the classical subgroups of schizophrenia was investigated. The former study yielded the following mean months of mental age: normals, 164; catatonic, 165; simple, 156; paranoid, 155; unclassified, 144; and hebephrenics, 129. Kendig and Richmond report on these subtypes as follows: paranoid, 148; catatonics, 144; hebephrenics, 138; and simple, 127.

Harper (38) using the Wechsler-Bellevue, Form I (39), found that average Full Scale I.Q. levels for the subtypes were: mixed and undifferentiated, 92; paranoid, 92; simple, 85; catatonic, 83; and hebephrenic, 81. Wechsler Verbal I.Q.'s from Harper's study were: mixed and undifferentiated, 95; paranoid, 92; simple, 87; catatonic, 86; and hebephrenic, 84.

That paranoids are relatively high and hebephrenics are low seems definite. With regard to the other subtypes, the results are too variable to permit conclusions. Further research on more adequately defined samples is indicated. Nevertheless, it is clear that even when the poorly specified, classical subtype diagnostic scheme is employed, intellectual level is variable among the groups of schizophrenics. Roe and Shakow put the matter well when they wrote, "A careful intercomparison of the various dementia praecox groups indicates that there is no justification for lumping all types into a total dementia praecox group, at least in psychometric research, since the differences among the types are in many instances greater than between the dementia praecoxes and the other groups" (33, p. 474). It is well to note that this does not necessarily imply that retention of the traditional subtypes

---

* Based on work by Weisenburg, Roe, and McBride (37).

would best reflect this psychometric heterogeneity. Some alternative categorical scheme or dimensional conceptualization could serve as well or better.

A feature of the Roe and Shakow study is their utilization of a rating of cooperation to constitute "representative" and "nonrepresentative" groups within patient groups. Less cooperative groups were generally less adequate than the representative groups but did not show any trends remarkably different from those reported above. The added deficit in performance of the nonrepresentative or uncooperative groups is attributed by Roe and Shakow to attitude differences. Just how the attitudes arise, the nature of the attitudes, and the way in which the attitude differences are to be interpreted in relation to the symptomatologies are the problems left unresolved. Effort, interest, and self-confidence are terms employed in defining cooperation. Although psychopathological variables are not necessarily implied by these defining terms, adjustment and personality variables, in addition to motivational variables, seem implicit.

Differential Deficit   Clinical assessment has suggested not only that schizophrenics perform below the general population average, but that the deficit is not uniform with regard to all aspects of intellectual functioning. By 1930, scattered psychometric studies had indicated that among schizophrenics the vocabulary score on the Stanford-Binet was less disrupted than the other items of the scale. Babcock (40) assumed that the basic level and the efficiency phases of intelligence can vary independently. She attempted to devise tests of efficiency and used the Terman Vocabulary Test as a measure of level, adjusting the scoring method so that for normals the discrepancy between efficiency and level was zero. There have been some reports of successful discrimination of pathological from normal groups, but, in general, the Babcock Test has proved inadequate (33, 41). Similar tests have been proposed by Simmins (42) and Shipley (43), but these have not been satisfactory in cross-validation studies. These tests in their existing forms are clearly inadequate, but they did suggest leads for further investigation, particularly the tests of learning and concept formation. The assumption that vocabulary is sustained seems to be in part an artifact of the relative laxness of scoring standards. In other words, many schizophrenics show deficit on vocabulary tests if abstractness and precision are emphasized in scoring (*e.g.*, 44, 45).

There have been two major defects in these studies of differential deficit. First, it is abundantly clear that chronological age, sex, education, and intelligence quotient have not been controlled, nor have other variables, such as socio-economic level and subculture. Second, tests have been short, inadequately standardized, and they lack scale homogeneity. Discrepancy scores can be informative only if the separate scales are homogeneous and reliable. All scales used in any differential deficit approach must be pure scales, *i.e.*, have high internal consistency, and should be uncorrelated with the other tests involved. The requirements of high scale purity and reliability have simply not been met in work to date. Additional requirements are that populations sampled and the sampling procedures employed be rational in terms of the objectives of the research.

Although the Stanford-Binet age-scale type of test is not logically appropriate for investigation of differential deficit, groupings of items on the basis of clinical experience may provide clues as to the directions that should be taken in developing instruments that could demonstrate differential deficit. In such an effort, Roe and Shakow grouped the test items into four categories: "(1) conceptual thinking; (2) immediate learning; (3) sustained associative thinking, immediate associative thinking, vocabulary; (4) old learning" (33, p. 467). Performance on old learning and vocabulary items seemed more resistant to disruption than any of the former. The dementia praecox groups were especially deficient on conceptual thinking items and in addition were characterized by greater variability than the normal group. Kendig and Richmond (32) made the same kind of analysis with essentially the same results. But, again, defects on old learning and vocabulary tests might become apparent if the tests were scored in ways that could show the defects of schizophrenics.

Shakow (20) has reported a careful study of deficits among schizophrenics. The work is a 15-year follow-up study. Schizophrenic patients score higher on vocabulary than on other intelligence-test items. Normals do not show this discrepancy. Part of this discrepancy can, however, be attributed to chronological age of the schizophrenics and part to their lower mental age, because there is a correlation between lower mental age and the occurrence of this discrepancy. Shakow shows that it is the vocabulary level of the hebephrenic subgroup which is lower than could be expected on the basis of educational level of the group. Even taking into account the current research on inadequacy of scoring of the vocabulary test, the study seems to suggest intellectual deficit associated with hebephrenia. But the extent of hebephrenic linked deficits would be exaggerated if age, ability level, and extent of cooperation of the patients were not taken into account. It would be of interest to know what the discrepancies among scoring standards are for subtypes of patients; *e.g.*, it seems likely that hebephrenics would show a differentially greater discrepancy on stringent rather than on lax scoring standards.

There are a very large number of studies (39, 46, 47) attempting to use the Wechsler tests as the instrument in differential diagnosis. These studies proceeded from the proposals of Wechsler (39) and Rapaport (18) that schizophrenics show characteristic deficits on certain subscales of the Wechsler tests. These tests were developed as measures of a general factor (39), a fact that reduces the likelihood of effective use in demonstrating unequal loss of various abilities. The subscales have only moderate reliabilities, are correlated with each other, and are not pure tests (48, 49). Thus, the many studies reporting negative or borderline results on differential deficit are not surprising. Several reviews of this literature are available, *e.g.*, Rabin and Guertin (50) and Schofield (51).

Of investigations using the Wechsler tests in differential diagnosis which are relevant to the study of differential deficit, those of Harper (38, 52) are most sophisticated. He employed a statistical technique known as the discriminate function, which achieves an optimum weighting of several tests in prediction of a categorical criterion. Harper's samples were of minimum size though much larger than those typically employed. There were 245 patients and 237 normals matched on age and Full Scale I.Q. The multiple correlation between the 10 Wechsler-Bellevue Intelligence Scale, Form I subscales, and diagnosis (schizophrenic vs. normal) was .44, which would occur less than 1 in 100 times by chance. The differentiation of the groups is thus clearly an improvement on chance, but the power of the discrimination is poor as only 67 per cent of schizophrenics would be correctly diagnosed by this method and a proportion of normals would be misclassified as schizophrenic. The Digit Symbol, Information, Block Design, and Picture Completion Tests contribute most in this discrimination between schizophrenics and normals. The schizophrenics are poorer on Digit Symbol and Picture Completion and are above normals on both Information and Block Design. Almost 37 per cent of the patients in this study are paranoid schizophrenics, and since Harper has demonstrated that this subgroup has W-B I subscale characteristics different from the nonparanoids, any effort to discuss in detail deviations typical of the total group of schizophrenics would be almost entirely speculative.

Harper (38) found some evidence suggesting that paranoids tend to be strong on Picture Arrangement, Object Assembly, Performance I.Q., and Full Scale I.Q.; that hebephrenics tend to be weak on Comprehension, Similarities, Performance I.Q., Verbal I.Q., and Full Scale I.Q.; and that catatonics tend to be low on Performance I.Q. and Full Scale I.Q. Should such trends be clarified and confirmed, there would then be a basis for the proposition that subgroups of schizophrenics have differing patterns of differential deficit.

In the studies discussed, Harper proceeded by matching groups on the basis of age and Full Scale I.Q. Certainly, this is far better than failing to achieve any control with respect to such variables. The point to be made is that Harper's practice is minimal in studies of the nature of relationships between the schizophrenics and intellectual functioning. More elaborate procedures may well be necessary. For example, Garfield (53) has shown that 21 of 31 patients in the above 120 Full Scale I.Q. group have higher verbal than performance scores. The reverse is true for 23 of 33 patients in the below 90 Full Scale I.Q. group. This is only one of several such differences. Garfield suggests in studying intelligence and schizophrenia that at least three age, three Full Scale I.Q. and three education-level groupings be used; this would be in addition to some discrimination among varieties of schizophrenia.

The problem of differential deficit has been studied within the group-factor intelligence theory (54, 55) by Binder (56). Surveying the literature, Binder reached the conclusion that the differential-deficit hypothesis had not been subjected to adequate test. He selected for study the very prevalent hypothesis that schizophrenics are deficient in those tests requiring ability to abstract as contrasted with those which require reproduction of learned material. Using well-matched samples of schizophrenics and controls, divided into those 40 years old and over and those younger, neither group differing on average age or education, he found by administering a Thurstone test that the younger schizophrenics are inferior to their control group when each of five group-factor tests was considered separately (verbal meaning, space, reasoning, number, and word fluency). The same is true of the older groups but not so dramatically.

Two tests that seem to involve abstract thinking were then contrasted with three tests that seem only to require reproduction of previously learned material in a familiar and routine fashion. The schizophrenics studied were not more deficient on abstract thinking tests. Thus, while there is evidence for general deficit among the schizophrenics, there is no evidence in Binder's work of differential deficit of the kind studied. But even in this highly controlled study, in which a group-factor type of test was used, Binder expresses a necessary doubt about his methodology. Specifically, although one may conclude that there is no major differential deficit, there could be an effect of this kind which would not appear in the study because of the restricted range of the test in comparison with the magnitude of the over-all deficit in the schizophrenic group. Also, it is possible that application of the Thurstone type test to subtype samples would yield results supporting a refined differential-deficit hypothesis. A further point is that Binder used multiple-choice type tests which may be somewhat easier for schizophrenics than tests requiring the subject to construct his own answers.

Such research employing the Stanford-Binet and the Wechsler tests justifies further exploration of the differential-deficit problem. When a Thurstone type test was applied in this area, the results suggested that any differential intellectual deficits which may be demonstrated in the schizophrenias will be restricted in magnitude. It seems very plausible that differential deficit will be found only in certain schizophrenics, not as a characteristic of all or even the majority of schizophrenic patients.

Deterioration   Classically, deterioration has meant a progressive irreversible loss of capacity that has an organic basis. While the concept has referents other than the performances required on intelligence tests, these do seem to measure some of the essentials referred to by this venerable term. On the basis of Shakow's evidence that among hebephrenics the average educational level is underestimated by 28 months by average vocabulary level, and that vocabulary level is more stable than other types of intelligence items, the conclusion might be drawn that deterioration at the physiological or structural level may be characteristic of some substantial proportion of hebephrenics. Or does this indicate that these people were carried along in school even though many were already low in intellectual efficiency? It must be noted that Kendig and Richmond find, as do many other investigators, that recovery of intellectual functioning is typical of chronic patients in whom the more dramatic psychotic manifestations subside. Cooperation is definitely predictive of performance on intelligence tests; *e.g.*, Shakow (20) reports correlations of .56 between the Stanford-Binet and cooperation and .61 with the Army Alpha. It is certainly not apparent that lack of cooperation is primarily related to so-called deteriorative processes. Many organic patients seem to strive very diligently despite deterioration, and there is a zero order correlation between cooperation and intelligence-test performance among these patients (57).

Another kind of finding also inspires caution regarding the deterioration hypothesis. Shakow (20) has reported data which show that schizophrenics have special difficulty on an Army Alpha subtest that requires a combination of conceptual thinking and social analysis, but do adequately on other subtests that also require sustained attention and conceptual thinking. It seems possible that it is material suggesting interpersonal experience that disrupts intelligence test performances of these patients. Because schizophrenics showed no deficit on this test if given as much time as they needed

(Senf, Huston, and Cohen [58]), it seems at least as likely that schizophrenics are inefficient as that they are deteriorated in an organic sense.

Still other evidence which must be considered is exemplified in a study by Mainord (59), who found that there was an average increase of about 10 I.Q. points when the Wechsler-Bellevue Verbal Scale was given under amytal. Subsequent administration without amytal produced results back at the lower level of the first administration. Hence, the increase with amytal was not due to practice effects. Other investigators have also found schizophrenics improving intellectual performance with amytal (60). Senf, Huston, and Cohen (58) find that amytal gives improvement if the deficit is linked to lowered verbal responsiveness or the effects of social content, but interferes with giving or selecting a very precise answer.

Current utility of the vague clinical concept "intellectual deterioration" seems small indeed. That individual patients show deficits in the area of intellectual functioning is certain both from clinical observation and from psychometric research. One must conclude that this topic is in an infant stage of conceptualization and investigation. The term "deterioration" is in fact still only a statement of a research problem that will be elucidated as particular aspects of intellectual deficit are conceptualized and traced so that antecedent factors may be identified. Although retrospective studies of intellectual functioning can be done, it would seem that only longitudinal study will yield definitive data. Unexpected results may emerge from such work. This is illustrated by Fitzherbert's finding of an increase in intellectual level at the onset of schizophrenia in three adolescent cases which were studied longitudinally (61).

PSYCHOMOTOR FUNCTIONING

Studies of voluntary actions indicate that it is desirable to make a distinction between gross and fine psychomotor abilities (62–64). Gross ability refers to actions wherein a premium is placed on strength, as in labor or athletic performances. Fine ability refers to actions with priority on speed and precision, as in typing and assembly of small objects. Fine psychomotor performances of pathological groups have been studied much more than gross tasks.

Reaction Time   Among the aspects of fine psychomotor performances, the most thoroughly investigated is reaction time.* It is perhaps fortuitous that reaction-time measures cluster together to form one, basic, personal

* More extensive discussions and bibliography have already been published (17, 62).

tempo factor (65), but it is interesting that the results are consistent from study to study to a greater extent than in most areas of research on schizophrenia.

Simple reaction time is quite clearly slower and more variable among schizophrenics than among normals (62). The deficit is more pronounced if the reaction-time procedure is made more demanding of continuous attention and effort. Rodnick and Shakow (66) developed a procedure on which scores of a group of schizophrenics did not overlap with those of a group of controls even though the latter were of low intelligence and little motivated. It was found that normal subjects have slower reaction times when responding after longer preparatory intervals and under irregular procedure and that many schizophrenics show these same effects in an exaggerated form. When preparatory intervals are long, some schizophrenics take longer to respond to the same preparatory interval under regular as compared with irregular presentation. Not only did this finding permit the development of an index of schizophrenic performance but it also shows the difficulty that many schizophrenics have in maintaining a set under conditions that are apt to allow distraction or avoidance.

Given the task of beginning at will and executing a simple response as quickly as possible, schizophrenics are again slow (67). Thus, whether the preparatory signal is external or internal, reaction-time deficit is demonstrated. Patients who are rated as more cooperative in the experimental situation and those more recently hospitalized tend to perform more like normals (68, 69). Though the matter has not been adequately investigated, organic patients seem to show less intraindividual variability than do schizophrenics (70, 71).

Not only is reaction time slow and variable, but nonparanoid schizophrenics, at least, show what has been called a "paradoxical" slower reaction time rather than a faster reaction with more intense stimuli. Venables and Tizard (72) show that this paradoxical effect disappears if the patients are studied in a second experimental session. These investigators favor the explanation that familiarization reduces the state of emotional excitation assumed for such subjects in an initial session. In other situations, such as rote learning, schizophrenics have been observed to improve with simple, repeated exposure to the task, but sometimes they perform less adequately if the repetitions are extended. The extent of the improvement with simple repetition seems to be related to degree of chronicity, the less chronic patients improving more with practice. These vagaries of performance do not seem to be typical of organic patients, but adequate comparison studies are lacking. Researches designed to vary affective arousal should help to clarify the factors involved in performances of schizophrenic patients.

Rosenbaum, Mackavey, and Grisell (73, 74) present evidence that defective reaction-time performance can be modified by manipulation of social motivation and electric shock motivation. Many patients reacted as quickly and as consistently under social or shock motivation as did normals, showing that they had the capacity to perform. More disorganized patients and older patients were least affected and were not approaching the normal level even with electric shock. Rather disorganized patients on closed wards were least improved by increased social motivation. Regularly presented shock generally increased performance but was least effective with older patients. Whereas shock tended to be associated with improved performance, unpredictable shock resulted in disorganization of a group of young, cooperative patients who were equal to normals under other conditions. An implication is that, because effects of different motivating conditions are not uniform with all groups of schizophrenics, there are etiological differences. Rosenbaum *et al.* discuss shock as a biological motivation as distinguished from social motivation. An alternative contrast is that of social motivation as reward and shock as punishment. The special importance of punishment will become apparent below.

The research design involving variations in motivating conditions, instructions, and set has not been sufficiently employed. Interactions of such factors with kind or degree of schizophrenia needs clarification.

Speed of Tapping   A large-scale study of typical mental-hospital patients has been reported by Shakow and Huston (75). As with reaction time, speed of tapping is slow and variable. King and Clausen (76, 77) report slowed tapping rates in both schizophrenic and pseudoneurotic schizophrenic patients, a finding in contrast to that of many other investigators who report relatively normal functioning among pseudoneurotic or atypical schizophrenics. Since there is no appreciable relationship between the personal tempo factor on which reaction times have heaviest loadings and the factor on which tapping speeds have heaviest loadings (65), it is plausible that there is a difference in reaction time but no difference in tapping speed between typical and atypical schizophrenic groups. This difference seems to focus on the problem of maintaining set in the absence of continuing action as distinct from maintaining action. It seems plausible that increased motivation would result in a differential increase in speed of tapping by the pseudoneurotic schizophrenics.

The above studies were of maximum speed of tapping. An alternative procedure is to instruct the subject to establish the rate of tapping which is most comfortable for him. Meyerson and Landau (78) found slow rates of tapping under these instructions. Schizophrenics are also slow in beginning to follow a rhythmic pattern and in doing so reduce the number of taps (67).

Dexterity, Precision, and Steadiness of Movements   Given the task of holding a horizontal stylus in a small hole without touching the sides, schizophrenics were slightly less successful than a normal control group (79). However, cooperative patients did as well as normals, permitting the investigators, Huston and Shakow, to argue that schizophrenia, *per se*, does not create a loss in fine neuromuscular coordination. Studying performances of schizophrenic and pseudoneurotic groups, King and Clausen (76, 77) report greater loss in simple dexterity tasks among the more disturbed group. Analogous results were obtained in eye-hand coordination, the subject being required to maintain stylus contact with a moving target (80, 81).

King (62) has made an unusually comprehensive study of fine psychomotor abilities in psychopathology, employing groups of normal controls, chronic schizophrenics, pseudoneurotic schizophrenics, and neurotics. Reaction time, speed of tapping, and finger dexterity were selected as representative tasks. Neurotics differ very little from normals, if at all; pseudoneurotic schizophrenics differ somewhat more; but the chronic schizophrenics are inferior to all other groups. King argues that the data require a conclusion that psychomotor capacity is reduced in schizophrenia, rejecting a motivational hypothesis on the grounds that learning curves of the several groups seem very similar and that performances on the more complex tasks are possibly less disturbed than on the simple tasks. In regard to the latter point, the assumption is that a motivational deficit would be reflected more in the more complex tasks.

Using the same procedures as King, but omitting tapping speed, Stotsky (82) introduced a manipulation of motivation. Groups studied were normals, remitted schizophrenics, and regressed schizophrenics. Remitted patients approximated normals, but the regressed patients were impaired on all tasks. After initial training and test periods, positive reinforcement in the form of praise was introduced. Whereas remitted schizophrenics had improved most, simply with repetition of the task, both patient groups showed relatively large improvements on reaction time under the reinforcement condition. However, on a more complex task with reinforcement, normals improved the most. In order to explain the greater improvement of patients on the simpler but not on the more complex task, Stotsky proposes that a multiple factor theory is necessary, *e.g.*, motivational deficiency and constitutional maladaptation. There is the alternative that reinforcement strengthens relevant responses on the simple task for all groups but more irrelevant responses on the complex task for patient groups. This assumes that normals were making fewer irrelevant responses in the complex tasks, which seems plausible.

Psychomotor Instability   Though speed and vigor in psychomotor reaction are often appropriate, stability or quiescence in many situations seems adaptive. Following Luria (83), finger tremor has been widely employed as a measure in studies of conflict and stress. Patients' reactions during stress were studied in this way by Malmo and his associates (84). An acute psychotic group was made up primarily of schizophrenics, and there were groups of chronic schizophrenics and anxiety neurotics. All patient groups were less stable than the normal control group; but over a series of stress tests, it was the chronic schizophrenics who were consistently poor. It is possible to conclude that the chronic schizophrenics sustain high anxiety and hence continue to give the maladaptive response.

Studies cited are representative of the work which has been done in assessing adequacy of psychomotor performances among schizophrenics, but this does not constitute an exhaustive survey. More complex performances have been studied. For example, Wulfeck (85) has required sequential, integrative patterns of movements, such as star tracing and following rhythmic patterns. Schizophrenics were less adequate than manic-depressive, psychoneurotic, and normal groups. Similarly, mirror tracing is done less successfully by deviant groups, including schizophrenics, as reported by Peters (86). Bender-Gestalt test performance is deficient (*e.g.*, 87, 88). Typically, studies sample only a very few pathological groups, assess a very few aspects of psychomotor functioning, do not relate psychomotor functioning to other aspects of behavior, and employ diagnostic procedures that are impressionistic.

There is some evidence to support the view that psychomotor efficiency is related to clinical status and increases with improvement (89, 90). Among typical schizophrenics, impairment is marked but can be reduced under special motivational conditions. There is, however, a residual deficit even under these conditions. What would be the outcome if training were continued over an extended period of time? Huston and Shakow (91) show that schizophrenics learn to perform at a level which normals surpass only with considerable practice and effort. Atypical schizophrenics are slightly deficient compared with normals, they improve simply with practice under generally encouraging conditions, and the performance level can usually be modified to the extent that there is no statistically significant difference from a matched normal group. Special motivating conditions seem to affect the schizophrenic groups differently. We are left with the tentative conclusion that deficits are reversible in atypical schizophrenia, but among chronic patients psychomotor deficits, while modifiable, do not yield entirely to motivating techniques investigated. In the one relevant study, even typical schizophrenics achieve a high level of proficiency after extended practice (91).

PERCEPTION

Perception is a topic which presents many difficulties of discourse. It is possible to maintain coherence within the rules of operationalism in connection with this subject (92), though this has not certainly been achieved in all aspects of the following discussion. In a general way, perceptual research is concerned with factors in the organization of sensory input, and a major complication is that clear distinctions between the "perception system" and the "response system" are difficult to achieve.

Primitive Processes   Arguing from the position that there is compelling evidence of metabolic disturbances in schizophrenia, Wertheimer (93) predicted that "satiability" would be less among patients than among normals. Essentially, Wertheimer adopts the proposal of Kohler and Wallach (94) that a polarization occurs in brain tissue activated during perception. One evidence of this polarization is figural after-effect—the effect of relatively prolonged attention to a first stimulus on the perception of a second stimulus (*i.e.*, when a first stimulus has been perceived, the perception of a second stimulus is distorted or modified, and this distortion is called figural after-effect).

When visual stimuli were used, the figural after-effect measure (amount of distortion of dot patterns) was found to have a reliability of .82 over a period of one month. Normal male subjects showed more satiation than did the schizophrenics, who when given longer exposure time became as satiated as did the normals on the initial test. Wertheimer has extended this line of investigation (95), showing that schizophrenics manifest (a) a smaller kinesthetic figural after-effect, (b) less increase in figure reversal rate from a first test period to a second, (c) less discoordination when there is experimental disruption of visual and kinesthetic images of the hand, and (d) less rapid decay of figural after-effect and discoordination. The question would now appear to be: What are the antecedents of these functional characteristics? In particular, what relationship exists between anxiety and these effects? And can the deviation be modified by chemotherapies?

Figure reversal refers to the shift that seems to occur in certain line drawings (*e.g.*, of a cube) as one continues to look at them. These shifts or reversals continue as the subject fixates on the figure, and reversal rate is simply the number of such shifts occurring during any convenient unit of time. Investigation of disturbed figure reversal in psychosis seems to have developed out of early work in which it was believed that reversal rate of extroverts would be less than that of introverts. Manic-depressives and dementia praecox patients were taken as extreme examples. The whole issue is now in doubt on the basis of experimental results, except that many psychotics manifest a slower reversal rate than normals. Working with manic-depressives, schizophrenics, and normals, Philip (96) finds evidence that reversals on certain stimulus figures called Lissajou figures occur at a slower rate and infrequently among psychotics. For example, about 35 per cent of psychotics see no reversals in contrast to 7 per cent of normals.

Autokinetic Phenomenon   If in a darkened room a subject fixates a dim stationary light, the light will usually appear to move to some extent. This is known as the autokinetic phenomenon and is of material interest as there are many organismic and social factors which relate to the amount of movement perceived. Voth (97) seems to have been the pioneer in applying this methodology in the study of behavior pathology. Test-retest reliability on a sample of 54 hospital patients was high, the correlation coefficient being .92. Catatonic, hebephrenic, and simple schizophrenic patients reported much movement of the light, but paranoid and unclassified-mixed schizophrenics reported relatively little movement. Among these patients, a moderate amount of perceived movement was a better prognostic sign than either little reported or much reported movement. In psychodynamic terms, it appears that either excessive control of or extreme acquiescence to the illusion is indicative of defective ego function in interaction with the environment. Because kinesthetic sensations, self-instructions, and social factors influence amounts of movement, this seems to be a global index of adaptive adequacy. It is of importance that subtypes of schizophrenics are deviant in different ways and in line with clinical expectations.

Confirmation that chronic, nonparanoid schizophrenics report high amounts of movement and constant movement is provided by Hahn (98). Among his subjects a success experience decreased, and failure increased, perceived movement. If perception of moderate amounts of movement is characteristic of individuals with favorable prognosis, then in terms of this measure, success is therapeutic.

Schizophrenic pathology is related to amount of autokinetic movement, and autokinetic movement is sensitive to interpersonal relatedness. This sets the context for the study by Diamond (99) of matched groups of male schizophrenics and a control group of nonschizophrenic drug addicts. Matching variables were age, education, intelligence, race, and socio-economic background. At issue was the hypothesis that in this experimental situation pairs of schizophrenics would not make their estimates of perceived movement as congruent as would pairs of control subjects. The results support this prediction. In line with the interpretations of Sherif (100) and others, these results support the conclusion that schizophrenics are deficient in adopting social norms. If substantiated with larger, more representative groups of subjects, these deficiencies lend support to social-learning concepts as a necessary component of an explanation of schizophrenia, unless it is shown that organic conditions alone produce such effects. Further, this seemingly artificial situation might yield an estimate of social withdrawal which would be relatively free of such extraneous influences as personality of ward personnel.

Constancy   The same object, seen in different contexts and at different distances, tends to be experienced as very similar in size, color, and shape even though the momentary stimulus input does not justify the perception. Thus, a person is experienced as person size and shape even though he is far off and at an angle producing a retinal image very different from that of the person standing near and directly in front of the viewer. This phenomenon is known as perceptual constancy. It can be destroyed in all of us under special and unfamiliar conditions (101). The progressive development of constancies has been studied somewhat over a range of ages in childhood (102); size, form, and brightness, if not all constancies, improve progressively from age 2 to 10, when constancy is quite adequate under relatively familiar and simple conditions. Since constancy is a developmental achievement of the organism, and since schizophrenics report many bizarre perceptions, deficiency of constancy would not be surprising.

Raush (103) reasoned that the perceptions of most schizophrenics would be characterized by less size constancy than those of normals, that they would perceive more in terms of retinal-image size than do normals. Paranoid schizophrenics, however, should be the exception and should, in compensation for threats to ego stability, show overconstancy, *e.g.*, see the farther of two identical objects as larger. His results lend support to his hypotheses.

In a subsequent study, Lovinger (104) studied three groups: good-contact schizophrenics, poor-contact schizophrenics, and nonpsychiatric hospital patients. Placement on open vs. closed ward was the basis for judging contact, though raters were also employed to confirm degree of contact. Size constancy was determined under three conditions: maximized distance cues, minimized distance cues, and no distance cues. All groups were very similar under conditions of maximum or absent cues. But, when minimal cues were offered, poor-contact schizophrenics achieved less constancy than the good-contact and control groups, which did not differ significantly from each other.

In possible disagreement with Raush, Lovinger failed to find a difference between paranoids and nonparanoids. This discrepancy might, however, be due to differing degrees of heterogeneity of the paranoid groups with respect to some other variable. For example, employing a maturity level concept, my colleagues and I have the impression that many paranoid schizophrenics are in good contact and are rated as relatively mature on the basis of Rorschach performance, but other patients carrying the paranoid diagnosis are lower on Rorschach maturity level and seem less in contact clinically. If Raush's paranoid group was made up of good-contact patients, the apparent discrepancy between his study and that of Lovinger is of no necessary consequence, provided there is a difference on the constancy measure between Lovinger's good-contact and poor-contact paranoids. These two relatively adequate studies illustrate the general fact that research samples must be described more adequately in terms of specific, objective measures which are mostly yet to be developed. Otherwise, research studies cannot be compared and contrasted with assurance and work is not additive. In particular, while conventional nosological subtype diagnosis is still mandatory, it is not sufficient as the description of patients in studies.

Earlier, Sanders and Pacht (105) reported a comparison of neurotics and schizophrenics who were patients at a V.A. mental hygiene clinic and a college student group. Normals tended toward slight departure from constancy in the direction of retinal-image size, neurotics maintained constancy most accurately, and psychotics departed from constancy in the over-constancy direction. This suggests that psychotics who are still making an adaptation must do so by excessive control.

A variation on simple constancy procedure introduces the element of object value or symbolic implications. Raush (106) had the same subjects as above select the one of a series of circles which most closely approximated an average overcoat button, an average scoop of ice cream, and the cross section of an average cigar. According to psychoanalytic theory, the button would have little symbolic significance or value, the ice cream and cigar much. Furthermore, affectively significant stimuli tend to be enhanced in size more than neutral stimuli. Operation of subjective factors was possibly enhanced as there is no exact, agreed size of such objects. Schizophrenics gave disproportionately larger estimates for the ice cream and cigar. These results were confirmed with a second group of patients and a nonprofessional control group. Added comparison objects were a seemingly neutral spool of thread and a presumably affectively significant milk bottle cap. The latter yielded the greatest difference between normals and patients. Pursuing the hypothesis that paranoid schizophrenics would attribute unusual stability to a class of objects, Raush also called for selection of those circles that would represent the smallest and largest buttons, scoops, and cigars as a way of measuring the range of ambiguity tolerated. Paranoids gave a relatively narrow range compared with controls and nonparanoids, these latter groups not differing on this measure.

A further step has been taken by Weckowicz (107), who has related size constancy to the response to mecholyl. This work was based on the hypothesis that schizophrenia involves disturbed functioning of the hypothalamus and reticular formation, and on the evidence of Callaway and Thompson (108) that size constancy breaks down during sympathetic-nervous-system discharge. After showing that retest reliabilities of the size constancy measures used were .64 and .89, it was found that schizophrenic patients whose blood pressure rises (following the initial reduction) after mecholyl injection had better constancy than the remaining subjects. Weckowicz interprets this response to mecholyl as indicating the effective functioning of "a homeostatic reaction of the higher hypothalamic sympathetic center" (107, p. 69). Size constancy was reduced among the chronic schizophrenics.

Constancy is an achievement which introduces a degree of stability into the perceived environment. Some paranoid schizophrenics manifest overconstancy, which may, as Weckowicz suggests, indicate increased awareness of and sensitivity to events in the external environment. In any case, overconstancy is a perversion of the basic processes and suggests a variation in etiology in contrast with failure to achieve or sustain constancy.

These explorations appear to be a fruitful line of investigation, and it would appear that research on physiological and motivational manipulations of constancy should be emphasized. There is no commanding general theory of constancy; hence, the implications of the findings are in some doubt. Yet, attainment of constancy would seem to depend in part on opportunity for exploration of and communication about perceptions. Conditions that promote adequate ego development seem basic in permitting achievement and maintenance of constancy.

Rorschach Technique   These inkblots are nonsense stimuli with various association values, and the vast majority of people who view them report having impressions of representations of real or fantasy objects. Hence, the assumption that the Rorschach technique permits inferences regarding perceptual processes. Serious clinical use of the Rorschach seems to involve the assumption that it is the adaptive processes as these function in the most vital life situations which are reflected in the Rorschach performance. If one assumes that some form of primitivization (*e.g.*, regression or social disarticulation) is characteristic of adaptations which are called schizophrenic, Rorschach performance becomes a measure of degree of primitivization. A cogent way to define levels of primitivization is in terms of children's Rorschach norms (109).

An empirical proposition which follows from the above view is that Rorschach age level of schizophrenics will be less than that of normals. And more severely schizophrenic patients will have lower age-level scores than will patients who are less disorganized and more in contact with the external environment. Friedman (110) selected aspects of Rorschach responses such as vague concepts, concepts which do not fit the blot, and bizarre concepts and predicted that schizophrenics would show these characteristics, as would children, in contrast to normal adults. His data confirm that the formal or structural organization of Rorschach responses of schizophrenics are like those of young children. Siegel (111) used Friedman's scoring system and showed that a more severe group of catatonic and hebephrenic patients was similar to children of ages three to five, but a group of paranoid schizophrenics was more similar to children of ages six to ten. These results are congruent with the hypothesis that regressive adaptation or arrest of ego development is a central aspect of the schizophrenias.

Confirmation of this work seems to be furnished by Becker (112). Rather than use the subtype specification of the schizophrenics, he scored each patient on a modification of the Elgin Prognosis Scale (113). It is reasonable to assume that there is a degree of agreement between this scale and the traditional subtypes, the scale having some advantages of objectivity and possibly of comprehensiveness. Becker elaborated Friedman's Rorschach scoring system and demonstrated a substantial correlation of it with the Elgin Prognosis Scale. These very similar results lend weight to the conclusion that whereas an undifferentiated total group of schizophrenics show a deficit in Rorschach performance, there is variation in extent of perceptual primitivization among these patients. Becker's results suggest in particular that the degree of perceptual regression is related to degree of clinical severity, to premorbid adjustment, or to both, as the Elgin Prognosis Scale reflects information about these areas.

In an earlier study, Kantor, Wallner, and Winder (114) had formulated a preliminary scheme for differentiation of reactive schizophrenics and process schizophrenics. Reactive cases were characterized by good premorbid adjustment, sudden onset, and adequate precipitating events. Process cases were those with poor premorbid adjustment, gradual onset, and absence of adequate precipitating factors. There was a significant relationship between psychotic Rorschach performance and process ratings, the reactive cases giving less deviant Rorschach responses. All of these cases had been diagnosed as schizophrenic on the basis of psychiatric examination. These results suggested a relationship between premorbid adjustment and type of schizophrenic breakdown. Using the same subjects, Brackbill and Fine (115) found that the process group gave a number of organic signs not significantly different from a group of organic patients. Reactive cases gave significantly fewer organic signs. Though the implications could be variously interpreted, Kantor and Winder (116) propose the speculative hypothesis that very early, sustained pathological life circumstances may result in developmental anomalies which eventuate in organic conditions.

Kantor and Winder (116) have developed an age-level scoring system by assembling children's Rorschach norms for each of Sullivan's (117) developmental epochs. For each patient, all of whom were veterans who had become overtly schizophrenic after making an acceptable adjustment as adults, the degree of primitivization or regression when schizophrenia was measured by the Rorschach age-level score. Each patient was also rated from life-history information obtained from relatives as to the earliest developmental epoch during which as a child the patient had experienced a life situation that would be considered pathogenic according to general mental health concepts. There is a substantial correlation between the Rorschach age-level score and the ratings from the case histories. This line of investigation should now be focused by studying the relationships of more accurately defined premorbid adjustment factors and specific Rorschach factors. (An example of needed refinement of the Rorschach is Barron's work on threshold for the perception of human movement in inkblots [118].)

Because it might be tempting to conclude that schizophrenics are deficient in all aspects of perception, mention is made here of a study by Cohen, Senf, and Huston (119). Schizophrenics whose Rorschach records were deficient in terms of form level, with chronic patients more deviant than early cases, did not show a deficit on a test requiring identification of right and left hands pictured in various orientations. There were other tests involved; and, with sodium amytal, patients tended to improve any deficiencies in performances.

Taken as a group, these studies support the general hypothesis that although perceptual processes of schizophrenics are often disturbed, there are significant differences in degree of disturbance, that degree of disturbance is related to premorbid factors and adjustment, and that the deficits are reversible. Further, the regression hypothesis seems to gain credence, though a hypothesis emphasizing deficiencies in ego development might be more encompassing.

Symbolism   Because symbols have an illusive, personal quality, objective study in this area often seems distinctly tangential to the clinician and hopelessly obscure to the experimentalist. Yet, in any given culture, participation in ceremonies, social activities, and direct personal relationships must involve appreciation for communications in terms of symbols. One procedure employed in exploring this area involves the matching of abstract figures with personal names. If elongated and pointed figures are matched with male names and rounded or containing figures with female names, sexual symbolism is said to be demonstrated. In studies by Starer (120) and Jones (121), there were associations of figures and names as predicted. Normals assessed the figures more "accurately" than the patients, most of whom were schizophrenics. This could be interpreted as evidence of inadequate social learning, or a deficit in abstract thinking could be emphasized as the basis of the performance. Starer makes the comment that greater clinical severity of psychosis is correlated with less success in this symbolism test. Together with Raush's results, discussed above, there is support for certain aspects of Freudian symbolism theory, for social disarticulation, and for views which emphasize failure of learning the tools which permit social participation as one factor in the etiology of schizophrenia.

Stimulus Content   Much of the work on disturbed perceptual and cognitive processes in the schizophrenias has focused on deficit without regard to stimulus content, or on deficit in terms of the so-called formal aspects of the responses made. Psychodynamic theories and learning theories tend to focus interest on the stimulus content. It is the personal significance or affectivity which presumably operates to cause deviations in interpretations of and reactions to the stimulus. Many hunches regarding the care and treatment of particular cases are gained from this type of analysis of tests, projective techniques, and clinical interactions. But systematic investigation proceeds slowly.

Rodnick and Garmezy (122) and their students have done a series of studies based on the hypothesis that there is "a functional relationship between social censure (on the stimulus side) and behavior deficit (on the response side)" in the schizophrenias. In other words, any representation of social censure produces deficit. Interaction themes other than social censure have been included by these investigators, but this is the crucial one. In assessing the hypothesis that picture content is a cause of behavior deficit,

Dunn (123) required that the subject judge whether or not a second picture is identical to a first. Some of the second pictures were identical but five other sets of pictures were progressively more dissimilar. Sets presented were pictures of scolding, whipping, feeding, and neutral scenes. Schizophrenics had difficulty discriminating pictures of the scolding scene, tended to have difficulty with the whipping scene, and did not differ from a control group of nonpsychiatric hospital patients on the feeding and neutral scenes. A subsequent analysis of the results revealed that the deviation was produced by schizophrenics with poor premorbid adjustments as measured by the Phillips scale (124).

There is a body of evidence indicating that distortion of object size is greater if an object has value or affective significance to the subject than if it is a neutral object.

With this in mind, Harris (125) presented pictures suggesting maternal domination, rejection, and overprotection in order to reflect problems thought to be important in the mother-child relationships of schizophrenics. Schizophrenics had difficulty making consistent size judgments for the significant pictures as compared with neutral pictures. Good premorbid adjustment patients tended to underestimate the sizes of the pictures, compared with the control group, but only the deviation on the dominance picture was statistically significant. Poor premorbids tended to overestimate sizes and deviated significantly from the control group on the ignoring and overprotection pictures. The good and poor premorbid groups differed from each other on dominance, acceptance, ignoring, and overprotection pictures with the normal group intermediate. This is one of the more striking demonstrations of lack of homogeneity among the schizophrenias. The poor premorbid groups tended to attribute a greater amount of rejection to their mothers when asked to answer questions on parent-child practices and attitudes of their mothers. The overreaction of the poor premorbid group to the ignoring and overprotection pictures in contrast to the sensitivity of the good premorbid group to the dominance picture could be interpreted in terms of passivity and activity. One interpretation would be that the poor premorbid group had experienced pathogenic relationships at an earlier age than did the good premorbid group. Rodnick and Garmezy (122) suggest that the poor premorbid group had dominating, restrictive, and powerful mothers and indifferent or ineffectual fathers, whereas these father and mother roles are the opposite in the good premorbid group. In any case, these studies support the proposition that stimuli depicting domination, rejection, ignoring, and overprotection do in fact lead to deviant responses. These are just the themes, of course, that clinical literature suggests would be crucial.

The Thematic Apperception Test pictures, chiefly of people, can be defined as a set of stimuli designed to tap personal and affective topics. The sample of interpersonal themes is small, but taken as a whole failures to include the commonly used elements of the pictures and failures to produce coherent stories in conformity with instructions constitute maladaptive behavior. A scoring system based on such features of performance has been used to differentiate normal, neurotic, and psychotic groups (126). This differentiation is congruent with the general hypothesis that interpersonal stimuli tend to be associated with deficits among schizophrenics.

The stories may be taken as a sample of interpersonal relationships especially significant for the particular patient and as a way of sampling important motivations. Clinical use has seemed to indicate heterogeneous problems and defenses; schizophrenics tend to give evidence of deviation in almost every conceivable way. But beyond this general confirmation of disturbance, the results have not been very informative.

Time Concepts   Schizophrenics are less notable for inaccuracy in estimating time intervals of a few seconds or minutes or two hours than they are for variability of such time estimates. Dobson (127) found that matched groups of neurotics, normals, oriented schizophrenics, and nonoriented (for time) schizophrenics did not differ in mean accuracy in estimating intervals of a few seconds, but differed in variability of sets of estimates. Neurotics were least and nonoriented schizophrenics were most variable. Greater variability of schizophrenics for long time intervals is confirmed by Rabin (128).

Schizophrenics are deficient in using time concepts, in ordering past events, and in giving a coherent order for anticipated future events (129, 130). Wallace (129) reports a curtailing of future time span. A group of "apathetic, dull, regressed" patients, hospitalized for many years, tended to retain the past as a frame of reference (131). In part, these results suggest the difficulties of conceptualization demonstrated in other areas of functioning. Failure to register events in memory is also suggested and is expected where interest and attention have been minimal. Motivated distortion of events and of the social frame of reference is possibly involved, also. There is little basis, as yet, for any detailed interpretations of disturbances of time concepts because methods and subjects have been heterogeneous.

Self-concept   There are a variety of ways in which personality theories construct the problem, but there is an abiding interest in the subject's assessment of the congruity of what he does in fact and the ideals he holds for himself. Similarly, interest is taken in any discrepancy between the subject's view of his own effectiveness in dealing with problems of living as compared with his view of how others seem to be doing. Paranoid and mixed delusional schizophrenics who had been recently hospitalized, normals, and neurotics were compared by Hillson and Worchel (132). The schizophrenics assessed themselves as favorably as did normals, but anxiety neurotics gave a relatively unfavorable self-report. The ideal self is reported significantly lower in schizophrenics than in normals and neurotics. Self-ideal discrepancy (corrected for level of self-rating) was greater for the neurotics than for the other groups. The patient groups tended to see themselves as less adequate than others in general, whereas the normals indicate that others are not doing so well in adjusting. Thus, the neurotics fall short of their ideal and feel inadequate in meeting life. The schizophrenics seem defensively to distort adequacy of adjustment and lower their ideals, while seeing others as more adequate. Among patients of this kind, self-acceptance seems to be related to defensiveness rather than to adequacy of adjustment. This is a familiar interpretation in the clinical literature. The relatively lower conscious ideal of these schizophrenics, if confirmed, would be of considerable interest within a psychodynamic framework since it suggests a defensive maneuver in addition to those usually postulated among neurotics. This in turn suggests a more severe degree of anxiety. Unfortunately, results from study to study in this relatively new area of investigation are not consistent (e.g., 133).

CONCEPT FORMATION AND PROBLEM SOLVING

Under usual testing conditions, hospitalized schizophrenics as an undifferentiated group are deficient in many aspects of problem solving and concept formation (e.g., 17, 134–137). Yet, despite a rather long history, this research area continues to manifest a plethora of persistently used, inadequately refined tests, and appealing but overly global concepts.

The Abstract-Concrete Hypothesis   Goldstein (e.g., 138) focused and crystallized research work in this area with his formulation of abstract vs. concrete thinking. It may be that his conceptualization will endure, but there do seem to be very important variations in degree and pervasiveness of the abstract attitude. There are at least three major lines of reasoning that require consideration in connection with the abstract-concrete hypothesis. First, if there are two or more major categories of schizophrenics, concrete thinking could characterize only one or only some such categories. Second, because much research by people holding the hypothesis has rested on qualitative assessment of performance, it is unlikely that alternative formulations would have received support. Third, the abstract-concrete formulation can be viewed as misleading, one which would be better transformed into a dimensional conceptualization, *i.e.*, degree or level of abstractness.

An attempt to clarify the matter has involved use of the Goldstein-Gelb-Weigl Object Sorting Test (18, 139), which requires the grouping of a variety of everyday items, together with an explanation of the reasons for the particular solutions. Clinicians who have given this test to normal and psychiatric groups usually seem to find that schizophrenics and organics manifest disturbances of conceptualization. It is, however, difficult to convey successfully the nature of these conceptual deficits to someone who has not administered the test to several typical patients. Goldstein's abstract-concrete dichotomy only approximates an account of the deficits. McGaughran and Moran (140, 141) assume that the test measures two dimensions. The first reflects the extent to which a concept is public rather than private, and the second reflects the extent to which a concept is open or abstract rather than closed or concrete. The scoring system is elaborate and complex in its present form, but these investigators find differences between chronic paranoid schizophrenics and normals in that the patients' concepts lack in publicness, although they show no defect in abstraction ability. The paranoid group also differs from an organic group, the latter using fewer open concepts and being lower on an autism index. It seems possible that by studying paranoid schizophrenics, McGaughran and Moran may have demonstrated their ideas under the most favorable of conditions. Nevertheless, they have taken a step in breaking the stagnation of thinking in terms of the abstract-concrete dichotomy. The tentative conclusion is that schizophrenics deviate because of increased privateness of concepts, whereas organics deviate by using more closed concepts.

Interpretation of proverbs has served as another method for evaluating abstractness of thinking. When Becker (112) devised an explicit and reliable scoring system for this type of material, there was no evidence of a bimodal distribution, but rather the schizophrenics distributed themselves in a fair approximation of a normal curve. Better performances on the proverbs was associated with a better rating on the Elgin Prognosis Scale for the male schizophrenics, but there was a zero order correlation for the women. These results obtain when intelligence has been partialed out statistically. Gorham (142) has developed more extensive proverbs tests and presents no data to suggest that particular patients perform in either an abstract or concrete manner.

Stimulus Content   Another approach in extending understanding of deficits in concept formation hinges on the hypothesis that the essence of schizophrenia is social disarticulation (143). This view suggests the prediction that schizophrenics are more deficient on social concept problems than on formal concept problems. In the latter, the stimulus materials do not suggest interpersonal themes. Whiteman (144) presents evidence on this hypothesis. Tests of formal-concept formation were a verbal analogies test and a test requiring sequential arrangement of pictured objects on the basis of logical-relational concepts such as size. A first result, based on controls and patients matched for age, Wechsler-Bellevue vocabulary, and education, is that the schizophrenics were poorer on these formal-concept tests. This confirms the findings that schizophrenics show thinking deficits in general, and the social disarticulation hypothesis does not necessarily account for this result. The result is congruent, however, in that social disarticulation of any duration could be the basis of lower motivation for achievement, unrealistic concern about consequences of inadequate performance, weakening of discrimination skills in general, or other such factors.

The measure of social-concept formation consisted of sets of pictures, several of each set being examples of a social concept and one or more of each set being extraneous. The cards were to be grouped, and the grouping explained. Scores on this test were corrected for level of performance on each formal-concept test in order to test the proposition that stimulus content contributes to thinking deficit. Normals were definitely superior to the patients, who gave more unique responses, fewer explicitly verbalized concepts, more rejections, and more physicalistic interpretations in which social significances of pictures were ignored (145). This last type of error is of interest in suggesting an avoidance which could easily be misinterpreted as an instance of disinterest in human contacts or a preoccupation with cosmic forces.

Confirmation of the differential difficulty of dealing with stimuli having human content is found in another problem-solving study by Davis and Harrington (146). The patients were described as being in good contact. The task was to select stimulus cards on the basis of successive bits of information. Normals and schizophrenic patients having been matched for performance on the stimulus cards presenting human content, there was no difference between groups when they were tested on stimulus cards depicting nonhuman content. But, the groups having been matched on nonhuman content cards, schizophrenics were inferior when tested on the human content cards. Hypotheses regarding the essential processes of schizophrenias must deal with this fact: unless stimulus complexity or some other formal characteristic can be made the basis for an explanation of the differences found, human content, *per se*, increases the difficulty of concept formation for schizophrenics.

Using Whiteman's tests, Cavanaugh (147) introduced special motivating conditions to determine the effect on concept formation performance. Nonpsychiatric hospital patients were contrasted with schizophrenics, the groups not differing on Wechsler-Bellevue vocabulary, age, education, or vocational level. Control groups of nonpsychiatric and schizophrenic groups were tested under usual testing conditions, and experimental groups took the tests while being subjected to loud "white noise" (an unpleasant auditory stimulus), which was terminated upon successful completion of each item or expiration of the maximum time allowed. Nonpsychiatric groups did not differ, so it would seem that they are strongly motivated under the ordinary testing conditions. Schizophrenics in the usual conditions were inferior to the nonpsychiatric groups, but under the noise condition the schizophrenics were indistinguishable from the nonpsychiatric groups and were superior to the schizophrenics tested under usual conditions. Escape from this aversive stimulus proved to be a condition evoking very adequate performance by many schizophrenics although some did not cooperate. One is inclined to assume that escape from an aversive stimulus would prompt at least minimal participation in simple action and learning procedures on the part of many so-called uncooperative schizophrenics. The technique should be exploited in future research. In any case, the deficiency under rapport conditions did not persist under the escape condition.

Apparently there is no direct research on the possible difference among subtypes of schizophrenics in the amount of deficit consequent upon human content of the stimulus material in concept formation and problem solving. Possibly relevant is a study by Senf, Huston, and Cohen (148), in which comic cartoons were analyzed by early and chronic schizophrenics, depressives, and neurotics. Subjects were asked to describe the picture, identify the speaker, and describe the action, the social roles depicted, the motivations, and what was humorous. Early schizophrenics showed deficits in specifying action and basis for the humor, but chronics were impaired in all aspects of the task except picture description. These results seem to indicate that degree of impairment is related to severity of schizophrenia, specifically for stimuli involving human content in a task which is akin to concept formation.

Rather than group schizophrenics, Flavell (149) approached the problem in terms of dimensional analysis. Normals and patients were matched on education and vocabulary and were compared on an abstractness score derived from a word-meaning test in which alternative multiple-choice answers of eight kinds were offered. As usual, the schizophrenics were deficient. Furthermore, among the schizophrenics the correlation between abstractness score and a ward social behavior rating was .60. This supports the proposition that there are important variations among schizophrenics and the proposal that dimensional concepts are fruitful in the study of schizophrenia.

Concept Implementation   When a subject has attained a concept, he may then apply the concept with greater or less success in dealing with additional materials. In particular, most concepts can be employed in ways narrower than usual or broader than usual. Thus underinclusiveness and overinclusiveness may be thought of as one dimension of consensual validation. Thinking disturbance of schizophrenics has often been discussed in these or essentially similar terms. Cameron (143, 150, 151), in particular, has proposed that schizophrenic disorganization involves these deviations.

Using a 50-item, paper-and-pencil test, Epstein (152) found that schizophrenics, in using concepts, overinclude but do not underinclude. Each item consisted of a key word, such as man, and five response words, such as arms, shoes, hat, toes, head, and the alternative "none." The subject was instructed to select all response words required in designating the complete thing described by the key word. Items were so designed that both overinclusion and underinclusion could occur. In addition to demonstrating overinclusion, the results are interpreted as indicating that overinclusion is correlated with disorganization or "intellectual impairment." A proportion of his schizophrenic subjects performed adequately. Qualitative analysis suggested the appropriateness of the terms "concrete" and "loose associations" in describing the overinclusive thinking. To reverse the speculation, do the widely found instances of concrete thinking and loose associations indicate that it is overinclusivensss which has been observed? If the overinclusiveness in dealing with concepts is viewed as a consequence of looseness of associations, then there is implicit the suggestion that somehow the associative bonds have been weakened. But if overinclusiveness is made primary, then there is implicit the suggestion that the stimulus word evokes a wide range of responses. This suggests a strengthening of remote associations, *i.e.*, a wide range of responses is associated with the stimulus. One explanation could be that schizophrenics have learned many inappropriate associations; another that schizophrenics have not had the experiences which would strengthen the association with the highest probability of relevance; and another that schizophrenics are in a high drive state (possibly because of anxiety) and so remote associations are strengthened to the point where they occur often.

Chapman and Taylor (153) reasoned that overinclusiveness would not be random among distraction stimuli, but would be greater with regard to similar rather than dissimilar categories. Thus, when instructed to select all words naming fruits, schizophrenics include some of the cards presenting names of vegetables, but not those naming birds. A trend was found supporting the idea that severe schizophrenia as evidenced by closed ward placement is associated with greater tendency to overinclusiveness. In two related studies, Chapman (154, 155) has provided evidence that schizophrenics show disproportionately more thinking disturbance than normals on increasingly difficult tasks, and more deficit with greater similarity of distraction stimuli to correct alternatives. In all these studies, the errors made by the patients are only more numerous, not different from those made by normals. In fact, one must describe many of the errors made by patients as depending upon conceptual thinking. The point is that schizophrenics perform like inefficient normals. Failure of inhibitory control of associative processes is suggested, as are heightened generalization gradients.

Before leaving the topic of overinclusiveness in thinking, a complication must be noted. Much of the research on schizophrenia, and no doubt much of the clinically inspired thinking, has ignored careful assessment of similarities and differences over the range of psychopathology. Specifically, Payne and Hirst (156) assessed overinclusive thinking of psychotic depressives by means of Epstein's test. Eleven depressives were contrasted with 14 normals matched for age, sex, occupation, education, and vocabulary level. Whereas the normals from this and from Epstein's study (152) had almost exactly the same average score, the depressives showed so much more overinclusion than did Epstein's schizophrenics as to suggest that depressives are more deviant than schizophrenics. Certainly, overinclusiveness seems not to be exclusively the deficit of the latter group. Should this be taken as evidence that overinclusiveness is associated with psychoticism, or that schizophrenics are depressed, or what? The psychoanalytic emphasis on deep regression in both groups is only one instance of earlier suggestions that psychotics have more in common than not.

Threat and Anxiety   On the basis of clinical literature, systematic studies, and psychodynamic theory, one would expect threat of failure to reduce adequacy of performance among schizophrenics. Webb (157) put the proposition to the test by injecting a report of failure between two sessions of testing for conceptual ability. The control group, schizophrenics who did not receive a failure report, improved in the second session (a result of interest in supporting the notion that among some groups of schizophrenics there is substantial improvement simply with further exposure to the task, testing situation, and tester). Performance in the second session of the experimental group was no better than during the first session, indicating that the report of failure set off some disruptive process.

Heath (158), assessing anxiety about parental relationships, sex, and aggression for each subject, was able to show that schizophrenics showed more response disorganization when these anxiety topics or contents were involved than when neutral stimuli were used. Because the areas of greater and lesser anxiety thresholds were assessed for each subject, it was also possible to find evidence that the degree of response disorganization and the level of each anxiety threshold are related. A replication of the study would be welcome, but, for the moment, a specific anxiety type of formulation rather than a general anxiety conceptualization is supported. The specific anxiety formulation represents a refinement of the proposition that schizophrenics are disorganized because of general anxiety, although, in contrast to normals, schizophrenics may have so many areas of high anxiety as to give the impression of uniformly high or general anxiety. Assuming confirmation of these results, high priority should be given to studies of groups with good and poor premorbid adjustment with regard to differential areas of highest anxiety, number of high anxiety areas, and adaptation in dealing with any specific high anxiety content.

Multiple Level Analysis   Given the rather widespread agreement that schizophrenia is probably best conceptualized in terms of several levels of analysis of the organism, psychological variables should be related to variables applicable at other levels. A stimulating example of the approach is given by Meadow and Funkenstein (159). Type of response to mecholyl was related to abstraction scores on various psychological techniques. One is reminded of the demonstration of a relationship between measures of physiological response and perceptual constancy mentioned earlier. Adequacy of premorbid adjustment is related to adequacy of conceptual behavior, which is related to type of physiological response, as is perceptual constancy. Both physiological response and presence of ability to engage in abstract thinking are related to prognosis. Loosely defined clinical concepts are gradually being displaced by more precisely defined variables which relate to the general knowledge in the fields of physiology and psychology. The problem of schizophrenia will probably become understandable only when this approach is greatly expanded.

LEARNING

Although even the most pessimistic points of view regarding prognosis among schizophrenics would not necessarily deny the possibility of learning, they have probably played a role in the apparent lack of interest in intensive study of this area. Though learning studies date from at least 1909 (5), there are still only scattered research reports, which indicate that although schizophrenics do not always perform increasingly well with practice, they do, generally speaking, learn (*e.g.*, 6, 7, 8, 80, 160). Just as typically, the final level of performance is low except with very extended practice and the rate of learning is slow (*e.g.*, 161–163).

Huston and Shakow (*e.g.*, 161, 162) seem to have triggered renewed interest in research on learning among schizophrenics. On a motor-learning task, these investigators showed that schizophrenics are poorer than normals and manic-depressives, but that all groups continue to improve with practice and that many schizophrenics show unexpected improvement as they adapt upon repeated exposures to the task. Additional aspects of their findings will be considered below. The point for the moment is that data were presented showing that learning was occurring, and this interpretation placed emphasis on the possibility that improved learning might be evident if appropriate conditions were arranged.

Correlates of Deficit   One approach to trying to understand deficits is in terms of a relationship to cooperativeness. Wittman (57) found a median correlation of +.75 between cooperativeness ratings and a series of memory and reasoning tests for schizophrenics but a zero order correlation for paretics. Later, Shakow (20) reported a median r of +.56 with tests of motor function, general intelligence, reaction time, and such. In studying learning, Huston and Shakow found lack of cooperation very evident, especially at the beginning of exposure to the task (*e.g.*, 161, 162). Certainly, it is the experience of all who work with schizophrenics clinically and in research that rapport is a critical problem, but one which can often be solved with carefully applied techniques. Perhaps an effort to train directly for cooperation, as has been done in related areas with young children (*e.g.*, 164–166), would permit an assessment of the level of performance possible for the various schizophrenics and would result in better general adaptation. Peters (167, 168) has reported transfer to other activities of the favorable effects of extended training in problem solving.

Subgroup differences in degrees of deficit may become informative. Hall and Crookes (163) report that chronic, impaired patients perform relatively poorly and are like organics in that they adopt stereotyped response patterns. Acute cases perform better and resemble neurotics in showing emotional interference with performance. These differences may, in part, be a function of the Hall and Crookes tasks, which were a relatively difficult paired-associates verbal-learning list and sequence problems done with a panel of three switches. Huston and Shakow (*e.g.*, 161, 162) had previously reported motor-learning deficit among schizophrenics and had found that the conventional subtypes in order of better to poorer learning performance are paranoid, unclassified, hebephrenic, indeterminant, and catatonic (161). Peters (169, 170) adds to the evidence that chronic patients are more deficient in learning ability than are acute patients. Although this association of greater deficit with severity seems established, there is need for extension of the range of learning tasks and learning conditions studied, as well as more explicit designation of severity by means of objective measures. A further problem is suggested in that Huston and Shakow report that adaptation occurs at different rates among the classical subtypes so that the ordering of subtypes in terms of deficiency is somewhat different on later exposures to the same learning task. Analogously, the longer term effects of special motivating conditions should be studied in relation to type of schizophrenia.

Learning deficit is much less apparent—and may be absent—among many schizophrenics if the experimenter establishes good general rapport with the patient. If the experimenter-patient relationship is improved, some evidence supports the proposition that there is marked improvement in output (160, 171). Furthermore, typical organic patients do not show this effect, nor do such organics as paretics show correlations of favorableness of attitude toward the task and output or the great variability of performance sometimes found among schizophrenics (*e.g.*, 57, 160, 171). Learning deficits seem relatively modifiable among many of the schizophrenics.

Additional analyses of the performances of schizophrenics are suggested. For example, Hall and Crookes (163) make some fascinating observations on the adaptations to errors on their sequence learning task. Some schizophrenics seem disposed to adopt a pattern of purposeless movements when a hypothesis is disconfirmed. On the paired-associates learning, many of the errors were "easy" associations to the stimulus word. Both are suggestive of negativistic and defeatist reactions as well as avoidance.

Reward and Punishment   Except for a few early conditioning studies and those studies in which experimenters tried to develop better general rapport, research employing varied motivating conditions in a systematic way has appeared only recently. Garmezy (172) trained normals and relatively acute, cooperative schizophrenics on an auditory discrimination problem, using a reward condition as contrasted with a mild stress-reward-punishment condition. In the reward condition, the correct selection of the second lowest pitched of five tones was rewarded. In the second condition, subjects were instructed to try harder, were rewarded for selection of the second lowest of five tones, and were punished for responding incorrectly to the highest tone. It is worth noting that unusual efforts were made to interest the patients in cooperating. With reward only, the patients were slightly less adequate than the normals. Under the second condition, patients did not discriminate as well, gave fewer responses to the correct alternative, and had a flatter response gradient. Comparing the patients who had two reward sessions with those who had first a reward session and then the mild stress-reward-punishment condition, Garmezy found that the latter group under the second condition showed fewer potentially correct responses to all stimuli and failed to improve the discrimination performance. The normals improved by making more correct responses to the training stimulus and fewer responses to test stimuli. When mild stress and punishment were interjected, the schizophrenics reacted by gradually making fewer efforts to succeed. It is as though the schizophrenic had too little appreciation of the possibility of mastering a problem, or as though frustration tolerance was insufficient to bridge the time required for learning. It is reasonable to think of the reduction in responsiveness as a generalization of avoidance.

Pursuing these differential effects of reward and punishment, Bleke (173) studied normals, schizophrenics with histories of good premorbid adjustment, and schizophrenics with histories of poor premorbid adjustment. Learning a list of nouns was the task. There were no differences in rate of learning, but when the subjects were tested for retention, those poor premorbids who had learned under punishment conditions were superior, showing a positive reminiscence effect. Interpretation of these results can vary in detail, but in some way punishment seems to have resulted in more learning by the usually inferior group. This learning was obscured initially by inhibitory or interference effects. The finding raises the question as to whether or not much faith should be placed in any findings of initial deficits in any complete assessment of the ways in which schizophrenics function.

Buss and his associates (*e.g.*, 174, 175) tend to confirm the superiority of punishment, although the applicability of their work to schizophrenia is not known specifically. The subjects are described only as neuropsychiatric hospital patients who were neither organic or mentally retarded; nevertheless, it is likely that most were schizophrenics. These studies are of interest because the tasks required the learning of concepts as contrasted with simple discrimination or rote learning.

Further evidence is provided by Pascal and Swensen (176), who modified motivation by introducing "white noise" during the learning of a complex discrimination problem. A patient group had been inferior to normals under the initial nondistraction conditions, but both groups had improved in performance. With introduction of the loud noise, both groups improved further, and the schizophrenics were no longer significantly below the normals. Pascal and Swensen suggest that the deficit of the patients was in response to unspecified stress and that the introduction of a strong, specific stressor motivated adaptive behavior. If the noise is interpreted as punishment, these results are congruent with other evidence suggesting that specific punishments are very effective in promoting learning by schizophrenics.

In a related study, hospitalized schizophrenics and normal controls were studied by Cohen (177) with regard to the effects of "rapport" and electric shock as sources of motivation. Learning a sequence of left and right pushes of a lever was required. Schizophrenics were poorer on the initial learning sequence, even though the less cooperative and more disorganized patients were eliminated. Shock did not produce any significant increase in the learning efficiency of the normal groups. There was improvement with shock in the patient group, though borderline statistical significance makes a confirmation study necessary. In learning three different sequences, the last two under either the special rapport or the shock condition, the shocked patient group improved their performance on each successive sequence. The rapport patient group showed some improvement on the second sequence but were less efficient on the third. Cohen suggests that in situations such as this, schizophrenics are not adequately aroused by acquired motivational cues. If the responses of the schizophrenics were simply irrelevant or represented avoidance, the results would be the same.

Effects of verbal reward and verbal punishment on paired-associates learning were assessed by Atkinson (178), who worked with schizophrenic and normal women. In this study, responses were rewarded or punished, failure to respond within a brief time being treated as an error. Normal women tended to learn more quickly under the reward condition—in agreement with general findings on learning. Schizophrenic women clearly learned more efficiently in the punishment condition. The verbal punishment consisted of such comments as, "That's an error," "No," "Wrong," and "That's wrong." Robinson (179) has conducted a similar study employing chronic, male patients as subjects and adding a control group of patients who were neither rewarded nor punished explicitly. All groups showed steady progress in acquisition of the correct associations. The punished patients learned more efficiently than either the control patients or the rewarded patients. A most interesting trend, which requires confirmation by added research, was that more personalized reward may result in less adequate learning than either impersonal reward or control treatment. In other words, personalized reward may tend to disrupt learning as contrasted with all other conditions of this study. The personalized reward was remarks such as "Good," "Right," "Mmm-hmm," and "That's right." Impersonal reward was a machine sound.

Robinson argues that the studies of the parent-child antecedents of schizophrenics indicate that, for these patients, the childhood period was one of sustained trauma resulting in an orientation to avoiding threats, harm, and rejection. Further, the inconsistent, shifting overprotection and rejection by the parents make rewards of specific responses confusing and unreliable guides to adaptive behavior. Consequently, for the schizophrenic, punishment operates with unusual force and reward has little or debilitating effect. These remarks pertain to mild or moderate rewards and punishments as applied to specific responses. Very general, unspecific approval and disapproval operate respectively to facilitate and disorganize performances of schizophrenics. Participation of the schizophrenics in both the Atkinson and the Robinson studies was facilitated by the usual relationship rapport building techniques used in clinical work with schizophrenics.

Peters (169) reports on an effort to control the arousal of motivation with nine chronic schizophrenics. Unfortunately, the control group consisted of seven mild schizophrenics and three anxiety reactions. The chronic patients were first given insulin in amounts which produced a subcoma condition, and then they were given a multiple-choice learning task, earning fudge candy by achieving a correct solution on each trial. Though these patients typically persisted on every trial until they found the correct solution and received the fudge, learning was slow and often progressed only when guidance was provided by the experimenter. Peters had planned to give guidance as he was following the views of N. R. F. Maier on frustration. (In brief, Maier proposes that if a pattern of behavior occurs during severe frustration, the behavior becomes fixated and will be changed only under special conditions such as guidance.) With guidance, chronic schizophrenic subjects would usually make some progress in learning. But, despite guidance, performances were particularly disrupted by distraction. More severely disturbed patients might be described as attempting to utilize too many cues. Again, excessive generalization seems to be the process most likely to be involved.

Conditioning   Investigation of conditioning of schizophrenics has followed a sporadic course, but currently there seems to be a phase of increased interest. Early research yielded inconclusive results (17, 180). More recent studies are at least more adequate in terms of numbers of subjects. However, there are as yet no studies in which adequate numbers of patients representing the subtypes of schizophrenia have been compared with each other and with suitable control groups. Clarification of conflicting trends will be necessary.

Spence and Taylor (181, 182) report studies of classical or Pavlovian conditioning where electric shock was not involved. Eyelid closure to a puff of air directed on the eye was the unconditioned response and a change in brightness of a visual field was the conditioned stimulus. These investigators assume that conditioning will occur more rapidly among subjects in whom drive state is high. Further, it is assumed that anxiety operates as a drive. Thus, the prediction was that anxiety neurotics and certain anxious psychotic patients would condition more rapidly than a normal control group. The prediction was confirmed. Most of the psychotic patients were apparently early, acute schizophrenics. The results tend to indicate that these schizophrenics are characterized by high anxiety or other high drive states.

Another major conditioning study was done by Howe (183), who predicted that chronic schizophrenics would condition slowly because of inadequate stress adaptation. The galvanic skin response to electric stimulation was conditioned to a tone. Howe worked with 60 neurotic subjects most of whom were anxiety reactions, 60 functional schizophrenics who had been hospitalized for at least two years, and 60 college students. The most definite result is that the neurotic group conditions more readily than the normal and schizophrenic groups. The latter seem to condition less readily than the normal group. Contrasting the studies of Spence and Taylor with this one of Howe, and placing them in the framework of many demonstrations that acute and chronic cases differ in essential ways, it is plausible that it is the difference in groups of schizophrenics that is reflected in the divergent results. One conclusion might be that chronic schizophrenics are relatively low on anxiety. However, Malmo, Shagass, and Smith (184), for example, offer evidence that the chronic schizophrenic reacts emotionally in terms of certain fundamental physiological processes, but that purposive responses are not made adequately. If this is so, then processes that interfere with development of adaptive responses are an essential aspect of the more severe schizophrenias, as contrasted with the acute group.

Gantt (185–187) has reported on conditioning of schizophrenics using an escape-shock procedure. The impression is that schizophrenics condition more readily than organics who are very resistent to conditioning. Analogously, patients who are more conditionable seem to be those who have more resources for adjustment. With these studies in mind, Peters (167) contrasted normals, treated chronic schizophrenics, and untreated chronic schizophrenics. The first two groups were more readily conditioned in procedures where the PGR to a loud horn and the PGR to shock were the conditioned responses and lights were the conditioned stimuli. These results seem to support those of Howe, but a study contrasting chronic and acute groups on eyelid conditioning and the same groups on a PGR procedure would permit much firmer conclusions. For the moment, the combined results suggest that chronic schizophrenics do not condition as rapidly as normals unless they have received some special treatment, but acute schizophrenics condition more rapidly. Because slower conditioning may result from low motivation, weak stimulus intensity, too strong stimulus intensity, and several other factors, a firm conclusion is not possible now.

Operant Conditioning   Learning often occurs under conditions in which a "spontaneous" response made by the organism is either rewarded or punished. Here, the response is not prompted by the use of an unconditioned stimulus. In a sense, prompting the desired response is indirect in operant conditioning, whereas it is direct in classical conditioning. Interest in operant, or instrumental, conditioning has been most intensified as a result of work of Skinner (188) and his students. Verbal and motor behaviors can be increased or decreased by a variety of reinforcing stimuli. Positive reinforcing stimuli include such verbalizations as "Mmm-hmm," "Good," "Fine," and paraphrasing, such gestures as the head nod, smile, and leaning forward, and such signals as a light, a buzzer, and a bell tone. Negative reinforcing stimuli include the head shake and "Huh-uh."

Operant conditioning is a procedure that permits an orderly exploration of the modifiability of various responses and the relative effectiveness of reinforcing stimuli. The technique's utility will depend upon success in applying the paradigm to attitudes, values, and goals as responses and to defined, measured roles and relationships as reinforcing stimuli. Part of the appeal of the procedure is that responses and reinforcing stimuli can be modified systematically and independently. For example, censure as a negative reinforcement could be compared with any variety of other reinforcers as they effect responses ranging from very simple to very complex. That the rather overly simplified, very general classes "reinforcement" and "response" will have to be more elaborately conceptualized seems apparent.

Application of the technique to schizophrenics seems to be in the stage at which investigators are still exploring the range of reinforcing stimuli that have effects, the range of responses that can be modified, and the effects of reinforcement schedules. Lindsley (*e.g.,* 189) notes that about 30 per cent of a patient group did not condition and that these were the patients with very low response rates and that apparently these are the more severely disturbed patients. Another group of investigators (190) finds evidence that, among acute schizophrenics, the relationship of operant-response rate to severity of illness is curvilinear with the least ill being slower than the middle group and the most severely ill being slowest of all. In another study (191), operant conditioning of verbal behavior proved difficult, but there is the suggestion that schizophrenics sustain existing response tendencies not so much because of ineffectiveness of social rewards but because of unusually strong habit structures.

INTERPERSONAL-RELATIONSHIP HISTORY

The emphasis to this point has been on the functioning of the patient. Although the relationship history may be reflected in the content of fantasies, in the stimuli which are associated with inadequate performances in perception and thinking, and in the relationships established with those involved in study, care, and treatment of the patient, additional methods must be devised and employed to test the proposition that interpersonal relationships have contributed to the patient's becoming schizophrenic, or have contributed to the particular manifestations which characterize the patient's schizophrenia, or have effects in determining the outcome of the psychosis, or combinations of these.

In many of the studies of characteristics of family members, authors have assumed that any characteristics different from those of relatives of persons making adequate adjustments are evidence that these characteristics are causal of schizophrenia. But, because the studies are made after onset of the psychotic episode, the differences may be reactions to having a family member become psychotic. On the other hand, if it is assumed that this cannot account for all differences found, the family characteristics may be causal to the variety of schizophrenic reaction and not to the occurrence of the psychotic episode. Furthermore, most often the studies have been of relatives of the total, undifferentiated group of schizophrenics and may therefore be of minimal power. Also, other pathological groups are seldom used as controls, so the specificity of interpersonal history to schizophrenia is unknown. Sometimes, too, an inferential error is made when it is argued that the logical difficulties in retrospective studies of interpersonal-relationship history somehow make the theories ascribing causal significance to history necessarily implausible, untestable, meaningless, or invalid.

The concept of the schizophrenogenic mother arose out of intensive psychotherapeutic work. Other studies of mothers of schizophrenics have usually employed one of three methodologies: (1) questionnaires regarding family relationships, child-rearing beliefs and practices, and attitudes about self and child; (2) interviews focused on these same areas; and (3) psychotherapy with the mothers. A fourth method, that of personality testing of these women, is little represented in published studies. Fathers of schizophrenics have been studied less often than mothers but are receiving more attention currently.

Major published studies based on questionnaires completed by mothers are those of Mark (192), Freeman and Grayson (193), and Zuckerman, Oltean, and Monashkin (194). Mark gave a parent-attitude scale (see Shoben [195]) to mothers of male schizophrenic veterans and a control group. Of 139 items regarding parent-child relationships and attitudes, the groups differed on 65. Mothers of the schizophrenics expressed restrictive attitudes and attitudes of both excessive devotion and cool detachment. In the Freeman and Grayson study, the mothers of male schizophrenic veterans were again contrasted with a control group using the Shoben scale. These mothers had generally poor attitudes, being possessive, ignoring, subtly dominating, with overconcern about the child's sexual behavior.

Zuckerman *et al.* administered an attitude inventory developed by Schaefer and Bell (196). The mothers of male and female schizophrenics in an acute-treatment hospital were contrasted with a control group with negative results. This failure to find differences, in contrast to the studies by Mark and by Grayson and Freeman, might be due to differences in questionnaires used, although Schaefer and Bell used many items similar to those of Shoben. Or there may be some difference between veteran and nonveteran populations. A comparison of mothers of male patients with mothers of female patients in the Zuckerman study shows that the failure to find differences does not seem to be due to a sex difference. Perhaps the interpretation should be that the veterans were the more chronic patient group. Considering the association of poorer, earlier interpersonal environments with more severe pathology found, for example, by Kantor and Winder, it would not be surprising if mothers of acute cases were similar to control mothers on an attitude questionnaire, with mothers of chronic cases being deviant. Neither of these questionnaires, it might be added, was developed specifically to focus sharply on those attitudes ascribed in the clinical literature to schizophrenogenic mothers.

Interview assessments of characteristics of parents of schizophrenics, as well as assessments based on psychotherapy with such parents, suffer typically from two major deficiencies: (1) the lack of a control group, and (2) the absence of a set of topics on which all interviewees are assessed. Such systematic coverage does not require a static interview outline or stereotyped procedure, as some clinicians would assume. The interview may be very flexible and questions may be very indirect and subtle, while at the same time ranging over standard topics. Also, it remains to be seen if a semistructured interview is really less sensitive as an attitude measure than is an unstructured procedure.

Two of the better studies based on interviews are those of Gerard and Siegel (197) and Prout and White (198). Both studied control groups as well as parents of patients. The impression created by the findings of these studies is that the parents of schizophrenics are immature, inadequate people, sometimes with extreme reaction formations. It also appears that the person who became schizophrenic had been, when a child, the focal point of distorted relationships within the family. Many clinical studies support and amplify this picture (e.g., 199–203). The next step in this line of investigation might well be studies designed to test more specific hypotheses, employing several methodological approaches and utilizing such control groups as the families of neurotics, depressives, and character disorders. Interview methodology which might appropriately be employed in this way is aptly illustrated in studies of the relationship of parent characteristics and child-rearing practices to personality in nursery-school-age children done by Sears et al. (204). In particular, systematic coverage of a range of topics, coding, and the making of ratings from interview data would be a substantial improvement over the more spontaneous and impressionistic procedures so often followed in studies done by clinicians.

Psychological study of parents and other relatives of schizophrenics might be pursued with any relevant and valid measurement technique. It is somewhat surprising, for example, to find no study of the intellectual level of parents and siblings of schizophrenics in comparison to control groups. There is a study by Davids (205) which lends support to the view that mothers of schizophrenic children are brighter than average, whereas the children score lower on intelligence tests than do other emotionally disturbed children.

Apparently, the Rorschach technique has been used more often in the study of relatives of schizophrenic patients than have other psychological tests. Two Rorschach studies (206, 207) suggest unusual frequency of pathological characteristics in relatives of schizophrenics. More specifically, Prout and White (198) gave the Rorschach to the two groups of mothers in their study and found that these mothers of male schizophrenics seemed to indicate more pathological personality configurations than the control mothers. Winder and Kantor (208) applied their age-level scoring procedure, described above, to these same Rorschachs and found that the mothers of patients were less mature, on the average, than the mothers of nonschizo-phrenic young adult males. As usual, the overlap of these groups was large. Such studies lend support to the position that the interpersonal environ-ments of schizophrenics have been deviant. One cannot conclude that any particular etiological position is favored by these results. Rather, intensive investigation into the operation of such unfortunate families is indicated.

A more global and elaborate approach has been used by Block, Patter-son, Block, and Jackson (209). These investigators studied parents of schizo-phrenic and neurotic children—probably a more difficult discrimination than contrasting any one pathological group with a normal group. These parents were tested with the Rorschach, the MMPI, and selected TAT cards. Interpretation of the battery of tests on each case was made in terms of a so-called Q-sort. On the basis of total group comparisons, there were no dif-ferences between parents of schizophrenic and neurotic children. But sub-clusters of certain neurotogenic and schizophrenogenic mothers and fathers do appear. In other words, some parents in each group are not distinguish-able from a proportion of the parents in the other group, but on the basis of case to case similarity, certain clusters of neurotogenic and schizophrenogenic parents do appear. These mothers of schizophrenics tend to be manipulative, exploitive, distrustful, hostile, and devious. Fathers of schizophrenics who cluster separately are described as expressing hostility directly and being assertive to the point of being counterphobic.

The study of interpersonal-relationship history strongly suggests use of the parents or other relatives as the subjects. But an alternative approach involves systematic study of what the patients themselves can report of the past. Rodnick and Garmezy (122) report that poor premorbid schizophrenics attribute more rejecting attitudes to their mothers than do good premorbid patients. The latter indicate more dissatisfaction with what their mothers did, expressing more disapproval of dominating, rejecting, and overprotec-tive practices. Even though the poor premorbids indicated more maternal rejection, they were not so critical as were the good premorbids.

Kohn and Clausen (210), in a study which has some excellent meth-odological features, found that schizophrenics remember their mothers as stricter, more self-assured, and more dominating than their fathers. But the extreme variations suggested a further study to Rodnick and Garmezy (122). Their preliminary evidence suggests that poor premorbid patients report mothers as more dominating, restrictive, and powerful, whereas good pre-morbid cases more frequently report their fathers as harsh, dominating, and oppressive. In both instances the other parent was seemingly seen as nice but not effective. It appears also that poor premorbids are more "mother-ori-

ented" in that they assign more adjectives to mother than to father when
there is a choice. Good premorbids assign more negative adjectives to father.
Thus, the patient's report of his memory of parents during the developmental years seems to furnish evidence of deviant relationships. And, of great
potential significance, possible differential family patterns for poor and good
premorbid cases are suggested. In clinical, psychotherapeutic, psychometric,
and other types of studies of the interpersonal history, attention to these
suggested differences is now imperative.

The study of interpersonal history could profitably be influenced by
findings of general studies of parent-child relationships, just as these general
studies have been influenced by clinical theory and evidence. From studies
of parents in general, there is emerging a set of dimensions which seem
applicable to all parent-child settings. These dimensions are related in very
important ways to the developing personality characteristics in children.
These dimensions, such as permissiveness and warmth, can replace such categorizations as rejecting, overprotective, dominating, and overly demanding.
Part of the benefit of such a translation will be to contribute to a clearer
discrimination between parent-personality traits and the child-rearing behaviors of the parents, leading to greater conceptual clarity. Of great benefit,
also, would be the progressive clarification of the kinds and degrees of deviation from parents in general which characterize pathogenic parents. There
is clearly, also, a need for conceptualization of families as functional units
(e.g., 211).

But to return to child-rearing behaviors, a summary of variables based
on five studies (Sears, Maccoby, and Levin [204], Baldwin, Kalhorn, and
Breese [212], Schaefer and Bell [213], Sewell, Mussen, and Harris [214], and
Milton [215]) will suggest the appropriateness of the dimensional concepts
and measures to the analysis of the relationship histories of schizophrenics.
The particular manifestations which define all these variables depend upon
age of the child. But all can be specified in terms of specific behaviors, a procedure which is an absolute necessity in research. A first variable is parental
permissiveness, though it may be useful eventually to distinguish among several permissiveness variables (214). A second variable is warmth. Neither of
these variables is new to clinicians, but the factor analysis yields the new
information that these variables are quite independent of each other, so
that all combinations are observed in the general population. The question
of one or a few combinations as typical of schizophrenogenic parents becomes meaningful. Further, the question of the necessary additional components in the pathogenic families could be more pointedly asked with such
information in hand. Among the other variables suggested by the above

studies are a family-adjustment variable, a variable having to do with the handling of overt aggression, and a variable having to do with general use of rewards and deprivations in training children. Carefully specified measures of such variables can be developed and would put the study of the interpersonal-relationship history on a much firmer basis than has so far been achieved.

The dilemma of those who place emphasis on the interpersonal history as a major etiological factor can only be resolved by longitudinal studies. Retrospective studies reflect the effect of the psychotic family member on the feelings, attitudes, and memories of relatives, and the kind and magnitudes of these effects are a mystery. To unravel these effects, a step by step process will be required, where retrospective studies will give way to studies of young adults and adolescents, the age group in which the probability of development of schizophrenia is relatively high. Fortunately, the study of personality development is becoming widespread, and from these studies some developing cases of psychosis will be found. More important, the increased certainty about factors generally important in personality development will provide an instructive perspective on the results of studies of schizophrenics.

COMMENTS IN CONCLUSION

Taken as a total group as found in public hospitals, patients diagnosed as schizophrenic manifest deficits in psychomotor performances, distortions in perception, deficits in thinking, deficits in intellectual efficiency, and deviations in learning. The strategy in future research will be to test hypotheses regarding antecedents of these deficits and deviations and to find means of correcting, compensating for, and preventing them.

As these deviations and deficits have been systematically measured, heterogeneity among schizophrenics has been confirmed repeatedly. Because the variations appear to be other than inconsequential, individual differences, the possibility of defining meaningful dimensions of schizophrenia emerges. What research has been done suggests that acute and chronic groups differ from each other in psychomotor performances, perception, thinking, learning, intellectual efficiency, and physiological functioning, as well as in adequacy of premorbid adjustment. This dichotomy does not necessarily indicate that there are two "types" of schizophrenics, but it certainly does indicate that the variable of premorbid adjustment and the heterogeneity of manifestations during psychosis must be taken into account if tests of hypotheses are to be maximally sensitive.

Deficits in psychological functioning are so characteristic of schizophrenics that it is vital to establish which can be reduced and how much reduction is possible by manipulation of instructions, structure of the interpersonal situation, patient's set, motivational factors, reinforcements, and chemical agents. Because these deficits do not seem to be of the kind implied by the classical concept of deterioration and at the same time are not totally reversible, the conditions under which there are varying degrees of motivational arousal of schizophrenics are open for intensive investigation.

The findings of the punishment-reward studies suggest that in some way these patients either have not developed or have lost the expectation that rewards and satisfactions can be attained. The further implication is that escape from noxious conditions focuses the pattern of living, and it is tempting to believe that rewards have come to provoke anxieties. Seemingly congruent with this finding are the clinical formulations which emphasize total domination of the offspring by a parent or parents, resulting in an isolated, unrealistic, symbiotic parent-child unit. The relation between differential response to punishment *vs.* reward and other variables such as specific areas of anxiety has yet to be explored.

In studies of perception and thinking, a definite pattern has become apparent: the content of the stimulus materials and of the problems to be solved is related to the degree of deficit. Content suggesting interpersonal relationships is associated more with deviations and deficits than is content having little relationship to persons or social processes. These data lend support to points of view that assign much significance to the interpersonal-relationship history in the etiology of the schizophrenias. There is, of course, a methodological defect in these published studies; *i.e.,* inadequate control of complexity of the stimulus material. If the effect can be confirmed with proper procedures, the results will mesh with the hypothesis that schizophrenics have experienced especially deviant interpersonal environments.

In connection with this hypothesis, it is cogent to assume that the pathogenic environment will have resulted in anxieties which are extreme and are reduced only by symptomatic behavior. In other words, it is plausible that particular kinds of parent-child interactions, at particular childhood ages, produce anxieties which become evident when particular stimulus contents are the occasions for disrupted performances. Can relatively specific predictions for each individual patient be made on the basis of the attitudes held by his parents and on the basis of that patient's life history?

Conceptualizations of acute schizophrenics as severely anxious people receive considerable support in clinical observation as well as in evidence such as that of Malmo and his associates (*e.g.,* 216) on physiological reactions. They are further supported by the ease of classical conditioning, seemingly reflecting heightened drive, and by the perceptual deviations associated with affectively significant stimulus content. But in many respects, performances of groups of acute schizophrenics do not differ greatly from those of normals, *e.g.*, performance on intelligence tests. As Rodnick and Garmezy (122) have pointed out in another connection, the more frequent failure to find differences in psychological functioning between acute or good premorbid schizophrenics and normals (contrasted with the many differences found comparing poor premorbids and normals) may have much to do with the fact that the methods employed have been based primarily on hunches derived from observation of more chronic patients.

It may well be, however, that the many similarities between acute schizophrenics and normals on many tasks should be taken as a key to an essential difference between the more acute and the more chronic schizophrenics. The acute cases resolve some anxieties, some of the time, in ways which are realistic and adjustive—or at least in ways not distressing to people in general. The patient who resolves most anxieties, most of the time, with unrealistic and unadjustive responses becomes a chronic patient. Here, the unrealistic, unadjustive nature of his behavior tends to precipitate more and more problem situations in which further anxieties are aroused. The pattern of living becomes a succession of disarticulated, disorganized responses which serve to reduce anxieties, temporarily, without resolving the problems. Disorganized perceptual and cognitive processes become the basis of the predominant response styles. The research task is to demonstrate the conditions under which socially adaptive responses so persistently fail to be adopted as important aspects of the patterns of reaction which are anxiety reducing.

Certainly, psychodynamic, especially psychoanalytic, points of view have much to offer in the guidance of further research on all of these matters. Such points of view will become more precise if reformulated in terms of social learning or behavior theory, *e.g.*, Dollard and Miller (217). Mednick (218) has presented a learning theory formulation of thinking disturbance in schizophrenia, which is admittedly sketchy and preliminary, but which illustrates the possibilities of the theoretical approach.

Psychological research on schizophrenia can come of age at this point in its history (1) if there is increased attention to many aspects of methodology; (2) if the multilevel manifestations of schizophrenia in any one patient and the significant variations among schizophrenics are recognized and are taken as consequent events to be explained in every serious theory; and (3) if progress is made in integrating psychosomatic, psychoanalytic, and social learning points of view as guides for developmentally oriented researches, particularly longitudinal studies.

References

1.   G. BERGMANN, *Mind,* 52: 122–140, 1943.
2.   R. R. SEARS, in Hunt, J. McV. (Ed.), *Personality and the Behavior Disorders,* Vol. I, New York: Ronald, 1944.
3.   N. E. MILLER, *Am. J. Psychol., 13:* 100–108, 1958.
4.   W. BEVAN-LEWIS, *Text Book of Ment. Diseases,* London: Blakiston's, 1899.
5.   L. C. GATEWOOD, *Psychol. Monogr., 11* (No. 45), 1909.
6.   G. H. KENT, *Psychol. Rev., 18:* 375–410, 1911.
7.   E. G. BORING, *Psychol. Monogr., 15* (No. 63), 1913.
8.   C. L. HULL, *Am. J. Psychol., 28:* 419–435, 1917.
9.   J. W. DE BRUYN, *J. Abnorm. Psychol., 3:* 378–385, 1908–1909.
10.   J. MC V. HUNT, *Psychol. Bull., 33:* 1–58, 1936.
11.   G. P. GRABFIELD, *Boston Med. Surg. J., 173:* 202–205, 1915.
12.   F. L. WELLS and C. M. KELLEY, *Amer. J. Insan., 77:* 17–45, 1920–1921.
13.   S. L. PRESSEY, *J. Abnorm. Psychol., 12:* 130–139, 1917.
14.   M. M. WENTWORTH, *J. Abnorm. & Social Psychol., 18:* 378–384, 1924.
15.   T. V. MOORE, *Am. J. Psychiat., 9:* 719–738, 1930.
16.   M. F. HAUSMANN, *J. General Psychol., 9:* 179–189, 1933.
17.   J. MC V. HUNT and C. N. COFER, in Hunt, J. McV. (Ed.), *Personality and the Behavior Disorders,* Vol. II, New York: Ronald, 1944.
18.   D. RAPAPORT, M. GILL, and R. SCHAFER, *Diagnostic Psychological Testing,* Vols. I & II, Chicago: Yr. Bk. Pub., 1945.
19.   H. O. SCHMIDT and C. P. FONDA, *J. Abnorm. & Social Psychol., 52:* 262–267, 1956.
20.   D. SHAKOW, *Nerv. & Ment. Dis. Monogr.,* No. 70, 1946.
21.   M. LORR, *Psychol. Bull., 51:* 119–127, 1954.
22.   P. R. MC REYNOLDS, E. L. BALLACHEY, and J. T. FERGUSON, *Am. Psychol., 7:* 340, 1952.
23.   P. BARRABEE, EDNA L. BARRABEE, and J. E. FINESINGER, *Am. J. Psychiat., 112:* 252–259, 1955.
24.   L. PHILLIPS and B. CORVITZ, *J. Pers., 22:* 270–285, 1953.
25.   R. B. CATTELL, *Factor Analysis,* New York: Harper, 1952.
26.   J. W. DEGAN, *Psychometr. Monogr.,* No. 6, 1–41, 1952.
27.   J. R. WITTENBORN, *J. Consult. Psychol., 15:* 290–302, 1951.
28.   W. H. GUERTIN, *J. Consult. Psychol., 16:* 308–312, 1952.
29.   M. LORR, R. J. JENKINS, and J. P. O'CONNOR, *J. Abnorm. & Social Psychol., 50:* 78–86, 1955.
30.   C. F. MASON, *J. Consult. Psychol., 20:* 297–300, 1956.
31.   J. B. MINER and J. K. ANDERSON, *J. Abnorm. & Social Psychol., 56:* 75–81, 1958.
32.   ISABELLE KENDIG and W. V. RICHMOND, *Psychological Studies in Dementia Praecox,* Ann Arbor: Edwards, 1940.
33.   ANNE ROE and D. SHAKOW, *Ann. New York Acad. Sc., 42:* 361–390, 1942.
34.   J. B. MINER, *Intelligence in the United States,* New York: Springer, 1957.

35. J. S. PEARSON and IRENE B. KLEY, *Psychol. Bull., 54*: 406–420, 1957.

36. L. W. SONTAG, C. T. BAKER, and V. L. NELSON, *Monogr. Soc. Res. Child Development, 23* (No. 2), 1958.

37. T. WEISENBURG, ANNE ROE, and K. B. MC BRIDE, *Adult Intelligence,* New York: Commonwealth Fund, 1936.

38. A. E. HARPER, *J. Consult. Psychol., 14*: 290–296, 1950.

39. D. WECHSLER, *The Measurement of Adult Intelligence,* Baltimore: Williams & Wilkins, 1944.

40. H. BABCOCK, *Arch. Psychol., 18* (No. 117), 1930.

41. H. F. HUNT in Brower, D., and Abt, L. E. (Eds.), *Progress in Clinical Psychology,* Vol. I, New York: Grune, 1952.

42. C. SIMMINS, *J. Ment. Sc., 79*: 704–734, 1933.

43. W. C. SHIPLEY, *J. Psychol., 9*: 371–377, 1940.

44. A. I. RABIN, G. F. KING, and J. C. EHRMANN, *J. Abnorm. & Social Psychol., 50*: 255–258, 1955.

45. A. J. YATES, *J. Ment. Sc., 102*: 409–440, 1956.

46. D. WECHSLER, *The Wechsler-Bellevue Intelligence Scale: Form II, Manual for Administration and Scoring the Test,* New York: Psychological Corp., 1949.

47. D. WECHSLER, *Manual for the Wechsler Adult Intelligence Scale,* New York: Psychological Corp., 1955.

48. B. BALINSKY, *Genet. Psychol. Mongr., 23*: 191–234, 1941.

49. I. LORGE, *J. Consult. Psychol., 7*: 167–168, 1943.

50. A. I. RABIN and W. H. GUERTIN, *Psychol. Bull., 48*: 211–248, 1951.

51. W. SCHOFIELD, *J. Clin. Psychol., 8*: 16–22, 1952.

52. A. E. HARPER, *J. Consult. Psychol., 14*: 351–357, 1950.

53. S. L. GARFIELD, *J. Consult. Psychol., 13*: 279–287, 1949.

54. L. L. THURSTONE, *Psychometr. Monogr.,* No. 1, 1938.

55. L. L. THURSTONE and T. G. THURSTONE, *Examiner Manual for the SRA Primary Mental Abilities (Intermediate),* Chicago: Sci. Res. Assoc., 1949.

56. A. BINDER, *J. Abnorm. & Social Psychol., 52*: 11–18, 1956.

57. M. P. WITTMAN, *Am. J. Psychiat., 93*: 1363–1377, 1937.

58. RITA SENF, P. E. HUSTON, and B. D. COHEN, *J. Abnorm. & Soc. Psychol., 50*: 383–387, 1955.

59. W. A. MAINORD, *J. Consult. Psychol., 17*: 54–57, 1953.

60. J. W. LAYMAN, *J. General Psychol., 22*: 67–86, 1940.

61. JOAN FITZHERBERT, *Brit. J. M. Psychol., 28*; 191–193, 1955.

62. H. E. KING, *Psychomotor Aspects of Mental Disease,* Cambridge: Harvard, 1954.

63. H. G. SEASHORE, *Psychol. Bull., 38*: 608–609, 1941.

64. R. H. SEASHORE, C. E. BUXTON, and I. N. MC CULLOM, *Am. J. Psychol., 53*: 251–259, 1940.

65. H. J. A. RIMOLDI, *J. Abnorm. & Social Psychol., 46*: 283–303, 1951.

66. E. H. RODNICK and D. SHAKOW, *Am. J. Psychiat., 97*: 214–225, 1940.

67. W. H. WULFECK, *Psychol. Rec., 4*: 271–323, 1941.

68. P. E. HUSTON, D. SHAKOW, and L. A. RIGGS, *J. General Psychol., 16*: 39–82, 1937.

69. P. H. VENABLES and J. TIZARD, *J. Abnorm. & Social Psychol., 53*: 23–26, 1956.

70. E. W. SCRIPTURE, *J. Ment. Sc., 62*: 698–719, 1916.

71.   F. L. WELLS and C. M. KELLEY, *Am. J. Psychiat.*, 2: 53–59, 1922.

72.   P. H. VENABLES and J. TIZARD, *J. Abnorm. & Social Psychol.*, 53: 220–224, 1956.

73.   G. ROSENBAUM, W. R. MACKAVEY, and J. L. GRISELL, *J. Abnorm. & Social Psychol.*, 54: 364–368, 1957.

74.   G. ROSENBAUM, J. L. GRISELL, and W. R. MACKAVEY, *J. Abnorm. & Social Psychol.*, 55: 202–207, 1957.

75.   D. SHAKOW and P. E. HUSTON, *J. General Psychol.*, 15: 63–108, 1936.

76.   H. E. KING and J. CLAUSEN, in *Psychosurgical Problems*, Vol. I, Columbia Greystone Associates (2nd Group). Philadelphia: Blakiston, 1952.

77.   H. E. KING and J. CLAUSEN, in *Psychosurgical Problems*, Vol. II, Columbia Greystone Associates (2nd Group).

78.   P. G. MEYERSON and D. LANDAU, *Arch. Neurol. & Psychiat.*, 63: 351, 1950.

79.   P. E. HUSTON and D. SHAKOW, *J. General Psychol.*, 34: 119–126, 1946.

80.   P. E. HUSTON, *Psychol. Bull.*, 29: 662, 1932.

81.   D. SHAKOW, *Psychol. Bull.*, 29: 661, 1932.

82.   B. A. STOTSKY, *J. Pers.*, 25: 327–343, 1957.

83.   A. R. LURIA, *The Nature of Human Conflicts* (Tr., W. H. Gantt), New York: Liveright, 1932.

84.   R. B. MALMO, C. SHAGASS, D. J. BELANGER, and A. A. SMITH, *J. Abnorm. & Social Psychol.*, 46: 539–547, 1951.

85.   W. H. WULFECK, *Psychol. Rec.*, 4: 326–348, 1941.

86.   H. N. PETERS, *J. Abnorm. & Social Psychol.*, 41: 437–448, 1946.

87.   G. R. PASCAL and B. J. SUTTELL, *The Bender-Gestalt Test*, New York: Grune, 1951.

88.   J. A. BOWLAND and H. L. DEABLER, *J. Clin. Psychol.*, 12: 82–84, 1956.

89.   A. S. EDWARDS and A. C. HARRIS, *J. General Psychol.*, 49: 153–156, 1953.

90.   H. E. SHIMOTA, *Dissert. Abstr.*, 16: 2530, 1956.

91.   P. E. HUSTON and D. SHAKOW, *Am. J. Psychiat.*, 105: 881–888, 1949.

92.   W. R. GARNER, H. W. HAKE, and C. W. ERIKSEN, *Psychol. Rev.*, 63: 149–159, 1956.

93.   M. WERTHEIMER, *J. General Psychol.*, 51: 291–299, 1954.

94.   W. KOHLER and H. WALLACH, *Proc. Am. Phil. Soc.*, 88: 269–357, 1944.

95.   M. WERTHEIMER and C. W. JACKSON, JR., *J. General Psychol.*, 57: 45–54, 1957.

96.   B. R. PHILIP, *Canad. J. Psychol.*, 7: 115–125, 1953.

97.   A. C. VOTH, *Am. J. Psychiat.*, 103: 793–810, 1947.

98.   I. N. HAHN, *Dissert. Abstr.*, 16: 1504–1505, 1956.

99.   M. D. DIAMOND, *J. Consult. Psychol.*, 20: 441–444, 1956.

100.   M. SHERIF, *Arch. Psychol.*, No. 187, 1935.

101.   C. H. GRAHAM, in Stevens, S. S. (Ed.), *Handbook of Experimental Psychology*, New York: Wiley, 1951.

102.   A. L. BALDWIN, *Behavior and Development in Childhood*, New York: Dryden, 1955.

103.   H. L. RAUSH, *J. Pers.*, 21: 176–187, 1952.

104.   E. LOVINGER, *J. Abnorm. & Social Psychol.*, 52: 87–91, 1956.

105.   R. SANDERS and A. R. PACHT, *J. Consult. Psychol.*, 16: 440–444, 1952.

106.   H. L. RAUSH, *J. Abnorm. & Social Psychol.*, 52: 231–234, 1956.

107.   T. C. WECKOWICZ, *Psychosom. Med.*, 20: 66–71, 1958.

108.   E. CALLAWAY and S. V. THOMPSON, *Psychosom. Med.*, 15: 443–455, 1953.

109.   B. KLOPFER *et al.*, *Developments in the Rorschach Technique,* Vols. I and II, Yonkers, N.Y.: World Bk., 1954, 1956.

110.   H. FRIEDMAN, *J. Proj. Tech., 17:* 171–185, 1953.

111.   E. L. SIEGEL, *J. Proj. Tech., 17:* 151–161, 1953.

112.   W. C. BECKER, *J. Abnorm. & Social Psychol., 53:* 229–236, 1956.

113.   PHYLLIS WITTMAN, *Elgin State Hospital Papers, 4:* 20–33, 1941.

114.   R. E. KANTOR, J. M. WALLNER, and C. L. WINDER, *J. Consult. Psychol., 17:* 157–162, 1953.

115.   G. A. BRACKBILL and H. J. FINE, *J. Abnorm. & Social Psychol., 52:* 310–313, 1956.

116.   R. E. KANTOR and C. L. WINDER, unpublished manuscript, 1957.

117.   H. S. SULLIVAN, *The Interpersonal Theory of Psychiatry,* New York: Norton, 1953.

118.   F. BARRON, *J. Consult. Psychol., 19:* 33–38, 1955.

119.   B. D. COHEN, RITA SENF, and P. E. HUSTON, *J. Abnorm. & Social Psychol., 52:* 363-367, 1956.

120.   E. STARER, *J. Consult. Psychol., 19:* 453–454, 1955.

121.   A. JONES, *J. Abnorm. & Social Psychol., 53:* 187–190, 1956.

122.   E. H. RODNICK and N. GARMEZY, in Jones, M. R. (Ed.), *Nebraska Symposium on Motivation,* Lincoln: Univ. Nebraska Press, 1957.

123.   W. L. DUNN, JR., *J. Pers., 23:* 48–64, 1954.

124.   L. PHILLIPS, *J. Nerv. & Ment. Dis., 117:* 515–525, 1953.

125.   J. G. HARRIS, JR., *J. Pers., 25:* 651–671, 1957.

126.   R. H. DANA, *J. Abnorm. & Social Psychol., 50:* 19–24, 1955.

127.   W. R. DOBSON, *J. General Psychol., 50:* 277–298, 1954.

128.   A. I. RABIN, *J. Clin. Psychol., 13:* 88–90, 1957.

129.   M. WALLACE, *J. Abnorm. & Social Psychol., 52:* 240–241, 1956.

130.   C. O. DE LA GARZA and PHILIP WORCHEL, *J. Abnorm. & Social Psychol., 52:* 191–194, 1956.

131.   J. LANZKRON and W. WOLFSON, *Am. J. Psychiat., 114:* 744–746, 1958.

132.   J. S. HILLSON and P. WORCHEL, *J. Consult. Psychol., 21:* 83–88, 1957.

133.   P. H. CHASE, *J. Consult. Psychol., 21:* 495–497, 1957.

134.   I. S. VIGOTSKY, *Arch. Neurol. & Psychiat., 31:* 1063–1077, 1934.

135.   E. HANFMANN and J. KASANIN, *Nerv. & Ment. Dis. Monogr.,* No. 67, 1942.

136.   M. M. BOLLIS and K. GOLDSTEIN, *Psychiatric Quart., 12:* 42–66, 1938.

137.   H. WEGROCKI, *Arch. Psychol.,* No. 254, 1940.

138.   K. GOLDSTEIN, in Kasanin, J. S. (Ed.), *Language and Thought in Schizophrenia,* Berkeley: Univ. California Press, 1946.

139.   K. GOLDSTEIN and M. SCHEERER, *Psychol. Monogr., 53:* No. 2 (Whole Number 239), 1941.

140.   L. S. MC GAUGHRAN and L. J. MORAN, *J. Abnorm. & Social Psychol., 52:* 43–50, 1956.

141.   L. S. MC GAUGHRAN and L. J. MORAN, *J. Abnorm. & Social Psychol., 54:* 44–49, 1957.

142.   D. R. GORHAM, *Psychol. Rep. Monogr.,* Suppl., No. 1, 1956.

143.   N. CAMERON, *The Psychology of Behavior Disorders,* Boston: Houghton Mifflin, 1947.

144.   M. WHITEMAN, *J. Abnorm. & Social Psychol.*, *49*: 266–271, 1954.

145.   M. WHITEMAN, *J. Nerv. & Ment. Dis.*, *124*: 199–204, 1956.

146.   R. H. DAVIS, *J. Abnorm. & Social Psychol.*, *54*: 126–128, 1957.

147.   D. K. CAVANAUGH, *J. Abnorm. & Social Psychol.*, *57*: 8–12, 1958.

148.   RITA SENF, P. E. HUSTON, and B. D. COHEN, *Am. J. Psychiat.*, *113*: 45–51, 1956.

149.   J. H. FLAVELL, *J. Abnorm. & Social Psychol.*, *52*: 208–211, 1956.

150.   N. CAMERON, *Psychol. Monogr.*, *50*, No. 1 (Whole Number 221), 1938.

151.   N. CAMERON, *J. Abnorm. & Social Psychol.*, *34*: 265–270, 1939.

152.   S. EPSTEIN, *J. Consult. Psychol.*, *17*: 384–388, 1953.

153.   L. J. CHAPMAN and J. A. TAYLOR, *J. Abnorm. & Social Psychol.*, *54*: 118–123, 1957.

154.   L. J. CHAPMAN, *J. Abnorm. & Social Psychol.*, *53*: 286–291, 1956.

155.   L. J. CHAPMAN, *J. Abnorm. & Social Psychol.*, *56*: 374–379, 1958.

156.   R. W. PAYNE and HEATHER L. HIRST, *J. Consult. Psychol.*, *21*: 186–187, 1957.

157.   W. W. WEBB, *J. Abnorm. & Social Psychol.*, *50*: 221–224, 1955.

158.   D. H. HEATH, *J. Abnorm. & Social Psychol.*, *52*: 403–408, 1956.

159.   A. MEADOW and D. H. FUNKENSTEIN, in Hoch, P. H., and Zubin, J. (Eds.), *Relation of Psychological Tests to Psychiatry*, New York: Grune, 1952.

160.   J. MC V. HUNT, *Am. J. Psychol.*, *48*: 64–81, 1936.

161.   P. E. HUSTON and D. SHAKOW, *J. Pers.*, *17*: 52–74, 1948.

162.   P. E. HUSTON and D. SHAKOW, *Am. J. Psychiat.*, *105*: 881–888, 1949.

163.   K. R. L. HALL and T. G. CROOKES, *J. Ment. Sc.*, *97*: 725–737, 1951.

164.   L. M. JACK *et al.*, *Univ. Iowa Stud. Child Welf.*, *3* (No. 9): 7–65, 1934.

165.   M. E. KEISTER, *Univ. Iowa Stud. Child Welf.*, *14*: 27–82, 1938.

166.   G. E. CHITTENDEN, *Monogr. Soc. Res. Child Devel.*, *7* (No. 1), 1942.

167.   H. N. PETERS and O. D. MURPHEE, *J. Clin. Psychol.*, *10*: 126–130, 1954.

168.   H. N. PETERS, *Am. J. Occup. Therapy*, *9*: 185–189, 1955.

169.   H. N. PETERS, *J. Clin. Psychol.*, *9*: 328–333, 1953.

170.   H. N. PETERS, *J. Clin. Psychol.*, *12*: 170–173, 1956.

171.   G. H. KENT, *J. Nerv. & Ment. Dis.*, *48*: 313–324, 1918.

172.   N. GARMEZY, *J. Pers.*, *20*: 253–276, 1952.

173.   R. BLEKE, *J. Pers.*, *23*: 479–498, 1955.

174.   A. H. BUSS and E. H. BUSS, *J. Exper. Psychol.*, *52*: 283–287, 1956.

175.   A. H. BUSS, W. BRADEN, A. ORGEL, and E. H. BUSS, *J. Exper. Psychol.*, *52*: 288–295, 1956.

176.   G. R. PASCAL and C. SWENSEN, *J. Pers.*, *21*: 240–249, 1952.

177.   B. D. COHEN, *J. Abnorm. & Social Psychol.*, *52*: 186–190, 1956.

178.   RITA L. ATKINSON, *Dissert. Abstr.*, *18*: 292, 1958.

179.   NANCY L. ROBINSON, *Dissert. Abstr.*, *18*: 1502, 1958.

180.   E. R. HILGARD and D. G. MARQUIS, *Conditioning and Learning*, New York: Appleton, 1940.

181.   K. W. SPENCE and J. A. TAYLOR, *J. Exper. Psychol.*, *45*: 265–272, 1953.

182.   J. A. TAYLOR and K. W. SPENCE, *J. Abnorm. & Social Psychol.*, *49*: 497–502, 1954.

183.   E. S. HOWE, *J. Abnorm. & Social Psychol.*, *56*: 183–189, 1958.

184.   R. B. MALMO, C. SHAGASS, and A. A. SMITH, *J. Pers.*, *19*: 359–375, 1951.

185.   W. H. GANTT, *Arch. Neurol & Psychiat.*, *40*: 79–85, 1938.

186.   W. H. GANTT, *Am. J. Psychiat.*, *99*: 839–849, 1943.
187.   W. G. REESE, R. DOSS, and W. H. GANTT, *A.M.A. Arch Neurol. & Psychiat.*, *70*: 778–793, 1953.
188.   B. F. SKINNER, *The Behavior of Organisms*, New York: Appleton, 1938.
189.   O. R. LINDSLEY, *Psychiat. Res. Reports*, No. 5, 118–139, 1956.
190.   G. F. KING, D. W. MERRELL, E. LOVINGER, and M. R. DENNY, *J. Pers.*, *25*: 317–326, 1957.
191.   C. H. HARTMAN, *Dissert. Abstr.*, *15*: 1652, 1955.
192.   J. C. MARK, *J. Abnorm. & Social Psychol.*, *48*: 185–189, 1953.
193.   R. V. FREEMAN and H. M. GRAYSON, *J. Abnorm. & Social Psychol.*, *50*: 45–52, 1955.
194.   M. ZUCKERMAN, MARY OLTEAN, and I. MONASHKIN, *J. Consult. Psychol.*, *22*: 307–310, 1958.
195.   E. J. SHOBEN, JR., *Genet. Psychol. Monogr.*, *39*: 101–148, 1949.
196.   E. S. SCHAEFER and R. Q. BELL, unpublished Memorandum, National Institute of Mental Health.
197.   D. L. GERARD and J. SIEGEL, *Psychiatric Quart.*, *24*: 47–73, 1950.
198.   C. T. PROUT and MARY A. WHITE, *Am. J. Psychiat.*, *107*: 251–256, 1950.
199.   TRUDE TIETZE, *Psychiatry*, *12*: 55–65, 1949.
200.   SUZANNE REICHARD and C. TILLMAN, *Psychiatry*, *13*: 247–257, 1950.
201.   T. LIDZ, A. R. CORNELISON, S. FLECK, and D. TERRY, *Psychiatry*, *20*: 329–342, 1957.
202.   L. EISENBERG, *Am. J. Orthopsychiat.*, *27*: 715–724, 1957.
203.   G. BATESON, D. D. JACKSON, J. HALEY, and J. WEAKLAND, *Behavioral Sci.*, *1*: 251–264, 1956.
204.   R. R. SEARS, E. E. MACCOBY, and H. LEVIN, *Patterns of Child Rearing*, Evanston, Ill.: Row, Peterson, 1957.
205.   A. DAVIDS, *J. Consult. Psychol.*, *22*: 159–163, 1958.
206.   C. MODOESI, *Rass. studi psichiat.*, *40*: 118–146, 1951.
207.   U. G. MULLER, *Nervenarzt*, *21*: 29–35, 1950.
208.   C. L. WINDER and R. E. KANTOR, *J. Consult. Psychol.*, *22*: 438–440, 1958.
209.   JEANNE BLOCK, V. PATTERSON, J. BLOCK, and D. D. JACKSON, *Psychiatry*, in press.
210.   M. L. KOHN and J. A. CLAUSEN, *Am. J. Orthopsychiat.*, *26*: 297–313, 1956.
211.   D. D. JACKSON, Paper presented at Academy of Psychoanalysis, San Francisco, Calif., 1958.
212.   A. L. BALDWIN, J. KALHORN, and F. H. BREESE, *Psychol. Monogr.*, *63* (No. 4), 1949.
213.   E. S. SCHAEFER and R. Q. BELL, *Am. Psychol.*, *10*: 319–320, 1955.
214.   W. H. SEWELL, P. H. MUSSEN, and C. W. HARRIS, *Am. Sociol. Rev.*, *20*: 137–148, 1955.
215.   G. A. MILTON, *Child Development*, *29*: 381–392, 1958.
216.   R. B. MALMO and C. SHAGASS, *Psychosom. Med.*, *11*: 9–24, 1949.
217.   J. DOLLARD and N. E. MILLER, *Personality and Psychotherapy*, New York: McGraw-Hill, 1950.
218.   S. A. MEDNICK, *Psychol. Bull.*, *55*: 316–327, 1958.

9. ANXIETY, PERCEPTION, AND SCHIZOPHRENIA

Paul McReynolds

This chapter will consider certain aspects of schizophrenia from a somewhat new point of view. The central thesis in the conceptualization to be proposed is that anxiety is the pre-eminent factor in the development of schizophrenia. This thesis itself is not, of course, new: on the contrary, it is quite widely held. What is new here is a particular interpretation of anxiety and an attempt to spell out just how anxiety, in terms of this particular interpretation, can lead to those behavioral characteristics which define schizophrenia.

In order to put an interpretation of schizophrenia based on anxiety on a scientific footing it is obviously unsatisfactory simply to posit that intolerable anxiety leads to schizophrenic reactions, without specifying the basic nature of anxiety in concepts which are meaningful in terms of schizophrenic symptomatology. That is, simply to say that extreme anxiety is extremely unpleasant and that the schizophrenic therefore develops extreme ways of dealing with it is to imply a circular and hence scientifically inade-

Paul McReynolds, Ph.D., is Director of Research at the Veterans Administration Hospital, Palo Alto, and is Consulting Associate Professor of Psychology at Stanford University.

For both critical and creative suggestions in the preparation of this chapter the author is indebted to a number of persons, in particular to the editor of this volume and to Richard C. Hamister, Leonard Ullmann, and Richard L. Jenkins.

248

quate definition of anxiety. Clearly, any advance in an interpretation of schizophrenia based on anxiety is dependent upon an improved conceptualization of anxiety. One of the first aims of this paper will be to propose such a conceptualization.

Because it implicates anxiety as the principal etiologic factor in schizophrenia, the present interpretation is, of course, a psychological one and contrasts with biochemical interpretations. To posit that psychological factors are primary is not, however, to claim that physiological factors are never involved. It must not be forgotten that all psychological processes have neural and thus chemical bases and that when we speak of psychological processes we are implicitly speaking in terms of underlying—albeit unknown —neural processes. A functional interpretation of schizophrenia thus does not deny that neural entities are involved but argues only that schizophrenia can result—under certain conditions—when these neural entities are themselves functioning in a natural and nonpathological manner.

But if the existence of underlying physiological mechanisms is granted, how can we be certain that direct pathology in these entities cannot *also* lead to—or at least contribute to—schizophrenia? The answer is, we cannot be sure: hence, my purpose here is not to hold that schizophrenia cannot be caused by physiological factors, but only that it can be caused by primarily psychological factors.

It is worth remembering that even though schizophrenia may be primarily functional it is still important to understand it physiologically, and that even though it might prove to be primarily physiological it would still be important to understand it behaviorally.

The general plan of this paper is as follows. The first two sections will be devoted to the development of a general conceptual framework, and the last six sections will concern the application of this theoretical formulation to certain problems of schizophrenia. Specifically, the purposes of the succeeding sections are: first, to describe the underlying theoretical orientation; second, to present an interpretation of the nature of anxiety; third, to show how this interpretation applies to the general problem of schizophrenia; fourth, to examine the problems of schizophrenic avoidance and withdrawal; fifth, to consider some of the problems of hallucinations; sixth, to consider distortions in reality perception in terms of the general theoretical orientation; seventh, to offer an interpretation of thinking disorder in schizophrenia; and eighth, to indicate and consider several general questions raised by the interpretation of schizophrenia presented in the earlier sections.

Many of the ideas to be proposed are somewhat speculative and programmatic, and they are not presented as constituting a completed theory of schizophrenia. The purposes of this paper will be met if it serves to open new possibilities for the understanding of schizophrenia.

THE PERCEPTUALIZATION PROCESS

The theoretical model to be employed here is framed in terms of the process whereby one perceives his world. It does not ignore overt behaviors, but it sees these behaviors as being energized and directed by tendencies to obtain or to avoid certain kinds of perceptions. In order to develop a theoretical structure, it is useful to have a basic conceptual unit in terms of which more elaborate concepts can be evolved, and in the present interpretation this unit will be the *percept*. Although the process of perceiving is phenomenally continuous and implies an on-going procession of changing content, it is possible to conceive of its content as being constituted of separate, static units. These units are what I have chosen to call *percepts*. A succession of conscious percepts would be equivalent to the stream of subjective life. These percepts could arise either from the just preceding sensory input or from re-examination and reorganization of older percepts retained as memories. As used here *percept* will refer not only to content that is substantively present, but also to content that once was perceived but is now a part of the memory system. Thus, *percept* will be the generic term for data that pass through an individual's awareness and remain with him. This is somewhat broader than pure information or cognition; feelings are represented in percepts quite as much as formal, affectless pieces of information.

Although it would be desirable to define *percept* more rigorously, and preferably in neurological terms (1), there are not sufficient data in this field to make such an attempt more than mere speculation. Actually, the term can be quite useful as a *conceptual* unit for theoretical exposition, quite apart from whether the course of perception actually is divided into separate units, or percepts. As a matter of fact, in the area of personality, *percept* can probably be used with as much precision as the more familiar *stimulus* and *response*. Many people mistakenly tend to think of *stimulus* and *response* as being quite precise and as referring to completely specifiable conditions. This impression is probably due to the use of these terms in studies of reaction time, serial learning, conditioning, and other artificially limited situations. When one applies these terms to the more dynamic personality processes, however, they lose their sharply defined quality. Consequently, the major personality theories—such as those of Freud, Goldstein, Sullivan, and Rogers—have not found stimulus-response concepts helpful, and a unit framed directly in terms of mental processes, such as percept, would appear to be useful. It goes without saying, of course, that, regardless of the terms used, the major deductions of any theory must be stated in terms of testable predictions.

One can conceive of mental life as consisting of two processes: (a) obtaining and receiving percepts, and (b) assimilating or integrating these percepts. This is what one does, hour after hour: it is the substance of the stream of mental life. These two processes—the reception of new percepts, and their assimilation into perceptual systems—appear to be complementary and can be considered as two aspects of a single, unitary function. We may refer to this whole process as perceptualization. Although since proposing this term (2) I have learned that it is used somewhat differently by Grayson (3) and Arieti (4), it seems best to adhere to my original usage.

Let us examine the two aspects of perceptualization in detail.

The Influx of Percepts   There appear to be two sources of perceptual input. The first is chance. These percepts are not actively sought, but instead are thrust upon the individual. A great many, perhaps most, of our percepts are of this nature—*e.g.*, percepts of natural realities such as the alternation of day and night; or of events like the death of a loved one or the loss of a job; or of the actions of other people toward one. However, while the environment usually tends to provide for a relatively constant influx of new percepts, it does not always do this. If the theories that hold that the dominant motivational tendency is to reduce stimulation to a minimum (5, 6) were correct, then persons would tend to seek minimal perceptual influx and to resist changes from this state. Observation, however, clearly indicates that this is not the case. On the contrary, when there are few new percepts naturally present, the individual tends to feel bored and to seek new percepts actively.

The second source of perceptual influx, then, is those percepts actively sought. It is particularly to be noted that the percepts sought must have some variability, some novelty; it is not so much percepts *per se* which are sought, as new percepts.

I have accounted for this characteristic of people by postulating the existence of *a natural tendency to experience new percepts* (2). The existence of this kind of human proclivity has been commented upon by others. Fenichel (6) discussed a "stimulus hunger," though he saw this as a detour toward the goal of not being stimulated. Linton (7) noted that the need for novel experiences appears to be common to all cultures. Woodworth has proposed that ". . . perception is always driven by a direct, inherent motive

which might be called the will to perceive" (8, p. 123). Nissen concluded
that "A function or capacity of the sense organs is to perceive and to know,
and this is one of the more important drives of all organisms" (9, p. 318).
And Hebb has referred to the necessity of accepting "a sort of exploratory-
curiosity-manipulatory drive, which essentially comes down to a tendency to
seek varied stimulation" (10, p. 247).

In recent years a number of studies have dealt with this tendency, by
whatever name it may be called. Harlow and his associates have demonstrated that monkeys learn to solve puzzles "when no motivation is provided other than the presence of the puzzle" (11, p. 29; 12). Using rats as
experimental subjects, Montgomery (13) and his associates demonstrated
that what they term "the exploratory drive" can provide a basis for discrimination learning. Berlyne has written: "More and more psychologists
have recently been turning to a certain set of related and hitherto neglected
phenomena. These include curiosity and exploratory behavior in infra-
human animals, curiosity in the human being, manipulatory drives and
attention to change" (14, p. 238).

Aside from these and similar studies on animals, there have been several
pertinent studies (15–19) on human subjects. Among theoretical psychologists the manifest facts of human curiosity and desire for variety have received attention for many years—e.g., from James (20), McDougall (21),
Troland (22), and most recently, White, who has written: "There is reason
to believe that the urge to explore, and to manage what we explore, is a
human urge as fundamental as the urge to procreate" (23, p. 40).

On the basis of the great intensity, and the apparent ubiquity of the
tendency to maintain perceptual novelty and variability, it is reasonable to
conceive of it as innate, although it may to some extent be based on, or
inhibited by, early experiences (24). Evidence for the intensity of the tendency has come especially from studies on sensory deprivation.

In the first of these studies, carried out by Bexton, Heron, and Scott
(25) at McGill University, students were isolated in a small room. There
was a bed, and opportunity was allowed for eating and going to the toilet.
There was a light, but the subjects wore translucent glasses to minimize
visual pattern perception and heavy gloves to cut down tactual stimulation.
The room was soundproofed although there was some sound from an air
conditioner. After some time in this environment all the subjects became
restless and bored and made dramatic attempts to provide perceptual variety
by singing, whistling, tapping their cuffs together and the like. Vernon and
Hoffman (26) and Lilly (27) also studied the effects of drastic reduction in
sensory input on normal subjects. Vernon noted the need to communicate,
and Lilly noted the strong desire for stimuli and activity.

Ormiston (28) postulated that sensory deprivation should increase the need for stimulation. He used apparent movement thresholds as a measure of stimulus need and obtained results in accord with his prediction.

The Assimilation of Percepts By *assimilation* I mean that process whereby percepts enter harmoniously and congruently into systematic conjunction with percepts which were experienced previously and have been incorporated into the apperceptive mass. Essentially, assimilation appears to consist of a kind of *classification,* or *categorization,* of percepts in such a manner that they fit congruently with previous percepts. Percepts can be classified in many different ways, but it can be hypothesized that people tend to develop particular patterns according to which given percepts are assimilated. These patterns may be termed *conceptual schemata (schema).* They may be thought of as relatively enduring plans or programs for the ordering of percepts. A person may assimilate percepts according to the conceptual schemata that he is intelligent, or that his wife loves him, or that people are untrustworthy. The construct of conceptual schema is related to concepts such as attitude, belief, and expectation.

If incoming percepts fit harmoniously into conceptual schemata already present, they may be assimilated easily; if they do not so fit, considerable *restructuring* of the schemata may be required before assimilation can occur. In psychotherapy this restructuring is often called "working through," but it is not peculiar to psychotherapy. Restructuring frequently requires additional percepts which modify the conceptual schemata involved. For example, suppose that one tends to assimilate percepts of an acquaintance around the conceptual schema that this acquaintance is punctual; suppose, however, that the acquaintance is late for an appointment; the percepts of this tardiness cannot easily be assimilated, and the person may then seek percepts that will permit assimilation without modification of his conceptual schema (*e.g.,* his watch is fast and his acquaintance was not really late); if such attempts fail the person may find it necessary to revise the schema of punctuality in terms of which he perceives his acquaintance.

The term *incongruency* may be used to refer to those characteristics of either percepts or conceptual schemata which make assimilation difficult. It implies the existence of contradictions, anomalies, and discordances among percepts and conceptual schemata. The simplest example of this is perhaps ambivalence. Other examples are: An individual loses by death someone close and important to him—the percepts associated with the death are incongruent with the conceptual schemata according to which the individual has assimilated percepts concerning the lost person. An individual fails in an examination—the perception of this failure is incongruent with his conceptual schema that he is extremely intelligent. A man, on the basis of casual conversation with someone at a cocktail party, surmises that this person teaches art in a college, but after the party his wife remarks to him that during other conversation the person indicated that he had never heard of Picasso—these percepts are incongruent with the conceptual schema that the person is an art teacher.

It appears that conceptual schemata are sometimes organized into more inclusive conceptual systems. For example, it can be hypothesized (29) that in most people conceptions of what is good and what is liked, and also of what is bad and what is disliked, are to some extent linked together. Percepts which are congruent with regard to one conceptual schema may be incongruent with regard to another. Thus, the perception of something as both good and liked would be congruent and hence easy to assimilate, whereas the perception of something as bad and liked would be incongruent and hence difficult to assimilate.

We may suppose that the greater the number of percepts assimilated according to a given conceptual schema the greater the stability of that schema and the stronger the resistance to restructuring. If the number of percepts incongruent with a given schema become great enough, then the schema may become untenable, resulting in the unassimilation of the previously assimilated percepts, and touching off a search for more adequate conceptual schemata.

Herbart (30), in 1824, was perhaps the first to attempt a psychological analysis of that process I am calling assimilation. In recent years, Lecky (31) proposed a theory of self-consistency to which I am very much indebted. Rogers' (32) theory of the self proposes that man reacts not so much to environmental stimuli *per se* as to his perceptions of these stimuli, and that these perceptions tend to be integrated into a consistent interrelationship. Rogers uses the term incongruence to refer to "a discrepancy between the actual experience of the organism and the self picture of the individual insofar as it represents that experience" (33, p. 96). Peak (34) has hypothesized that certain attitudes are due to *disparities* between perceptions. Festinger (35) has presented a theory of cognitive *dissonance,* which postulates the seeking of cognitions that will reduce dissonance. Kelly's (36) theory of personal constructs concerns ways of construing perceptions in such a manner as to minimize incompatibilities.

As I understand them, Lecky, Rogers, Peak, Festinger, and perhaps Kelly also, are alike in implying that the basic tendency is to achieve harmony, to get rid of incongruence, dissonance, or disparity. To me, it seems more satisfactory to postulate a tendency to assimilate percepts. In this way we can avoid the very questionable assumption that persons always seek a state of minimal incongruency, and we can allow for the active seeking for novelty, since novelty frequently implies a certain degree of incongruency.

I am grateful to Dr. Leona Tyler for calling my attention to the similarity of my views on assimilation to the theory of Piaget (37, 38). Piaget considers assimilation to be the fundamental fact of psychic development and points out that it is a concept common to both physiology and psychology. His concept of assimilation is a little broader than that presented here, particularly in his emphasis on sensorimotor functions. His concept of accommodation and my term *restructuring* are at least somewhat related, as are his *schema* and my *conceptual schema*.

So far I have discussed the two aspects of perceptualization—the tendency to seek novel and variable perceptual influx and the tendency to assimilate percepts. It is my contention that it is necessary to keep in mind the complementary nature of these two tendencies in order to see anything approaching the whole picture. Perceptualization is not to be thought of as working toward the *end* of complete stability, but rather as a continual *process,* which may proceed at various rates. The hypothesis may be offered that there exists—as a function of a number of conditions—an *optimal perceptualization rate* and that the affect concomitant with such a rate is one of pleasure. Similarly, it can be suggested that a very high perceptualization rate is felt as exciting and a very low rate as boring. This connection of pleasure with process rather than end is not new (39, 40); Lecky speaks of pleasure in connection with the overcoming of difficulties and notes that "continuous pleasure demands the continuous solution of new problems" (31, p. 67).

Perceptualization is not to be conceived of as an instinct, or a motive, or a need, but simply as something that the nervous system does, in the same basic manner in which the stomach digests food, the circulatory system distributes blood, and the like. If this is the case, then it is reasonable to look for disturbances and anomalies in perceptualization in order better to understand the functional psychopathologies.

ANXIETY

This section will examine the situation which arises when assimilation of percepts is difficult or impossible. It is proposed that unassimilated percepts tend to accumulate and that it is meaningful to speak of the total quantity or magnitude of unassimilated material. This quantity, it is further suggested, underlies the feeling of anxiety (2, 29). Although the nature of this relationship is problematical, it seems most reasonable to suppose that anxiety is related directly to the ratio of unassimilated to assimilated percepts. Thus it appears that in children—in whom there is presumably a lower absolute quantity of assimilated material than in adults—a lesser quantity of unassimilable material is required to cause anxiety. For the present, however, we will hypothesize merely that *anxiety is some function of the magnitude of unassimilated material.*

This is in accord with the view that anxiety can result from a plethora of changes and new circumstances. A sudden great increase of unassimilated material probably underlies the states of psychic trauma and panic. In most instances this would result not from new experiences *per se,* but from the destabilization of previously assimilated systems of percepts.

Although the present view is not framed along neurological lines, it must be taken for granted that the functions proposed here have ultimately anatomical and physiological bases. Therefore, certain physiological conditions or biochemical intrusions might under certain conditions affect directly the neural representations of anxiety in the absence of unassimilated percepts. There is some evidence that certain drugs (*e.g.,* epinephrine [41]) and certain biochemical imbalances can result in what is apparently a feeling of anxiety. The possibility must not be overlooked, however, that what is affected might be the perceptual apparatus, so that strange and incongruous percepts, difficult to assimilate, would be received.

Anxiety as described here is a feeling-tone of mental anguish and is to be distinguished from restlessness and readiness for action. It seems likely that certain muscular and glandular changes associated with preparation for heightened action sometimes result from anxiety, but it would be a mistake to equate such tensions with anxiety, because it is doubtful that anxiety invariably leads to heightened tension, and because conditions other than anxiety—such as alertness, fatigue, and metabolic factors—also affect the tension level.

The present interpretation may, of course, be too simple. It might turn out to be necessary to take account of the nature of the percepts involved, so that unassimilated percepts in some areas (*e.g.,* marital relations) could cause more anxiety than an equal quantity of unassimilated percepts in other areas (*e.g.,* one's progress in school). Such a change, however, would remove much of the elegance of the present interpretation. That certain areas of experience are more anxiety-provoking than others is, of course, obvious. But because of their importance the total mass of percepts in those areas is far higher than in others, so that there appears to be no necessity for positing any actual differences among percepts as to the anxiety which their lack of assimilation may provoke. Further, it should be remembered that the amount of anxiety actually generated by incoming unassimilable percepts is more a matter of the extent to which they bring about the unassimilation of previously assimilated material than of their quantity *per se*—and in this regard there would, of course, be considerable variation among percepts of different contents.

There appear to be at least four factors that can make assimilation difficult and thus result in anxiety.

(a) Excessively high rate of influx. If too many things happen too quickly percepts may accumulate more rapidly than they can be assimilated.

(b) Extreme novelty. If incoming percepts are extremely novel—without being so unique as to be meaningless—considerable restructuring might be required and hence assimilation would be retarded.

(c) Additional percepts necessary to assimilation will not be available until later. To the extent that there is excessive uncertainty about the future, percepts depending for their assimilation upon what is to happen in the future would be difficult to assimilate.

(d) Incongruencies in the content of percepts and the systems into which they would be assimilated.

The first three factors would tend to disappear over time; hence, the last—incongruency—would seem to be most significant in the generation of long term, fairly stable patterns of anxiety. While most incongruencies are developed through experiences, it is possible that certain innate factors also play a role; the work of Hebb (42) on anthropoid fears may be so interpreted.

In order to test the hypothesis of a relationship between incongruency and anxiety, the author devised a technique for estimating the extent of incongruency between one's values—his judgments of what is proper and improper—and his feelings—what he likes and dislikes. In this technique the subject is given a number of items, such as "marriage," "the way my father treats me," "telling someone off," and is asked for each to indicate how he evaluates it (basically Good or Bad) and how he feels about it (basically Like or Dislike). The subject's total incongruency score is a weighted average of the discrepancies between his values and his feelings. Thus, liking something which he considers bad indicates an incongruency, whereas disliking it is considered congruent. Several studies (29) with this technique, while not completely unambiguous in their results, have tended to support the correlation between incongruency and anxiety. Clemes (43), studying relations among self-percepts of subjects, also found evidence for this relationship. It is to be noted that the present view does not predict a perfect relationship between incongruency and anxiety, because factors other than incongruency

contribute to anxiety, and because a person may be able to avoid experiences
—and hence the build-up of unassimilable percepts—in his areas of incongruency.

In addition to these studies performed in the context of the present
conceptualization, there are several other pertinent papers in the literature.
Funk (44) found a correlation of .43 between anxiety and "religious conflict"; since conflictive material can be interpreted as incongruent, this finding is consonant with the present view. Block and Thomas (45) reported a
correlation of —.69 between self to self-ideal congruency and the Pt scale
of the MMPI; inasmuch as the Pt scale is highly correlated (46) with a measure of anxiety (Taylor MAS), this finding can be interpreted as lending
tentative support to the present conceptualization.

It can be hypothesized that *the greater a person's anxiety the stronger
should be his tendency to assimilate new percepts that cannot be avoided.*
This is based on the assumption that an anxious person already has a high
level of unassimilated material and so would strive to prevent the level from
rising still higher. Suinn (47) presented subjects with ambiguous material in
such a manner that they could either leave it ambiguous or attempt to make
sense of it. He assumed that making sense of the material represented attempts at assimilation and predicted that more anxious subjects should
manifest such attempts to a greater extent than less anxious subjects. His
results failed to reach statistical significance but were in the predicted direction. Two other studies, although performed in different theoretical contexts, lend support to the above hypothesis. Smock (48) found that subjects
under stressful conditions tended to attempt resolution of ambiguous stimuli
more quickly than subjects under nonstressful conditions (the work of
Binder [49], however, indicates that this relationship is quite complex).
Brim and Hoff (50) found frustrated subjects to show an increased desire
for certainty. Because it seems reasonable to interpret an increased desire
for certainty as one expression of a stronger tendency for assimilation, this
finding also appears to support the present view.

Another hypothesis this view suggests is that *the more anxious a person
is the more he should resist giving up a conceptual schema according to
which percepts have been assimilated.* The reason is that to give up the
schema would add still further unassimilated percepts to an already high
level. As will be seen later, this hypothesis is particularly important to an
understanding of the persistence of delusions. It also appears to be capable
of rationalizing Smock's findings (48) that threatened subjects cling to incorrect interpretations of ambiguous stimuli longer than do non-threatened
subjects, and the findings of Moffit and Stagner (51) that previously estab-

lished perceptual interpretations are adhered to more tenaciously under conditions of threat.

A third prediction seems reasonable also: *anxious persons should tend to deny or avoid the perception of incongruent stimuli.* Another study by Smock (52) indicates that psychological stress retards the recognition of stimuli containing incongruous elements. Hunt and Schroder (53), using measures of the tendencies to assimilate or to deny negative material (criticism), found anxious persons to show a greater tendency than less anxious persons to deny negative information. If we assume that criticism was incongruent with conceptual schemata relating to the self, as seems reasonable, then this finding is in accord with the above prediction. We will utilize this prediction in our examination of schizophrenic withdrawal.

This formulation of anxiety in terms of the level of unassimilated percepts may be compared with other views of anxiety. In a rough way it is related to the Freudian theory (6, 54), which emphasized, first, blockage of the discharge of accumulated tensions, and, second, threats to the ego. More directly related are other theories already mentioned, which relate anxiety to disharmonies among perceptions. Thus Peak writes that "when disparity increases beyond a certain point it would be expected to result in anxiety" (34, p. 175). And Festinger (35) posits that the existence of dissonance is psychologically uncomfortable. Kelly (36) conceives of anxiety in terms of a person's recognizing that his ways of construing his world are incapable of embracing events which happen to him. Anxiety comes "when the facts at hand do not fit into one's construct system . . ." (36, p. 501). Rogers conceives of anxiety thus: "If an individual dimly perceives . . . an incongruence in himself, then a tension state occurs which is known as anxiety" (33, p. 97).

The emphasis of these authorities on incongruency seems to me correct enough as far as it goes. But in my view incongruency is neither a direct determinant nor the sole determinant of anxiety. Rather, incongruency contributes to anxiety only to the extent that it hinders assimilation and thus results in a backlog of unassimilated material. The existence of marked incongruencies in certain areas of personality thus need not lead to anxiety—if experiences can be avoided in these areas so that new unassimilable percepts do not occur. Unlike the formulations of Rogers and Kelly, the present conceptualization does not depend on the awareness of incongruencies in order to explain anxiety. It is, however, important to note that incongruency must be defined in terms of the individual personality. Thus, two sets of percepts which to one individual are completely irrelevant can hardly be incongruent, though for someone else they might be.

There seems no reason to posit any formal difference between "normal" and pathological anxiety, if both are due to unassimilated material. The difference is seen as one of degree and techniques for dealing with anxiety. Inasmuch as man is held to have inherent tendencies to obtain and assimilate new material, it follows that a certain quantity of as yet unassimilated percepts is to be considered as the natural situation—not as a defect which most people unfortunately have, but rather as a characteristic of optimal functioning. It is posited only that an excess of such material leads to mental stress, and it seems best therefore to restrict the term anxiety to such instances.

The present theory, like those of Rogers and Kelly, differs considerably from those in the Hullian tradition. According to the latter, anxiety is similar to fear, or to conditioned responses to fear (55, 56). Their basic paradigm is: A signal, such as a tone, is paired closely in time with a painful stimulus, such as an electric shock. Eventually the tone itself will cause fear. These conditioned fear responses are termed anxiety, and the implication is that human anxiety is similarly caused.

Many ingenious experiments have been based on this theory (55–58), and the studies have been quite informative on the relationship of fear and fear reduction to learning. But the usefulness of these experiments in the study of learning (56) does not justify acceptance of their assumption that all human anxieties are based ultimately upon reactions to inherently painful stimuli.

A complete understanding of the relationship between anxiety and fear of painful events is hampered by our inadequate understanding of the nature of pain. A tentative interpretation may be suggested: Anxiety and pain are quite different; but the actual experiencing of pain is unpleasant, and thus might be incongruent with the wish to avoid unpleasant percepts. Thus pain percepts would be difficult to assimilate and hence would result in anxiety. Pain does not necessarily lead to anxiety, however. If a particular conceptual schema were such as to be capable of assimilating percepts of pain, then pain would not lead to anxiety, though it would still be unpleasant. Thus a person who conceived of himself as stolid and stoical might find pain percepts relatively easy to assimilate. It is possible to conceive of situations in which pain percepts could actually serve to reconcile unassimilated material and hence lower anxiety.

It is not denied that feelings of anxiety are frequently concomitant with situations of fear, but this does not mean that the two concepts are synonymous. As I have already suggested, percepts concerning a future event might be difficult to assimilate, provided that there is uncertainty or that the future event seems likely to be difficult to assimilate. Thus anticipations of pain, *i.e.*, fear, may yield unassimilable percepts and thus anxiety. In this manner we might explain, *e.g.*, the anxiety which develops in the dentist's waiting room.

The above comments are not intended to deprecate the importance of learning in the development of anxiety. The effects of learning appear to be most profound in the development of particular conceptual schemata leading to incongruencies, but the present view does not deny that certain cues may become linked with anxiety by associative learning and hence capable in themselves of evoking anxiety. My objection to the stimulus-response interpretation of anxiety is not that it is wrong, but that it is inadequate.

GENERAL NATURE OF SCHIZOPHRENIA

We are now in a position to examine in more detail the thesis stated in the opening paragraph of this chapter—that schizophrenia can result from a condition of overwhelming anxiety. But in accordance with the interpretation of anxiety that has been developed in the previous section, this thesis may now be modified to read that schizophrenia can result from an extremely high level of unassimilated percepts. The difference between the present view and others (*e.g.*, Arieti [4]) which emphasize the role of anxiety in the development of schizophrenia is thus in the way in which anxiety is defined.

The general assumption here is that in his living experiences each individual develops conceptual schemata to assimilate the multitude of percepts which his particular environmental exchanges present to him. Depending upon the nature of his experiences, various incongruencies may exist among these conceptual schemata, both the schemata and the incongruencies being unique to the individual. If a series of events occurs, the perceptions of which the individual is unable to assimilate, he will attempt to restructure his conceptual schemata in order to facilitate assimilation. If this attempt is unsuccessful the percepts will accumulate, and if their quantity becomes great enough the resultant effects and reactions will comprise that symptom picture we term schizophrenia.

It is posited, then, that the primary "cause" of schizophrenia is an extremely high quantity of unassimilated percepts. Whether this condition is in itself sufficient to generate schizophrenia is problematical. It is conceivable, for example, that in persons with certain kinds of incongruencies, or having certain typical techniques for dealing with unassimilable material, the outcome of an excessive quantity of unassimilated percepts would be schizophrenia; and that for persons with other kinds of incongruencies, or having other techniques for dealing with unassimilable percepts, the outcome of an excessive quantity of unassimilated percepts would be psychotic depression. Although this question is too conjectural for discussion here, it may be assumed that in any event the particular pattern of symptoms appearing in an instance of schizophrenia is determined largely by the particular personality pattern of the patient.

It is possible that certain kinds of incongruencies make assimilation especially difficult and occur with unusual frequency among schizophrenics. Although this problem is beyond the scope of the present chapter, I would like to call attention to two contemporary research programs which seem to me to be especially pertinent to it. The first of these (Rodnick and Garmezy [59]; Atkinson [60]; Robinson [61]) has produced evidence to indicate that many schizophrenics, primarily those near the "process" (62) end of the morbidity continuum, are relatively more motivated—as compared with normals—by punishment than by reward. This finding suggests that the incongruencies of many schizophrenics concern difficulties in avoidance rather than difficulties in attainment. A second pertinent line of investigation (Bateson, Jackson, Haley, Weakland [63]) concerns the identification in some schizophrenics of what is termed a *double-bind*. This is a peculiar kind of inner problem situation in which alternative choices are contradictory and the person feels forbidden to recognize this fact. It seems apparent that such a complexity of contradictions would make assimilation especially difficult.

It seems likely that if the input of unassimilable percepts were great enough schizophrenic reactions might occur even in the absence of widespread incongruencies. A disorder of this type would be expected to be quite brief. Pertinent to this point is the observation that during World War II patients would sometimes be classified as schizophrenic and then recover very quickly, sometimes even before reaching base hospitals. Such cases were sometimes called "three-day schizophrenia" (64).

I know of no direct evidence that schizophrenia typically is preceded by the condition of a very high level of unassimilated material, although there are a number of observations which can be interpreted to imply that such is the case. For example, schizophrenic reactions often follow a drastic change in one's pattern of living such as is likely to present many new percepts for assimilation. The changes may be such things as making the transition from dependent adolescence to independent adulthood, entering or leaving the armed service, changing jobs, and losing someone close. The more radical or comprehensive the change, *i.e.*, the more new percepts it generates, the more likely a schizophrenic development would be. It would be a mistake, of course, to attribute the sudden development of schizophrenia solely to a period which affords an unusually large number of percepts, because everyone faces such periods and yet few develop schizophrenia. The crucial factor is rather the extent to which, over previous years, such incongruencies have been developed as will prevent the assimilation of the new percepts.

AVOIDANCE AND WITHDRAWAL IN SCHIZOPHRENIA

It can be assumed that the reactions to a large quantity of unassimilated percepts are primarily of two kinds: first, attempts to keep the quantity of unassimilated material from getting even greater; and second, attempts to bring about assimilation of the unassimilated percepts. The first of these kinds of reactions in the case of schizophrenia involves selective avoidances, withdrawal behavior, and apathy; the second concerns delusions and thinking disorders. This section will be concerned with behaviors which can be interpreted as being oriented toward the prevention of an increase in the quantity of unassimilated percepts in an individual in whom this quantity already is very great—that is, the first of the problems just mentioned.

When an individual has a set of percepts that are difficult to assimilate— *i.e.,* a problem situation—his reaction is ordinarily to seek such additional percepts as will resolve the incongruencies and hence permit assimilation— *i.e.,* solution of the problem. If he is unable to attain solution he may keep "trying" older percepts, in an unsuccessful and ruminative manner, or he may stop thinking about the problem and simply "carry" the anxiety engendered by the unassimilated material. Because the data were unassimilable, the likelihood is that any further percepts in the same area of incongruency would likewise be unassimilable. For the person to continue to receive percepts in this area, then, would be tantamount to increasing his level of unassimilated material still further.

On the basis of this analysis it may be hypothesized that persons tend to avoid situations likely to yield percepts in their own unique areas of incongruency. Thus some individuals might avoid situations requiring emotional involvement, others might avoid competitive situations, or heterosexual relations, or contacts with their relatives, and so on. The particular patterns of avoidance presumably would be unique for each person. It is to be noted that so long as a person was able to maintain his *selective avoidances* he would not be particularly anxious. An individual living within the fences of his uniquely circumscribed world is relatively safe from intense anxiety, but he is in a very precarious position since the environment is likely to thrust upon him experiences which he cannot avoid. Hebb, from a somewhat different orientation, has suggested that culturally devised avoidances serve as a protective cocoon to shield man against many emotionally disturbing stimuli, and that "the development of what is called 'civilization' is the protective elimination of sources of acute fear, disgust, and anger . . ." (24, p. 830).

The concept of *selective avoidance* is related to Sullivan's (65) concept of *selective inattention*. The former concept refers to attempts of a person to avoid getting involved in situations likely to yield unassimilable percepts; the latter concept refers to the tendency of a person to fail to recognize the import of stimuli because to do so would cause anxiety. In the present view selective inattention, as well as selective avoidance, can be conceptualized in terms of the attempt to avoid unassimilable percepts.

There is one recent experiment, in our laboratory, which illustrates the phenomenon of selective inattention in areas of incongruency. Byrne, Terrill, and McReynolds (66), using a technique similar to that described earlier, obtained separate measures of incongruency (between values and feelings) in the areas of sex and hostility for 32 psychiatric patients. In one part of the experiment the subjects were shown a series of cartoons and asked to indicate, for each one, whether it represented sex or hostility. It was found that the greater the subject's incongruency in the area of hostility, the fewer cartoons he called hostile and the less accuracy he showed in deciding which ones represented hostility. These relationships reached significance at the .05 level. Analogous trends—though below statistical significance—were found with regard to sexual incongruency and the sex cartoons. The specificity of selective inattention to incongruency is further indicated by the facts that there were no appreciable trends for persons with marked incongruency in the sexual area to misperceive hostile cartoons, nor for persons with marked incongruency in the hostility area to misperceive sexual cartoons.

Probably selective inattention and selective avoidance are to some extent characteristic of all people, but it appears that, in their extreme form, such behaviors are particularly characteristic of many tramps and hoboes, and—within the realm of the psychoses—of what is termed simple schizophrenia. This suggestion, though different in context, is actually very similar to a point made by Arieti, who writes: "Rather than change reality, the simple schizophrenic limits reality. He narrows his horizon to a large extent, so that he will be able to make some kind of compromise with what is left of reality . . ." (4, p. 187).

Along this same line of thought, it seems possible that many hospitalized schizophrenics come to use the pattern of selective avoidance to a predominant extent, regardless of what their diagnosis is or what their admitting symptoms were. The large neuropsychiatric institution is in many respects ideally suited to the facilitation of patterns of avoidance of problem areas.

A person who utilizes selective avoidances to a marked extent may appear quite odd—not only because of the things he does not do, but also because of the things he does. In order to maintain an adequate perceptualization rate, the individual would need to engage in activities which would provide sufficient novelty and change. But many of the normal, typical activities of his fellows would not be open to him because of his selective avoidances: he would thus be forced to engage in more idiosyncratic kinds of interests and activities. This suggestion may explain to a limited extent the rather odd kinds of collections (4) or hobbies characteristic of certain schizophrenics.

In addition to the avoidance of certain perceptual areas there appears to be a general tendency whereby increased anxiety attenuates the tendency to obtain novel percepts. The hypothesis I am suggesting here is that *the strength of the tendency to obtain novel, or variable percepts*—which I have proposed as a basic human characteristic—*is decreased as a function of the quantity of unassimilated material.* Descriptively, this hypothesis states simply that when a person has a large quantity of unassimilated percepts he is less likely to seek still additional percepts that might be unassimilable than he is when he has few unassimilated percepts.

In a preliminary attempt to evaluate the above hypothesis, Bryan and McReynolds (67) attempted to create differing levels of unassimilated percepts in two groups of psychiatric patients. They then presented the subjects with opportunities to choose cards judged to represent novelty or familiarity. As predicted, those subjects assumed to have the lower level of unassimilated percepts chose more novel cards. Although the results of this study were in accord with the hypothesis, it should be pointed out that the experiment was somewhat artificial and that the hypothesis should be tested in a more naturalistic manner.

The hypothesized reduction in the tendency to obtain novel or variable percepts, as a function of the magnitude of unassimilated material, may be the basis of schizophrenic withdrawal. This suggestion is somewhat similar to Pavlov's (68) theory of increased inhibition in schizophrenics as a result of their inability to cope with stimulation. Whereas schizoid withdrawal is probably best described as a pattern of selective avoidances, actual schizophrenic withdrawal appears to be describable as a condition of extremely minimal influx of novel percepts. The most direct evidence for this statement is provided, of course, by the schizophrenic patient who sits mute and

unmoving, uninterested in anything, participating in only the most routin-
ized and unvarying behavior. Such a person would seem to be the very picture of minimal influx of novel perception. Schizophrenic withdrawal, I
suggest, is a kind of functional sensory deprivation. The decrease in the
novelty-seeking tendency should, according to the hypothesis, be most prominent in schizophrenics who have a large quantity of unassimilated material.
Patients who by psychotic reorganization or other symptomatology have
effected assimilation would not be expected to differ appreciably from normals in the strength of the novelty-seeking tendency.

Though the phenomenon of schizophrenic withdrawal has been commented upon widely, systematic studies which would bear upon the above
interpretation are rare. Kanner (69) has reported a condition termed *early
infantile autism* in young children. One of the traits characteristic of this
condition is "an obsessive desire for sameness." As White comments, this
"conveys the impression that the child cannot tolerate anything new; his
sense of security depends upon keeping the environment constant and free
from surprises." It is not certain, of course, that early infantile autism is
related to schizophrenia, but, as White notes, "most workers are inclined to
view it as at least the start of a strong trend in that direction" (70, p. 561).

Since a person does not always know, before he perceives something,
whether it will be novel or familiar, it might be supposed that actually there
would tend to be some inhibition of the influx of all percepts. In connection
with this possibility a report by Goldfarb is especially interesting. He writes:

> Our observations confirm the generalization that the childhood
> schizophrenic seems to lack interest in the outer world. He resists
> social engagement. He accomplishes this by cutting off the major
> perceptual channels used in normal social intercommunication,
> *i.e.,* vision and audition, despite the fact that there is no detect-
> able defect in the sensory apparatus and neuroanatomic substrate
> for hearing and seeing. Indeed there is good evidence that the
> schizophrenic child can hear and see, but he does not look or
> listen. He does not use visual and auditory experiences, so that, in
> effect, he behaves as a nonhearing, nonseeing child (71, p. 650).

There is some evidence that the characteristic of being nonresponsive
to external stimuli is reflected in the EEG. Blum (72) reported that schizophrenics show less alpha responsiveness to photic stimulation than do normals. And Saucer (73) found an impairment in the perception of visual
apparent movement in undifferentiated schizophrenics.

The most dramatic example of schizophrenic withdrawal is catatonic stupor. Straus and Griffith (74) have presented evidence to indicate that this condition is not due to a deficit in motor capacity and that it is not a sleeplike condition. Although their data suggest that the catatonic patient is not nearly so oblivious of what is going on as he may appear to be, yet it would seem undeniable that the catatonic condition does serve effectively to cut down on the influx of new and variable percepts. Not only does the catatonic patient avoid participation in social interactions and normal activities, but also—and in particular—his inhibition on action permits him to avoid having percepts of self-initiated movements. That it is the *perception* of movements, rather than movements *per se,* which is avoided is indicated by the fact that the patient's sleep movements are normal. It is as if the patient had developed a selective avoidance of percepts concerning self-initiated action. Why this particular technique for avoiding novel and possibly unassimilable percepts should appear in some schizophrenics and not in others cannot be explained in terms of the present theoretical model, but we may hypothesize that it would most frequently be utilized by schizophrenics whose habitual modes of categorizing percepts include awareness of voluntary movements.

If it is true that many schizophrenics have a reduced tendency to seek novelty in perception, then their rate of perceptualization would be low, because perceptualization is based upon having a relatively constant input of novel percepts for assimilation. As previously suggested, a low rate of perceptualization appears to underlie the feeling of boredom. If, according to the general conceptualization underlying this paper, an optimal perceptualization rate is necessary for feelings of pleasure and zest, then it follows that the withdrawn schizophrenic is experiencing few such feelings. In a very real sense, if he tends to block all novel percepts then he has nothing to look forward to. The symptom picture of *apathy* would seem to be due to some extent to a continued condition of very minimal perceptualization. A difference between apathy and extreme boredom is that in the latter the afflicted person is eager to do something about the condition, whereas in the former he is resigned to it.

I do not mean to imply that the symptom of apathy can be explained solely in terms of decreased perceptualization, but only that this may be an important factor in apathy. Strassman, Thaler, and Schein (75) reported the development of apathy in some of the United States prisoners of war repatriated by the Chinese and North Koreans. During their imprisonment many of the men exhibited a marked withdrawal of involvement in their situation and became listless and indifferent. In some instances the apathy reached such a degree that the prisoners seemed inclined simply to lie down and wait for death. "Two things," according to the authors, "seemed to save the men close to 'apathy' death: getting him on his feet doing something, no matter how trivial, and getting him interested in some current or future problem" (75, p. 999). Both of these things can be interpreted as affording an increase in perceptualization rate.

It seems probable that low perceptualization, if extreme enough, can be implicated in at least some problems of difficulty in concentrating. Many schizophrenics report great difficulty in maintaining attention, and it is a reasonable conjecture that this characteristic may be due in part to the lessened perceptualization brought about by the schizophrenic's withdrawal. In the pioneering study on experimentally minimized input of variable sensory stimuli—by Bexton, Heron, and Scott—the authors observe that "the subjects reported that they were unable to concentrate on any topic for long while in the cubicle. Those who tried to review their studies or solve self-initiated intellectual problems found it difficult to do so. As a result they lapsed into day-dreaming, abandoned attempts at organized thinking, and let their thoughts wander" (25, p. 72). Similar results are reported by other investigators (27, 76).

Why should a minimal influx of novel percepts make directed, problem-oriented thinking difficult? One possibility is that proposed by Bexton, Heron, and Scott (25), in accordance with Hebb's (10) conception of the vital role of sensory input in maintaining proper functioning of the brain. These investigators believe that maintenance of efficient behavior requires a continually varied sensory input. Their conceptualization is that sensory input has two functions, one a cue function in which specific information is transmitted, and the other a nonspecific or arousal function (77–79) in which the input serves to maintain efficient functioning. This arousal function would be mediated through the reticular system (10, 80). Sharpless (81) has demonstrated that, for a stimulus to evoke the arousal reaction, it must change frequently, and Fuster (82) has supported the role of reticular facilitation on attentive behavior by showing that the efficiency of visual discrimination is improved by direct mild electrical stimulation in the reticular formation.

Regardless of the question of reticular system involvement, however, it seems clear that for some reason organized, directed thinking is affected adversely by an insufficiency of novel perceptual input. And if it is true, as postulated here, that in those schizophrenics who have not achieved resolution of their unassimilated material by psychotic reorganization there is a tendency to avoid novel percepts, then it follows that such patients should manifest difficulty in organized, directed thinking.

THE PROBLEM OF HALLUCINATIONS

Various studies on experimental isolation (25, 27, 76, 83–85) have produced in their subjects not only difficulties in ordered thinking but also various hallucinatory experiences. In general the hallucinatory activity is reported to have appeared after the effects on organized thinking noted above. There were also reports of body image alteration and feelings of depersonalization.

The fact that hallucinations may be produced by drastically reducing the input of variable percepts raises the possibility that the same process may be involved in the hallucinations of schizophrenics. The suggestion here is that in the hallucinating schizophrenic the high level of unassimilated material has led to a drastic decrease in the influx of new percepts, so that the patient can be considered as analogous to the hallucinating subject in experimental isolation. That experimental hallucinations are caused by lack of novel data for perceptualization, rather than by social isolation *per se,* is indicated by a report (86) of a prisoner, now in Alcatraz, who has been in solitary confinement since 1920, yet who has maintained extremely wide intellectual activities and interests, and who has remained completely rational and well-integrated mentally.

This functional interpretation of hallucinations is not incompatible with the fact that hallucinations can sometimes be induced by biochemical means. It is possible that certain drugs and perceptual isolation affect the perceptual apparatus in a similar manner. A study which illustrates this possibility is that by Keller and Umbreit (87), who report that a certain peculiar head-shaking response in reaction to touching an area on the back of the head can be produced in mice by injections of LSD (lysergic acid diethylamide), and that exactly the same response can also be produced in mice by solitary confinement.

Other investigators have directly or indirectly suggested a parallel between hallucinations in schizophrenia and hallucinations induced by perceptual isolation. Lilly, *e.g.,* raised the question: "If the healthy ego is freed of reality stimuli, does it maintain the secondary process, or does primary process take over?" (27, p. 1). Maier (88) specifically suggested that hallucinations under sensory deprivation may be regarded as similar to those reported by mental patients. And Fenichel stated that "it is probable that the mental systems, the stimulation of which produces perceptions, becomes sensitive to stimuli from within whenever the acceptance of further external stimuli is blocked. A blocking of this kind may be caused in very different ways. In the state of sleep the doors to the external world are closed for biological reasons, and therefore thoughts are transformed into hallucinations; in schizophrenia, it is the pathogenic withdrawal of the object cathexes which has the same effect" (6, p. 426).

It should be emphasized that the present proposal actually does not require that there be an absence of novel or changeable situations in order for hallucinations to occur. It is required rather that there be a minimal amount of *assimilation* of novel percepts, *i.e.*, a condition of continued low perceptualization. While obviously perceptualization can be minimized by preventing the input of novel percepts, it is also possible to conceive of a situation in which there is an input of new percepts, yet because the percepts cannot be assimilated there is minimal perceptualization. I am aware that, put this way, the hypothesis would be extremely difficult to test. It is to be noted, however, that hallucinations sometimes occur in individuals under extremely traumatic conditions—*i.e.*, when there is an influx of percepts which cannot be assimilated. Azima and Cramer-Azima (84) have reported the development of hallucinatory activity in one isolation subject for whom there was no experimental blocking of visual input. It is further to be noted that the present hypothesis is not intended to account for the content of hallucinations (which presumably is determined by personality factors), or for the extent to which a patient uses his hallucinations in a psychologically economic manner.

Why should a continued low perceptualization rate contribute to the occurrence of hallucinations? We will examine this question briefly, though to do so will require us to indulge in speculation even more freely than heretofore. A necessary condition for the occurrence of hallucinations appears to be a loss of the capacity for discriminating as to whether percepts are based on stimuli from within one's own self, or upon stimuli from "out there." The nature of this "external-internal" discrimination is unknown, though factors involved in it have long been discussed (*e.g.*, 20). Recently, Maier (88) proposed that the discrimination is hindered by a person's being excessively preoccupied with internal sensations: this suggestion is similar to earlier conceptions that percepts arising from within attain a greater vividness when there is no contrast with the usually more dominant sensations arising from external stimuli and thus "seem like" external stimuli. Dember and Earl (89) have proposed that when a person is bored and is given no assistance by his sensory receptors in obtaining material to relieve this boredom, he may resort to creating new stimuli—as, *e.g.*, in an hallucination.

I would like to offer the conjecture that the "internal-external" discrimination is probably based upon a number of different kinds of cues. An analogy would be depth perception, in which a number of different cues appear to be involved. Some—but not all—of the kinds of cues involved in the "internal-external" discrimination may be: (a) the *vividness,* or relative vividness of the percepts, with the more vivid being judged external (providing they concern data normally received through external receptors); (b) the extent to which the various pertinent percepts are *congruent* with each other (*e.g.,* a person may suppose, on the basis of visual percepts, that the table he perceives is "out there": he predicts, therefore, that if he reaches out his hand he will touch the table; he does so and his prediction is confirmed); and (c) the extent to which one has *control* over the pertinent percepts. If the locus for the perception is actually "out there" the actual structure of the reality perceived will determine predominantly the percepts the person has, whereas if the perception actually is fantasy, the person himself will have predominant control over it—with regard to altering or terminating the perception.

Of these three possible cues, it appears that utilization of the last one, in particular, may be adversely affected by low perceptualization. As noted in the last section, there is reason to believe that continued low perceptualization affects adversely the ability to maintain organized, directed thinking. If one loses the feeling of control over certain of his thoughts, then the percepts involved may to this extent be indistinguishable from percepts arising from external stimuli. It appears possible, then, that one reason why continued low perceptualization makes hallucinations possible is that it renders unusable one cue ordinarily utilized, albeit automatically, in making the discrimination between inner and outer reality.

This particular suggestion, even if valid, of course does not go very far toward unraveling the puzzle of hallucinations, but evidence for the more general hypothesis of low perceptualization's somehow being an important condition for hallucinations is impressive. One way by which this hypothesis could be tested is by experimentally increasing perceptualization in subjects who are active hallucinators. If the hypothesis is valid their hallucinations should decrease. This suggestion is similar to Maier's (88) idea of treating schizophrenics with intense external stimulation, but it is also different. According to the present conceptualization intense stimulation would not be effective unless it yielded novel, variable percepts, and even this would not be effective unless the patient assimilated such percepts. It seems likely that unless carefully carried out, experimentation of this kind could increase the patient's anxiety.

In concluding this section I would like to note that hallucinations—*i.e.,* distorted perceptions—and delusions—*i.e.*, distorted beliefs—need to be kept separate, though they are closely related. Whether a person *believes* his hallucinatory images actually to be "out there" is a different matter from whether the images *appear* to be external. In the isolation studies with normals, *e.g.*, the subjects did not accept their hallucinations as reality.

THE STRUCTURE OF REALITY

The last two sections were devoted to a consideration of those characteristics of schizophrenia which, it was held, can be attributed in part to the existence of a large accumulation of unassimilated percepts. This and the next section will examine certain characteristics of schizophrenia which, it will be proposed, can be attributed in large part to attempts to bring about the assimilation of unassimilated material. The symptoms of schizophrenia which will be considered are, in this section, reality distortion and, in the following section, thinking disorder.

In order to examine the question of why people sometimes strongly believe that which is "unreal," *i.e.*, the question of reality distortion, we must first examine why they so frequently believe that which is "real"—or, more broadly, we must ask how it is that people come to believe anything. We are not concerned here with ultimate reality, but rather with the process whereby people come to *believe* that certain things are real—*i.e.*, with the origin and persistence of beliefs and attitudes.

The ancient Chinese philosopher, Chuang-Tze, once dreamed that he was a butterfly. When he awoke he questioned whether he were a man who had dreamed he was a butterfly, or a butterfly now dreaming he was a man (90, pp. 691–92). This is the old problem of cognizing reality, on which James (20) wrote so effectively. Our concern here is not in the nature of reality, but in the determinants of what seems real. It would be a mistake to consider that people "naturally" perceive reality correctly and that the only mystery is why they sometimes misperceive reality: both kinds of beliefs are equally in need of explanation.

As suggested earlier, assimilation of percepts is assumed to occur according to particular conceptual schemata which an individual develops. In certain instances, it appears, conceptual schemata may have the form of propositions, such as "the world is round," "Joe is reliable," or "the world is against me." Conceptual schemata of this kind may be described as indicating convictions or beliefs concerning the relationships between given categories. It is proposed that all beliefs can be conceptualized in terms of this paradigm—*i.e.*, a belief is a propositional schema that one uses in assimilating his perceptual world. Our attempt is to bring within one system of explanation both rational and irrational beliefs, and beliefs extending all the way from those in which there may be considerable doubt—as, *e.g.*, one's belief that he will get a high grade in an examination—to those in which there is complete certainty—as, *e.g.*, one's belief that the sun will rise tomorrow.

It can be posited that, other things being equal, the greater the number of percepts assimilated according to a belief, the stronger and more persistent is that belief. For example, a person who had assimilated numerous percepts according to the conceptual schema that people in general are trustworthy would tend to believe this more strongly, and to exhibit greater persistence in it, than a person who had assimilated few percepts according to this particular conceptual schema. Actually, of course, beliefs cannot be considered in isolation: a possible belief that might assimilate a large number of percepts might nevertheless not be adopted if, by virtue of being incongruent with some other belief, it would threaten the assimilation of an even greater amount of material.

Each person has an extremely large number of beliefs or interpretations of reality which, since they are never called into question, are ordinarily not thought of as beliefs at all. These are conceptual schemata according to which the great multitude of percepts concerning the objects and events of one's environment are assimilated and which help to give stability to his perceptual world. I refer to such underlying principles as that night follows day, that effects have causes, that time passes and the events of yesterday are gone, and the like.

One implication of the present view is that one's picture of reality is determined largely by the extent to which elements of this picture facilitate the assimilation of his perceptions. It may appear at first glance that such an interpretation is inadequate to account for the correspondence between the way people generally believe the world of physical objects to be and the way this world actually is. It can be assumed, however, that actually reality of this kind is consistent and that as additional percepts are received which reflect this reality there would typically be a tendency for the individual to find unsatisfactory those conceptual schemata that are incongruent with reality. As time passes, therefore, the individual would tend to restructure his schemata in such a manner as to bring them in closer accord with the real world.

The present interpretation of beliefs appears to be somewhat related to Krech's (91) proposal that attitudes can be conceptualized as problem-solving attempts, and also to Osgood and Tannenbaum's (92) theory of attitude change, in which incredulity is related to incongruity.

The hypothesis that beliefs can be conceptualized as ways of interpreting things in such a manner as to resolve incongruences and hence bring about or maintain assimilation of percepts is not the same as saying that people necessarily believe what they want to believe. For example, a person may be convinced that the world is against him, despite the fact that in a certain sense he would very much prefer the world to be for him. But if he has assimilated innumerable percepts around the conception that the world is against him—if he has made sense of things in this way—then the potency of this view will be extremely great, and indeed to give it up—though this might seem to be "pleasant"—would result in the unassimilation of a large number of percepts and hence anxiety.

With this background let us turn to the problem of deviant beliefs in schizophrenia, in particular to the problem of delusions. It appears that delusional beliefs are not formally different from nondelusional beliefs: both exist because they serve to facilitate the assimilation of percepts, and both are held strongly to the extent that they do this.

We have supposed that in the onset of schizophrenia there is an extremely high level of unassimilated material, due to the fact that the patient has not been able to assimilate the perceptions of his experiences according to his existent conceptual schemata. To the extent that the unassimilated material remains at a high level the symptoms discussed in the two preceding sections would be expected to appear. But the patient may be able, by drastic restructuring of conceptual schemata, to bring about marked reduction in the level of unassimilated material. Such restructuring—in line with the above discussion—would necessarily bring about a change in the patient's interpretation of reality. Examples of this would be: the patient may come to assimilate previously unassimilable percepts of failure around a new belief that certain persons are preventing him from succeeding; or he may assimilate percepts of being apparently ignored by certain other persons—which previously, let us say, meant that he was less important than he wanted to be, and hence were unassimilable—around the new view that actually he is too superior for other people to approach and has a God-given mission. If the changes in conceptual restructuring are widespread enough, they may comprise what Jenkins has referred to as *psychotic reorganization*. In describing this process Jenkins states: "A system of fixed false beliefs may be evolved which serves to reduce some of the intolerable inner tensions of the personality at the expense of reality distortion" (93, p. 745).

The use of new schemata in assimilating material is clearest in those instances in which there is first a period of rumination concerning unassimilated percepts and then a *sudden clarification* (94) in which the unassimilated material dramatically becomes organized according to a new conception. Cameron has noted that "what the patient reports as sudden clarification seems to belong to the group of terminal reactions which in normal behavior we call *closure*. In delusions the closure consists of the patient's sudden discovery of a formulation which justifies all of his suspicions and premonitions by uniting them all under one plausible hypothesis" (94, pp. 397–98).

Although almost all schizophrenics apparently utilize delusions to some extent, it is the paranoid schizophrenic who most characteristically devises special conceptual schemata in order to bring about assimilation. Outside the realm of pathology this same process can perhaps be seen in cases of dogmatic cultists and may be related to the sudden crystallization of percepts in religious conversions (I am indebted to Dr. Richard Jenkins for these suggestions). A rationalization is a common example of adopting a new conceptual schema according to which material previously unassimilable can be assimilated.

In order to test the hypothesis that delusions represent one way of reacting to anxiety Beach (95), in our laboratory, studied a group of schizophrenics manifesting delusional thinking. She conceptualized delusions as tendencies toward closure (94) and predicted that this tendency would be greater in patients with high anxiety than in patients with low anxiety. She used a measure of auditory closure preference and an anxiety inventory (96) and obtained a significant positive correlation (.46)—in accordance with the prediction—between these measures for patients judged to have relatively systematized delusions; for patients judged to have relatively unsystematized delusions, however, the correlation was insignificant (−.27). The reason for this discrepancy is unclear, and the matter merits further experimental study.

In terms of the present interpretation the intensity of a schizophrenic delusion is a function of the quantity of percepts integrated by the delusion —or, to put it another way, of the extreme anxiety that would result if the delusion were dispensed with. This does not mean that any particular delusion is necessarily persistent. But it does imply that the patient, if he gives up one delusion, is likely to turn to another which will handle a greater number of otherwise unassimilable percepts. Indeed, it may be suggested that many apparently new delusions actually are only replacements for previous, perhaps less dramatic delusions. A patient who develops a delusion of omnipotence, *e.g.*, may be reacting to a delusional interpretation of his own degree of uniqueness.

If it is true that the formal characteristics of delusional beliefs are the same as for other beliefs, then we must ask why it is that certain persons can develop and maintain delusions, despite their irrational nature. Part of the answer would be that the mass of unassimilated material is so extreme, and the incongruencies so great, that the socially irrational schema is the best the patient can do. Still, how can the patient so conveniently overlook contrary evidence, evidence which in many instances is seemingly obvious? There are two answers here, I think: the patient avoids percepts incongruent with his delusion, and he seeks percepts congruent with it—or, to put it another way, he avoids percepts contradictory to his delusional beliefs, and he seeks percepts supportive of them. I know of no experimental evidence bearing directly upon this hypothesis, but many behavioral characteristics of paranoid schizophrenics appear to be in accord with it. Thus paranoid schizophrenics frequently appear to be unable or unwilling even to consider evidence contrary to their delusions. At the same time they often seem to show a remarkable facility for interpreting all kinds of behaviors in terms of their delusions.

The postulated tendencies to avoid evidence contrary to and to seek evidence supportive of delusional beliefs, in order to maintain assimilation of the material these delusions encompass, are apparently similar to Cameron's (94) concepts of *reaction-sensitivities* and *reaction-insensitivities*. I would like also to call attention again to Festinger's (35) theory of cognitive dissonance. Festinger notes that dissonance may be reduced either by changing certain elements or by selectively adding new cognitive elements which are consonant with the view which one would maintain. With regard to the latter, he gives the example of a person who wishes to smoke but feels that he should not because of danger to his health, and who therefore seeks out information indicating that smoking will not, after all, injure his health. Festinger's view here and my inference that patients with delusions seek percepts congruent with their delusions appear to have much in common.

As is well known, many schizophrenic delusions include interpretations of the world as threatening, hostile, and untrustworthy. This is another way of saying that many schizophrenics assimilate percepts according to such schemata. It has been called to my attention by Dr. Leonard Ullmann that patients manifesting such projective, externalizing kinds of delusions would tend, in order to maintain the delusions, to be particularly sensitized to percepts of threat—the externalizing delusional patient has a vested interest, as it were, in perceiving the world as threatening. He would, paradoxically, actively seek percepts which, considered *per se*, without reference to the total context, would appear to be stressful and anxiety-provoking. Shannon (97) and Ullmann (98), in our laboratory, have found evidence that patients judged to externalize their problems do in fact show marked sensitivity to presumably threatening stimuli, as indicated both by recognition thresholds and by emotional verbal expressiveness.

Schizophrenic disturbances in reality perception include not only idiosyncratic and bizarre beliefs, as discussed above, but also certain *feelings of unreality*. These feelings appear often to take the form of doubt as to what is real and what is unreal. This doubt would imply that in the patient's searching for conceptual schemata according to which he might assimilate large masses of percepts he has hit upon two or more quite different, yet equally adequate, sets of conceptual schemata and consequently is unable to reject either. A common nonpathological example of this situation is afforded by a person awaking from a vivid dream: there is a brief period when the dream-world schemata of where he is, what he is doing, etc. and the schemata according to which the actual world may be assimilated are equally plausible. While this situation persists, the person may have a feeling of confusion, of lack of orientation, a sense of unreality. The situation is terminated when the percepts which may be assimilable in terms of "actual-world" schemata become dominant over percepts which may be assimilable in "dream-world" schemata. In order to hasten this development, the person may take some action—such as getting up and turning on a light--which is calculated to increase the influx of percepts from the real world.

THOUGHT DISTURBANCES IN SCHIZOPHRENIA

It would be expected that many schizophrenics would show highly idiosyncratic patterns of perception, both with regard to the percepts induced by given stimuli and the conceptual schemata used in assimilation. There are a number of reasons for this prediction. One is that in most instances the schizophrenic has for some time been relatively withdrawn and isolated from the normal course of experiences and so has not had adequate opportunity for developing normal perceptual responses to stimuli. Another reason is that, because of his patterns of selective inattention and selective avoidance and his needs to obtain certain percepts in order to maintain precarious conceptual schemata, the percepts of the schizophrenic would tend to be determined to a disproportionate extent by unique personality factors. Still another reason is that as a result of his low rate of perceptualization the withdrawn schizophrenic finds it difficult to maintain concentrated attention on given stimulus factors and so would tend to have erratic and haphazard patterns of thought.

The perceptual idiosyncrasies of schizophrenics are most apparent in the hebephrenic and mixed types of the disorder, but they are to some degree apparent in all schizophrenics. It is largely this characteristic—including the succession of percepts which makes up the train of thought—which makes it difficult for other persons to establish emphatic rapport with schizophrenic patients. The idiosyncratic nature of the percepts of many schizophrenics, particularly in those areas in which they have numerous unassimilated percepts, is indicated not only by bizarre and highly personal verbal associations, but also by psychological tests which sample the perceptual process, such as the Rorschach.

A study by the author (99, 100) provides experimental evidence that many of the perceptions of schizophrenics differ from those of normal people. Schizophrenics and normals (as well as other groups) were shown 50 blot areas on the Rorschach cards and asked questions such as "Could this be a bat?" "Could this part be a butterfly?" It was found that the schizophrenics —not including those of the paranoid type—differed significantly from the normals in terms of the concepts they reported seeing and not seeing. Some of the schizophrenics reported seeing almost all of the concepts presented, and others reported seeing very few of them; but even when the data were evaluated in such a manner as to be independent of these tendencies the schizophrenics' responses still differed significantly from those of the normals. The findings of this study have been corroborated and extended by Johnson (101).

With this background we are prepared to examine the question of thinking disorders in schizophrenia. Actually delusional thinking, which we have already considered, represents a disorder in thinking since it is based upon faulty premises, but the term *thinking disorder* is more typically applied to difficulties in the adequate use of concepts and in the formation of appropriate abstractions, and it is in this sense that the term will be used here. It is generally accepted that thinking disorders are characteristic of many, though not all, schizophrenics. It seems apparent that perceptual idiosyncrasies, as discussed above, would be a major contributing factor to thinking disturbance, since efficient thought processes require the maintenance of attention on the appropriate stimulus aspects of a problem, irrespective of the personal meanings of the stimuli.

But in addition to this factor, there is reason to believe that in some schizophrenics there occurs a more specific kind of change which is also importantly involved in thinking disturbances. In order to describe this factor it is necessary to examine in more detail the process of assimilation. As suggested earlier, assimilation is assumed to involve the assignment of percepts to categories in such a manner that they are congruent with previous assimilations of percepts. Although the categories involved in the assimilation process in any given individual would be difficult to specify, they would presumably consist of such groupings of percepts as, *e.g.*, those having to do with certain qualities, like being heavy; traits, like honesty; persons, like one's father; objects, like automobiles; and so on. These examples indicate that categories can be quite complex, and accordingly raise this question: how completely must a given percept "fit" a given category in order to be grouped with the other percepts in that category? It seems reasonable to conceive that individuals may differ in this regard, that some individuals tend to utilize stringent criteria in assigning percepts to categories, whereas other persons tend to utilize loose, or lax standards. In a purely figurative way the point intended here can be illustrated as follows. Suppose a new percept to have four of the five attributes of category A, and three of the five attributes of category B: then, the suggestion is that for a person in whom the process of assimilation occurs in terms of exacting standards the new percept would not fit into either category; that for a person in whom the assimilation involves the use of moderately stringent standards the new percept would fit into category A but not into category B; and that for a person in whom assimilation occurs in terms of relatively inexact criteria the new percept would fit into either category.

This postulated variable refers to the habitual and automatic manner in which one assimilates percepts. It is not the same as carelessness or inattention: these factors are largely under one's conscious control, whereas it is assumed that the degree of strictness or laxness one uses in categorizing incoming percepts is not subject to voluntary control. Further, it should be noted that we are not concerned here with the question of capacity for perceptual discriminations, *i.e.*, determinations as to whether two objects are identical. A person may assign to the same category two dogs, or two grains of sand, or two persons: this does not mean that he cannot distinguish between them, but only that in ordinary patterns of thought he does not do so.

The assigning of percepts to categories amounts to grouping percepts together in terms of similarity and dissimilarity. Consequently, for a person who tends to use stringent criteria in assimilation the percept groupings would tend to be narrow, and for a person who habitually uses lax standards the percept groupings would tend to be broad or overlapping. It is hypothesized that in some instances of schizophrenia *the existence of a high level of unassimilated percepts tends to reduce the degree of rigorousness, or strictness which the patient habitually requires for assimilating percepts,* or, to put it in another way, tends to increase the range of available categories to which given percepts may be assigned.

Except in terms of theoretical context and method of derivation, the present hypothesis—that the standards according to which percepts are grouped tend to be lax and to lead to overly broad groupings in some schizophrenics—appears to be similar to the formulations of certain other investigators. Cameron (94, 102, 103) has used the term *overinclusion* to refer to the tendency of some persons to include in a given classification or type of reaction a greater range of stimuli than is appropriate. He believes extreme overinclusion to be characteristic of schizophrenic disorganization and to explain to some extent why patients' attitudes of hostility, resentment, and the like sometimes generalize indiscriminately to strangers or to people in general (94, p. 458). Chapman and Taylor had schizophrenics do sorting tasks and found that they tended toward "an inappropriate broadening of the conceptual basis of sorting" (104, p. 123). McGaughran and Moran (105) reported that the categorizations of schizophrenics tend to be more "open" (in their terminology) than those of normals, *i.e.*, to permit greater freedom in the variety of objects which could be included in a given category (106).

While it is framed in a different theoretical context, the concept of loose standards, or criteria for assimilating percepts, appears to be related to Cameron's concept of overinclusion, Chapman and Taylor's concept of breadth of concepts, and McGaughran and Moran's concept of openness. It is also related, though perhaps less closely, to interpretations proposed by Arieti (4), Von Domarus (107), Hyman (108), and Peters (109). Von Domarus and Arieti see the thinking of some schizophrenics as being characterized not by a broadening of categories *per se,* but by a defect in logical thinking such that objects may be related on the basis of some single quality they possess, regardless of whether this quality is pertinent to the relationship. Hyman proposes that the schizophrenic tends to conceptualize on the basis of "partial" similarities, and he presents experimental evidence in support of this hypothesis. Peters suggests that maladjusted persons have a tendency to think in terms of higher level abstractions, or supraordinates. Peters' interpretation thus implies an increase in the breadth of conceptual categories in schizophrenia.

One important effect of a reduction in the strictness of standards used for assimilation and the concomitant increased breadth of percept groupings would be to afford an individual a greater availability of categories to which percepts could be assigned in order to avoid incongruencies. *A decrease in the strictness of the standards used in categorizing percepts would thus facilitate the assimilation of otherwise unassimilable percepts.* In this deduction, the present view is similar to that of Kelly (36) who proposes that loosening of one's constructs may serve as a defense against anxiety. Arieti and Hyman also suggest that the loss of precision in conceptual behavior can reduce anxiety.

But although a decrease in the habitual degree of exactitude required for assimilating percepts would tend to facilitate assimilation it would also make thinking less precise. This fact can be used to explain to a considerable extent the difficulty that many schizophrenics show on concept formation tests (94, 105, 108, 110). In these tests the patient is presented with a set of objects or words which have been preselected in such a manner that they can be grouped according to certain appropriate concepts. It is often noted that some schizophrenics, when asked to group them, fail to group them according to the appropriate concepts. In terms of the present model this behavior can be rationalized by supposing that the patient's loose standards for categorizing percepts affords him an increased number of categories, or groups to which a given object can be assigned, and consequently increases the likelihood of his making "wrong" assignments. This interpretation, except in systematic derivation, is somewhat similar to that proposed, with experimental support, by Chapman (110, 111) and Chapman and Taylor (104). The indication seems to be not so much that some schizophrenics do not use abstractions as that they do not use the abstractions the tester has in mind.

Whether or not schizophrenics are seen as deficient in abstract thinking depends on how the term *abstract thinking* is used. If this term is used to refer to the degree of breadth or inclusiveness of conceptual categories, then it appears that many schizophrenics show an increased tendency to think abstractly. But if it is used to refer to the capacity to identify and deal conceptually with an essential quality common to several objects, then it appears that many schizophrenics are deficient, as maintained by Goldstein (112, 113). There is considerable evidence that schizophrenics frequently interpret remarks or statements (*e.g.*, proverbs) in a concretistic manner. This can perhaps be explained to some extent by supposing that some patients who have difficulty in handling conceptual material tend to compensate by reacting to unstructured stimuli in an extremely literal fashion.

With regard to the patients' own verbalizations, their lax categorizing standards would contribute to peculiar and inexact uses of metaphor and to looseness and disjointedness in association. Both effects would be predicted on the basis that imprecise categorizing standards would increase the range of percepts which would seem appropriate to the subject. That looseness in association is determined partly by the same factors which cause poor performance on tests of abstract behavior is indicated by a study by Meadow, Greenblatt, and Solomon (114), which reported significant positive correlations between these two variables. It can further be conjectured that emotional flattening, *i.e.,* the tendency to behave as if nothing is important or significant (94), can be attributed in part to this same factor. The extent to which events or choices seem significant to a person appears to be a function of the sharpness of the differences between alternate choices or possibilities, and these differences would tend to be decreased by imprecise standards for categorizing percepts.

So far in this section it has been proposed that the thinking disorders characteristic of many schizophrenics can to a large extent be accounted for by two main factors: first, the idiosyncratic nature of the perceptions of schizophrenics; and second, a reduction in the "goodness of fit" required for assigning given percepts to given categories in the process of assimilating percepts. These two factors appear to be somewhat related to two variables proposed by McGaughran and Moran (105, 106) as being important in conceptual behavior. Thus, the notion of extent of idiosyncrasy in perception appears to be somewhat similar to McGaughran and Moran's variable of public *vs.* private concepts; and the concept of degree of strictness or looseness habitually utilized in categorizing percepts appears to be somewhat related to their variable of closed *vs.* open concepts.

While the first of these factors is probably applicable in some degree to all schizophrenics, it seems likely that the second is characteristic only of certain schizophrenics. All studies measuring concept formation in normals and schizophrenics report a large overlap between the two groups. In the study by the author already cited (99), in which subjects were presented with various Rorschach blot areas and asked if these could represent given concepts such as bat, butterfly, etc., it would seem that the less stringent a subject's criteria for assimilation the more frequently he would have accepted the suggested concepts as being adequately represented by the blot areas. It is noteworthy, then, that the means for the normals and schizophrenics were not appreciably different on this variable, though the standard deviation was considerably greater for the schizophrenics. Unfortunately this study did not control for negativism, perseveration, or suggestibility, so that its results must be considered as tentative, but its suggestive implication is that not only do many schizophrenics *not* tend to think loosely and overinclusively, but also some of them actually conceptualize according to very strict criteria. It is possible to wonder, in a speculative manner, if some patients vary from day to day, even from hour to hour in the strictness or looseness of their standards for assimilating percepts: such an inconsistency would be in keeping with the unpredictability of much schizophrenic behavior.

Why some schizophrenics would tend to utilize less stringent criteria for assimilation under the condition of a high level of unassimilated percepts and other schizophrenics would not is unclear. It is possible that the question of whether one's criteria for assimilation become more or less strict in reaction to anxiety is a function of learned patterns or styles of behavior.

It has been assumed here that anxiety, or the level of unassimilated percepts, is a major factor in altering the standards one uses in assimilation. If this is the case, then one would expect conceptual performance to become poorer under conditions presenting percepts especially difficult to assimilate. No direct test of this prediction is available, but a study by Webb (115) appears to be pertinent. Webb found that schizophrenics tended to perform more poorly on a similarities test when it was preceded by mild criticism—which presumably yielded percepts difficult to assimilate—than when it was not.

It is likely that the degree of "goodness of fit" one requires in assimilating percepts may also be influenced by certain physiological factors. The author found that categorizing standards, as evaluated by the Rorschach blot procedure described earlier, became significantly less stringent after prefrontal lobotomy. Senf, Huston, and Cohen (116) reported that intravenous sodium amytal impaired performance on conceptual tasks requiring precise responses. And within the realm of normal behavior, it is suggested that dreams represent a kind of loose thinking characteristic of imprecise categorizing standards.

GENERAL CONSIDERATIONS

What determines the particular constellation of symptoms that a patient will show? The central hypothesis of this chapter has been that schizophrenia results primarily from an extremely high level of unassimilated material and that the symptoms of schizophrenia represent—or are the "by-products" of—tendencies to prevent this from becoming even greater and to bring about assimilation. It is not possible to specify the magnitude which the quantity of unassimilated percepts would have to attain in order to generate schizophrenic symptoms, but this value would be determined, probably, in any given case, by factors such as what other adjustive alternatives are available to the individual and how long the quantity of unassimilated percepts has been excessive. Further, it is possible that individuals differ, as a function of unknown physiological and genetic determinants, in their capacities for maintaining unassimilated material. Thus, while the development of incongruencies, and hence the accumulation of unassimilated percepts, is based on experimental factors, the effects of these factors in the development of schizophrenia probably are considerably influenced by physiological and genetic variables.

In the preceding sections I discussed various characteristics of schizophrenia one at a time, as if these characteristics were isolated from each other. I did this in the interest of clarity, and did not mean to imply that the different symptoms are unrelated. Actually, of course, the same patient may utilize techniques of withdrawal, may create delusional schemata for assimilating percepts, and may develop deficiencies in cognitive processes. The particular techniques for dealing with unassimilated material which a given patient uses most predominantly and which comprise his symptom picture are probably exaggerations of the same techniques he would use if he were not schizophrenic.

In what way is schizophrenia different from neurosis? According to the present formulation neurosis, like schizophrenia, would be interpreted in terms of reactions to unassimilable percepts. The fundamental difference between schizophrenia and neurosis appears to be that in the former the quantity of unassimilable percepts is much greater, thus leading to more exaggerated perceptual and behavioral effects and reactions. I do not mean to imply, however, that the only difference between schizophrenia and neurosis is that one represents a higher point on a continuum than the other. There does appear to be a certain qualitative difference between neurotics and schizophrenics. The point—or area—where neurosis leaves off and schizophrenia begins is, I suggest, that point where the patient's perceptions become sufficiently idiosyncratic and his behaviors arising from these perceptions become sufficiently disorganized as to lie outside the range of experience of other people, with the result that the patient's behaviors cease to elicit a normal degree of corrective feedback from the reactions of other people. In other words, it is suggested that when one's idiosyncrasies become so pronounced as to be personally meaningless to most other people—as in the case of a schizophrenic—then the reactions of other people to these idiosyncrasies become less useful in correcting them. For this reason the perceptual and behavioral characteristics of the schizophrenic tend, to much greater degree than those of the neurotic, to become increasingly idiosyncratic.

Why does schizophrenia tend, in general, to be so persistent? In solving the problem of schizophrenia it is important not only to determine what its causes are, but also why it so frequently tends to persist for many years. In terms of the present conceptualization the persistence of schizophrenia would be attributed primarily to the continued existence of a large quantity of percepts which either are unassimilated or else are assimilated only because of certain manifestations of the psychosis—such as delusional conceptual schemata. Further, as indicated in the foregoing paragraph, the perceptual idiosyncrasies characteristic of schizophrenia would tend to perpetuate the disorder.

There is, however, another factor which needs to be considered. It would seem that in many instances of schizophrenia the environmental circumstances that tend to generate unassimilable percepts would tend to disappear, or to be alleviated over a span of years. Further, it seems possible that the effects of unassimilated percepts might tend to disappear over a long period of time, as the material underlying the percepts is forgotten and as numerous additional and assimilable experiences are perceived. These points are conjectural, of course, but the possibility must not be excluded that while a large quantity of unassimilated percepts may be primary in bringing about schizophrenia, something else is required to account for its long-term persistence.

Such an additional factor might be this: certain schizophrenic patterns, once established, tend to become fixed and to exist in a functionally autonomous manner. In the case of delusions, this kind of persistence could be rationalized by supposing that once a delusional schema is created to handle a certain problem, innumerable percepts would be assimilated according to this schema, so that even after the problem was no longer meaningful the delusion would persist because of the large quantity of percepts assimilated in terms of it. Reasons for the possible persistence of withdrawal behavior and of thinking disorders beyond the duration of the problems which brought them about are less clear. Perhaps such patterns tend to become habitual; perhaps they become characteristic styles of behaving.

What are the implications of the present conceptualization for the treatment of schizophrenia? The present approach to the problem of schizophrenia does not lead to the proposing of any radically new techniques of treatment. Thinking of schizophrenia in the way it has been described here, however, does serve to emphasize certain aspects of a treatment program. The primary therapeutic problem—at least for schizophrenics for whom the disorder has not become an habitual way of life—would be to help the patient resolve his incongruencies and restructure his conceptual schemata in such a manner as to permit the assimilation of percepts in socially appropriate ways. The major purpose of psychotherapy would be to help the patient achieve adequate restructuring: thus, in the present view, successful psychotherapy is not primarily a process of deconditioning and extinction but rather a process of restructuring and integration.

For some schizophrenics hospitalization probably serves as a kind of selective avoidance and has the effect of cutting down on the input of unassimilable percepts. This may not only halt the further development of the psychosis but may also afford the patient an opportunity to develop adequate ways of assimilating material. On the other hand, the manifold percepts associated with being hospitalized—with the possible connotation of being labeled as "crazy"—are themselves presumably difficult to assimilate. And for those patients for whom being hospitalized facilitates patterns of selective avoidance, hospitalization itself may become a preferred way of life, thus serving to hinder actual recovery.

Successful restructuring—whether in the context of formal psychotherapy or in the process of the patient's daily living experiences—is difficult at best for a schizophrenic patient to accomplish, but it is undoubtedly sometimes made even more difficult by certain side effects of the disorder. I am referring to those side effects hypothesized to arise in part from a low rate of perceptualization, *i.e.*, feelings of strangeness and depersonalization, difficulties in concentrating and maintaining attention, and hallucinations. It seems likely that in some instances hospitalization may actually enhance these effects and thus contribute to the worsening of the psychosis. I am thinking here of institutions in which, because of lack of personnel or lack of vision, patients are not afforded adequate opportunity for new kinds of experience and so exist in psychologically isolated states not markedly different from some of those reported in the literature on sensory deprivation. According to the present conceptualization a therapeutic program should be designed to provide considerable novelty and variety of experiences for the patient. It is important to emphasize, however, that these experiences should be of a kind and at a rate that the patient can assimilate; otherwise they would accentuate his anxiety and hence his psychotic symptomatology.

If it is true, as conjectured earlier, that in some instances of long-term schizophrenia certain behavioral patterns tend to persist in a functionally autonomous manner, then these symptoms could not be alleviated by efforts directed at facilitating assimilation. Rather, the problem would be to help the patient develop more adequate and satisfying patterns of behavior.

The present view has emphasized psychological factors in the development and treatment of schizophrenia, but the question arises as to how the fact that tranquilizing drugs often have therapeutically desirable effects can be reconciled with this view. It seems doubtful that any drugs can directly resolve incongruencies and hence bring about assimilation. It is possible, however, to conceive that drugs could affect certain side effects of schizophrenia—such as agitation and tension—in a desirable manner and thus contribute to the patient's over-all improvement. Further, it can be conjectured that drugs might alter the strictness or looseness, or possibly the consistency, of the standards used by a patient in assimilating percepts. As an example of how this might be therapeutic, suppose a patient to have loosened standards as a result of anxiety, but not to require these loosened standards in order to assimilate percepts. In such an instance a drug which would tend to increase the strictness of his categorizing standards would help to alleviate symptoms resulting from loose standards. I mention these possibilities not with the implication that they are valid, but rather to indicate that a psychological interpretation of schizophrenia is not incompatible with the fact that chemical agents often are therapeutic.

SUMMARY

This chapter has presented a programmatic and somewhat speculative formulation of certain aspects of schizophrenia. The formulation is framed in terms of the process whereby one receives and assimilates percepts. It is suggested that anxiety may be conceptualized as a function of the quantity of percepts which are unassimilated. The major detriment to assimilation is incongruencies among the conceptual patterns according to which assimilation occurs. The development of incongruencies is attributed to the nature of one's life experiences.

It is proposed that the primary cause of schizophrenia is an excessively high level of unassimilated percepts. Certain characteristics of schizophrenia, including avoidance tendencies, withdrawal behavior, apathy, and hallucinations may be attributed in part to attempts—or side effects of attempts —to prevent the quantity of unassimilated material from becoming even greater, and delusional beliefs are seen as representing attempts to bring about the assimilation of otherwise unassimilable percepts. Thinking disorders are conceptualized as reflecting alterations in the general standards required for assimilation: it is proposed that such alterations are brought about by an increase in the magnitude of unassimilated material and in some instances can serve to facilitate assimilation.

It is felt that the present conceptualization may be useful in two respects: first, in bringing a number of otherwise diverse behavioral phenomena within a single conceptual structure; and second, in suggesting needed areas for further research.

References

1. P. MC REYNOLDS, Thinking conceptualized in terms of interacting moments, *Psychol. Rev.*, *60*: 319, 1953.
2. P. MC REYNOLDS, *A Restricted Conceptualization of Human Anxiety and Motivation*, Psychol. Rep. Monograph Supplement 6, 1956, p. 293.

3.   H. GRAYSON, *Psychological Admissions Testing Program and Manual*, Los Angeles: VA Center, 1951.

4.   S. ARIETI, *Interpretation of Schizophrenia*, New York: Brunner, 1955.

5.   J. DOLLARD and N. MILLER, *Personality and Psychotherapy*, New York: McGraw-Hill, 1950.

6.   O. FENICHEL, *The Psychoanalytic Theory of Neurosis*, New York: Norton, 1945.

7.   R. LINTON, *The Cultural Background of Personality*, New York: Appleton, 1945.

8.   R. WOODWORTH, Reinforcement of perception, *Am. J. Psychol., 60*: 141, 1947.

9.   H. NISSEN, "The Nature of the Drive as Innate Determinant of Behavioral Organization," in Jones, M. (Ed.), *Nebraska Symposium on Motivation*, Lincoln: Univ. Nebraska Press, 1954.

10.   D. HEBB, Drives and the C.N.S. (conceptual nervous system), *Psychol. Rev., 62*: 243, 1955.

11.   H. HARLOW, Mice, monkeys, men, and motives, *Psychol. Rev., 60*: 23, 1953.

12.   H. HARLOW, M. HARLOW, and D. MEYER, Learning motivated by a manipulation drive, *J. Exper. Psychol., 40*: 228, 1950.

13.   K. MONTGOMERY and M. SEGALL, Discrimination learning based upon the exploratory drive, *J. Comp. & Physiol. Psychol., 48*: 225, 1955.

14.   D. BERLYNE, The arousal and satiation of perceptual curiosity in the rat, *J. Comp. & Physiol. Psychol., 48*: 238, 1955.

15.   D. BERLYNE, A theory of human curiosity, *Brit. J. Psychol., 45*: 180, 1954.

16.   D. BERLYNE, An experimental study of human curiosity, *Brit. J. Psychol., 45*: 245, 1954.

17.   D. BERLYNE, The influence of complexity and novelty in visual figures on orienting responses, *J. Exper. Psychol., 55*: 289, 1958.

18.   J. KAGAN, L. SONTAG, C. BAKER, and V. NELSON, Personality and I.Q. change, *Am. Psychologist, 12*: 364, 1957 (Abstract).

19.   P. MC REYNOLDS, Exploratory behavior as related to anxiety in psychiatric patients, *Psychol. Rep., 4*: 321, 1958.

20.   W. JAMES, *Principles of Psychology*, New York: Dover, 1950.

21.   W. MC DOUGALL, *The Energies of Men*, New York: Scribner, 1933.

22.   L. TROLAND, *The Fundamentals of Human Motivation*, New York: Van Nostrand, 1928.

23.   R. WHITE, Inside the space-man, *Saturday Review*, July 6, 1957, p. 40.

24.   D. HEBB, The mammal and his environment, *Am. J. Psychiat., 111*: 826, 1955.

25.   W. BEXTON, W. HERON, and T. SCOTT, Effects of decreased variation in the sensory environment, *Canad. J. Psychol., 8*: 70, 1954.

26.   J. VERNON and J. HOFFMANN, Effect of sensory deprivation of learning rate in human beings, *Science, 123*: 1074, 1956.

27.   J. LILLY, Mental effects of reduction of ordinary levels of physical stimuli on intact, healthy persons, *Psychiatric Res. Rep., 5*: 1, 1956.

28.   D. ORMISTON, The effects of sensory deprivation and sensory bombardment on apparent movement thresholds, *Am. Psychologist, 13*: 389, 1958 (Abstract).

29.   P. MC REYNOLDS, Anxiety as related to incongruencies between values and feelings, *Psychol. Rec., 8*: 57, 1958.

30.   J. HERBART, *Psychologie als Wissenschaft,* discussed by Boring, E., *A History of Experimental Psychology,* New York: Appleton, 1950.

31.   P. LECKY, *Self-consistency, A Theory of Personality,* New York: Island Press, 1945.

32.   C. ROGERS, *Client-centered Therapy,* Boston: Houghton Mifflin, 1951.

33.   C. ROGERS, The necessary and sufficient conditions of therapeutic personality change, *J. Consult. Psychol.,* 21: 95, 1957.

34.   H. PEAK, "Attitude and Motivation," in Jones, M. (Ed.), *Nebraska Symposium on Motivation,* Lincoln: Univ. Nebraska Press, 1955.

35.   L. FESTINGER, *A Theory of Cognitive Dissonance,* Evanston: Row, Peterson, 1957.

36.   G. KELLY, *The Psychology of Personal Constructs,* Vol. I, New York: Norton, 1955.

37.   J. PIAGET, *The Origins of Intelligence in Children,* New York: Internat. Univ. Press, 1952.

38.   E. ANTHONY, The significance of Jean Piaget for child psychiatry, *Brit. J. M. Psychol.,* 29: 20, 1956.

39.   E. FROMM, *Man for Himself,* New York: Rinehart, 1947.

40.   D. HEBB, *The Organization of Behavior,* New York: Wiley, 1949.

41.   H. BASOWITZ, S. KORCHINS, D. OKEN, M. GOLDSTEIN, and H. GUSSACK, Anxiety and performance changes with a minimal dose of epinephrine, *Arch. Neurol. & Psychiat.,* 76: 98, 1956.

42.   D. HEBB, On the nature of fear, *Psychol. Rev.,* 53: 259, 1946.

43.   S. CLEMES, "The Relationship Between Manifest Anxiety and Congruency Among Self-Perceptions in Schizophrenics," Master's thesis, Stanford University, 1958.

44.   R. FUNK, Religious attitudes and manifest anxiety in a college population, *Am. Psychologist, 11:* 375, 1956 (Abstract).

45.   J. BLOCK and J. THOMAS, Is satisfaction with self a measure of adjustment? *J. Abnorm. & Social Psychol., 51:* 254, 1955.

46.   G. BRACKBILL and K. LITTLE, MMPI correlates of the Taylor Scale of manifest anxiety, *J. Consult. Psychol., 18:* 433, 1954.

47.   R. SUINN, "The Tendency to Assimilate Incoming Percepts as a Function of the Level of Anxiety," Master's thesis, Stanford University, 1955.

48.   C. SMOCK, The influence of psychological stress on the "intolerance of ambiguity," *J. Abnorm. & Social Psychol., 50:* 177, 1955.

49.   A. BINDER, Personality variables and recognition response level, *J. Abnorm. & Social Psychol., 57:* 136, 1958.

50.   O. BRIM and D. HOFF, Individual and situational differences in desire for certainty, *J. Abnorm. & Social Psychol., 54:* 225, 1957.

51.   J. MOFFIT and H. STAGNER, Perceptual rigidity and closure as functions of anxiety, *J. Abnorm. & Social Psychol., 52:* 354, 1956.

52.   C. SMOCK, The influence of stress on the perception of incongruity, *J. Abnorm. & Social Psychol., 50:* 354, 1955.

53.   D. HUNT and H. SCHRODER, Assimilation, failure-avoidance, and anxiety, *J. Consult. Psychol., 22:* 39, 1958.

54.   R. MAY, *The Meaning of Anxiety,* New York: Ronald, 1950.

55.   N. MILLER, Fear as motivation and fear-reduction as reënforcement in the learning of new responses, *J. Exper. Psychol., 38*: 89, 1948.

56.   R. SOLOMON and E. BRUSH, "Experimentally Derived Conceptions of Anxiety and Aversion," in Jones, M. (Ed.), *Nebraska Symposium on Motivation*, Lincoln: Univ. Nebraska Press, 1956.

57.   O. MOWRER and P. VIEK, An experimental analogue of fear from a sense of helplessness, *J. Abnorm. & Social Psychol., 43*: 193, 1948.

58.   N. MILLER, "Learnable Drives and Rewards," in Stevens, S. (Ed.), *Handbook of Experimental Psychology*, New York: Wiley, 1951.

59.   E. RODNICK and N. GARMEZY, "An Experimental Approach to the Study of Motivation in Schizophrenia," in Jones, M. (Ed.), *Nebraska Symposium on Motivation*, Lincoln: Univ. Nebraska Press, 1957.

60.   R. ATKINSON, "Paired-associate Learning by Schizophrenic and Normal Subjects under Conditions of Verbal Reward and Punishment," Ph.D. dissertation, Indiana University, 1957.

61.   N. ROBINSON, "Paired-associate Learning by Schizophrenic Subjects under Conditions of Personal and Impersonal Reward and Punishment," Ph.D. dissertation, Stanford University, 1957.

62.   R. KANTOR, J. WALLNER, and C. WINDER, Process and reactive schizophrenia, *J. Consult. Psychol., 17*: 157, 1953.

63.   G. BATESON, D. JACKSON, J. HALEY, and J. WEAKLAND, Toward a theory of schizophrenia, *Behavioral Sci., 4*: 251, 1956.

64.   E. STRECKER, F. EBAUGH, and J. EWALT, *Practical Clinical Psychiatry*, New York: Blakiston, 1951.

65.   H. SULLIVAN, *The Interpersonal Theory of Psychiatry*, New York: Norton, 1953.

66.   D. BYRNE, J. TERRILL, and P. MC REYNOLDS, Unpublished data.

67.   J. BRYAN and P. MC REYNOLDS, The tendency to obtain new percepts as a function of the level of unassimilated percepts, *Percept. Motor Skills, 6*: 183, 1956.

68.   I. PAVLOV, *Conditioning and Psychiatry*, New York: Internat. Pubs., 1941.

69.   L. KANNER, Autistic disturbances of affective contact, *Nervous Child, 2*: 217, 1943.

70.   R. WHITE, *The Abnormal Personality*, New York: Ronald, 1956.

71.   W. GOLDFARB, Receptor preferences in schizophrenic children, *Arch. Neurol. & Psychiat., 76*: 643, 1956.

72.   R. BLUM, Alpha-rhythm responsiveness in normal, schizophrenic, and brain-damaged persons, *Science, 126*: 749, 1957.

73.   R. SAUCER, A further study of the perception of apparent motion by schizophrenics, *J. Consult. Psychol., 22*: 256, 1958.

74.   E. STRAUS and R. GRIFFITH, Pseudoreversibility of catatonic stupor, *Am. J. Psychiat., 111*: 680, 1955.

75.   H. STRASSMAN, M. THALER, and E. SCHEIN, A prisoner of war syndrome: apathy as a reaction to severe stress, *Am. J. Psychiat., 112*: 998, 1956.

76.   P. SOLOMON, H. LEIDERMAN, J. MENDELSON, and D. WEXLER, Sensory deprivation: a review, *Am. J. Psychiat., 114*: 357, 1957.

77.   G. FREEMAN, *The Energetics of Behavior*, Ithaca: Cornell Univ. Press, 1948.

78.   E. DUFFY, The psychological significance of the concept of "arousal" or "activation," *Psychol. Rev., 64*: 265, 1957.

79.   R. MALMO, Anxiety and behavioral arousal, *Psychol. Rev., 64*: 276, 1957.

80.   G. MORUZZI and H. MAGOUN, Brain stem reticular formation and activation of the EEG, *Electroencephalog. & Clin. Neurophysiol., 1*: 455, 1949.

81.   S. SHARPLESS, *Symposium on Brain Mechanism,* 14th International Congress of Psychology, June, 1954.

82.   J. FUSTER, Effects of stimulation of brain stem on tachistoscopic perception, *Science, 127*: 150, 1958.

83.   H. AZIMA and F. CRAMER-AZIMA, Effects of the decrease in sensory variability on body scheme, *Canad. J. Psychiat., 1*: 59, 1956.

84.   H. AZIMA and F. CRAMER-AZIMA, Studies on perceptual isolation, *Dis. Nerv. System, 18*: 1, 1957.

85.   H. AZIMA and F. CRAMER, Effects of partial perceptual isolation in mentally disturbed individuals, *Dis. Nerv. System, 17*: 117, 1956.

86.   C. STONG, On "the amateur scientist," *Scient. Am., 197*: 143, 1957.

87.   D. KELLER and W. UMBREIT, "Permanent" alteration of behavior in mice by chemical and psychological means, *Science, 124*: 723, 1956.

88.   N. MAIER, Frustration theory: restatement and extension, *Psychol. Rev., 63*: 370, 1956.

89.   W. DEMBER and R. EARL, Analysis of exploratory, manipulatory, and curiosity behaviors, *Psychol. Rev., 64*: 91, 1957.

90.   W. DURANT, *The Story of Civilization,* I, *Our Oriental Heritage,* New York: Simon and Schuster, 1954.

91.   D. KRECH, Attitudes and learning: a methodological note, *Psychol. Rev., 53*: 290, 1946.

92.   C. OSGOOD and P. TANNENBAUM, Congruity in the prediction of attitude change, *Psychol. Rev., 62*: 42, 1955.

93.   R. JENKINS, The schizophrenic sequence: withdrawal, disorganization, psychotic reorganization, *Am. J. Orthopsychiat., 22*: 738, 1952.

94.   N. CAMERON, *The Psychology of Behavior Disorders,* New York: Houghton Mifflin, 1947.

95.   A. BEACH, "Preference for Auditory Closure as a Function of Anxiety in Schizophrenics," Master's thesis, Stanford University, 1958.

96.   J. TAYLOR, A personality scale of manifest anxiety, *J. Abnorm. & Social Psychol., 48*: 288, 1953.

97.   D. SHANNON, "The Effects of Ego-defensive Reactions on Reported Perceptual Recognition," Ph.D. dissertation, Stanford University, 1955.

98.   L. ULLMANN, Clinical correlates of facilitation and inhibition of responses to emotional stimuli, *J. Proj. Tech., 22*: 341, 1958.

99.   P. MC REYNOLDS, Perception of Rorschach concepts as related to personality deviations, *J. Abnorm. & Social Psychol., 46*: 131, 1951.

100.   P. MC REYNOLDS, The Rorschach concept evaluation technique, *J. Proj. Tech., 18*: 60, 1954.

101.   L. JOHNSON, Rorschach concept evaluation test as a diagnostic tool, *J. Consult. Psychol., 22*: 129, 1958.

102.   N. CAMERON, *Reasoning, Regression, and Communication in Schizophrenia*, Psychol. Monograph 50 (No. 1), 1938.

103.   N. CAMERON, Deterioration and regression in schizophrenic thinking, *J. Abnorm. & Social Psychol.*, *34*: 265, 1939.

104.   L. CHAPMAN and J. TAYLOR, Breadth of deviate concepts used by schizophrenics, *J. Abnorm. & Social Psychol.*, *54*: 118, 1957.

105.   L. MC GAUGHRAN and L. MORAN, "Conceptual level" vs. "conceptual area" analysis of object-sorting behavior of schizophrenic and nonpsychiatric groups, *J. Abnorm. & Social Psychol.*, *52*: 43, 1956.

106.   L. MC GAUGHRAN, Predicting language behavior from object sorting, *J. Abnorm. & Social Psychol.*, *49*: 183, 1954.

107.   E. VON DOMARUS, "The Specific Laws of Logic in Schizophrenia," in Kasanin, J. (Ed.), *Language and Thought in Schizophrenia*, Berkeley: Univ. California Press, 1944.

108.   M. HYMAN, "An Investigation of Cognitive Process in Schizophrenia," Ph.D. dissertation, University of California, 1953.

109.   H. PETERS, Supraordinality of associations and maladjustment, *J. Psychol.*, *33*: 217, 1952.

110.   L. CHAPMAN, Distractibility in the conceptual performance of schizophrenics, *J. Abnorm. & Social Psychol.*, *53*: 286, 1956.

111.   L. CHAPMAN, The role of type of distractor in the concrete conceptual performance of schizophrenics, *J. Pers.*, *25*: 130, 1956.

112.   K. GOLDSTEIN and M. SHEERER, *Abstract and Concrete Behavior: an Experimental Study with Special Tests*, Psychol. Monograph 53 (No. 2), 1941.

113.   K. GOLDSTEIN, "Methodological Approach to the Study of Schizophrenic Thought Disorder," in Kasanin, J. (Ed.), *Language and Thought in Schizophrenia*, Berkeley: Univ. California Press, 1944.

114.   A. MEADOW, N. GREENBLATT, and H. SOLOMON, "Looseness of association" and impairment in abstraction in schizophrenia, *J. Nerv. & Ment. Dis.*, *118*: 27, 1953.

115.   W. WEBB, Conceptual ability of schizophrenics as a function of threat of failure, *J. Abnorm. & Soc. Psychol.* 50: 221, 1955.

116.   R. SENF, P. HUSTON, and B. COHEN, Thinking deficit in schizophrenia and changes with amytal, *J. Abnorm. & Soc. Psychol.* 50: 383, 1955.

PART V

Sociology

10. SOCIAL RELATIONS AND SCHIZOPHRENIA: A RESEARCH REPORT AND A PERSPECTIVE

John A. Clausen and Melvin L. Kohn

Schizophrenia poses a problem at the core of social-psychological theory—the problem of the relationship of the individual to his society, of the personality to its social matrix. Are there recurrent, patterned features of particular cultures and social organizations that encourage the development, shape the form, or modify the natural history of the schizophrenic process? Sociological concern with the topic has taken a variety of forms, including the investigation of: the incidence and prevalence of recognized schizophrenia in various cultures and subcultures, differences in residential distribution among subtypes of schizophrenia, the early social experiences of schizophrenics reared in neighborhoods characterized by apparent high incidence of schizophrenia, the cultural coloring of the symptomatic manifestations of schizophrenia, and, most recently, social processes within the therapeutic milieu and the posthospital functioning of patients returned to the community.

We begin with a summary of a study of selected childhood experiences and relationships of all persons hospitalized for schizophrenia during a twelve-year period from a city of under 40,000 population. Parts of this study have been reported elsewhere in greater detail (1, 2, 3); here we shall give

John A. Clausen received his Ph. D. in sociology from the University of Chicago. He was Assistant Professor of Sociology at Cornell University before joining the NIMH in 1948. He is now Chief of the Laboratory of Socio-environmental Studies, NIMH. Melvin L. Kohn, a Cornell Ph.D., is Chief of the Laboratory's Section on Community and Population Studies.

an overview of the research, relating it to other studies of schizophrenia, and then turn to theoretical and methodological issues that are posed in such research.*

Our major points of departure were afforded by two types of previous research: (1) studies, largely by sociologists, of the apparent incidence or prevalence of schizophrenia among neighborhoods, social classes, racial and ethnic groups; and (2) studies, largely by psychiatrists, of the dominant trends in relationships between the schizophrenic and his parents.

Knowledge of the true incidence of schizophrenia would require periodic examination of the population to ascertain all new cases which have occurred in a given time span. Periodic examinations are patently not feasible for most populations. Therefore, an index of the number of new cases of schizophrenia such as the number of first admissions to mental hospitals is most often used in sociological research involving population segments having roughly comparable access to mental hospitals. The most influential of the early studies of the distribution of schizophrenia among neighborhoods in American cities, Faris and Dunham's *Mental Disorders in Urban Areas* (4), used such an index. This and other "ecological" studies of the distribution of mental disorder conducted in American and European cities (5, 6) consistently show a tendency for rates of first admissions to public and private mental hospitals to be highest in the central areas of the city—areas of low economic status and high population mobility.

Subsequent studies of the prevalence of treated schizophrenia within different social strata, defined in terms of occupational and educational levels, have also indicated a marked inverse relationship between rates of treated schizophrenia (very largely, of course, accounted for by hospitalized cases) and social status (7).

Because social status carries a wide range of social and cultural implications, such gross correlations cannot readily be interpreted in a single frame

* The authors are indebted to the Maryland State Department of Mental Hygiene and its late Commissioner, Dr. Clifton Perkins, for making available patient files, granting access to patients at State hospitals, and aiding our research with a grant-in-aid; to the hospitals of the State of Maryland, especially Springfield State Hospital and Brooklane Farm Hospital, for contributing their case records and enabling us to interview their patients and former patients; to the physicians of Washington County for aid in arranging interviews and in providing valuable data; and to the Public Health Methods Division of the USPHS (especially Dr. Philip Lawrence, Chief of the Familial Studies Unit in Hagerstown) for granting access to their files of Morbidity Studies (basic to our control-group selection) and for valuable suggestions and aid in the field work.

The senior author was afforded the opportunity to work on this paper as a Fellow at the Center for Advanced Study in the Behavioral Sciences during 1957–58.

of reference. There is, first, the question of whether observed differences in the incidence of treated schizophrenia represent true differentials in disease incidence. Some critics of the ecological studies have argued that the high rates of schizophrenia in lower status areas are to be explained by the "drift" of incipiently ill persons into these areas, especially persons who have become detached from stable family life. Whether or not mobility is related to etiology, there is a good deal of evidence that schizophrenics tend to move around more than normals do. On the other hand, evidence of the *social* mobility of schizophrenics, as indexed by their occupational careers or by a comparison of their social statuses to those of their fathers, is markedly conflicting. Before their hospitalization, schizophrenics have been found to be upwardly mobile in New Haven (8), downwardly mobile in Chicago and New Orleans (9, 10), and neither upwardly nor downwardly mobile in Buffalo (11). In our research we planned to examine the mobility of subjects drawn from areas or social strata showing different rates of hospitalization.

If we assume for the moment that the ecological findings are not simply an artifact of the "drift" of incipient schizophrenics into lower status occupations and neighborhoods, a second question becomes pertinent: Do the differences in rates of schizophrenia derive from the nature of social interactions in the areas of residence, from subcultural aspects of social class (*i.e.*, differences in way of life, family relationships, values), from the effects of economic deprivation, from a linkage between social status and genetic factors significant in schizophrenia, or from some other associated phenomenon? One hypothesis, which has been especially congenial to sociologists, is that the areas of the city with highest rates of hospitalization for schizophrenia are precisely the areas whose inhabitants are most subjected to social isolation, and that social isolation—especially when experienced during childhood—is directly predisposing to schizophrenia. Dunham found that catatonics nurtured in such areas had, as children, great difficulty in coming to terms with the "harsh, often brutal aspects of slum life" (12). Rebuffs from peers were seen as leading to a progressive isolation of the child, eventuating in schizophrenia. As developed by Faris and Dunham, the social-isolation hypothesis incorporated consideration of initial personality tendencies, parental oversolicitude, and difficult peer group relationships (5, 12, 13, 14). These workers did not simply postulate that children growing up in high-rate areas are more generally isolated than children growing up in other neighborhoods; they asserted that social isolation was a necessary precursor to schizophrenia. The testing of the social-isolation hypothesis was a major objective of our research.

Another point of departure, it will be recalled, was provided by studies of the relationship between the schizophrenic and his parents (most often, the mother alone) in childhood (15–23). These studies found the mothers of schizophrenics to be dominant and controlling figures, either overprotective or rejective of the offspring who later develop the illness. Underlying the overprotectiveness or rejection, there was felt to be a basic inability of the mother to meet the child's emotional needs by a spontaneous giving of affection.

Most of these studies derive their data from research interviews with, or therapy of, the mothers. Control groups representing normal families of social backgrounds comparable to those of the schizophrenics were usually either lacking or quite inadequate. The present study sought to secure information from patients (and former patients) themselves on a limited number of dimensions of family relationship. Comparable data were secured from a control group matched with the patients on those social variables most likely to have some bearing upon the structuring of parent-child relationships.*

THE HAGERSTOWN STUDY

Setting of the Research   Our research procedures were influenced by the availability of certain types of data in a community under consideration. This community, the city of Hagerstown, Maryland, had been the locus of a series of morbidity studies for nearly three decades before the beginning of our own research. These studies gave us invaluable information on the composition and residential history of a high proportion of Hagerstown families—information that greatly facilitated the selection of a control group for the patients under study and afforded a check on other data relating to mobility.

* Controls were individually paired with the patients on the basis of age, sex and occupation (or father's occupation), using records derived from Public Health Service morbidity studies conducted periodically in Hagerstown since 1921. By this method it was possible to accomplish matching as of a period well before the onset of illness—on the average, 16 years before hospitalization. (In roughly half the cases the patient and his control had attended the same class in public school.) In addition to individual matching on the characteristics mentioned, over-all frequencies were balanced with respect to family composition and ecological area of residence.

Interviews were conducted with all patients and former patients who were physically and psychologically accessible and willing to be interviewed, 45 of the 62 schizophrenic patients. In 12 of the remaining 17 cases we were able to interview a close relative and to ascertain that the noninterviewed patients did not differ appreciably from those interviewed except as regards accessibility.

Hagerstown is an industrial and trading center located at the junction of three major railroads, a major east-west highway, and a less important north-south highway, in northwestern Maryland. It has a large aircraft plant and several smaller factories. It is an old and settled community, although the war years brought an influx of workers to the aircraft plant. On the whole, however, the population has been relatively stable in recent decades, with an average annual increase slightly under one per cent per year since 1920. The majority of in-migrants during the war years were from nearby counties of Pennsylvania and West Virginia and did not represent a different cultural group from the old inhabitants. The population is remarkably homogeneous—preponderantly white, Protestant, and native-born.

Residential and Occupational Distribution   We found no differences in average annual rates for first hospital admission for schizophrenia among census-enumeration districts of varying socio-economic status. In part, this finding may be an artifact of the relatively small population on which the rates are based. The failure to find higher rates of schizophrenia in the more deteriorated areas of the city appears more cogent, however, in the light of two other findings. (1) The areas *do* show significant differences in the rate of hospitalization for the much less frequent manic-depressive reactions. Rates of manic-depressive psychosis were three times as high in the upper two strata as in the lower three. (2) Rates of schizophrenia do not vary significantly by *occupational group* either: the rate for professional, technical, and managerial persons is almost identical with that for operatives, service workers, and laborers.

Could the absence of differences among Hagerstown social strata in the rates of hospitalization for schizophrenia be illuminated in any way by a knowledge of the social mobility of the patients? Data on social mobility were secured by direct interview of the patients (or close relatives) and control subjects. Comparison of the residential and occupational histories of patients and controls revealed that Hagerstown schizophrenics changed their places of residence and their jobs more frequently than did normal persons of comparable background. But there was no greater shift to residential areas or jobs of different status by patients than by normal controls. The data on mobility throw no light on our failure to find significant socio-economic differentials in hospitalization for schizophrenia.

Several possible explanations of the absence of socio-economic differentials have been considered at length in another publication (3). We believe that the lower socio-economic strata do produce somewhat more schizophrenics than higher strata but that the lack of "collecting areas" for detached individuals in a city as small as Hagerstown results in the outward migration of some lower-status schizophrenics prior to their hospitalization. In addition, it appears that the narrowed range of social status in a city of this size, coupled with a relatively high degree of integration of blue-collar workers into neighborhood, church, and community, may make for a less marked relationship between social class and aspects of personality development that are critical for schizophrenia than would be found in a metropolis.

Social Isolation and Schizophrenia   Schizophrenic patients and their controls were interviewed at some length to collect information about their friendship patterns and social activities during early adolescence. From their replies (transcribed from the interview schedules and coded "blind" by two judges), patients and controls were classified as having been "isolates" or "partial isolates," as having played primarily with brothers or sisters, or as having been "non-isolates."

Roughly a third of schizophrenics reported activities and friendship patterns (as of age 13–14) that led us to classify them as isolates or partial isolates, whereas only 4 per cent of our normal subjects reported such patterns. The data attest that schizophrenics are more likely than are normal persons of their background to have been isolated from their peers early in adolescence; nevertheless, two-thirds of the schizophrenics seem to have had normal patterns of social participation at that age. So isolation can hardly be considered to be a *necessary* precursor of schizophrenia.

Our further problem was to ascertain whether the isolation of the one-third of the patients could be considered etiologically significant. We could find no evidence that the patients classified as isolates or partial isolates had different experiences in respect to availability of playmates, childhood illness, residential mobility, or parental restrictions upon their activities or their choice of friends. They were not kept from social participation. Nor were the isolates and partial isolates likely to have been hospitalized at an earlier age, to remain hospitalized longer, or to function at a reduced level after return to the community. Their illness was no more severe than that of the non-isolates.

On the other hand, information from the hospital records (based upon interviews with family members) suggests that the patients classified as isolates had withdrawn from prior social relationships. They were almost all perceived by their families as shy, timid, or fearful persons during early childhood. But none of the patients classified as non-isolates had been so perceived (according to hospital records) at age 13–14. The "isolation" of some patients seems to have resulted from their early and progressive alienation from others. It reflects inadequacies in social relationships and a mode of dealing with such inadequacies. Further study of the subtler aspects of social isolation is needed, however, to ascertain whether under some circumstances the process of alienation and consequent isolation can be reversed in a favorable environment.

Family Relationships   Although isolated and non-isolated patients did not differ in those aspects of family relationships that we studied, patients did differ from their controls. It may be of interest to note that, in this sample, patients and former patients were no more likely to come from families broken by death or divorce prior to the child's thirteenth birthday than were their matched controls.

Analysis of family relationships is confined to those cases in which both the patient and his matched control were raised by both natural parents or by one parent and one stepparent from an early age (39 cases). Our interview inquired into the relative positions of the parents in decision making, authority, and general control of the child as recalled by that child years later. Using a series of items relating to strictness, the making of day-to-day decisions, restrictiveness, and dominance, we developed scales of maternal and paternal authority behavior (relative to the given child). A larger proportion of schizophrenics than of controls reported that their mothers had wielded a great deal of authority over them and their fathers relatively little. The pattern of strong maternal and weak paternal authority was reported most often by paranoid schizophrenics, less often by catatonics.

Any further subdivision of our cases left us with very small numbers, but at least two findings seem worthy of further examination. One concerns the relationship between perception of parental authority and socio-economic status: our schizophrenic subjects tended to report maternal rather than paternal dominance regardless of the socio-economic status of the parental family (as indexed by father's occupation). Our controls, on the other hand, reported decreasing maternal authority and increasing paternal authority with increasing occupational status. That is, at the lower status levels, controls also tended to report that the mother had been dominant, differing little if at all from the patients and former patients in this respect. At the higher status levels, on the other hand, controls showed a strong tendency to report relative paternal dominance or equal (usually moderate) authority roles for mother and father.

A second apparent relationship, based on even fewer cases and therefore no more than suggestive, is that male schizophrenics who reported strong maternal and weak paternal authority more often said they had felt closer to their mothers than to their fathers; female schizophrenics who reported this authority pattern more often felt closer to the father. Insofar as maternal dominance has relevance to schizophrenia, then, we might hypothesize a linkage with sex-role identification and affectional ties.

Duration of Hospitalization and Subsequent Experience   The length of time that any patient spends in the mental hospital is determined by a variety of circumstances, such as his psychopathology, the therapeutic aims and administrative policies of the hospital, the availability of a family to which the patient can return, and the patient's ability to play a role appropriate to parole or discharge. These circumstances appear to be influenced by attributes of the patient's personality and his social background, though our knowledge of the ways in which these interact and of the consequences is meager and unsystematic.

The status of the former schizophrenic patients in the Hagerstown study at the time of interview (2–14 years after hospitalization) was:

Still in hospital	28%
Seriously ill, but at home	7
Much impaired, at home	19
Somewhat impaired, but working	11
Not apparently impaired	32
No data	3
	100%

For those patients who had been admitted to the hospital five or more years prior to our interview with them, we attempted to assess status as of five years after admission. Nearly a third were still (or again) in a mental hospital; another third were employed or occupied at home in pursuits similar to those engaged before the illness; a fourth were discharged but were functioning at a markedly reduced level; and the remainder were discharged but could not be classified as to the level at which they were functioning.

In general, it appears that status as of one year after admission to the hospital was a good index of status five years after admission. Indeed, the proportions of patients in the hospital or in the community at any given time beyond the first year seemed just about stable: roughly 30% in the hospital, 70% in the community. There was, of course, much shifting back and forth; 43% of the schizophrenic patients had been admitted more than once at the time of the follow-up. In general, however, circumstances or characteristics associated with initial discharge in less than a year were also associated with relatively good functioning in the community as of five years after admission. Consistently favorable prognostic indicators were: initial hospitalization in a private mental hospital; marriage and residence with family of procreation; low maternal and medium-high paternal authority; very good childhood health history; residence in higher status areas. Socio-economic status seems to be positively associated with favorable prognosis for males, but by virtue of the small sample of male patients the finding does not reach a high level of statistical significance.

For those former patients who were in the community at the time of the follow-up, it is of interest to note their current social relationships as compared with their controls. Three rough indices have been used: the number of formal organizations (churches, unions, clubs, etc.) to which individuals belonged; the number of informal groups (neighborhood, social); and whether or not they had close personal friends. The data are summarized below:

	SCHIZOPHRENICS	CONTROLS
Belong to one or more formal organizations	15%	41%
Belong to an informal social group	9%	35%
Meet with friends at least once weekly	15%	53%

Thus, even those patients who are back in the community show much constriction of social relationships as compared with controls of the same age, sex, and early social background. Incidentally, there was no association between social isolation in adolescence and participation in social relationships at the time of the follow-up.

General Summary of the Hagerstown Findings   The major findings of the Hagerstown research, summarized in general terms (though clearly not to be generalized to other communities without a number of qualifications and limitations), are as follows:

1. The probability of being hospitalized with a diagnosis of schizophrenia did not vary significantly by socio-economic status of one's neighborhood or occupation.

2. One third of the schizophrenics, as compared with almost none of their matched normal controls, were isolated from social activities with peers early in adolescence, but lack of participation reflected feelings of alienation and seclusiveness which had characterized the "isolated" patients from an early age. At some later period, many of the other patients became alienated from their fellows.

3. Schizophrenic patients reported a substantially greater frequency of strong maternal authority and weak paternal authority than did their matched, normal controls. This difference between patients and controls was greatest at the upper levels of socio-economic status and least (or nonexistent) at the lower levels.

4. The Hagerstown data suggest that social characteristics influence duration of hospitalization and subsequent performance in the community. They also clearly indicate a marked constriction in the posthospital social relationships of the patients.

In Hagerstown, then, it appears that socio-economic status may be more closely linked to family structure and to what happens to a person after he is hospitalized for schizophrenia than to the incidence of schizophrenia. On the other hand, studies of larger cities in the United States have almost uniformly shown higher rates of hospitalization for schizophrenia from lower than from upper socio-economic strata. It appears probable that out-migration of incipient schizophrenics of low socio-economic status from communities like Hagerstown may obscure the link between lower status and schizophrenia in the small community while contributing to its overstatement in the metropolitan centers to which many schizophrenics migrate.

RECENT RESEARCH ON THE
FAMILIES OF SCHIZOPHRENICS

In the six years since the Hagerstown project was undertaken, intensive studies of the families of schizophrenics have added much to our knowledge of interaction patterns associated with schizophrenia. Investigators, combining clinical and behavioral-science skills, have carried conceptualization beyond gross characterization of the personalities of the parents of schizophrenics. In taking stock of our own data and as a step toward planning further research, we should like to consider some of the recent work from a sociological perspective. There appear to be both important convergences and areas of disagreement among the recent formulations and findings. We shall not try to summarize the studies, nor shall we be able to do justice to the formulations derived from them. Several are, of course, reported elsewhere in this volume. We shall here attempt to state the most relevant formulations and findings bearing upon the possible role of family interaction in the etiology of schizophrenia, point out some of the differences in orientation or in data reported, and then examine the research critically from our perspective as sociologists.

It seems fair to say that all of the research with which we shall be concerned regards schizophrenia as the outcome of a pathological process of personality development, beginning relatively early in life.* Furthermore, the family is seen as the matrix of personality development; here the child learns to perceive his world, to relate to others, to test his capacities, to build an identity. The writings most explicit on this score have been those of Lidz and his associates, but all those we shall cite share a common core of social psychological and psychiatric theory on personality development.

The Mother-Child Relationship in Schizophrenia   Whether the data have been secured from studies of patients, of their mothers, or of the interaction of the whole family group, certain common impressions are derived from nearly all of the studies that are concerned with the mothers of schizophrenics. The earlier investigators (see reference 16 for a review of studies prior to 1950) used a variety of trait names—cold, perfectionistic, anxious, overcontrolling, restrictive—to connote a type of person unable to give spontaneous love and acceptance to the child. Mark, using an inventory of attitudinal items, added a trait best described as "intrusiveness" (18). These mothers were often unwilling to accord the child any privacy, even in his thoughts.

Lidz, too, finds widespread pathology among schizophrenics' mothers (24-26). Some he describes as showing seriously scattered thinking, most as cold, rigid, or overindulgent toward the children. He also stresses their imperviousness to the feelings of others.

Implicit in these characterizations of the personality of the mother is the nature of her tie to the child. Intensive clinical studies of the families of schizophrenics have recently given us more adequate formulations of the pathological features of that tie. Hill (27) and the research group of Bowen (28) have described the symbiotic entanglement of mother and child, who are characterized as "living and acting and being for each other." They have noted the frequent transfer of anxiety both within the pair and within the larger family; movement toward autonomous identity by any member is met by a display of anxiety in another.

The theory advanced by Bateson, Jackson, and their associates (29-31) focuses attention upon conflicting messages that are communicated to the child at different levels. The mothers of schizophrenics are seen as catching the child in a "double bind," wherein the mother verbalizes love and warmth but rebuffs the child's tendencies to respond to her words. The basic feelings

* It is not entirely clear how large a role is ascribed to heredity, but several of the research teams clearly do not rule out the possibility that pathologic processes in the family may be specific for schizophrenia only with genetically vulnerable persons.

of the mother for the child are suffused with hostility or anxiety, but her inability to face these feelings leads to their denial and to the expression of loving behavior. This formulation seems quite consonant with the earlier interpretations of the overprotective, oversolicitous mother who lacks basic warmth for her child. The new note is the stress on the communication process. In this research and in that of Bowen, the role of the father is seen as significant largely in terms of his failure to counteract the pathological tendencies of his wife.

The Fathers of Schizophrenics   Prior to the recent group of studies, the fathers of schizophrenics had been noted primarily as the passive, inadequate marital partners of the dominant "schizophrenogenic mother," although Reichard and Tillman (16) called attention to the occasional "domineering, sadistic" father and Lidz and Lidz (32) noted the instability of many fathers of schizophrenics. Of the more intensive recent studies, only that of Lidz (33) has subjected the fathers of adult schizophrenics to the detailed scrutiny usually reserved for mothers. He has tentatively characterized five patterns of paternal personality and role in the families he has studied. But in our opinion the cases described by him and by others can be roughly subsumed under three general clusters or types: (1) passive, immature, retiring; (2) domineering, sadistic; (3) aloof, grandiose, narcissistic.

The quantitative studies are in agreement that the first of these types is most prevalent, as it would have to be in order to accord with the "typical mother." Lidz (33) has described several subtypes of the "domineering" father, including tyrannical, wife-derogating men and prestige-seeking, child-derogating men who become rivals of the child for the mother's attention. The "aloof" father seems to resemble closely the dominant type found by Kanner (34) and Eisenberg (35) in studies of the fathers of autistic children.

It may be noted that these three types of fathers are quite similar to the types revealed by Jackson's factor analysis of psychiatrists' conceptions of the "schizophrenogenic father" (36). Clearly there is more diversity in the characterizations of the fathers of schizophrenics than in those of the mothers.

The Family Network   The characterizations of the family structure itself derive largely from those of the personalities of husband and wife. With reference to marital conflict, two grossly divergent patterns have been described: extreme marital schism, with mutual distrust and derogation; and the masking of conflict and difference to achieve what Wynne (37) has called "pseudomutuality." In the latter instance, divergence or independence of expectations within the family is regarded as a threat to family existence. Collaborative but unwitting efforts are made to exclude from recognition any evidence of divergence. The mechanisms supporting pseudomutuality include indiscriminate approval, contradictory, mutually obscuring levels of communication, and the use of intermediaries and of projections to pressure other members when they threaten the illusion of complementarity. What Wynne has called "pseudomutuality" seems to characterize some of the families described by Bateson, Bowen, Lidz, and Hill in the works previously referred to.

Marital schism can frequently be inferred in families with domineering fathers; it is most clearly described by Lidz and by reports from the Mayo Foundation (38). In these families, husband and wife tend to undercut and derogate each other, competing for the attention and affection of the children. Both husband and wife tend to be closely bound to their own parental families, preventing a full commitment to the conjugal unit. By virtue of parental pathology and conflict, these families do not afford adequate role models for the children. They are deficient in the consistency and appropriateness of controls upon behavior, traumatizing the child in his attempt to achieve stable nonpunishing expectations of others.

It may be noted that, while different aspects and degrees of parental pathology are described in the several studies, there is general agreement that the observed patterns of family life militate against the child's achieving a self-respecting identity and an ability accurately to discriminate emotionally tinged communications. These research teams do not imply that the phenomena to which they have called attention represent *the* cause of schizophrenia. Indeed, they recognize explicitly that such distortions are found also in the families of neurotics and even in normal families. But given certain degrees of distortion and certain not wholly specified concomitants, they suggest that schizophrenia may result. Lidz, for example, eschews direct effort at etiological explanation, although he does propose "the hypothesis that these persons are prone to withdraw through altering their internal representations of reality because they have been reared amidst irrationality and intrafamilial systems of communication that distort or deny instrumentally valid interpretations of the environment" (25).

The emphasis on communication and on how the child comes to make (or is prevented from making) "instrumentally valid interpretations of his environment" seems to us a most promising approach to the study of what

is critically important. But we cannot wholly reconcile this formulation
with the fact that many preschizophrenic adolescents do make instrumentally
valid interpretations of their environments before the onset of overt symptomatology. When one has known well a capable and well-oriented young
adult and has seen the gradual or sudden alteration of his behavior as
schizophrenia manifested itself, it is difficult to accept the notion that he
had never learned to assess the real world. Something is lost or surrendered;
but that is not to say that it never existed. Thus far, only Bateson and his
associates have alluded to this problem in their publications, recognizing
the need to study the disintegration of patterns of discrimination and interpretation.

The Need to Consider Alternative Explanations   Concentrating attention
on the descriptions of the pathological parental personalities and the
devastating features of the socialization process in these families, one can
readily believe that they could not fail to produce pathological children.
But such convictions are in the last analysis still unproved hypotheses.
Alternative explanations must be considered.

Theoretical discussions of personality development usually begin with
a recognition that the interaction between an infant and his environment
is influenced by the genic constitution of the organism, the intrauterine experience and birth process, and the nature of the environment, past and
present. Having recognized the interaction between constitution and environment in the forging of personality, we tend, however, to pass immediately to exclusive consideration of one or the other. Perhaps we do so
because the inseparability of the two sets of potentialities precludes any attempt at quantitative analysis of their interaction. Yet the failure to formulate a theoretical model of the interaction between genotypes and environments leaves us with incomplete research designs when we attempt to study
the relationship between such a phenomenon as schizophrenia and the psychodynamics of family life.

Study after study has characterized the apparent psychopathology of
the parents of schizophrenics. Sometimes the parents have themselves been
hospitalized for mental illness; more often they manifest behaviors which
are a token of conflict and of pent-up hostility but are not classified as psychosis. Within the families that produce schizophrenics are other children,
some showing gross psychopathology and some seemingly unimpaired. Kallmann (39) reports the incidence of schizophrenia among full siblings of an
index case as 14 per cent. Some of the recent studies of highly selected families suggest that many more of these children are enveloped in a pathological
integration, with alternation of symptomatology during the therapy of the

index case (28, 31, 37); but systematic data on the siblings have not yet been presented in any of these studies.

Parental personalities showing gross pathology antedating the child's birth could support equally well a genetic or a psychogenic explanation of the schizophrenia. The fact that not all children in these families are schizophrenic suggests that parental pathology is not enough. Some interaction between genic susceptibility and a social matrix within which the child is impaired in efforts to achieve a viable identity seems most probable.

A METHODOLOGICAL CRITIQUE

Part of the difficulty of interpreting the data in hand undoubtedly stems from our inability to specify unequivocally the nature of the phenomenon or phenomena to be called "schizophrenia" and the lack of agreement among investigators as to what is the expected range of "normal" behavior. To this topic we shall return. *But a not inconsiderable part of the problem of disentangling the interacting variables seems to derive from our failure in study after study to specify and analyze sufficiently the selective processes whereby patients and their families are brought under investigation, the family histories of behavioral pathology, and the socio-cultural matrix within which the disorder is recognized and responded to.*

Can further light be cast on the meaning and generalizability of the various findings summarized above by examination of selection of cases and the sources of data, and by consideration of genetic or socio-cultural bases for some of these characteristics? We believe that it can.

Selection of Cases for Study   The Hagerstown study, as well as many others, suggests that there are rather marked differences in prior experiences, in social status, and in personality orientation between schizophrenic patients who leave the hospital after a few weeks or months of hospitalization and those who stay on for many years. For a long time, statistics based on the average stay as of a given date were quoted as though they represented the average duration of hospitalization for all schizophrenics. It is now recognized that such statistics are grossly misleading, because more than half of all hospitalized schizophrenics are returned to their homes in less than a year—perhaps even within six months. As Kramer and his associates (40) have demonstrated, the only defensible way to assess the course of illness for a representative sample of patients is to accumulate data for a "cohort" of successive admissions to the hospital—that is, a consecutive series of cases, each followed over a comparable period of time.

A sample of patients designated sequentially at the time of first treatment for schizophrenia will differ markedly from a sample chosen as representative of a resident hospital population. Several of the studies of family pathology have taken patients who had been resident in mental hospitals for a number of years. There is abundant evidence that relatively sudden onset of schizophrenia is in general a good prognostic indicator and that among chronic schizophrenics a high proportion had a slow, insidious onset (41). For many of the families of chronic schizophrenics selected for study, it appears, then, that there has been a longer than usual period of struggle with the patient's problem even before his hospitalization. Family pathology *may* have been the cause of the problem, but we cannot rule out the possibility that the family looks so pathological because it has been faced for so long with a devastating stress. Also, to the extent that family pathology *does* contribute to the severity and duration of schizophrenia, these patients would, of course, come from the more pathological backgrounds.

The selective factor becomes even more critical for those studies which require, before admitting the patient to the study population, that one or both parents agree to participate in the treatment-research process. It may be, as Lidz has suggested, that these families are better organized, less torn by conflict than a cross section of the families of schizophrenics. The opposite may, however, be the case. They may well be more intensely involved in a struggle with problems they have been unable to resolve or to escape from, by virtue of parental pathology and of pathological integrations of need. This is not to imply that such involvements are without significance, or to deny that they are more often found in the families of schizophrenics than in the general population. But we cannot dismiss the matter of selection without examining further data. One would like to have at least minimal data on social status, schizophrenic relatives, expressions of conflict, authority patterns, etc., within the families of those patients *not* selected for study within the particular population.

When one selects patients *because* they exhibit some characteristics to an atypical degree (as, for example, patients having an intense symbiotic relationship with the mother), one will want to know something about the other respects in which they differ from a representative sample. But here, of course, there can be no possibility of investigating the etiological significance of the characteristic on which selection was based, regardless of how fruitful such samples may be for an analysis of family dynamics in the treatment situation. If one studied only schizophrenics from broken homes, he might well conclude that broken homes caused schizophrenia. The principle of overdeterminacy in psychic phenomena makes selection a critical matter.

The Sources of Data   The Hagerstown study relied chiefly upon the patient's own report of his childhood experience and of the structure of relationships within the family group, as given to a strange interviewer not affiliated with any treatment service. The former patient's cooperation was sought for this single interview, with no implication that he was still ill or would gain any benefit from the interview. In such an interview, it would obviously not be possible to explore deep feelings about family relationships. On the other hand, direct questioning about childhood activities and about the general patterning of family relationships seems here to have yielded direct answers without giving rise to intense anxiety or to the massing of defenses and evasions. One cannot make inferences about parental pathology from these data, but one can make reliable classifications of such patterns as authority relationships using objective criteria applying equally to patients and controls.

Data have been secured in a variety of ways in the other studies cited. In some instances, patient and family members are jointly under therapy. At one extreme is the situation in which patient and parents are resident together in the mental hospital, with parents sharing in the task of caring for the patient, described by Dr. Bowen in Chapter 12 and elsewhere (28). Such a situation would seem likely to increase the difficulties of almost any relationship. In the midst of a strange group, persons only slightly acquainted will often form close bonds very quickly. In a strange setting, whose norms are not at all those of the larger community, there are both pressures to closer emotional involvement within the family and pressures to learn how to behave appropriately to the situation. This same phenomenon exists in the visiting situation, so often commented on judgmentally by hospital staff. Family visitors to the mental hospital seem so ill at ease, so lacking in warmth, that pathology is often ascribed to them. A sociological perspective would lead one to anticipate such difficulties when strong emotional ties are involved but when interpersonal expectations are unclear because the situational framework is almost wholly new.

Even when the parents are not involved in the hospital setting but are seen in individual or group therapy, it is not surprising that they frequently seem quite disturbed. Whether or not their behaviors "caused" the schizophrenia, they have had to evolve some defenses in order to survive with it. Therapy calls these defenses into question. It raises questions as to whether the parents have, indeed, been "good" parents. The cultural injunction is there, even if the therapist does not take an accusatory stand. To say that the behavior displayed by parents in these circumstances seems pathological is to raise the issue of standards of comparison. Response to extreme stress is different from normal resting response. To the extent that coping with the schizophrenic illness of a family member is a stress quite different from those normally encountered, and to the extent that surveillance of a family is likely to lead to some masking techniques, one wonders whether the cards are not somewhat stacked against obtaining, from the study of current interactions, data that can be used to construct an adequate picture of the family prior to the onset of schizophrenia.

There is another issue that must be faced, relating not only to the selection of cases and the sources of data, but also to the criteria and instruments for assessing pathology. There is something less than complete agreement among investigators as to the overtness of the pathology of the parents. Some (38) comment on the frequency with which the most gross, overt pathology is manifest. Jackson (31) and Lidz (26), however, stress that in many instances these families had appeared quite normal until they had been under intensive study for some months, when chinks began to appear in the family armor. The earlier study by Lidz and Lidz (32), based on 50 consecutive admissions to a private psychiatric clinic, noted the extent to which "the grossest features of the family environment" manifested overt disturbance and obviously deleterious effects on the children. The later papers of Lidz, based on intensive study of a small number of families, describe the same gross pathology, but many of these families were apparently better able to conceal their difficulties.

It would seem desirable to distinguish, in analyses of family functioning, those instances in which one or both parents show signs of overt psychotic behavior from those in which atypical attitudes and relationships prevail but manifest personality disturbance is less severe or less apparent. If, as Lidz finds, "minimally 60 per cent of the patients had at least one parent who was an ambulatory schizophrenic or was clearly paranoid" (26), it would appear likely that some of these parents would be recognized as pathological without months of intensive interviewing. It would be most helpful if relatively objective, even though crude, indices could be used to differentiate types of parent personality. These could also be applied to appropriate control populations, either of families that have no problematic "index case" or of families that are faced with a comparable problem of distinctly organic etiology.

At present, we may have no instrument, except the sensitive clinician, for making relevant assessments of parental personalities and modes of family communication. But until we evolve more explicit criteria for such assessments, which can be applied with equal validity to the families of schizophrenics and to control families, we simply cannot rest easy with assertions that pathology prevails almost completely in the former group. It *may*, but the investigator's conviction that it does makes unbiased assessments very difficult. We are not by any means suggesting that the parents of schizophrenics do not differ in their attitudes, personalities, and relationships from the parents of normals. The evidence is overwhelming that a high proportion do differ. But we have too little unequivocal data on either the source or the degree of pathology in the parents.

The Socio-cultural Matrix of the Family   There is no question that *some* of the parents of schizophrenics suffer from severe mental illness. But we have noted that the proportion who appear atypical in attitudes and family relationships is not just a minority; it is the overwhelming majority. Are there sources of these characteristics other than severe individual pathology? Are they, for example, to some degree distorted reflections of rather pervasive tendencies within the larger socio-cultural matrix in which personalities are formed and in which families build up their patterns of interaction?

We are sufficiently interested by the socio-economic differential in parental authority behavior among our controls to want to secure more data on the structure and functioning of a cross-sectional sample of families of working-class and middle-class status. This new study has entailed interviewing mothers—and in a fourth of the families, fathers and children as well—in 200 middle-class and 200 working-class families in Washington, D.C., each family having at least one child in the age range 10–11.* Very preliminary tabulations suggest a number of respects in which these working-class mothers differ from the middle-class mothers in the direction of having attributes and roles similar to those ascribed to the mothers of schizophrenics. Working-class mothers are somewhat more often the dominant parent for both authority and affectional ties; they far more often express a desire to know everything that is going on in the child's mind; they are more concerned with obedience and control over their children (while middle-class mothers are more concerned with the happiness and interpersonal competence of the children); and they more often refer to their husbands (or to males generally) in disparaging ways. Our working-class sample is weighted toward the upper, stable working-class family. Studies of lower-class slum-dwelling families show these tendencies to a much greater extent, according to the work of Spinley (42), Kardiner and Ovesey (43), Plant (44), and others.

In several respects, then, it appears that a significant number of work-

---

* The first published findings of this research and details of the design are contained in a paper by Melvin L. Kohn, "Social Class and Parental Values," *American Journal of Sociology, 64*: 337–351, 1959.

ing-class mothers tend toward patterns that characterize the so-called "schizophrenogenic mother." At this point it does not appear fruitful to say either that the working-class patterns are primarily reflections of individual pathology or that they are necessarily productive of pathology. Minimally, it would be agreed that these patterns may not be salutary for the mental health of the child, especially of the male child. Certainly it is relevant to keep in mind that most of the studies of the incidence or prevalence of schizophrenia in larger cities in the United States have suggested a marked inverse relationship between social status and the occurrence of schizophrenia. More recent efforts to establish the frequency of *any* kind of psychiatric disturbance in various social strata have suggested the willingness of some psychiatrists to label more than one-fourth of their lower class samples "severely disturbed" (45).* To what extent can the families of schizophrenics be clearly differentiated from this fourth of the working-class population, and in what ways? To the extent that they are characterized by similar interactional processes, are the sources of atypical attitudes and interpersonal patterns to be traced to idiosyncratic experiences, to family transmission, to wider cultural influences, or to varying combinations of these?

The developing pathology of relationships in the families of schizophrenics must also be viewed within the larger framework of modes of handling deviance within the society generally. The families of schizophrenics are not alone in attempting to avoid dissension in their interactions with the patient and in their concerns about what is going on in the patient's thoughts. The person whose behavior frequently violates expectations, especially if he is prone to feeling slighted or to being enraged without apparent provocation, tends to be handled with "kid gloves" while on his good behavior and to be watched closely for signs of trouble. The maintenance of goal-oriented activity (even therapy) is threatened by such persons. In most groups, defenses which exclude or extrude the difficult person will be brought into play when he gets out of hand. In the family, such defenses are morally unavailable, at least overtly.

A widely shared value in our culture (and in most others) is that parents should be loving and relaxed with their children. For a variety of reasons, relating to the personality of the parent, to situational factors surrounding

---

* There seems to be little question but that psychiatric diagnosis is "shaky" for the lower-class subject who frequently incorporates behavior tendencies that would be regarded as symptomatic of psychopathology in middle-class subjects but that are shared aspects of the lower-class subculture. This fact does not mean that real differences in significant symptomatology or in vulnerability are not linked with class. But much research is needed to delineate the interaction of variables involved.

the prenatal period and the natal event, and to the characteristics of the particular infant, a very substantial proportion of parents are unable to be as spontaneously warm and loving to their children as they perhaps think they ought to be. This is the less surprising when one considers that the relationship between husband and wife is likewise supposed to be suffused with relaxed love, yet a fourth or a fifth of all marriages end in divorce and perhaps a higher percentage endure with something less than ideal role relationships. When stresses become too great, a marriage can be dissolved. But once a child has been delivered, the injunctions to loving nurturance are for all infancy, childhood, and adolescence, if not for life. Only when an older child's behavior has become so monstrous as to suggest that he is "not really human" may parents disavow the child, especially if they can argue that he was different from the very beginning. In marriage, moreover, both partners choose each other, or at least one chooses and the other accedes to being chosen. In the parent-child situation, of course, neither party knows what he is getting until the infant begins to be a behaving stimulus and responder. Genes being distributed as they are, and adults having no great natural ability to take the role of the infant, the process of establishing a more or less stable pattern of parent-child relationships is likely to entail trauma for both parties. Fathers may, and very frequently do, handle their traumas in this process by leaving the problem to the mother. Indeed, in some instances the father seems to avoid much involvement beyond participation in the conception of the child. This tendency is frequently noted in our culture and is not by any means peculiar. Mothers cannot get off the hook so readily. They have to live with the child as he is, whether he is that way because of genes, bellyaches, or the distribution of dispositions surrounding it. The mother who is, for one reason or another, unable to measure up to the expectations she has internalized is faced with a threat to her identity. She may be expected to use a variety of defenses—denial, reaction formation, masking—to try to survive in this role which she cannot abrogate.

There are, then, a number of respects in which socio-cultural or situational influences may be involved in the interpersonal dynamics that are observed in the families of schizophrenic patients. Some of these influences may possibly be of etiological significance; others may simply be concomitants of the pathology. No matter how convinced the clinician may be that the observed family dynamics were antecedent to the schizophrenia and caused it, the dispassionate observer cannot accept such an interpretation until the several separate bodies of data can be reconciled more adequately than at present. At least one recent study, that by Klebanoff (46), indicates that mothers of schizophrenics and mothers of brain-damaged children both exceeded mothers of normal children in "overpossessiveness." It is hypothesized that a child who poses a problem for his parents by virtue of minor or marked atypicality or simply by virtue of characteristics that make it difficult for his parents to accept him may in time change the whole structure of family relationships.

To illustrate the kind of data we need in order to interpret the correlations between parental personalities, family dynamics, heredity, and schizophrenia, a hypothetical example may be useful. The formulation owes much to Hill (27), though it is not necessarily in keeping with his emphases. The illustration takes as its point of departure women sharing a specified aspect of personality type. It could equally well begin with a particular type of male. Our data on the process of mate selection are still very meager, but it does not seem reasonable to ascribe all the responsibility—or the pathology, whatever its degree—to one partner alone.

A Hypothetical Analysis   Suppose one were to follow the developmental course, from adolescence on, of young women from that not inconsiderable group who are constricted in their relationships with men, whom they tend to disparage, and whose attitudes towards sex or sensual gratification generally are tinged with anxiety and disgust. What kind of marriages are they likely to make and how will they perform the maternal role? It may be hypothesized that such women will not in general appeal to aggressive, sexually expressive males, nor will they be attracted to such males. Therefore, one would anticipate a general tendency to marry conforming, unaggressive or preoccupied males. One might, of course, expect the marriage rate of this group to be somewhat lower than that of women generally, but, on the other hand, one would anticipate a strong push toward conventional behavior among such women and therefore a strong desire to have a home and family. Deviation from the usual age-pairings in marriage might be expected, and it would be anticipated that both husband and wife would have had less experience with the opposite sex before marriage than would be typical of their subcultural groups. In a certain proportion of instances, the experience of marriage may be therapeutic with reference to the attitudes and constrictions that characterize the wife; in other instances, the marriage may accentuate these problems. For such women, physical gratifications in marriage are likely to be low and companionship not zestfully rewarding. Motherhood is then less likely to be enjoyed as a natural, enriching experience involving physical gratification and the unfolding of a new career; rather will it become an unpleasant burden unless intellectualized and moralized into a sacred duty and an altar for self-dedication.

It is hypothesized that to the extent that the marital relationship itself fails to provide satisfaction, a child will come more and more to be the mother's chief source of satisfaction and the basis for self-vindication. If this is so, the need for control over the child will become greater and the mother will tend to become more and more both the source of affection and the source of authority for the child. To the extent that the child shows tendencies to rebuff the mother or to behave in ways that contravene her wishes or moral standards, she is likely to react both with anxiety and with feelings of aggression. The moral imperatives of mother love cannot, however, be escaped, for to act in such a way as to deny them would deny the mother's claim to worth. There would seem to be a strong tendency toward one aspect of the double-bind situation with reference to the mother's own behavior—unacceptable impulses will be denied while stereotyped mother-role norms will be verbalized. If the father is not wholly lacking in assertiveness, conflicts over the mother's preoccupation with the child and her efforts at control are likely to ensue. If, however, the father is a very passive figure, one can see how tendencies toward pseudo-mutuality in family behavior might well occur.

What alternative outcomes would be noted in a hundred marriages of the general type described? What are the dominant interpersonal patterns of such husbands and wives outside the family? What are the consequences of individual differences among children of these parents? Can clinicians describe the most common integrations of individual pathology in these families? Can social scientists characterize the behavioral outputs and outcomes of such families as a group and characterize meaningful subgroups? These, we believe, are problems to be tackled. Naturally, an adequate analysis must trace the course of parent-child relationships for each child, including the shifting of identifications, dependency ties, and emotional responses as new members are added to the family and as new roles are assumed.

SUMMARY AND CONCLUSION

In this discussion of issues and problems, we have touched upon four major sources of ambiguity in the interpretation of research findings: (1) lack of joint consideration of genic and experiential factors; (2) failure to specify adequately the basis for selection of research subjects and the consequences of such selection; (3) the inadequacy of a reconstruction of early family patterns from observations, interviews, or therapy of family members after they have long been confronted by a severe relational problem; and (4) failure to take into account the socio-cultural matrix as it influences family patterns relevant to personality development and to the handling of extreme deviance in a child. Anyone who has done research in this difficult area has become aware of some of these problems. Perhaps this sharing by sociologists of their perspective entails at least an occasional phrasing that can lead to a fruitful reformulation in terms more congenial to a clinical investigator.

We have ranged far from Hagerstown and our data on correlates of schizophrenia there. Our effort, however, has been to explore ways of building upon both the Hagerstown findings and recent, more intensive studies of the families of schizophrenics. The significance of social class for schizophrenia or for normal personality development can be ascertained only by studies which go more deeply into the process of personality development in the several social strata in a variety of communities. The significance of various clusterings of parental attitudes or traits for the personality development of children can best be established by following families through the developmental phase. Many more studies will be required to deal with the problems that have been mentioned. It is our belief that more adequate answers will be forthcoming if some of these studies shift from focus upon the patient to focus upon different types of families, defined by family histories (*i.e.*, genetic linkages), by subcultural orientations, and by personality orientations of the marital partners, examining alternative outcomes to patterns which to a greater or lesser degree resemble those found in the families of schizophrenics.

The study of the normal family is, of course, as crucial to analysis of the families of schizophrenics as is the study of pathology. Longitudinal study—examining more intensely the process of mate selection, the meaning of children as each successive one is added to the family, the interaction among siblings and parents in the periodic crises posed by illness, accident, or by inevitable disappointments or failures in some enterprises, the crystallization of anxieties or of exorbitant hopes, the reactions of successive siblings to double-binding techniques—such study can add not merely to our efforts to understand the etiology of schizophrenia, but even more to our knowledge of normal development.

References

1.   M. L. KOHN and J. A. CLAUSEN, Social isolation and schizophrenia, *Am. Sociol. Rev.*, 20: 265–273, 1955.

2.   M. L. KOHN and J. A. CLAUSEN, Parental authority behavior and schizophrenia, *Am. J. Orthopsychiat.*, 26: 297–313, 1956.

3.   J. A. CLAUSEN and M. L. KOHN, The relation of schizophrenia to the social structure of a small city, in Pasamanick, B. (Ed.), *Epidemiology of Mental Disorder,*

Washington, D.C.: American Association for the Advancement of Science, 1959, pp. 69–86.

4.   R. E. L. FARIS and H. W. DUNHAM, *Mental Disorders in Urban Areas,* Chicago: Univ. Chicago Press, 1939.

5.   H. W. DUNHAM, The current status of ecological research in mental disorder, *Social Forces, 25:* 321–326, 1947.

6.   J. A. CLAUSEN and M. L. KOHN, The ecological approach in social psychiatry, *Am. J. Sociol., 60:* 140–151, 1954.

7.   A. B. HOLLINGSHEAD and F. C. REDLICH, *Social Class and Mental Illness: A Community Study,* New York: Wiley, 1958, Chap. 8.

8.   A. B. HOLLINGSHEAD *et al.,* Social mobility and mental illness, *Am. Sociol. Rev., 19:* 577–584, 1954.

9.   M. S. SCHWARTZ, "The Economic and Spatial Mobility of Paranoid Schizophrenics and Manic-depressives," Unpublished Master's thesis, University of Chicago, 1946.

10.   M. H. LYSTAD, Social mobility among selected groups of schizophrenic patients, *Am. Sociol. Rev., 22:* 288–292, 1957.

11.   R. LAPOUSE *et al.,* The drift hypothesis and socioeconomic differentials in schizophrenia, *Am. J. Pub. Health, 46:* 978–986, 1956.

12.   H. W. DUNHAM, The social personality of the catatonic-schizophrene, *Am. J. Sociol., 49:* 508–518, 1944.

13.   R. E. L. FARIS, "Ecological Factors in Human Behavior," in Hunt, J. McV. (Ed.), *Personality and the Behavior Disorders,* New York: Ronald, 1944, Vol. 2, pp. 736–757.

14.   R. E. L. FARIS, Cultural isolation and the schizophrenic personality, *Am. J. Sociol., 40:* 155–164, 1934.

15.   T. TIETZE, A study of mothers of schizophrenic patients, *Psychiatry, 12:* 55–65, 1949.

16.   S. REICHARD and C. TILLMAN, Patterns of parent-child relationships in schizophrenia, *Psychiatry, 13:* 247–257, 1950.

17.   D. L. GERARD and J. SIEGEL, The family background of schizophrenia, *Psychiatric Quart., 24:* 47–73, 1950.

18.   J. C. MARK, The attitudes of the mothers of male schizophrenics toward child behavior, *J. Abnorm. & Social Psychol., 48:* 185–189, 1953.

19.   J. KASANIN *et al.,* The parent-child relationships in schizophrenia, *J. Nerv. & Ment. Dis., 79:* 249–263, 1934.

20.   R. C. LANE, "Familial Attitudes of Paranoid Schizophrenic and Normal Individuals of Different Socio-economic Levels," Unpublished Ph.D. dissertation, New York University, 1954.

21.   J. MCKEOWN, The behavior of parents of schizophrenic, neurotic, and normal children, *Am. J. Sociol., 56:* 175–179, 1950.

22.   C. T. PROUT and M. A. WHITE, A controlled study of personality relationships in mothers of schizophrenic male patients, *Am. J. Psychiat., 107:* 251–256, 1950.

23.   J. L. SINGER, Projected familial attitudes as a function of socio-economic status and psychopathology, *J. Consult. Psychol., 18:* 99–104, 1954.

24.   T. LIDZ *et al.,* The intrafamilial environment of schizophrenic patients: II. marital schism and marital skew, *Am. J. Psychiat., 114:* 241–248, 1957.

25.   T. LIDZ et al., Intrafamilial environment of the schizophrenic patient: VI. the transmission of irrationality, *Arch. Neurol. & Psychiat., 79*: 305–316, 1958.

26.   T. LIDZ, Schizophrenia and the family, *Psychiatry, 21*: 21–27, 1958.

27.   L. B. HILL, *Psychotherapeutic Intervention in Schizophrenia,* Chicago: Univ. Chicago Press, 1955.

28.   M. BOWEN et al., Study and treatment of five hospitalized family groups each with a psychotic member. Paper presented at annual meeting, Am. Orthopsychiatric Assoc., Chicago, March 8, 1957.

29.   G. BATESON et al., Toward a theory of schizophrenia, *Behavioral Sci., 1*: 251–264, 1956.

30.   J. H. WEAKLAND and D. JACKSON, Patient and therapist observations on the circumstances of schizophrenic episode, *Arch. Neurol. & Psychiat., 79*: 554–574, 1958.

31.   D. JACKSON, "Family Interaction, Family Homeostatis and Some Implications for Conjoint Family Psychotherapy," in Masserman, J., *Individual and Family Dynamics,* New York: Grune & Stratton, 1959, pp. 122–141.

32.   R. W. LIDZ and T. LIDZ, The family environment of schizophrenic patients, *Am. J. Psychiat., 106*: 332–345, 1949.

33.   T. LIDZ et al., The intrafamilial environment of the schizophrenic patient: I. the father, *Psychiatry, 20*: 329–342, 1957.

34.   L. KANNER, To what extent is early infantile autism determined by constitutional inadequacies? *A. Res. Nerv. & Ment. Dis., Proc., 33*: 378–385, 1954.

35.   L. EISENBERG, The fathers of autistic children, *Am. J. Orthopsychiat., 27*: 715–724, 1957.

36.   D. JACKSON et al., Psychiatrists' conceptions of the schizophrenogenic parent, *Arch. Neurol. & Psychiat., 79*: 448–459, 1958.

37.   L. WYNNE et al., Pseudo-mutuality in the family relations of schizophrenics, *Psychiatry, 21*: 205–220, 1958.

38.   P. G .S. BECKETT et al., Studies in schizophrenia at the Mayo Clinic: I. the significance of exogenous traumata in the genesis of schizophrenia, *Psychiatry, 19*: 137–142, 1956.

39.   F. J. KALLMANN, "The Genetic Theory of Schizophrenia," in Kluckhohn, C., and Murray, H. A. (Eds.), *Personality in Nature, Society and Culture,* New York: Knopf, 1949.

40.   M. KRAMER et al., *A Historical Study of the Disposition of First Admissions to a State Mental Hospital,* Public Health Monograph No. 32, 1955.

41.   T. RENNIE, Analyses of one hundred cases of schizophrenia with recovery, *Arch. Neurol. & Psychiat., 46*: 197–229, 1941.

42.   B. M. SPINLEY, *The Deprived and the Privileged: Personality Development in English Society,* London: Routledge, 1953.

43.   A. KARDINER and L. OVESEY, *The Mark of Oppression: A Psychosocial Study of the American Negro,* New York: Norton, 1951.

44.   J. S. PLANT, *Personality and the Cultural Pattern,* New York: Commonwealth Fund, 1937.

45.   T. RENNIE et al., Urban life and mental health: socio-economic status and mental disorder in the metropolis, *Am. J. Psychiat., 113*: 831–836, 1957.

46.   L. B. KLEBANOFF, "Attitudes of Mothers of Schizophrenic, Brain-injured and Retarded, and Normal Children," Unpublished Ph.D. dissertation, Boston University, 1957.

PART VI

Family Dynamics

11. SCHIZOPHRENIA, HUMAN INTEGRATION, AND THE ROLE OF THE FAMILY

Theodore Lidz and Stephen Fleck

Our studies of the intrafamilial environment in which schizophrenic patients grow up follow the clinical observation that schizophrenic patients virtually always emerge from homes marked by serious parental strife or eccentricity (1–12). An earlier survey comparing the clinical histories of 50 schizophrenic patients with 50 depressive psychotic patients indicated that fewer than 10 per cent, estimating conservatively, had come from homes that were well integrated and contained two reasonably stable parents (13). Subsequent experience with intensive therapy with schizophrenic patients confirmed and heightened these impressions, which appeared to offer the most consistent leads concerning the etiology of schizophrenia. Disturbed homes are common, but the findings suggested that an intensive search be made for more specific factors within the radius of this circle. The observations gained significance when considered against an emergent theory of schizophrenia, a conceptualization of the nature of man and how he develops into an integrated individual, and an appreciation of the vital functions of the family in personality development (14–18).

The studies on which the paper is based are being carried out in conjunction with Alice Cornelison, Dorothy Terry, and Sarah Schafer, and are supported by grants from the NIMH and the Social Research Foundation.

Theodore Lidz, M.D., is Professor of Psychiatry in the Yale University School of Medicine and Psychiatrist-in-Chief. Stephen Fleck, M.D., is Associate Professor of Psychiatry and of Public Health in the Yale University School of Medicine and Medical Director of the Yale Psychiatric Institute. Both are psychoanalysts.

Our investigations have been primarily exploratory, an endeavor to learn what transpired within these families and whether common features exist among them. The conceptual framework has served as in all research to direct attention and filter observations; and the emerging material has, in turn, continuously modified and sharpened our theoretic approach. It demanded new concepts of the influence of parents and of family transactions upon the offspring and of the functions which the family must fill to meet the child's inborn needs and developmental patterns while also instilling the mores and instrumentalities required for adaptation. We shall try to discuss each of the interrelated aspects of our approach separately for purposes of clarity. As they are not discrete, and as we pursue our studies to clarify these very issues, the discussion must remain incomplete and tentative. We are seeking to convey an orientation, not a closed system of thought.

It may be well to state at the start that we do not seek to promulgate an environmental interpersonal approach as against a genetic or biochemical approach. We are observing, recording, and interpreting what transpires within the family. The disorganization and irrationality found in these families can well indicate parental aberration that is genetically transmitted via some endocrine, biochemical, or neuronal means. If genetic factors exist, they are still beyond the reach of study and modifiability except in the most general terms. The parental abnormalities must, of course, also exert an interpersonal and environmental influence upon their families. Studying these provides meaningful material concerning schizophrenia, about personality integration, and about family dynamics. Although we consider that these observations may clarify the etiology of the illness, others may prefer to regard them phenomenologically. However, the limitations imposed by unproven convictions that something genetic or organic must be involved, risk neglecting material that appears to provide new insights into the subtleties of human development and the family's role in it. We have, therefore, sought to interpret our observations in their own transactional frame of reference. In considering the child's unfolding biologic endowment and his needs that must be met, we recognize the potentiality of anomalous endowments that cannot be met, but we also consider the possibility, strongly supported by our studies, that families exist that can neither fill the imperative needs of the child nor coherently convey the cultural instrumentalities to the child.

Schizophrenic reactions, whatever their cause, are a form of disorganization of the personality—a failure to achieve or maintain ego integration. The faulty ego development and the aberrant mentation are traditionally attributed to some unknown inherent defect, and those who consider schizophrenia as a type of aberrant personality development are chided for neglecting the brain and problems of physiological homeostasis. The human brain, however, bestows upon man a unique way of adapting to his environment via symbolic processes, and distortion of this strictly human technique is the essence of schizophrenia. Efforts to achieve simplification by ignoring the complexities of human techniques of adaptation entail the risk of eliminating the essence of the problems of schizophrenia (19, 20).

The critical feature of schizophrenia lies in the aberrant symbolic processes. However, the distortions of perceptions, meanings, and logic differ from degradations of mental functioning due to any known impairment of the brain or to the effects of any toxic agent (21). Although the schizophrenic patient has often been characterized as being unable to think abstractly, even casual observation indicates that he ·often abstracts all too readily. Unless the schizophrenic is permitted to become dilapidated through social isolation, his thought disorder remains or becomes circumscribed to sensitive topics. Duration of illness need not be paralleled by increasing thought disturbance. A patient with long-standing, fixed delusional systems that pervade much of his behavior can still learn analytic geometry; and another who berates her family constantly with delusional material can, when reasonably calm, compose intricate music. Such highly abstract and new acquisitions are barred to patients with organic brain lesions that are sufficiently extensive or pervasive to cause behavioral disorganization. Those who have learned to listen find not only meaning but perspicacious insights into what a patient may seek to communicate and yet to conceal. Patients' responses to psychotherapeutic intervention and milieu therapy have forced reconsideration of concepts of schizophrenic deterioration.

Such observations warrant the hypothesis that schizophrenia is a condition in which the patient alters his internalized representation of reality in order to escape and withdraw from his insoluble conflicts, from a world grown untenable to him, and from social interaction. Perplexed in his efforts to establish meaningful relationships, caught between opposing contradictory desires that are often traceable to parental conflict, frightened by the violence of his aggressive and erotic impulses, and unable to find a path into the future or even to gain security through regression because of distrust or fear of those upon whom he would depend, the patient withdraws from others and their ways of thinking and communicating. Through altering the world autistically, by changing his perception of himself and others, and by abandoning the logic of his culture, he finds some room for living and some semblance of self-esteem. The thought disorder tends to be self-perpetuating because the patient no longer tests the usefulness of his ideas or behavior for mastering his environment or establishing communication. When the onset of the illness is acute, the abandonment of object relationships is often precipitated by fear of loss of control over incestuous, homosexual, or homicidal impulses; and the ensuing panic increases disorganization and interpersonal disorientation (4). Restitutive measures to re-establish some ways of relating to others usually follow.

Recognition of the far-reaching role of symbolic functioning in human adaptation permits consideration of how the illness can be the outcome of a life development that has gone astray, being then related to the total developmental process rather than the product of disordered brain functioning. The development of a brain that permits abstract symbolization provided man with a method and range of adaptation different from that of any other organism. It freed him from inborn or instinctive patterns, such as reflexes or imprints, by integrating them into complex motivational forces where the basic biological needs provide impulsion to behavior rather than the compulsion of fixed patterns (19). Able to recall selectively, he can be motivated by his distant past and even the experiences of past generations. Able to project the past through the present into the future, he becomes motivated by potential futures that he imagines and the ultimate future that he knows awaits him, as much as by the past. Able to communicate verbally and through writing rather than simply through example, he can transmit what he learns from generation to generation and across generations. Each human group has built up over countless centuries ways of doing and reacting that are termed the instrumentalities of the culture. These include the language itself with the potentialities and limitations it sets for mental activity, ways of perceiving that tint the inborn sense organs, ways of thinking and reasoning that free and enslave, mores and sentiments that qualify what becomes emotionally meaningful, as well as the tools, tangible and mental, with which man works upon nature and gains degrees of control over it.

These vital acquisitions are, of course, not transmitted via the genes. Unless we understand that man transmits two discrete and yet intimately interdependent heritages from one generation to the next, we can never understand his behavior or his physiological functioning correctly (22). Unless the infant, who is born with countless potentialities but little inborn direction, grows into and assimilates the instrumentalities of the culture in which he is born, he will be no more a person and no more capable of living in society than his primordial ancestors who first acquired the exquisite neuromuscular control essential for language and tool bearing. Man has developed during recent millennia not so much through genetic mutation as through the gradual acquisition of new ways of adapting to and modifying his environment. On the other hand, unless each culture develops and provides ways suited to the inborn needs of man and to his developmental pattern of unfolding his potentialities, it cannot survive.

Each human group must enable the infant to acquire ways of communicating, of thinking and doing, and he must be protected during long years of immature dependency while he learns. He must find ways of solving the tasks of each phase of development in order to move securely into the next stage with its new problems. The normal course of development requires movement toward increasing independence, with the insecurities and anxieties of additional responsibility for the self. The long period of dependency creates lasting bonds to others and provides a security that the child relinquishes reluctantly, whereas the concomitant limitations may be shed eagerly. Regression tempts repeatedly and can serve to help consolidation before he ventures onward again. By the end of adolescence or early in adult life, the individual is expected to have assimilated patterns of living, achieved an identity of his own, and found a way of life to enable him to leave parental shelter, guidance, and some of their limiting influences. The way of life, the needed emotional maturity, the workable set of mores do not come as part of his physical maturation but through learning and particularly through interaction with parental figures with whom he identifies and whom he introjects to gain their ways and their strengths. The process can progress in reasonably integrated fashion only if these models are not impossible to follow, do not obscure the way through using confusing signals, are not mutually contradictory, and transmit instrumentally valid ways of living with others in the society into which the youth must eventually emerge.

In virtually all societies, the family is the primary conveyor of the cultural instrumentalities that the child must acquire to become a person. Yet it carries out this basic function implicitly according to tradition with little awareness of how the personalities and interactions of its members become part of the child. There are countless chances for misdirection, confusion, and conflict between birth and the attainment of maturity. The wonder is how the family fills its functions so adequately and yet so unknowingly. Still, the structure of the family and the patterns of its activities are largely products of its culture, and they would not have developed and survived unless they were useful in forwarding essential functions. Perhaps it is a safeguard that aberrant products of deviant families tend to be excluded from parenthood (23).

The child grows in relation to others, and the bonds that attach him to others are no less real because they are diaphanous. Even as he begins to emerge from biologic dependent needs, his needs for others are given compulsive moment by his libidinal drives. Those essential figures from whom he separates become embodied within him and continue to provide direction and exert control upon his life. The human being can never be considered as an isolate, for even in isolation he is supported by earlier attachments to others, which become internalized, or symbolic. The loss of these relationships or their abandonment brings catastrophe. The need to maintain his relatedness fosters the relegation into the unconscious of impulses and wishes unacceptable to parental figures, whether real or introjected. The selection of that which is acceptable to parental figures or their replacements, and through them to the culture, fosters delimitation and channeling of thought and behavior culminating in an integrated ego development and structure. Even as man cannot be understood separated from his interpersonal attachments, he cannot be understood separated from his culture, which he carries within him. He has grown into it, and it has become incorporated in him. Indeed, psychiatry proper deals with just these problems, which arise because the biologically endowed infant must assimilate the instrumentalities of his culture to become a person, but the process of the assimilation is only in part controlled biologically.

The unfolding of the biologically endowed organism and its assimilation of the interpersonally transmitted heritage are so intimately intertwined that they can be differentiated only arbitrarily. The parents who carry the genetic traits are usually also the primary carriers of the culture and the primary figures for identification. While man's biological make-up sets requisites that each culture and subculture must take into account, the culture also sets imperatives to assure that each new member can live in it and transmit its mores, and these mores profoundly influence the physiological functioning of the individual. What stimulates or repels appetites, what frightens or angers, is influenced by where and how the child is reared. The human is integrated at a symbolic level, and what he thinks about what he feels and what he feels about what he thinks influence his functioning down to the cellular level.

With this general statement of the nature of human adaptation, we can return to the problems of schizophrenia and its distortions of the symbolic processes. The very capacity that distinguishes man and permits his inordinate range of adaptability contains a grave vulnerability. He depends fundamentally upon the instrumental utility of his thinking to cope with the many divergent environments in which he has learned to live. He is not endowed with an inborn system of meanings or logic. His brain permits thinking but does not guarantee rational thinking. What is considered rational varies with time and place, as history and ethnology amply testify. Still a trend toward "reasonable" thinking exists in all groups. Even though no one can perceive reality as it is, for the *ding an sich* ("the thing itself in an absolute sense" [24]) ever eludes our perception, a practical measure of reality and reason exists in how our perceptions and thinking lead to effective action and to mastery over our environment. Rationality of communication is measured by the degree of workable interaction with others that it provides. Meanings develop from sorting out experiences and through communication with others. However, percept and meaning develop and alter in the service of emotional needs while providing a useful adaptation to the environment. Effective communication with a significant person may also require disregard of logic and verbal expression in favor of response to the affective and unspoken (5). Meanings can give way before the need to permit gratification of drives and wishes in the face of restrictive realities. Percepts alter before the need to maintain a satisfactory image of the self and of others essential to the self. Not all shared ideas are reasonable or effective for controlling the environment. Man's need for security in an uncertain world leads to the systematization of ideas that run counter to experience. The acceptance of untestable axioms needed to provide emotional security often directs perception and understanding (25, 26). Such axioms form belief systems when shared and culturally acceptable and delusional systems when idiosyncratic.

The complex nature of human rationality, it may be reasserted, is such that rationality and irrationality cannot be considered primarily in terms of intactness of brain functioning. The nonperceptions and self-deceptions that arise to ward off anxiety when one's acceptability to oneself and others is threatened constitute the mental mechanisms of defense. But defenses may fail or even increase the dilemma by distorting the view of the situation that must be dealt with. This is apt to occur when essential needs and expectations are mutually exclusive, when the way into the future is barred and even regressive movement paralyzed because the persons upon whom one would depend cannot be trusted and arouse untenable impulses. Even then one other way still exists, but it leads beyond the confines set for life in society. The person can abandon the logic of his culture, change the meanings of events and the perception of his motivations and those of others. He can regress to a period when reality yielded to the power of fantasy and regain a type of omnipotence and self-sufficiency. Such means of escape from the untenable are so clearly available to man, and so often used in minor, individual ways and in major, culturally approved ways, that if we did not know of a syndrome such as schizophrenia we should have to search for it as an anticipated type of developmental failure.

Still, a theory of schizophrenia must explain not only a person's need to withdraw through symbolic distortions but also his capacity to do so. While it may be possible for many to escape into unshared and paralogical ways when under extreme stress, others probably cannot. It may be considered, for example, that some people develop psychosomatic illnesses because they cannot avoid the physiological dysfunctions produced by anxiety through distorting perception of reality. Such paths may be open only to those who have been poorly grounded in reality-testing in childhood (19, 27, 28, 29).

A corollary hazard in man's mode of adaptation, or perhaps one should say in the culture's means of adapting the infant to its ways, requires consideration. The culture depends largely upon the family to convey its mores and instrumentalities to its children. The individual's reactions in all subsequent group and interpersonal situations rest upon the foundations provided within the family. Yet the family has its own needs, which may take precedence over its educational functions. It may be deviant from the remainder of society, set mutually exclusive demands upon the child, provide inconsistent emotional experiences, teach paralogical ways, and in many other areas provide faulty schooling. Although the family is not the only influence upon the developing ego, it provides the most consistent or consistently inconsistent set of influences impinging upon the child (30–32).

Focusing attention upon the intrafamilial object relationships is consistent with other psychoanalytic and dynamic approaches (17). It includes a search for causes of ego weakness and unstable ego boundaries, for reasons for narcissistic withdrawal after object loss, for regression to infantile omnipotence, for loss of reality-testing, and so forth (33). Such a focus, however, considers particularly the ego's development in relation to others and especially the parental objects within the world of the family, created largely by the interaction of the parental figures. But our studies go beyond the intrafamilial object relations taken in a strict sense and focus also upon the influences of the family as a unit, in order to examine the structural requisites of the family that are essential to the promotion of integral ego structure in its offspring. The material derived from the study indicates that neglect of these structural essentials may be a major shortcoming in current approaches to the study of personality development.

When preliminary surveys indicating that schizophrenic patients almost always grew up in seriously disturbed homes were viewed from this orientation, it seemed imperative to scrutinize the family milieu for determinants of schizophrenic reactions (13, 34–45). But the investigation of the influence of the family and its members upon the emergent generation presents very grave methodological and conceptual difficulties. Neither suitable techniques of study nor an adequate conceptual framework for a dynamic study of family interaction exist (18, 27, 46–62). Preliminary studies indicated the need to examine the entire family situation rather than some segment of it. The father appeared to be seriously disturbed just as often as the mother (5, 11), and the vicissitudes and fortunes of the family life as a whole appeared of potential importance. The only basis for the belief that schizophrenia is determined by events in the early, oral phase of development is purely hypothetical, unsupported by evidence that the earliest mother-child relationships are more deleterious than those of other psychiatric patients (5). The cardinal symptomatology of schizophrenia would seem to indicate that later developmental periods also have critical significance. The symbolic distortions, the interpenetration of reality and fantasy, the confusion of sexual identity, the concerns over incestuous impulses, the attribution of omniscience and omnipotence to parental figures are all significant problems of the early Oedipal or late pre-Oedipal phases of development (63). Although it may be considered that disturbances in the oral phase are essential to the development of schizophrenia, they may only establish a potentiality to mental illness, whereas subsequent events may determine the degree and form of the individual's adjustment or maladjustment.

In a general way, we have considered schizophrenia to be essentially an illness of adolescence and early adult life even when the manifest illness appears later. We have considered the developmental forces that lead to the formation of an integrated person who can leave the parental home and assume responsibility for himself, and we have looked for factors that may have made such emergence impossible and led to withdrawal and regression. An effort was made by the investigators to eliminate preconceptions concerning specific causal factors and simply examine the material as it emerged.

The approach adopted, despite its many obvious shortcomings, has been essentially the intensive exploration of what transpired within the family from its inception through the time of study. Multiple techniques were utilized in an attempt to recreate the personalities, their interactions, the ways and the atmosphere of the family group. The core material derives from the long-term study of the families of 16 patients hospitalized in the Yale Psychiatric Institute. Only families in which the mother and at least one sibling were available for repeated interviews and projective testing were selected. In all except two families, the father was alive and participated. All the families were upper or upper-middle class and capable of supporting a mem-

ber in a private hospital for a prolonged period except for two families with
a somewhat lower socio-economic status. The sample had a clear bias toward
more intact families with status and prestige in their communities and cannot be compared directly with most other series. The bias was desired to
safeguard against the inclusion of families selected because of their disorganization or partial dissolution and to lessen complexities created by
economic distress and disturbed extrafamilial social environments.

The major method used was the repeated therapeutic and nonthera-
peutic interviewing of all available family members, often amounting to
hundreds of sessions with a single member and less frequent interviews with
others. Less immediate relatives, family friends, former teachers, and nurse-
maids were interviewed whenever possible, diaries and productions of the
patient and other family members were studied, and home visits were made
(1). The observation and study of the interaction of the family members
with each other and the hospital staff proved particularly valuable (2). All
members of the family were given projective tests when possible, and these
were interpreted to reveal family patterns of interaction and identifications
between members as well as to further understanding of the individual personalities (12). Families were studied for periods ranging from four months
to four years, lengthening as the study progressed and awareness increased
of the difficulties in obtaining a proper picture. Any attempt to reconstruct
a family environment as it existed over a period of 15 to 30 years will contain
grave deficiencies. The diffuse procedure was warranted because it seemed
impossible to structure a stricter methodological procedure without excluding avenues of investigation available and useful in some families but not in
all cases. Recently a similar study of the families of upper and upper-middle
class delinquents has been started to obtain comparative material concerning
families with similar problems, concerns, and motivations to participate (10).
Whatever the shortcomings, there is reason to believe that the studies have
yielded the most comprehensive and intimate pictures of any families yet
studied for any purpose.

The findings of the study, which are still being scrutinized, cannot be
reviewed here, and the reader must be referred to our articles, published and
pending, to obtain an impression of their worth and meaning (64, 1–18). The
extent and pervasiveness of the family pathology were unexpected. Not a
single family was reasonably well integrated, but it requires illustrative material to convey properly how seriously disorganized or aberrant these families were (6–8). Most of the marriages upon which the families were based
were gravely disturbed. The majority were torn by schismatic conflict between the parents that divided the family into two hostile factions, with

each spouse seeking to gain the upper hand, defying the wishes of the other, undercutting the worth of the spouse to the children, seeking to win the children to his side and to use them as emotional replacements for the spouse. The remaining families developed a skewed pattern because the serious psychopathology of the dominant parent was passively accepted by the other, leading to aberrant ways of living and of child-rearing. Their acceptance and masking of the serious problems that existed created a strange emotional environment that was perplexing to the child. In each family at least one parent suffered from serious and crippling psychopathology, and in many both were markedly disturbed. Although none of these parents had ever been in a mental hospital, at least 10 of the 16 families contained a parent who was an ambulatory schizophrenic or clearly paranoid, and our diagnostic cut-off point was arbitrary and conservative. Still others were chronic alcoholics, severe obsessives, or so extremely passive-dependent that they were virtually children of their spouses rather than another parent. Many parents constantly required support for their tottering narcissism that could not be gained from the spouse, and they chronically distorted situations to maintain their self-image and the single, narrow way of life that constituted their adjustment. Insecurity and confusion concerning sexual identity, often with fairly obvious homosexual trends, were common, and many of these parents had difficulty in controlling their incestuous impulses, both heterosexual and homosexual (4). Suspiciousness and distrust of outsiders pervaded some families and were taught directly to the children, and some degree of paralogical thinking was present in almost all these families (3, 8). These parents clearly provided faulty models for identification and for primary love objects that started the child in life with strange patterns of interpersonal relationships.

The organization of the material continues to present difficulties because of its inordinate complexity and the need to view it from a variety of overlapping perspectives. Articles have been published to focus attention and to analyze various facets that required study rather than to provide a comprehensive picture. In the absence of any single satisfactory frame of reference, several approaches to the material are being undertaken. These include examination of the parent-child relationships, the parental interaction and its influences upon the child, the dynamics of the family as a small group, the manner in which the family fills certain structural requisites that seem essential to the ego integration of the offspring, and the nature and characteristics of intrafamilial communication (17, 45).

Although particular attention has been paid to the characteristics of the mother and her relationship to her children, generalizations that apply to all the mothers are not found as readily as when one contemplates just those mothers who usually obtrude themselves upon psychiatrists because of striking characteristics (34, 44, 65, 66). The mother forms the primary love object for the child and the first figure for identification to boys as well as girls, and her influence requires intensive study. But if common denominators exist among all 16 mothers which explain the illness of their children, they are not readily apparent. Although we found many so seriously disturbed that it is difficult to see how they could bring up reasonably well-adjusted children (7, 10), very few had not done their utmost to be good mothers, and overt rejection of a child appears to have been unusual. We believe that some would or could have been reasonably adequate mothers, had they only been unimpeded by serious marital difficulties or the demands of their disturbed husbands. Others were strikingly "schizophrenogenic" because of their own ambulatory schizophrenic ways and needs.

We are still engaged in methodologic sorting of a large number of maternal traits in a search for common and significant features (38, 41, 65). It seems possible that the mothers of schizophrenic sons must be considered separately from mothers of schizophrenic daughters (10). Some traits, however, recur frequently. Among these are imperviousness to what the child seeks to convey, combined with an inordinate intrusiveness; a tendency to confuse the child's needs with her own needs projected on the child; disparity between what is expressed verbally and emphatically (67); failure to recognize ego boundaries between herself and the child; the need to have the child live out an existence closed to her because she is a woman (9, 26); undue restrictiveness because of her obsessive anxieties, or, conversely, an inability to set limits (8, 9). In addition, there are frequently such generalized difficulties as uncertainty concerning sexual identity, low self-esteem as a woman, projective trends, chronic distortions of situations in order to maintain a needed preconceived version of the self and the family.

Very early in the study of these families, our attention was drawn to the importance of the fathers, whose presence and influence could not be neglected (5, 11). They were as frequently and as severely disturbed as the mothers. Despite the relative neglect of the father in recent studies of the dynamics of schizophrenia and even of child development in general, the father's place in the developmental dynamics of the offspring is, of course, extremely involved, and his deficiencies can impede the child's progress in many ways at all stages of development. He is usually the first intruder into the child's mutuality with the mother, and the child should develop a sense of identification with him, as well as a sense of mutuality with both the mother and father as a unit. The mother's ability to be maternal and secure depends greatly upon the support she gains from the father and his ability to share her with the child. The child's appraisal of the mother's worth as a love object involves the father's esteem for her or his enmity toward her. To the son, he forms a critical object for identification, whereas to the daughter he should be a suitable love object, so that she can seek to gain the love of a man by growing into a woman like mother. This development will be difficult if the father despises the mother or is so inconsistent that no behavioral pattern appears to satisfy him. The fathers studied were very often insecure in their masculinity, needing constant admiration and attention to bolster their self-esteem. Even the domineering and more tyrannical fathers whom neither wife nor children could satisfy could be recognized as being basically weak and ineffectual by the members of the family. A goodly proportion were paranoid or given to paralogical and irrational behavior within the family that seriously affected the entire family interaction. The quality of imperviousness to the feelings and sensitivities of others that epitomizes many of the mothers also applies to many of the fathers. We have evidence which indicates that fathers can interfere with the mother's relationship to the child even during the first days and weeks of a child's life (7, 66); that he often fosters blurring of the line between the two generations in the family by competing with a child; and that his insecurity as a husband and father impedes the development of identity as a man in the son and as a woman in the daughter. The fathers, just like the mothers, are so caught up in their own unresolved problems that they can rarely fill the essentials of a parental role adequately.

It is apparent that the child is influenced by the parental interaction as well as by each parent's personality and the dyadic relationships with the child. The introjection of the parental relationship and its harmonies and dissonances is a process that has scarcely been studied specifically. It has also been described by Wynne and his collaborators (68, 69). The anxieties conveyed to the child by the mother may have less to do with her concerns about the child than with her concerns about her husband. Rejective behavior by a parent may reflect the wish to be rid of the marriage to which the child binds. The parent who regards a child as an intruder into the marital relationship, or, conversely, who uses the child as a substitute for the spouse, must influence the spouse's attitude and behavior toward the child. The child is influenced not only by the parent's own self-esteem but also by the spouse's esteem for this parent. A father who constantly derogates the mother influences the child's concept of "wife" and "mother" and opens the way for the daughter to compete realistically with the mother for the father. A father who is constantly being castrated by the mother provides a distorted image of the role of the man in the family and initiates in the son a fear of women that seems an important factor in the genesis of homosexual trends (4, 9). However, even such analyses of the effects of parental interaction upon children are but an arbitrary extraction from the study of the family in terms of small group dynamics, permissible because it appears essential for purposes of description of the complex interplay.

In some respects the family forms the epitome of a small group with an organic life and unity of its own over and above the lives of its constituents. The welfare of the family requires each member to give a degree of precedence to its needs above his own and those of outsiders. It provides a shelter for its members within and against the remainder of society. Perhaps more than in any other group, the actions of any member affect all and produce reactions and counterreactions. Its members must find reciprocally interrelating roles or leave one or more members in a state of imbalance requiring pathological defenses (59, 61, 68, 69). The family, in turn, relates as a unit to the broader society in which it exists and forms a focal point between individuals and their organization within society.

Nuclear family dynamics operate under some specific imperatives which are unlike those of other small groups. Beginning as a group of two the family enlarges to include the children, only to decline again in number over a period of two or three decades, reaching again a twosome. Besides this continual evolutionary shift in its composition and tasks, the group contains a clear biological division into two genders that cuts across the generations. There is also an imperative to observe and maintain the distinction between the two generations of parents and offspring.

In the families of schizophrenic patients, a number of deficiencies in such areas profoundly influenced their members. Many of these families provided a paucity of emotional shelter because of the schisms that existed, requiring members to erect stronger ego defenses and be less honest and trusting within the family than elsewhere (4, 6). Others provided a type of shelter within that fostered distrust of all without. In many cases a true nuclear family, which should form the emotional center of gravity of the parents, scarcely existed. The primary loyalties of one or both parents remained in their own parental homes, with major decision-making often left to their parents or siblings. Others formed units that provided little real contact with the remainder of society and taught divergent mores. When parents could not find reciprocally interrelating roles, children consciously or unconsciously sought roles that would fill voids, bridge gaps, satisfy mutually contradictory desires of parents. Some children were placed in the role of a scapegoat whose problems became the bond which kept the family together, or the child could be used as an excuse for the unhappiness of the group (61). The cultural differences and divergent backgrounds which some of our parents bring into marriage are also sources of difficulty that require careful scrutiny (59). The partners also contribute unresolved emotional needs stemming from their parental homes, which they hope will be resolved or satisfied in their marriage, either through the relationship with the spouse, the acquisition of children, or the altered status achieved by marriage (7). It would seem possible to study and include such cultural differences and unresolved emotional problems through studying the personalities of the parents and how they intermesh to form a family. The reasons why the parents selected a particular mate, why they married, and how they inter-relate are essential to the understanding of the group and its on-going interaction. Still, while the interrelationship between the spouses forms the foundation of most families in our society, a marital relationship is not the same as a family relationship. A marital partnership can permit a wide variation in role assignments if acceptable to both partners but causing imbalance when children are added. Gross reversals of culturally prescribed male and female roles need not disrupt a partnership but can only distort the development of children reared in such culturally deviant situations, especially if such deviations remain more or less covert.

Analysis of the more formal structure of the family provides a task foreign to psychiatrists accustomed to dealing with intrapersonal and interpersonal dynamics. Such procedure permits comparisons of families in nonpersonal terms and in turn sharpens appreciation of what is required of a family and its members (38, 39). For a child to develop properly, the family must provide a matrix with structural requisites that help shape the ego structure of the offspring. It currently appears that understanding the deficiencies of the family in such structural terms helps greatly to clarify the nature and origins of the ego weaknesses of schizophrenic patients. The material from our study drew our attention to the common failure of these families to maintain the essential boundaries between the two generations. This generalization included the childlike dependency of one parent upon the other, the rivalries between parents for the affection and loyalty of a child, intense jealousies between a parent and child for the other parent, and the incestuous proclivities of both parents and children (4). It was extremely helpful to find that Parsons and Bales had emphasized the same structural requisite of the family and had developed an analysis of the family structure based upon the study of small groups in general (16–18).

The division of the family biologically into two generations and two sexes provides a framework that serves to establish the roles of members and the cultural patterns for these roles.

How the analysis of the family in these terms works out will be illustrated briefly. In order to survive and grow, the infant, who is born helpless, must at first receive total care, which is gradually abrogated as he matures, and he must be indoctrinated in group living within the family to be able to leave the family and live in other groups and form a family of his own. The older generation must act in coalition and give of themselves to enable the offspring to grow through assimilation. Each generation has prerogatives denied the other. For example, children must be dependent upon parents, but undue parental dependence upon children creates difficulties. Parents are permitted and expected to have sexual relationships with each other, but all sexual relationships within the family are prohibited to children. Each sex has role expectations that are partly determined biologically. The mother has the role of providing the total care needed by the infant, which demands an erotically toned interest in the child. She becomes more involved in the affectional relationships and the internal structure of the family. The father is required to protect and supply the mother-child unit, emerges from the family into society more than the mother, and is more concerned with instrumental tasks. As Parsons points out, a cold and unyielding mother will be more deleterious than a cold and unyielding father, and a weak and ineffectual mother less harmful than a weak father (18).

The development and resolution of the Oedipal situation, which forms an essential and critical juncture in the child's life, provide a particularly pertinent example of the importance of structural requisites within the family (4, 16). The child requires the erotically motivated love of a parent during the pre-Oedipal period so that in turn he can invest his own total being in the task of growing and socializing within the family; yet, when these attachments are no longer vital to his existence, he must gradually be frustrated before he can gain a conflict-free role within the family. Thus energy is freed to be invested in peer groups and learning, and eventually the child can grow away from the family and find erotic gratification outside of it. The mother has the difficult task of giving herself completely enough to the child and then withdrawing the erotic bonds which had been temporarily vital to him, but they must be replaced gradually by non-erotic bonds of identification with her and the family. Her erotization of the relationship should be guided by the needs of the child rather than serve primarily to fill a void in her own life. It is probably best when the entire operation proceeds unconsciously, controlled by the marital bonds, the structure of the family, and the child-rearing customs of the group. A mutually supportive relationship between the parents safeguards the child from becoming a primary source of gratification to one of them, facilitates parental maintenance of an educative role as members of the adult generation, lets the parents assume proper sex-linked roles in relation to the child, and enables them to frustrate the child without frustrating the self or the marital partner (57, 70). These and other factors enable the mother and child to make the difficult transitions in their relationship. The continuation of Oedipal strivings into later, conscious incestuous wishes conflicts with an essential taboo and provokes fear and guilt, but the harmful effects go beyond this. The taboo not only is essential for the integrity of the family and the general structure of society but also fosters the achievement of ego identity with firm ego boundaries in every individual. The failure of the families of schizophrenic patients is often mirrored clearly in the incestuous problems that arise (4).

The family's ways and structure also require specific consideration in relationship to the society in which it exists. The indoctrination of the new generation to family living must also be preparation for living in the broader cultural group. When family ways are notably deviant, the offspring find themselves in a foreign world when outside the family, unable to grasp signs and signals and uneasy with the ways in which outsiders relate to them. When families have belief systems and ways of thinking and reacting emotionally that are unique, the child is ill prepared for emergence into the world, and forming an intimate marital union demanding intuitive understanding of another, is even more difficult (3, 8). The child has not only learned alien ways, but he has also been prepared to alienate himself from shared ways of regarding the world, even as have members of his family.

An attempt has been made to convey an orientation to the problems of schizophrenia which led to our current intensive exploratory studies of the total family environment in which the patient is reared. The very serious parental pathology found in all cases permeates and distorts the entire family interaction and structure and precludes the focusing of attention on any single facet. We have sought to indicate how pertinent data emerge from the study of the individual personalities, the dyadic relationships, the group interaction, the family structure, and the family's relationship to its societal matrix. Although various aspects can be singled out for study and clarification, they interpenetrate and influence almost all other phases of the family life, for the family forms a unique small group which cannot be fragmented without distortion of the material. In a general sense, however, we have studied the material by following the parents' personalities, including their subcultures and unresolved problems, which interrelate to form a marital union. Then we considered the parents in their roles as individuals and as a unit forming a family group after the arrival of children (7).

We have not sought to present discrete findings in organized form here but simply to indicate direction and potential meaning. In the most general terms, it would seem difficult for children who have grown up in these families to become reasonably well-integrated persons. The question often raised concerning the "normal" siblings reared within the same families forms a focal point of study and is one reason why only families containing siblings have been included. The problem is not so great as considered initially because many siblings are seriously disturbed and relatively few have made reasonably stable adjustments. Even these individuals, with rare exception, suffer from marked constriction of the personality (7, 12, 69). Consideration of the dynamics of role relationships, of the stresses linked to being a member of one sex or the other within a given family, and of the vicissitudes of the family as a whole appears to clarify the individual cases.

Brief consideration of a few of the problems and symptoms that seem basic to schizophrenic reactions may serve to indicate, in summary, how they have become more understandable when regarded against the family backgrounds. Irrationality and paralogical thinking may be tolerated or encouraged within the family, but they jeopardize interaction with and adaptation to the community. The family member who becomes the patient may exhibit more distorted communication, and, in his behavior, more irrationality than do his siblings or parents. But it is the parents who chronically distorted meanings and communications to defend a precarious equilibrium, either within one of them, or within the marriage, or within the family, or in all three spheres, providing, in a sense, training in irrationality.

Confusion of sexual identity is common among the patients, noted particularly in homosexual trends and fears and in delusions of impending change of sex. The parents also suffer from faulty sexual identity, often with apparent latent homosexual tendencies and with some degree of reversal of sex-linked social and parental roles. The parent of the same sex as the patient rarely provided an adequate model for identification; and, even if he could have done so, the worth of this parent as man or woman, husband or wife, father or mother often was seriously undercut by the spouse. Patients' needs to seek to fill the emotional needs of a parent in crossed sexual or asexual ways compounded the difficulties. The incestuous problems that bring fear of proximity and intense feelings of worthlessness and guilt were also often found to have their counterpart in the parents. At times, a patient was clearly justified, and not delusional, in fearing that if he lost control incest could well occur.

Further, the schism between parents, with efforts to seduce a child to side with one parent, opened the way for the patient to insert himself as a more essential object than the other parent. The broader effects upon ego development, designated above, will not be reconsidered here. However, the seductive or hostile attitudes of one or the other parent, more or less consciously perceived by the patient, suggest that the delusional patient is not simply projecting his own impulses but may be transferring attitudes of parents to others, just as occurs in therapy. The problem of the weak ego structure mirrors the confused identifications with irreconcilable and contradictory parental objects as well as the failure of parents to maintain ego boundaries between the self and the patient. The loss of cardinal objects with consequent delusions of world catastrophe which so frequently ushers in the overt psychosis, does not seem to follow abandonment of the patient but rather the patient's dire need to withdraw because of imminent loss of control over incestuous and murderous impulses. It will be realized that these and other aspects of schizophrenia and their potential origins cannot be kept discrete, for the study increasingly indicates that such developments are related products of the gross failure of the family to carry out many fundamental functions vested in it by society to provide each new member with a workable ego structure.

Although much remains hypothetical concerning the etiologic moment of the family interaction, it seems certain that these serious family disorganizations cannot be extraneous to the problem. While abstractions that can be considered as generalizations for the entire group must remain tentative, the work with specific families has led to much clearer understanding of the patient's problems and has fostered communication between patient and therapist. Family attitudes have often altered, with concomitant shifts in the patient's ways of relating to them. Perplexing symptoms take on tangible meaning so that work with them becomes less evanescent and more capable of being translated into terms of definite interpersonal difficulties with which both patient and therapist can work. It is encouraging to find that this approach to the study of schizophrenic reactions raises new and meaningful questions at every turn, and their investigation constantly broadens and sharpens our grasp of schizophrenia in general and of the problems of the specific patient. Beyond the study of schizophrenia, the investigations have entered upon the vast topic of the structure and pathology of the family and its relationship to personality development and maldevelopment. Following the subtle and far-reaching influences of family pathology upon the family members brings new dimensions to the study of personality development and analytically oriented psychopathology. The study of schizophrenia leads us into the study of basic issues of human integration.

References

1.   A. CORNELISON, Casework interviewing as a research technique in a study of families of schizophrenic patients, *Ment. Hyg.* To be published.
2.   S. FLECK, A. CORNELISON, *et al.*, The intrafamilial environment of the schizophrenic patient. III. Interaction between hospital staff and families, *Psychiatry, 20:* 343, 1957.
3.   S. FLECK, D. X. FREEDMAN, *et al.*, The intrafamilial environment of the schizophrenic patient. V. the understanding of symptomatology through the study of family interaction. Paper presented at Am. Psychiatric Assoc. Meeting, May 15, 1957.
4.   S. FLECK, T. LIDZ, *et al.*, "The Intrafamilial Environment of the Schizophrenic Patient," in Masserman, J. H. (Ed.), *Individual and Familial Dynamics,* Grune, 1959.
5.   T. LIDZ, A. CORNELISON, *et al.*, The intrafamilial environment of the schizophrenic patient. I. the father. Psychiatry, *20:* 329, 1957.
6.   T. LIDZ, A. CORNELISON, *et al.*, The intrafamilial environment of schizophrenic patients. II. marital schism and marital skew, *Am. J. Psychiat., 114:* 241, 1957.
7.   T. LIDZ, A. CORNELISON, *et al.*, The intrafamilial environment of the schizophrenic patient. IV. parental personalities and family interaction, *Am. J. Orthopsychiat., 28:* 764, 1958.
8.   T. LIDZ, A. CORNELISON, *et al.*, The intrafamilial environment of the schizophrenic patient. VI. the transmission of irrationality, *A.M.A. Arch. Neurol. & Psychiat., 79:* 305, 1958.
9.   T. LIDZ, A. CORNELISON, *et al.*, Zur Familienumwelt des Schizophrenen, *Sonderdruck Psyche,* XIII, 1959–60.
10.   T. LIDZ, S. FLECK, *et al.*, Studies in progress.
11.   T. LIDZ, B. PARKER, and A. CORNELISON, The role of the father in the family environment of the schizophrenic patient, *Am. J. Psychiat., 113:* 126, 1956.
12.   D. T. SOHLER, J. HOLZBERG, *et al.*, The prediction of family interaction from a battery of projective tests, *J. Proj. Tech., 21:* 199, 1957.
13.   R. W. LIDZ and T. LIDZ, The family environment of schizophrenic patients, *Am. J. Psychiat., 106:* 332, 1949.
14.   J. C. FLÜGEL, *The Psychoanalytic Study of the Family,* London: Hogarth, 1921.
15.   J. C. FLÜGEL, *Man, Morals and Society: A Psychoanalytic Study,* New York: Internat. Univ. Press, 1955.
16.   T. PARSONS, The incest taboo in relation to social structure and the socialization of the child, *Brit. J. Sociol., 5:* 101, 1954.
17.   T. PARSONS, Social structure and the development of personality: Freud's contribution to the integration of psychology and sociology, *Psychiatry, 21:* 321, 1958.
18.   T. PARSONS, A. BALES, *et al.*, *Family, Socialization and Interaction,* Glencoe, Ill.: Free Press, 1955.
19.   S. FLECK, Vigilance (orienting behavior), conditional reactions and adjust-

ment patterns in schizophrenic and compulsive patients, *Ann. New York Acad. Sc.,* *56*: 342, 1953.

20. A. MEYER, The dynamic interpretation of dementia praecox, *Am. J. Psychol.,* *21*: 385, 1910.

21. T. LIDZ, J. R. GAY, and C. TIETZE, Intelligence in cerebral deficit states and schizophrenia measured by Kohs Block Test, *Arch. Neurol. & Psychiat., 48*: 568, 1942.

22. H. J. MULLER, Progress and prospects in human genetics (sec. VIII), *Am. J. Human Genet., 1*: 1, 1949.

23. M. L. KOHN and J. A. CLAUSEN, Social isolation and schizophrenia, *Am. Sociol. Rev., 20*: 265, 1955.

24. I. KANT, *Kritik der reinen Vernunft* (1. Band), Leipzig: Deutsche Bibliothek in Berlin.

25. F. FROMM-REICHMANN, Notes on the development of treatment of schizophrenics by psychoanalytic psychotherapy, *Psychiatry, 11*: 263, 1944.

26. R. W. LIDZ and T. LIDZ, "Therapeutic Considerations Arising from Intense Symbiotic Needs of Schizophrenic Patients," in Brady, G. and Redlich, F. (Eds.), *Psychotherapy with Schizophrenics,* New York: Internat. Univ. Press, 1952.

27. E. M. GOLDBERG, Experiences with families of young men with duodenal ulcer and "normal" control families: some problems of approach and method, *Brit. J. M. Psychol., 26*: 204, 1953.

28. H. B. RICHARDSON, *Patients Have Families,* New York: Commonwealth Fund, 1945.

29. F. P. THOME, Epidemiologic studies of chronic frustration–hostility states, *Am. J. Psychiat., 113*: 717, 1957.

30. N. W. ACKERMAN, Interpersonal disturbances in the family, *Psychiatry, 17*: 359, 1954.

31. S. FISHER and D. MENDELL, The communication of neurotic patterns over two and three generations, *Psychiatry, 19*: 41, 1956.

32. H. J. LOCKE, G. SABAGH, and M. THOMAS, Primary communication empathy and family unity. Paper presented at Am. Sociological Soc. Meeting, Sept., 1955.

33. E. ERIKSON, The problem of ego identity, *J. Am. Psychoanalyt. Assn., 4*: 56, 1956.

34. J. DELAY, P. DENIKER, and A. GREEN, Le milieu familial des schizophrénics, *L'Encéphale, 46*: 189, 1957.

35. H. E. FRAZEE, Children who later become schizophrenics, *Smith College Studies in Social Work, 23*: 125, 1953.

36. F. FROMM-REICHMANN, Notes on the mother role in the family group, *Bull. Menninger Clin., 4*: 132, 1940.

37. D. L. GERARD and J. SIEGEL, The family background of schizophrenia, *Psychiatric Quart., 24*: 47, 1950.

38. L. HILL, *Psychotherapeutic Interaction in Schizophrenics,* Chicago: Univ. Chicago Press, 1955.

39. A. M. JOHNSON, P. G. S. BECKETT, et al., Studies in schizophrenia at the Mayo Clinic: I. the significance of exogenous treatment in the genesis of schizophrenia. II. observations on ego functions in schizophrenia, *Psychiatry, 19*: 137–148, 1956.

40. J. KASANIN, E. KNIGHT, and P. SAGE, The parent-child relationships in schizophrenia, *J. Nerv. & Ment. Dis., 79*: 246, 1934.

41.   J. D. MARK, The attitudes of mothers of male schizophrenics towards child behavior, *J. Abnorm. & Social Psychol., 48*: 185, 1953.

42.   C. T. PROUT and M. A. WHITE, A controlled study of personality relationships in mothers of schizophrenic male patients, *Am. J. Psychiat., 107*: 251, 1951.

43.   S. REICHARD and C. TILLMAN, Patterns of parent-child relationships in schizophrenia, *Psychiatry, 13*: 247, 1950.

44.   T. TIETZE, A study of mothers of schizophrenic patients, *Psychiatry, 12*: 55, 1949.

45.   C. W. WAHL, Antecedent factors in family histories of 392 schizophrenics, *Am. J. Psychiat., 110*: 668, 1954.

46.   N. W. ACKERMAN, A study in family diagnosis, *Am. J. Orthopsychiat., 26*: 66, 1956.

47.   N. W. BELL and E. F. VOGEL, A framework for the systematic analysis of a family. Unpublished report.

48.   E. BOTT, *Family and Social Network,* Tavistock, London, 1957.

49.   M. BOWEN, R. H. DYSINGER, *et al.,* Study and treatment of five hospitalized family groups each with a psychotic member. Paper presented at annual meeting, Am. Orthopsychiatric Assoc., Chicago, March 8, 1957.

50.   B. BUELL, *et al.,* Classification of disorganized families for use in family oriented diagnosis and treatment, Community Research Associates, New York, 1953.

51.   W. BURGESS, The family as a unit of interacting personalities, *Family, 7*: 3, 1926.

52.   I. CHEIN, The family of the addict. Paper read at Bellevue Hosp., New York, January, 1956.

53.   H. V. DICKS, Clinical studies in marriage and the family: a symposium. I. experiences with marital tensions seen in psychological clinic, *Brit. J. M. Psychol., 26*: 181, 1953.

54.   N. FOOTE and L. S. COTTRELL, *Identity and Interpersonal Competence: New Directions in Family Research,* Chicago: Univ. Chicago Press, 1955.

55.   R. HILL, J. J. MARK, and C. S. WIRTHS, *Eddyville's Families,* Chapel Hill, N.C.: Inst. for Research in Social Science, 1953.

56.   R. HILL, Marriage and family research: a critical evaluation, *Eugenics Quart., 1*: 58, 1954.

57.   D. D. JACKSON, The question of family homeostasis, *Psychiat. Quart. Suppl., 31*: 79, 1957.

58.   T. JANSEN, Measuring family solidarity, *Am. Sociol. Rev., 17*: 727, 1952.

59.   J. P. SPIEGEL, F. KLUCKHOHN, *et al.,* Integration and conflict in family behavior. Report No. 27, Group for the Advancement of Psychiatry, Topeka, Kansas, 1954.

60.   J. P. SPIEGEL, New perspectives in the study of the family, *Marriage and Family Living, 16*: 4, 1954.

61.   J. P. SPIEGEL, The resolution of role conflict with the family, *Psychiatry, 20*: 1, 1957.

62.   G. TOURRAINE and H. BRUCH, Obesity in childhood: the family frame of obese children, *Psychosom. Med., 2*: 141, 1940.

63.   D. D. JACKSON, Some factors influencing the oedipus complex, *Psychoanalyt. Quart., 23*: 566, 1954.

64.   T. LIDZ, Schizophrenia and the family, *Psychiatry, 21*: 21, 1958.

65. J. ABRAHAMS and E. VARON, *Maternal Dependency and Schizophrenia,* New York: Internat. Univ. Press, 1953.

66. Y. D. ALANEN, *The Mothers of Schizophrenic Patients,* Helsinki: Borga Tryckeri & Tidnings Ab., 1958.

67. G. BATESON, D. D. JACKSON, *et al.,* Towards a theory of schizophrenia, *Behavioral Sci., 1:* 257, 1956.

68. L. C. WYNNE, I. M. RYCHOFF, *et al.,* The family relationships of schizophrenics: a rubber fence hypothesis. Paper presented at Annual Meeting, Am. Psychological Assoc., Chicago, 1956.

69. L. C. WYNNE, I. M. RYCHOFF, *et al.,* Pseudo-mutuality and the family relations of schizophrenics, *Psychiatry, 21:* 205, 1958.

70. A. M. JOHNSON and S. A. SZUREK, The genesis of antisocial acting out in children and adults, *Psychoanalyt. Quart., 21:* 468, 1952.

12. A FAMILY CONCEPT OF SCHIZOPHRENIA

Murray Bowen

The schizophrenic psychosis of the patient is, in my opinion, a symptom manifestation of an active process that involves the entire family. This orientation has evolved during the three and one half years of a clinical research project in which schizophrenic patients and their parents have lived together on a psychiatric ward in a research center. The family unit is regarded as a single organism and the patient is seen as that part of the family organism through which the overt symptoms of psychosis are expressed.

This volume is devoted to papers about the etiology of schizophrenia. When schizophrenia is seen as a family problem, it is not a disease in terms of our usual way of thinking about disease, nor does it have an etiology in terms of the way those of us in the medical sciences have been trained to think of etiology. However, a family orientation does permit us to talk in terms of the origin and development of schizophrenia. When the family is viewed as a unit, certain clinical patterns come into focus that are not easily seen from the more familiar individual frame of reference. In this paper, I will describe some of the prominent clinical observations from the family research study and convey some thoughts about the way schizophrenia develops in the family group.

I will present my material in four sections. The first section will deal

Murray Bowen, M.D., Chief, Family Study Section, Adult Psychiatry Branch of NIMH, is especially concerned with the psychoanalytic therapy of schizophrenia and with psychoanalytically oriented studies of schizophrenic patients and their families.

with some important over-all considerations. The second section will include pertinent background information about the family research study. The third, and most important section, will include clinical material from the research project and theoretical considerations of the family concept. The fourth section will include a summary of the family concept and some thoughts about how this is related to the over-all problem of schizophrenia.

GENERAL CONSIDERATIONS
ABOUT SCHIZOPHRENIA

As this book demonstrates, the problem of schizophrenia is so basic and pressing that it has been approached from many angles and from the points of view of many different disciplines. Each of these disciplines—whether it be psychology, endocrinology, sociology, genetics, clinical medicine, or any other —has learned to think about data in a certain way and also to ignore data that it feels to be irrelevant to the study at hand. It could hardly do its work otherwise. But since each of these disciplines tends to ignore or minimize data that may be very important to those in another, it is not surprising that the study of schizophrenia sometimes seems to be nearly as confused as the patient, with, it is true, a great profusion of theories stemming from certain evidence but tending to ignore or overlook the evidence procured by other disciplines with a very different theoretical background and direction of thinking.

In this connection, we might do well to recall the

> . . . six men of Indostan
> To learning much inclined,
> Who went to see the Elephant
> (Though all of them were blind),
> That each by observation
> Might satisfy his mind (1).

Was the blind man who perceived the elephant as a wall more accurate than he who felt a tree or he who felt a fan? Perhaps they did not have time to feel the whole elephant, but certainly they would have proceeded more intelligently by pooling their information rather than by quarreling over partial concepts.

In the study of schizophrenia we are handicapped by the same sort of "blindness." What is needed is no less than a unified concept of man, a frame of reference that will enable us to understand the necessary connections between cell and psyche, and perhaps between psyche and the entity we know as soul. We are far from capable of such thinking at this time, but the recognition of the partial "blindness" and the limitations of each discipline should go far to discourage the sort of limited thinking that mistakes the part for the whole.

These initial thoughts are presented for several reasons. One is to reiterate a belief that the understanding of schizophrenia is right in front of our "eyes," that it has been there for a long time, and that more progress can be made in understanding why man thinks as he does about schizophrenia than in understanding why the schizophrenic patient thinks as he does. Another reason is to remind the reader that the family concept presented in this paper is based on psychological thinking. Even though we have made an effort to find a broader viewpoint from which to "see the elephant," we must remember that a psychological orientation has its own conceptual boundaries, and that, in the long run, the family concept is the perception of yet another "blind man."

BACKGROUND DATA ABOUT
THE FAMILY STUDY

This research study was started in 1954. The initial working hypothesis had been developed several years before during the course of individual clinical work with schizophrenic patients and also with their mothers. The hypothesis considered schizophrenia to be a psychopathological entity in the patient which had been influenced to a principal degree by the mother. It considered that the basic character problem in the patient, on which schizophrenic symptoms are later superimposed, was an unresolved, symbiotic attachment to the mother.* The initial focus of the study was on the mother-patient relationship. Three mothers and their schizophrenic daughters lived on the ward and participated together in the milieu treatment program. Each patient and each mother had individual psychotherapy. When mothers and patients were in a living situation together, certain facets of the relationship came into focus that had not been anticipated from work with each individually or from joint interviews with the two together. The details of

* This type of symbiotic relationship had already been discussed by a number of authors. Benedek (2) had discussed the theoretical aspects of the mother-child symbiosis. Mahler (3) had discussed clinical implications in her work with autistic and symbiotic children. Hill (4), Lidz and Lidz (5), and Reichard and Tillman (6) had considered symbiosis as it applies to the adult schizophrenic patient. Our present views about symbiosis have much in common with those of Limentani (7).

the mother-patient relationship will be discussed later in the paper. To summarize it briefly, there was increasing evidence that the mother was an intimate part of the patient's problem, that the mother-patient relationship was a dependent fragment of a larger family problem, and that the father played an important part in it.

At the end of one year, the hypothesis was extended to make it more consistent with the clinical observations. The psychosis in the patient was now considered to be a symptom of the total family problem. The research plan was revised to admit new families in which both father and mother could live with the patient on the ward. The psychotherapy plan was revised to make it more consistent with the new working hypothesis. The new psychotherapy plan, which we have called "family psychotherapy," was one in which the family members attended all therapy hours together.*

Four families consisting of father, mother, and patient have now lived on the ward and participated in family therapy for periods up to two and one-half years. Normal siblings have lived with two of the families for periods up to one year. The ward living space accommodates three families at a single time. Thus, a total of three mother-patient families and four father-mother-patient families have now participated in the in-patient study. Among these seven families, the maximum period of participation has been three years, the minimum period has been six months, and the average period of participation has been 18 months. An additional seven families consisting of father, mother, and moderately disturbed psychotic patient, have been treated in out-patient family therapy for periods up to two years. This is a total of 14 families in the research study. An additional 12 family groups have been seen in detailed preadmission evaluation studies as well. These families were not admitted to the research project, but the evaluation data has supplemented certain areas of data from the 14 research families.

A major part of the staff effort went into the creation of a ward milieu that would permit the family to remain with the patient in the ward setting. The patients were chronically and severely disturbed. All had been hospitalized, continuously or periodically, for a number of years before admission to the project. The ward administration was adapted, as nearly as possible, to permit the family to function as it would at home. Twenty people have worked full time on the combined clinical and research operation; three psychiatrists and a social worker make up the clinical research team, and twelve nurses and attendants staff the ward in eight hour shifts, seven days a week. The remainder of the staff includes an occupational therapist

* Details about these early clinical observations of the families, and the initial efforts at family psychotherapy, have been presented in another paper (8).

and various clerical and technical assistants. Consultants and members of other professional disciplines have participated on a part-time basis.

The parents assumed the principal responsibility for the care of the patients, but the medical and nursing staff worked toward making services available at the family's request. The parents were soon asking, and demanding, that the staff "come into the family problem" and solve it for them so that there was never a problem with the staff's "intruding into" or "being excluded from" the family situation. The close "helping" relationship of the staff made it possible for them to know the families better but it created new technical problems for the treatment program. There have been discussions about how our observations made in the ward setting might differ from those obtained by an observer in the home. This is impossible to answer. An essential element in our observations is equivalent to a psychotherapist's view of the patient in a psychotherapy relationship.

The ward living situation has provided an opportunity for subjective and objective research observations that has not been equaled by any other in our experience. It enables us to see the family as a whole in action as no other method could. To explain briefly, each family member has a perception of the family that is different from the perception of any other family member. Each family member is different in outside relationships from what he is in the presence of other family members. The psychotherapist, who meets with the family group in "talking" hours, has a view of the family different from any possible in any, or in all, individual perceptions of the family. This "family unit" view of the family, which is crucial to our theoretical orientation, will be discussed later. The ward living situation provides an additional "talking and action" view of the family drama that has not been possible in the more structured family therapy hours. There are views of the family eating, sharing, working, and playing together. There are views of the family relating to other families, to the ward staff, and to the outside environment. There are longitudinal views of the family adjustment to success, failure, crisis, and serious illness.

All of the changes in our working hypothesis and treatment approach have been based on clinical observations from the in-patient families. The nurses on each shift record observations on each individual family member, on the family unit, and on the relation of the family group to the environment. Each family therapy hour is tape-recorded while three additional written records are also made. Written records include a set of process psychotherapy notes, a summary of the verbal content, and a sociogram of the meeting. The daily material is then summarized into weekly and monthly summaries. The data from the out-patient families have been almost entirely supplemental to the more detailed data from the in-patient families.

The concept of the "family unit" or the "family as a single organism" is crucial to our way of thinking about schizophrenia. In addition to the theoretical reasons, which I will present later, there were practical reasons to institute the "family unit" approach. A family, in constant living contact with a psychotic family member, is in a state of intense conflict and emotional turmoil. Each family member solicits outside support for his particular emotional point of view. It is difficult for therapists and personnel to remain objective even if they are trained in handling countertransference problems. A nonparticipant observer might aspire to scientific objectivity, but, in the emotional tension that surrounds these families, he begins to participate emotionally in the family drama just as surely as he inwardly cheers the hero and hates the villain when he attends the theatre. Clinical staff members have been able to gain workable objectivity by detaching themselves emotionally from the family problem. When it was possible to attain a workable level of interested detachment, it was then possible to begin to defocus the individual and to focus on the entire family at once. Even though the family-unit orientation appeared to have a theoretical advantage, it was the presence of the family group on the ward, and the clinical necessity of dealing with the situation, that forced the staff to work toward a family unit orientation. Once it was possible to focus on the family as a unit, it was like shifting a microscope from the oil immersion to the low power lens, or like moving from the playing field to the top of the stadium to watch a football game. Broad patterns of form and movement that had been obscured in the close-up view became clear. The close-up view could then become more meaningful once the distant view was also possible.

Other factors have made the family-unit orientation difficult. We have all been trained to think of emotional problems as individual ones. The entire body of psychological and psychoanalytic theory was developed from perceiving the family through the eyes of the patient. Diagnostic and descriptive terms apply to the individual. It has been difficult to change this automatic way of thinking in ourselves. To facilitate the shift to family-unit thinking, we have attempted to discard as much of the "second nature" psychiatric terminology as possible and to force ourselves to use simple descriptive words. I do not like the terms "maturity" and "immaturity," as used later in the paper, but I have used them descriptively in an attempt to avoid terms with an association automatically connotative of an individual orientation. The conceptualization of the family has been a problem for others working in the field. We agree with those who would like to have a family diagnosis in addition to our individual diagnosis. Ackerman (9) and his group have attempted to define the interlocking of individual defense mechanisms. Mittelmann (10), working with different members of the same family, has described the reciprocal relationships between family members. After wrestling with this problem for over three years, we are working our way toward some kind of system that deals with "function" rather than with the static situation conveyed by a diagnostic label. This functional orientation has been approached by a number of investigators. Spiegel (11) emphasizes function in his work on role theory. Jackson (12) suggests a functional system in his stable-satisfactory, unstable-satisfactory, stable-unsatisfactory, unstable-unsatisfactory classification. Regensburg (13) suggested a functional classification of the marital relationship from her experience in social casework. It is probably part of the change in climate from static to dynamic concepts.

DEVELOPMENT OF SCHIZOPHRENIA IN A FAMILY: A THEORETICAL CONCEPT

Since the beginning of our family study, I have come to regard schizophrenia as a process that requires three or more generations to develop.* The clinical and research data will be presented in chronological order, beginning with the grandparents and progressing in successive stages to the acute psychotic eruption in the patient. It has been possible to obtain some fairly detailed historical data in line with the three-generation idea, but this area remains as the one where thinking is most speculative and supporting data are weakest.

This brief history from one of the families will be used to illustrate the points that I currently consider to be most important in the three-generation process: The paternal grandparents (first generation) were relatively mature and highly respected members of the farming community in which they lived. Their eight children were also relatively mature except for a son (second generation), who was the father of the patient and who was much less mature than his siblings. As a child he was very dependent on his mother. The other siblings regarded him as mother's favorite, but she either denied this and affirmed that she loved all her children equally, or she implicitly agreed and said that she would have done as much for any of the other children if they had needed as much attention as this son. With the need to be-

* The investigation of the three-generation idea began in 1955 with the statement of our consultant, Dr. Lewis Hill, that it requires three generations for schizophrenia to develop. This was an extension of the thinking in his book *Psychotherapeutic Intervention in Schizophrenia* (University of Chicago Press, 1955). Dr. Hill died in February 1958 while this paper was being written, but I believe the three-generation idea as expressed here is a fairly accurate representation of his thinking.

gin functioning in the outside world that came with adolescence, he suddenly became distant and aloof from his mother and began to function much more adequately outside the home. He applied himself to school and later to his business. He became more successful in business than his siblings and colleagues, but he was aloof, shy, and uncomfortable in close personal relationships. He never rebelled against his parents, but he maintained a distant, compliant relationship with them.

There was a similar pattern on the mother's side of the family. The maternal grandfather (first generation) was a respected professional man in a small town. It was the oldest daughter (second generation) who became the mother of the patient. She was the one in her sibling group who had the most intense attachment to her mother. At adolescence, she reacted to the parental attachment in a different way from that in which the father reacted in his family. He attained his area of adequacy outside the home, while she gained her area of adequacy in the home. She suddenly changed from a shy, dependent girl who could do nothing without her mother to a socially poised and resourceful young woman who could run the home without help. Here were two people with high levels of immaturity, but both had managed to deny their immaturity and to function adequately in certain areas. Both were lonely people and somewhat aloof in their relationships with others. They met while he was working in the town where she lived. Neither had been serious about marriage before they met. On one level there was a "made only for each other" quality about the relationship, but on the surface they appeared casual or even indifferent to each other. The casual relationship continued for a year. They married suddenly, a few days before the husband was transferred to a job in another state. Their relationship became conflictual as soon as they began to live together.

According to the speculative three-generation idea, these two people will have at least one child with a very high level of immaturity, and this child may develop clinical schizophrenia in an attempt to adapt to the demands of growing up. It is stressed that this is not a specific proposition about the origin of schizophrenia but that such a pattern has been present in several of the families. We have speculated about the implications of this pattern. It suggests that one child in each sibling group acquires a higher level of immaturity than the other siblings, that the immaturity is in the one who had the most intense *early* attachment to the mother, and that the immaturity is roughly equivalent to the combined levels of immaturity in the parents. It is a consistent clinical experience, among those who work with husbands and wives, that people choose spouses who have identical levels of immaturity but who have opposite defense mechanisms. To summarize this three-generation idea, the grandparents were relatively mature but their combined immaturities were acquired by one child who was most attached to the mother. When this child married a spouse with an equal degree of immaturity, and when the same process repeated itself in the third generation, it resulted in one child (the patient) with a high degree of immaturity, while the other siblings are much more mature. We have not worked with families with complicated family histories involving the death of a parent, divorces, remarriages, or multiple neuroses and psychoses in the same sibling group.

There are some characteristics of the early married life of the parents that are important in our theoretical thinking. A constant finding in all 11 father-mother-patient families has been a marked emotional distance between the parents. We have called this the "emotional divorce." There is considerable variation in the ways parents have maintained this distance. At one extreme was a family in which the parents maintained a very formal and controlled relationship. They had few overt differences. They saw their marriage as ideal. They reported an active and satisfying sexual relationship. They used conventional terms of endearment with each other, but it was difficult for them to share personal feelings, thoughts, and experiences. At the other extreme was a family in which the parents could not remain for long in each other's presence without arguments and threats. In social situations they were congenial. They controlled the conflict with physical distance from each other. They referred to their marriage as a terrible 25 years. In the middle of the scale were nine families in which the parents maintained the emotional divorce with various combinations of formal control and overt disagreement. They were consciously aware of their differences but they avoided the touchy points to keep arguments at a minimum. They saw their marriages as difficult situations to be endured.

In all the families, the parents have definite patterns of functioning in the emotional-divorce situation. Both parents are equally immature. One denies the immaturity and functions with a façade of overadequacy. The other accentuates the immaturity and functions with a façade of inadequacy. The overadequacy of one functions in reciprocal relationship to the inadequacy of the other. Neither is capable of functioning in the mid-ground between overadequacy and inadequacy. The terms "overadequate" and "inadequate" refer to functioning states and not fixed states. Overadequate refers to a functioning façade of strength that is greater than realistic. Inadequacy refers to a functioning façade of helplessness that is as unrealistic as the façade of strength is unrealistic in the other direction. When the mother functions as the overadequate one, she is dominating and aggressive and the father is helpless and compliant. When the father functions as the over-adequate one, he is cruel and authoritarian and the mother is helpless and whining.

There are some constantly recurring situations that accompany the overadequate-inadequate reciprocity. One is the "domination-submission issue." On personal issues, especially decisions that affect both parents, the one who makes the decision becomes the overadequate one and the other becomes the inadequate one. The overadequate one sees self as being forced to take responsibility and the other as a shirker. The inadequate one sees self as being "forced to submit" and the other as "dominating." The "domination-submission" term was introduced by the inadequate one who complains the most. This brings in the problem of "decisions." One of the outstanding clinical characteristics of the families is the inability of the parents to make decisions. They avoid responsibility, and the anxiety of "submission," by avoiding decisions. All levels of decisions are left undecided, to be decided by time, by circumstance, or by advice from experts. Decisions that are routine "problems to be solved" by other families become "burdens to be endured" by these families. The inability to make decisions creates the impression of weak families. One father illustrated the decision problem clearly. He said, "We can never decide together on anything. I suggest we go shopping Saturday afternoon. She objects. We argue. We end up doing nothing." When decision paralysis becomes intense, the mothers more often assume the decision-making function against the passive resistance of the fathers.

There is a fairly constant pattern in the conscious reasons of the parents for having chosen each other as mates. These are the kinds of personal things that are rarely said to each other. This material is usually fragmented and distorted until after they are comfortable in family psychotherapy. The fathers say they admired the mothers' strength, social confidence, and directness. One mother said, "I was so scared in social groups I would start chattering. It just came out. Now, after 25 years I hear my husband thought I was a brilliant conversationalist." The mothers say they admired the fathers' kindness, intelligence, and reliability. One father said, "I was too scared to do anything but agree and she thought it was kindness." The qualities they consciously admired in each other were qualities that were prominent in the façades of overadequacy.

In most of the families, the parental conflict began in the first few days or weeks after the marriage. The conflict began over decisions that dealt with routine problems of living together. A striking example of this occurred between an interne and nurse who were secretly married two years before they finished their hospital training. The marital relationship was calm and satisfying until they began to live together. According to our current thinking, the marital partners encountered the anxiety of overadequate-inadequate reciprocal functioning as soon as they were in a teamwork living situation. Parents have described "arguments over nothing" in situations like golf, a game of cards, or a work project for just the two of them. They found ways to avoid this anxiety. The usual mechanism was for each to work independently and to avoid joint activity. The conflict was less when a third or fourth person was present. Several couples spent much time visiting others or entertaining friends in their home. Marriage tensions would be reduced when one went to his or her parents for a visit. One father reviewed the dilemma of this prechildren period quite clearly. He said, "Our life was a cycle of too much closeness, too much distance, and fights. We fought when we got too close. Then we stayed mad and spoke only when necessary. One would start to make up. Then there would be a good period of a few hours or a few days until there would again be a cycle of too much closeness, a fight, and another cycle." When asked what he meant by too much closeness, he said, "When we were close, I would start acting like a little boy and she would make demands like a bossy mother. If I continued to act like a helpless child, she would purr like a kitten. The problem was that I gave up part of me when I was helpless. I had a choice. I could give in to her or balk. If I gave in, she would stay calm. If I balked, she would get nasty, I would get nasty, and we would fight." Of the distance phases, he said, "I did my best work when we were far apart. It was far from ideal. That is when I would get depressed and call myself names but I could somehow work better then." About the closeness phases, he said, "They occurred when either of us started to make up. I would be determined to have nothing to do with her but when she would start to make up, it was like a piece of bait I could not resist. I think it was the longing for closeness in both of us that made us respond so fast."

The decision to have a child was the most difficult of all decisions in these families. This problem began with the earliest thinking about having a baby. A history from a family in which the oldest child became schizophrenic will illustrate some of the crucial issues. The wife had a great desire for children for "my fulfillment as a woman." The husband opposed passively with comments about money and the right time. His opposition obscured her fears that she might not be able to have a normal baby. The wife became pregnant at a time when her wish for a baby was great. She immediately was in great conflict about the pregnancy. From the beginning of the pregnancy, her thoughts were almost totally invested in the developing fetus. Her thoughts were expressed as doubts, worries, and concerns about the normality and health of the child. When she was emotionally close to the husband, her thoughts were more invested in him and there was less preoccupation with the child. During periods of greatest distance from the husband, she wished she could abort to relieve the conflict. This mother did not have the same intense conflict during a later pregnancy with a normal child. She had the same kinds of fantasies, but they were much less intense. The conflictual state continued until after the mother could see that the child was alive and healthy. The mother said she had not been able to permit herself to realize, until after the child was born, how important this baby was to her. For her, the pregnancy had been a constant frustration between "promise of fulfillment" and a "threat that it could never be true." She worried so much that the baby would be deformed, or born dead, or be abnormal and die later, that she reached a point of saying to herself, "If it *is* going to be abnormal and die, I would rather abort now" and "I know *I* can never have a normal baby. I wish I could go on and have a miscarriage."

A significant shift in the husband-wife relationship began when the wife first knew she was pregnant.* At this point she became more emotionally invested in the unborn child than in the husband. The conflict of anticipating the baby continued until the baby was born. Another important shift in family relationships began the moment she could see that the baby was alive and well. Her thoughts immediately went toward caring for the baby. When she first saw this child, she thought, "This tiny, tiny, helpless little thing. I am its mother and I am the one who has to *protect it and care for it.*" She described an overwhelming surge of maternal instinct to do things for the baby. The intensity of the maternal instinct was much less with the second child who grew up to be normal. When she first saw the second baby, she thought, "A new baby is so tiny. It is a wonder that such a tiny thing *can grow up and become an adult.*" The first child came closer to completing "fulfillment" of the mother's need for an important other person than any other person in her experience.

As I currently see the mother-child equilibrium, the mother was securely in the overadequate position to another human being, this human belonged to her, and it was realistically helpless. She could now control her own immaturity by caring for the immaturity of another. With her emotional functioning more stabilized in the relationship with the child, the mother became a more stable figure for the father. He could better control his rela-

---

* Caplan (14) points out the shift in parental relationships during a pregnancy. He also suggests that the mother's relationship to the child can be predicted from her fantasies during the pregnancy.

tionship to her when her functioning did not fluctuate so rapidly. He tended
to establish a more fixed position of aloof distance from the mother, similar
to his relationship with his own mother. This new emotional equilibrium
came to be a fixed way of functioning for the father, mother, and child. I
have referred to this as the "interdependent triad." The child was the key-
stone. Through the relationship with the child, the mother was able to
stabilize her own anxiety and to function on a less anxious level. With the
mother's anxiety more stabilized, the father was able to establish a less
anxious relationship with the mother.

Two other mothers described maternal feelings of similar intensity
when they first saw the child who later became schizophrenic. The memory
of this feeling experience remained with them just as another person re-
members the most striking emotional experience in his life. The similar, but
less intense, feelings with other babies were not particularly noted at the
time. The meaning of baby to these mothers is reminiscent of a psychotic
girl who said many times, "I wish I could have a baby of my own. I do not
know how I could ever become pregnant, but if I could ever have a baby
of my own, I would never be lonely again." Freud (15), in writing about the
narcissistic mother, said, "In the child to whom they give birth, a part of
their own body comes to them as an object other than themselves, upon
which they can lavish out of their narcissism, complete object love."

For the purpose of this presentation, the period from the birth of the
child to development of the acute psychosis in the patient will be considered
as a single stage in the development of schizophrenia in the family. The
research data will be summarized in terms of the mother-child relationship,
the child-mother relationship, and the relationships of the father.* The
characteristics of the relationships are most pronounced during periods of
stress.

Perhaps it will make the discussion of general characteristics of such
relationships clearer if I present a brief chronological history of one of the
families for this period. This was a family with a psychotic older daughter
and a normal younger daughter. The father and mother continued their
emotional divorce in the marriage. To those outside the home, the marriage
was considered to be happy. After a difficult few years, the father did well in

* Our clinical findings are in close agreement with that of Lidz (16), Bateson and
Jackson (17), Wynne (18), and others working with schizophrenic patients and their
families. In many cases the main difference is the use of different terms to describe the
same phenomenon. For instance, I have used the term "reciprocal functioning,"
Wynne uses "pseudomutuality," and Jackson (12) uses "complementary" to describe
the same relationship phenomenon.

his own business. The mother devoted herself to the child and to the home. The father put his energy and thoughts into the business. The daughter did well intellectually, but she was extremely shy. Her problem was similar to that described for most of the patients in the research families. The parents said, "She had few close friends. She was more comfortable with adults. She never seemed to know what to do or what to say around other children." After adolescence, she was much more active and outgoing in school. Her psychotic break came the first year she was away from home at college. The father's business failed during the year after the daughter became psychotic. The second daughter, four years younger than the patient, was unusually outgoing and successful with minimal effort.

The mother-child relationship is the most active and intense relationship in the families. The term "intense" describes an ambivalent relationship in which the thoughts of both, whether positive or negative, are largely invested in each other. The mother makes two main demands on the patient. The most forceful is the emotional demand that the patient remain helpless. This is conveyed in subtle forceful ways that are out of conscious awareness. The other is the overt, verbalized, "hammered home" demand that the patient become a gifted and mature person. An example from a hospitalized family will illustrate these separate simultaneous levels of process. A psychotic son was eating a late lunch alone. The mother stopped to help him. She buttered his bread, cut his meat, and poured more milk for him. At the same time she was urging him, on an intellectually mature level, to become more grown up and to learn to do more for himself. It is incidental that the patient stopped eating. If the action story could be separated from the verbal story, there would be two separate themes. The action story would be appropriate between a mother and small child and the verbal one would fit best between a mother and teen-age child. Dysinger (19), in a paper "The Action Dialogue Between a Schizophrenic Girl and Her Mother," made an attempt to isolate the action story in one of the research families. To summarize this point, we think of two levels of process between the mother and the patient. Much of the emotional demand that the patient remain a child is conveyed on an action level and out of conscious awareness of either mother or patient. The verbal level is usually a direct contradiction to the action level.

A prominent feature of every mother-patient relationship is the mother's worries, doubts, and concerns about the patient. This is a continuation of the mother's overinvestment that began before the child was born. In the research families, there are some definite patterns to the worries of the mothers. In general, the worries are focused on the patients' development, growth, behavior, dress, and other such personal items. Each mother has a special grouping of worries that have to do with her own feelings of inadequacy. For instance, one mother was always concerned about disease and the inadequacy of her own internal organs. Her worries focused on her son's bowels, skin, sinuses, and endless other items about impaired organs. The son had multiple physical complaints. Several mothers had feelings of inadequacy in which they doubted their own physical attractiveness. Their worries focused on the patients' teeth, hair, complexion, posture, body build, dress, masculine or feminine characteristics, and other related subjects. These patients tended to be exaggerated examples of what the mothers had "fought against." The mothers doubted their own intellectual capacities. Their worries tended more toward intelligence tests, grades in school, and intellectual functioning. The patients in these two families appeared intellectually dull. To summarize this point, the subjects of the mothers' overconcerns about the patients and the focus of their "picking on the patients" are the same as their own feelings of inadequacy about themselves. This point is so accurate on a clinical level that almost any point in the mothers' list of complaints about the patient can be regarded as an externalization of the mother's own inadequacies. If a therapist or other outside figure suggests this, the mother and even the father and patient will attack or withdraw, or both. However, if either the patient or father confronts the mother with this, there is a significant beneficial emotional reaction.

The degree of negative response in the patients seems directly related to the intensity of the campaigns to *change* the "inadequacies" in the patients. The mothers' efforts to change the patients are timed with anxieties in themselves, and not with the reality situation in the patients.

We have used the term "projection" * to refer to the most all pervasive mechanism in the mother-child relationship. It has been used constantly by every mother in every aspect of her relationship with the patient. According to our thinking, the mother can function more adequately by ascribing certain aspects of herself to the child, and the child accepts. This is of crucial importance in the area of the mother's immaturity. The mother denies her own feelings of helplessness and her wish to be babied. She projects the denied feelings to the child. Then she perceives the child to be helpless and to wish to be mothered. The child, and even the entire family, accepts the

* The "projection" from the mother to the patient has been described in the literature. Reichard and Tillman did an excellent description of it in 1950. "Projection" accurately describes a mechanism in the individual, but, in a two-person relationship, it does not describe the reciprocating "introjection" of the other. The combined term "projection-introjection" also does not account for all the essential aspects of this complex mechanism.

mother's perception as a reality in the child. The mother then "mothers" the helplessness in the child (her own projected feelings) with her adequate self. Thus, a situation that begins as *a feeling in the mother, becomes a reality in the child.* There have been many examples of this mechanism in the families. One mother fed her child when she herself was hungry. When she was most anxious, she would force attention on the child and justify her actions by quoting an authority who recommended unlimited love for children. When she was not anxious, she would be relatively neglectful of the child and justify herself by quoting an authority who recommended firmness with children. In one sense, by using the child as an extension of herself, the mother was able to take care of her own inadequacies without having to depend on others. An example of another level of "projection" occurred in a mother who unrealistically perceived her daughter to have a voice of operatic quality. The daughter soon realized, from experiences outside the home, that this was not true. At home, she would sing for her mother's friends and act as if the good-voice myth were true. Outside the home, she related herself according to the reality of the situation. She said she continued the unreality at home to make her mother feel better. This daughter had a neurotic problem. In a family with a psychosis, neither daughter nor mother could have recognized the boundary between reality and unreality and both would have acted out the good-voice myth in all their relationships.

The "projection" occurs also on the level of physical illness. This is a mechanism in which the *soma of one person reciprocates with the psyche of another person.* There have been innumerable examples in which an anxiety in one person could become a physical illness in another. Before the ward internist was fully aware of this, there were many situations in which an overtly anxious mother would describe the patient's symptoms to the doctor. The patient would agree with the symptoms. The doctor would make a diagnosis and prescribe medication. Within a few hours, a process could change from anxiety in the mother to pain in the patient that had been diagnosed and was being treated. Pediatricians have told us that this is a troublesome problem in their practice. It is much easier to treat the compliant patient than to attempt to deal with the underlying problem. The somatic reciprocation often includes definite physical pathology. A striking series of such reciprocations occurred in a mother in response to rapid improvement in a regressed patient. Within a few hours after each significant change in the patient, the mother developed a physical illness of several days' duration. The somatic responses included a febrile respiratory infection, laryngitis with severe edema of the vocal cords, gastroenteritis, and severe urticaria. These marked reciprocating mechanisms are most common in, but not limited to, the mother-patient relationship. I believe the mechanism belongs primarily in the functioning reciprocation of extreme unrealistic overadequacy to extreme unrealistic inadequacy.

Another facet of the complex mother-child relationship was described by a mother and daughter who were far along in the process of untangling themselves from each other. The mother began to notice how much time she spent in thinking about the daughter. She had never been consciously aware of this before. She said she had always felt the same feelings and emotions as the daughter. She wondered about her intuitive ability to feel what another felt. She recalled an incident from the daughter's childhood. The child fell and injured her head. The mother's own head began to hurt in the exact spot the daughter's head was injured. She pondered the reason for this. She concluded that her own life was connected with the daughter's in some complex way. She decided to "put an invisible wall between us so I can have my life and she can have hers." The daughter confirmed this fusion of feelings. She had never been able to know how she herself felt. She had depended on the mother to tell her how she felt. When occasionally she had a feeling that was different from what the mother said, she discounted her own feeling and felt the way the mother said she felt. She had depended on the mother for many other things. She never knew how she looked, if clothes were becoming, or if colors matched. She depended on the mother for this. Away at school for long periods, she could begin to have her own feelings. When she returned home she would again lose the ability to know her own feelings. Then the daughter described the same intuitive ability to know how the mother felt.

Now to a consideration of the child's function in the child-mother relationship. An oversimplified description is to say that the mother "projects" her inadequacies to the child and the child automatically "introjects" the mother's inadequacies. In more detail, the child is involved in the same two levels of process as the mother, except that the mother actively initiates her emotional and verbal demands and the child is more involved in responding to the mother's demands than in initiating his own demands. In this sense, the child's life course is one in which he tries the best he can to remain the mother's baby and at the very same time to become a mature adult. I believe this is the same dilemma described in different terms by Bateson and Jackson (17) in their concept of the double bind.

In the research families, the response of the patient to the mother's demands varies with the degree of functional helplessness of the patient and the functional strength of the mother. A very helpless and regressed patient will comply immediately to emotional demands and pay little attention to verbal demands. A less regressed patient offers token resistance to emotional demands but disagrees vigorously with verbal demands. It requires a fairly high level of functional strength for the patient to oppose an emotional demand actively with comments like, "I refuse to let you get me upset." In response to such a stand the mother can become overtly anxious or physically ill. The compliance of an inadequate patient to the mother's emotional demand is almost instantaneous. As soon as the overtly anxious mother is in direct contact with the patient, the mother becomes less anxious and the patient more psychotic and regressed. The more adequate mother then babies the less adequate patient. It seems that anxiety in the mother is an automatic signal for the patient "to help the mother" by becoming her baby. The patient participates so actively in this process that I do not see the patient as a "victim" of the situation. In a certain sense, patients philosophically accept this position as a mission for which they were born. Of this, one patient said, "I was born when my mother needed someone. It could have been my brother or my sister if they had been born when I was." The patient lives his life as if the mother would die without his "help" and if the mother died, then he would die too.

The child makes his emotional and verbal demands on the mother by exploiting the helpless, pitiful position. Patients are adept at arousing sympathy and overhelpfulness in others. All the research families have eventually found their homes geared to the demands of the patient. The parents are as helpless in taking a stand against the patient as the patient in taking a stand against parents.

Now to a consideration of the father's relationships in the interdependent triad. His emotional divorce from the mother remains rather constant, but he can have a close relationship to the child any time the mother permits it. The parents follow a pattern very much like divorced parents who share their children. The mother, the overadequate one in relation to the inadequate child, is in charge of the child. The child has no direct voice in choosing between the father or mother, but the child can harass the mother until she goes away and leaves the child with the father. The father is then in the functioning position of a substitute mother. Even though he may function in this position a long time, he still remains a representative of the mother. In our experience it has not been possible for a father to have a primary relationship with the patient until he has first been able to change his own emotional divorce with the mother.

All 11 research families have followed the basic pattern of overadequate mother, helpless patient, and peripherally attached fathers. All the mothers have been concerned about the intensity of the child's attachment to themselves. The mothers see the attachment as due to the fathers' disinterest in the child. The fathers agree with this. This was especially true in the six families with psychotic sons. The parents all worried about implications of homosexuality if the sons remained attached to their mothers. All the parents agreed that sons needed close relationships with their fathers for proper masculine identification. All six fathers tried to be close to their sons. Every effort failed. The most successful was one in which the father and son spent an afternoon a week together for several years. The father was in the position of the mother's hired attendant for the son. One father initiated his own effort to win his son. He became a Boy Scout troop leader with the secret hope his son would become interested in the Boy Scouts. The mother did not relinquish any of her attachment to the son, and he never attended a scout meeting.

Our experience with normal siblings has been of great interest. At the beginning of the study, I thought all the siblings were heavily involved in the family problem. With increasing experience, I now lean strongly to the belief that the essential process is confined in the father-mother-patient triad. From the histories, and from superficial observation, there were data to indicate that every family member was somehow involved. A case will illustrate the point. A mother had the usual attachment to the older psychotic daughter. The family story indicated that the father and the younger daughter were as attached as the mother and older daughter, and observations during the first six months tended to confirm this. During the next two years the younger daughter sided with all three members of the basic family triad, but she was never involved to the point that she could not withdraw and leave the family. Over and over, normal siblings and in-laws have become involved for a time in the family conflict but they have always withdrawn so that the basic family triad remains, linked in the triangular interdependency.

Before attempting to follow the family pattern to the point of psychotic disruption, I will return to the beginning of the mother-child relationship and review some of the points that are crucial to the psychosis. According to our present thinking, the child becomes the "important other" to the mother. Through the child, the mother is able to attain a more stable emotional equilibrium than had otherwise been possible for her. The "tiny helplessness" of the infant permits her to function securely in an overadequate position. The emotional stabilization of the mother then enables the father to have a less anxious relationship with the mother. Thus, the functional helplessness of the infant makes it possible for both parents to have a less anxious adjustment. Even though both parents have a conscious wish for the child to grow and develop normally, they both automatically do things to keep the child in the helpless position. I have already described mechanisms by which the mother attempts to keep the child helpless. The father does this too. If the mother's effort to "make the child behave" is not immediately successful, the father will add his weight to her effort. I believe anxiety is the crucial issue. The research families all have a low tolerance for anxiety. They operate on a "peace at any price" principle. They quickly compromise important life principles to relieve anxiety for this moment. Of course, this "peace at any price" policy immediately causes greater anxiety for tomorrow, but they continue the compromising attitudes to relieve the anxiety of the moment.

The mechanisms by which either the mother or child can feel the same as the other, or "be for the other," are difficult to conceptualize. A number of possible explanations have been proposed in the literature. Why does the child enter into this situation in the first place? I believe the child is automatically protecting his own interests by doing the things that will insure a less anxious and more predictable mother. However, once the child enters into this "being (helpless) for the mother" and the mother enters into the opposite "being (strong) for the child," they are both in a functional bind of "being for each other." When the child's self is devoted to "being for the mother," he loses the capacity of "being for himself." I stress the functional "*being* helpless" rather than the fixed "*is* helpless" viewpoint. In other words, I regard schizophrenia as a functional helplessness in contrast to concepts that regard it as a constitutional helplessness. There are valid data on both sides of this issue.*

The process in which the child begins to "be for the mother" results in an arrest in his psychological growth. His physical growth remains normal. Each year there is a wider discrepancy between physical growth and psychological growth. The relationship requires that the child devote himself completely to the mother and that the mother devote herself to the child. The symbiotic state is precariously balanced at best. As the years pass and the child is no longer a baby in size, it is even harder to keep the symbiosis in emotional equilibrium. Each is threatened by change in the other. The child is threatened by any sign of aging, sickness, anxiety, weakness, or change in

* Bayley, Bell, and Schaefer (20) are among those investigating the early mother-infant relationship. They are searching for clues as to whether the character of the relationship is determined by inherent qualities in the infant to which the mother responds, or whether the character of the relationship is determined by factors in the mother.

the mother's attitude that might prevent her always being the strong, adequate mother. The mother is threatened by growth, sickness, or any circumstance that might prevent the child being always her baby. However, it is inevitable that they both change and inevitable that the relationship will one day be disrupted. The feelings that each experience in regard to the loss of the other are equated with death.

The mother threatens the child in many ways. Most important is the threat that she might have another baby and desert the child. I believe the mother's selection of a particular child for such an intense relationship is determined by her unconscious functioning in the prevailing reality situation. A good percentage of mothers will retain the initial relationship with the first child. One mother said the oldest was so pitiful when the second was born that the oldest needed her more. Other mothers have successive attachments to each new child and finally retain the youngest as "my baby." Others choose children from the middle of the group. One mother with five children had successive attachments with the first two and retained an attachment to the third, a daughter who looked like the mother. Another mother had normal relationships with her first two children and then an intense attachment to the third, who was born shortly after the death of her own mother. The birth of a physically deformed child might come closer to "fulfillment" of the mother's emotional needs than a normal child.

The main threat to the continuation of the mother-child symbiosis is the growth process in the child. The relationship might remain fairly calm and erupt into separation anxiety symptoms only during periods of rapid growth in the child. The growth can bring out threats, rejections, demands, and retaliation in both. Described as a phenomenon, the symbiosis attempts to make two lives stand still at a particularly pleasurable phase in both life cycles. In the beginning, the mother-infant symbiosis is a normal stage in the course of a life from birth to death. When it is perpetuated, it becomes a foreign thing, threatened by the biological progression of the very life process of which it was once a part.

Now to a consideration of events that lead to the acute psychosis. The rapid growth of the child at adolescence interferes with the functioning equilibrium of the interdependent triad. There is an increase in anxiety for all three members. The automatic mechanisms of the mother—and also the father—go toward forcing the child back into a more helpless position, and the automatic mechanisms of the child go toward compliance. The adolescent period is one in which the growth process repeatedly upsets the equilibrium and the emotional process attempts to restore it. The conscious verbal expressions demand that the child be more grown up.

The child's course from adolescence to the acute psychosis is one in which he changes from a helpless child, to a poorly functioning young adult, to a helpless patient. I will focus on the changes in the child without specifically describing the continuing reciprocating mechanisms in the parents. Adolescence activates intense anxiety in the symbiotic relationship. Before adolescence, the mother had remained calm as long as the child was infantile. He had handled his wishes to grow up with fantasies of future greatness. The growth period causes anxiety in the child and anxiety in the mother, until the symbiotic relationship itself becomes a serious threat. When the child is more grown up, the mother infantilizes. When he is child-ish, she demands that he grow up. After years of functioning as a helpless child, he has little "self" of his own and he is poorly equipped to do any-thing without the mother. His dilemma is one of finding a course between the opposing forces. The problem is much greater than that of the normal adolescent who can expect help from parents in growing up and who is basically capable of making a start outside the family. The child in this dilemma has to deal first with the mother's effort to hold him back and then with his own urge to return to her, before he can get to the problems of the normal adolescent. Once free of the mother, he faces outside relation-ships without a self of his own. Of this dilemma a male patient said, "It takes a lot of doing to hold your mother's hand and play baseball at the same time." A young woman patient said the situation was like a "magnetic field" around the mother. When she was too close to the mother, she would sud-denly be "pulled into the mother" and lose her own identity; when she was too far away from the mother, she had no "self" at all.

Our patients used denial and isolation, while still living in the home, to escape the mother's "magnetic field." One of our patients collapsed into psychotic helplessness at 15 years after failing in his initial efforts to func-tion without his mother. Most of our patients were successful in their first efforts to function without their mothers. This was the case with the daugh-ter described in the brief family history. She became more outgoing and comfortable with those outside the family. The family was sure that adoles-cence had solved her "adjustment problem." She looked forward to becom-ing completely free of the family when she went away to college. By increas-ing the denial and reassuring herself, she made it through one semester of college. Her work became impaired during the first examination period. The psychotic collapse developed over a period of a few days while she was still increasing the denial and redoubling her effort to "do it myself." In terms of our theoretical viewpoint, the psychosis represents an unsuccessful attempt to adapt the severe psychological impairment to the demands of adult functioning. The patient's denial of incapacity and her protestations of strength were now expressed in the distorted verbalization, while her helplessness was acted out by the psychosis.

The psychosis represented a disruption of the symbiotic attachment to the mother and a collapse of the long term interdependent father-mother-patient triad. Anxiety in the family became high. The mother handled her anxiety with an increased façade of strength, especially toward the father and the staff at the mental hospital. She had assumed responsibility for the hospitalization. The daughter was hostile and openly rebellious to the mother for the first time. The mother dealt with the daughter's total rejection by saying, "It is because she is sick," implying that the daughter would not behave this way if she were well. The father, without being aware of it, had automatically slipped back to inadequate functioning in relation to the extremely overadequate mother. His business began to fail. He went into bankruptcy within a year without any awareness that his bankruptcy could have any relation to the functional interdependency of the central family triad.

I believe that unresolved symbiotic attachments to the mother vary from the very mild to the very intense, that the mild ones cause little impairment, and that schizophrenic psychoses develop among those with the most intense unresolved attachments. There are a number of ways in which the individual with an intense attachment may find some solution to his dilemma. Certain individuals are able to replace the original mother with mother substitutes. The functional helplessness may find expression in somatic illness. The person with a character neurosis uses a flight mechanism to deal with the helplessness. The patients in our families attempted to find distant relationships. The psychotic collapse is seen as an effort at resolution that failed.

I have used the terms "emotional demand" and "emotional process" to describe the emotional responsiveness by which one family member responds automatically to the emotional state of another, without either being consciously aware of the process. Perhaps this can be understood as nonverbal communication, but I have chosen to use these terms descriptively. The process is unconscious in the sense that neither person is consciously aware of it, but it is not unconscious in our usual use of the term. This "emotional process" is deep and it seems somehow to be related to the *being* of a person. It runs silently beneath the surface between people who have very close relationships. It operates during periods of conflict and periods of calm harmony. In most of our families there is much conflict and open disagreement and many stories of injustices and misdeeds between family members. It is easy for the observer to become preoccupied with the conflict and turmoil. There are families with schizophrenic family members that have little or no conflict and no history of the factors we ordinarily associate with schizophrenia. I believe this emotional process may be intimately associated with schizophrenia and that the "silent" family may provide more clues to the process.

The question of "rejecting mothers" comes up. We have not had a rejecting mother in our small number of research families. Every mother in our group has been "called rejecting" by the patients. The amount of attention the mothers give the patients depends on their level of anxiety. When mothers are anxious, they are hovering and infantilizing. When mothers are not anxious, they give much less attention. The patients experience this decrease in attention as "rejection." My impression of the real rejecting mother is one whose baby could never be part of her defense system for her own emotional needs, so that she has to desert the baby to find her gratification elsewhere.

Among the families who have done well in family therapy, we have seen changes in the usual, fixed, family patterns. For instance, a change in one member would be followed by changes in the other two. It was observation of the changes that led to the description of the "overadequate-inadequate reciprocal functioning."

There are some other changes from the course of therapy that are of theoretical interest. The following is a brief account of some changes in a father-mother-daughter family. The intense conflict between the mother and psychotic daughter occupied the first several months of family therapy hours. The father remained on the periphery, and in an inadequate position. Gradually the father began to participate in the family problems. The conflict shifted to the mother-father relationship. As the father began to take some stands against the overadequate mother, she became much more anxious, challenging, and aggressive toward him. Eventually he assumed a position as head of the family, in spite of her marked anxiety, tremulousness, and protest. In a few days she rather quickly changed to a kind, motherly, objective person. She said, "It is so nice finally to have a man for a husband. If he can keep on being a man, then I can be a woman." The emotional divorce disappeared, and for two months they were as completely invested in each other as two young lovers. The patient tried to win back her lost symbiotic partner, but the mother remained firm and the patient made some solid progress. Under stress, they each fell back to their former ways of functioning, but thereafter it became easier for the father to move into an adequate position and less threatening for the mother to lose the overadequate position.

The striking observation was that when the parents were emotionally close, more invested in each other than either was in the patient, the patient improved. When either parent became more emotionally invested in the patient than in the other parent, the patient immediately and automatically regressed. When the parents were emotionally close, they could do no wrong in their "management" of the patient. The patient responded well to firmness, permissiveness, punishment, "talking it out," or any other management approach. When the parents were "emotionally divorced," any and all "management approaches" were equally unsuccessful.

CONCLUSION

The working hypothesis for this research project has been based on the theoretical assumption that the psychosis in the patient is a symptom of a larger family problem. This assumption is in contrast to the usual theoretical position which considers it a disease or pathological phenomenon in the patient. It has not been possible to run the clinical and the research operation in complete harmony with our theoretical position. Our own limitations and the generally accepted view that it is a disease in the individual make it necessary to retain part of the individual orientation. In other words, we may say that we regard psychosis as a family problem, but, in many basic ways, we must relate to it as a disease in the individual. However, our research institution has afforded unusual experimental flexibility, and it has been possible to achieve a reasonable degree of harmony between the hypothesis and the research operation. The more we have been able to see the psychosis as a family phenomenon, the more we have been able to see a different picture of schizophrenia. Thus, the working hypothesis is based on a theoretical assumption. The research operation, based on the hypothesis, has provided observations different from those possible from other theoretical viewpoints. The family concept is a correlation of research observations with the hypothesis. Our research project has been in operation four years. The hypothesis and operational approach has been modified, to some degree, every year. In this sense, the family concept, as here presented, could be called our current working conceptualization of schizophrenia as a family problem.

At the beginning of the paper I said our theoretical problem with schizophrenia was somewhat analogous to the problem of the blind men and the elephant. The analogy is probably more apt for those who work with the family than for others but I have been surprised to find that schizophrenia viewed from the family orientation is very different from schizophrenia viewed as an individual problem. The schizophrenia did not change; the only change was in the eyes that saw it. In this sense, the family concept provides another position from which to view one of man's oldest dilemmas.

References

1.   J. G. SAXE, "The Blind Men and the Elephant," in Stevenson, B. E. (Ed.), *Home Book of Verse,* New York: Holt, 1949.

2.   T. BENEDEK, *Studies in Psychosomatic Medicine, Psychosexual Functions in Women,* New York: Ronald, 1952, pp. 339–351.

3.   M. MAHLER, "On Child Psychosis and Schizophrenia," in *The Psychoanalytic Study of the Child,* Vol. 7, New York: Internat. Univ. Press, 1952, pp. 286–305.

4.   L. B. HILL, *Psychotherapeutic Intervention in Schizophrenia,* Chicago: Univ. Chicago Press, 1955.

5.   R. W. LIDZ and T. LIDZ, "Therapeutic Considerations Arising from the Intense Symbiotic Needs of Schizophrenic Patients," in Brody, E. B., and Redlich, F. C. (Eds.), *Psychotherapy with Schizophrenics,* New York: Internat. Univ. Press, 1952, pp. 168–178.

6.   S. REICHARD and C. TILLMAN, Patterns of parent-child relationships in schizophrenia, *Psychiatry, 13:* 247–257, 1950.

7.   D. LIMENTANI, Symbiotic identification in schizophrenia, *Psychiatry, 19:* 231–236, 1956.

8.   M. BOWEN, Family participation in schizophrenia. Paper presented at annual meeting, Am. Psychiatric Assoc., Chicago, May, 1957.

9.   N. ACKERMAN, "Interlocking Pathology in Family Relationships," in Rado, S., and Daniels, G. (Eds.), *Changing Concepts in Psychoanalytic Medicine,* New York: Grune, 1956, pp. 135–150.

10.   B. MITTELMANN, "Analysis of Reciprocal Neurotic Patterns in Family Relationships," in Eisenstein, V. (Ed.), *Neurotic Interaction in Marriage,* New York: Basic, 1956, pp. 81–100.

11.   J. P. SPIEGEL, The resolution of role conflict in the family, *Psychiatry, 20:* 16–18, 1957.

12.   D. JACKSON, Family interaction, family homeostasis, and some implications for conjoint family psychotherapy. Paper presented at Academy of Psychoanalysis, San Francisco, May, 1958.

13.   J. REGENSBURG, Application of psychoanalytic concepts to casework treatment of marital problems, *Social Casework, 25:* 424–432, 1954.

14.   G. CAPLAN, "Emotional Implications of Pregnancy," in *The Child: His Health and Development,* Cambridge: Harvard (in press).

15.   S. FREUD, "On Narcissism: an Introduction," in *Collected Papers,* Vol. IV, New York: Basic, 1959, p. 47.

16.   T. LIDZ, A. CORNELISON, S. FLECK, and D. TERRY, The intrafamilial environment of schizophrenic patients: II. marital schism and marital skew, *Am. J. Psychiat., 114:* 241–248, 1957.

17.   G. BATESON, D. JACKSON, J. HALEY, and J. WEAKLAND, Toward a theory of schizophrenia, *Behavioral Sci.*, *1*: 251–264, 1956.

18.   L. C. WYNNE, I. RYCHOFF, J. DAY, and S. H. HERSH, Pseudo-mutuality in the
family relations of schizophrenics, *Psychiatry*, 21: 205–220, 1958.

19.   R. H. DYSINGER, The "action dialogue" in an intense relationship: a study of
a schizophrenic girl and her mother. Paper presented at annual meeting, Am. Psychiatric Assoc., Chicago, May, 1957.

20.   N. BAYLEY, R. Q. BELL, and E. S. SCHAEFER, Research study in progress, Child
Development Section, National Institute of Mental Health, Bethesda, Md.

13. THE "DOUBLE-BIND" HYPOTHESIS
OF SCHIZOPHRENIA AND
THREE-PARTY INTERACTION

John H. Weakland

In a previous paper (1) my colleagues and I developed the concept of a "double bind" as a pattern of communication provoking behavior character-istic of schizophrenia. Our attention there centered on two-person interac-tion, especially communication between mother and child. Since that time we have become increasingly interested in the involvements of patients in three-party interaction, particularly the father-mother-child relationship and such institutional relationships as administrator-therapist-patient and doctor-nurse-patient. These three-party situations, while overtly different and more complex than the two-party ones previously studied, show important

This paper is a product of the Schizophrenic Communication research project directed by Gregory Bateson and carried out at the Veterans Administration Hos-pital, Palo Alto, California. This research has been aided by a grant from the Josiah Macy Jr. Foundation, administered by the Department of Anthropology, Stanford University; and currently is supported by the National Institute of Mental Health and administered by the Mental Research Institute of the Palo Alto Medical Research Foundation.

Naturally, I am indebted to the project director and other project members, Jay Haley, Don D. Jackson, M.D., and William F. Fry, M.D., for some of the ideas presented in this work.

John H. Weakland, originally trained as a chemical engineer and later as a sociologist and anthropologist, is working at the Mental Research Institute of the Palo Alto Medical Research Foundation on studies on the nature, etiology, and therapy of schizophrenia in terms of communication, using anthropological techniques to obtain data on behavior.

similarities if they are viewed in terms of the pattern of conflicting communication that the patient encounters.

Our general point of view and our particular concepts and hypotheses are based on detailed and intensive study of tape and film records of the actual communication of patients with people playing important parts in their lives. Initially we studied mainly the communication of patients and therapists in individual interviews, but for several years now we have been concentrating more and more on the interaction of patients with their family members, in family therapy sessions or just as a family group. This paper, however, presents only a limited amount of our own primary data. It centers on applying the approach and insights thus developed to the analysis of three-party interaction and to the interrelating of observations reported by various other investigators of schizophrenia. We hope in this way to give further evidence for our previous findings, to clarify a basic schizophrenogenic pattern common to a variety of particular situations, and to promote a communicational orientation that has been somewhat foreign to orthodox psychiatry but that we have found to be most illuminating.

THE BASIC DOUBLE-BIND CONCEPT: TWO-PERSON INTERACTION

In order to make ourselves clear to those unacquainted with our previous papers on the subject, we will first briefly review our original views of the double bind and then proceed to show how these views are helpful in clarifying three-party schizophrenogenic interaction. It should be understood that we are making no claim that double binds are the only factor of importance in the genesis of schizophrenia or that these more complex situations are "only double binds." But we do feel that this concept is helpful in discerning some similarities important for schizophrenia in certain different situations.

As we originally stated our position:

> The general characteristics of this [double-bind] situation are the following:
> 1. When the individual is involved in an intense relationship; that is, a relationship in which he feels it is vitally important that he discriminate accurately what sort of message is being communicated so that he may respond appropriately.
> 2. And, the individual is caught in a situation in which the other person in the relationship is expressing two orders of message and one of these denies the other.

3. And, the individual is unable to comment on the messages being expressed to correct his discrimination of what order of message to respond to, *i.e.*, he cannot make a metacommunicative statement (1).

(Other early statements by our research group were basically similar although with some differences of terminology and emphasis.)

This way of describing the double-bind communication situation tends to concentrate on characterizing a pattern of messages as sent by a "binder." In our early work there was an urgent need to emphasize this point, to insist, against a climate of opinion focused either on physiology or fantasy, that real people were giving real, observable messages that were provocative of schizophrenic responses. We depicted the situation as that of one person giving another two related but contradictory or incongruent messages, presenting conflicting injunctions of importance, while also acting to forestall escape and to inhibit notice and comment on the inconsistency by the "victim."

This view, however, is biased in two important respects. First, it must be stated explicitly that we do not think it a whole and rounded view of such relationships. Although this one-way picture of "binder" and "victim" might be correct to some extent very early in a parent-child relationship, the "victim" soon learns similar or reciprocal patterns of communication—such as giving incongruent messages of his own, or responding to any and all communications he receives as if they were incongruent and binding. This contributes strongly to maintenance of the over-all patterns of communication and interaction found in the families of schizophrenics, and to the difficulty of psychotherapy with such patients; persisting messages of these kinds strongly press the therapist toward similar pathogenic interaction with the schizophrenic patient.

Second, emphasis on the sending of messages restricts the viewing of the situation from the opposite pole—*i.e.*, that of the person receiving double-bind messages and behaving in response to them. This viewpoint is especially relevant here. It is schizophrenic response to certain two- and three-party communication situations that is of psychiatric interest and makes it in order to look back, from this common effect, for common factors in antecedent circumstances. Therefore, it is important to characterize the double-bind communication situation from the receiver-respondent's end of the system.

One of our more recent double-bind statements, concerned with investigating the circumstances facing a patient just before his psychotic break, partially demonstrates this viewpoint: "We have mentioned . . . our concept of the double bind as a situation: (1) in which a person is faced with contradictory messages, (2) which is not readily visible as such because of concealment or denial, or because the messages are on different levels, and (3) in which he can neither escape, nor notice and effectively comment on the contradictions" (2). This characterization of the double bind may be expanded as follows to insure maximum clarity:

(1) *In a double-bind situation, a person is faced with a significant communication involving a pair of messages, of different level or logical type, which are related but incongruent with each other.*

(2) *Leaving the field is blocked.* Such escape, presumably followed by establishment of more satisfactory communication elsewhere, would be one potential avenue of natural and adequate response. Its unavailability usually is an outcome of dependence on the person (or persons) giving the contradictory messages. When dependency is inherent in a situation (as with childhood or illness), this point is obvious. More complex, however, are the important situations where dependency (or effective belief in it) is fostered by other messages of total double-bind communication, to a degree far beyond the physical or emotional "realities" of the person's current life situation.

(3) *It is therefore important to respond adequately to the communication situation, which includes responding to its duality and contradiction.* Two contradictory significant messages mean two incongruent behavioral injunctions, because every message instigates behavioral response. Lack of recognition and response to the duality and incongruence of the messages received leads to further difficulties on the recipient's part at several levels of behavior: failure to discriminate the order of message being received; consequent subjective confusion and distortion of ideas and affects; and speech or action that manifests confusion and division either directly, or by an all-or-nothing reaction to one aspect of the sender's message. Further, such inadequate and incomplete responses are very apt to provoke a further message condemning the response; *e.g.,* "Why are you so silent when I speak to you?" or "You always get excited so easily." The total sequence, then, has the form of a larger, more encompassing double bind, and the situation is still further aggravated.

It appears that such incongruent communication can be handled adequately only by a response that recognizes and points up the incongruity. This might be done by (a) overtly labeling the incongruity as such—*i.e.,* by moving to a different level of communication and explicitly discussing the original communication situation. It might also be done by (b) giving a manifestly dual message in reply, or by (c) a humorous response exposing the nature of the double-bind incongruence, for humor always involves multiple message levels and incongruities. As an illustration we can consider possible responses to a mild sort of incongruent message situation: "Wouldn't you like to open that window?" said in a way or context that suggests that the speaker is really the one who wants it open, yet does not acknowledge this. Then: (a) "You speak as though you're asking what I like, but you really seem to be telling me what to do." (b) "I wouldn't like to, but if it's important to you I'll do it." (c) "Thank you for being thoughtful of me, but can it be opened from below?" But this is not to say that any of these responses is easy to carry off, even though we are throughout this paper considering the double-bind pattern in terms of a type of maneuver and various possible outcomes, not just the "successfully completed" bind.

(4) *An adequate response is difficult to achieve because of the concealment, denial, and inhibition inherent in or added to the basic contradictory pair of messages.* The communicational factors that may serve to restrain awareness and/or comment on duality and contradiction are many; some are gross and others very subtle, some explicit and others implicit, some verbal and others tonal, gestural, or contextual, some positive and others negative. It is probable that this variety and subtlety have played a major part in obscuring, for both patients and psychiatrists, the existence of the double-bind communication pattern and its etiological significance for schizophrenia. Related to this has been psychiatric overemphasis on specific trauma and neglect of repetitive patterns in basic learning situations (3). A few such factors of particular importance may be mentioned here, as they operate in two-party double-bind situations; some counterparts in three-party situations will be considered later.

(a) *Concealment:* Two major barriers to the overt recognition of the basic inconsistency in the double-bind communication are inherent in its nature. First, the messages, being of different level or logical type, do not confront one another directly, whether one verbal message qualifies another incongruously or a verbal message conflicts with tone or gesture. There is no clear confrontation—"A is true. No, A is false"—even if the two messages convey different and incompatible behavioral injunctions. In this connection, it is important to remember that objectively very slight signals— thus ones easily ignored or denied—can drastically modify or even reverse the significance of much more obvious or lengthy messages. Second, the fact that only one person is addressing the receiver carries an implication of "only one message," or at least of consistent messages, in a given situation. This is further reinforced by the fact that this person is important to the receiver; not only can he not be escaped or ignored, but also his messages are hard to doubt or question. These various factors may all be seen in such a simple example as a mother who says, "Come here to me, dear," with a slight edge of concealed hostility in her tone, or a little bodily withdrawal. The incongruence is real, but it is well concealed, and it is not easy to call one's mother to account on the basis of such apparently minor evidence.

(b) *Denial:* Obviously, the operation of the factors just mentioned can be reinforced by adding to the basic pair of incongruent messages other messages overtly denying that contradiction exists—and perhaps putting the onus on the receiver by claiming that he misunderstood, by emphasizing the unity of the sender or his important position *vis-à-vis* the receiver, and so on. Continuing the example above, if the child should go so far as to remark on the mother's tone, there might be a reply like "You just imagined that, dear; you know how much mother loves you."

(c) *Inhibition:* Reinforcement much like that obtained by denial may also occur via "no message"—*i.e.*, by strongly *ignoring* the actual complexities of communication and the possibilities of inconsistency and by acting as though they were out of the question. Investigation of the communication situation may also be inhibited by direct prohibition of comment or by various threats, such as signs of parental withdrawal or disturbance if any questioning is attempted. All of these factors are further reinforced when, as seems common in double-bind situations, the binder stresses his own benevolent position and concern for the other's welfare. In accordance with these possibilities, our hypothetical mother might behave as if her incongruent statement is perfectly simple and straightforward; if this were questioned, she might reply "Don't worry yourself making something out of nothing, dear; just leave things to mother"; or she might appear confused or hurt by an unjustified attack on her maternal love and nobility; or she might simply appear completely unable to see the point of the question raised, a reaction that can be one of the more devastating forms of withdrawal.

Whenever any such message of concealment, denial, or inhibition is added to reinforce an original double-bind communication, the combination produces another double-bind structure, on a wider scale. For example, when the occurrence of a pair of incongruent messages is followed by a further message denying that there was any contradiction, this combination comprises another pair of incongruent messages, of different levels, whose incongruence is difficult to detect and handle. And this process may repeat itself, enlarging each time. If the child is still questioning about the mother's denial, then mother might say "Something must have upset you to make you behave that way to your own mother, who loves you so." The pathogenic power of double-bind communication patterns and the difficulty of altering them seems importantly related to this progressive and cumulative tendency. (It is instructive in this connection to compare descriptions by Stanton and Schwartz of how covert, institutional conflicts tend to build up and spread [4].)

FATHER, MOTHER, AND
SCHIZOPHRENIC CHILD

Our original conceptions of a double-bind situation focused on the case in which one person is receiving from one other person two related but conflicting messages, of different levels, where escape is not feasible and response is important, but where there are certain major difficulties in the way of detecting and commenting on the inconsistency. In our earlier studies, however, we noted briefly the existence of more complex possibilities and recognized that such a situation was not necessarily produced by the mother alone but could be created by a combination of mother, father, and/or siblings (1). If we now consider the mother and father in relation to a child as the particular three-party situation that is probably, in practice, most important for schizophrenia, it is evident that most of the factors listed for the two-party situation can occur equally well in this three-party case. Clearly, parents can, on a given matter, give conflicting messages to a child. Clearly, it is important for the child, who is in an over-all or collective sense *more* dependent on both parents than on one, to deal with the conflicting behavioral influences resulting by dealing with the inconsistency of these messages. But, equally clearly, one or both parents may also be giving messages that conceal, deny, or inhibit exploration of the inconsistency in much the same variety of ways considered above.

It is less obvious at first—but especially striking when perceived—that even those obscuring factors that would seem inherent in the two-person situation may easily have parallels or equivalents in the three-person situation. Comparison and confrontation of possibly contradictory messages from one sender are difficult because the message cannot readily be separated. It may be equally difficult with two senders because the messages are *too much* separated—by person, by time, by different style of phrasing. And they still may differ in level: "When the double bind is inflicted not by one individual but by two, . . . one parent may negate at a more abstract level the injunctions of the other" (1). Even the matter of "oneness" and its implications of single or consistent messages may also occur readily enough when two individuals are in fact communicating separately to a third, by *grouping* the two into an apparent unity. Language forms provide this possibility in plural pronouns ("*We* want you to do such-and-such") or in collective nouns like "parents." Another avenue lies in the explicit identification of the messages of the two as the same ("Your father and I agree that you are not well enough to come home yet"). Or one parent might appear silent, dominated, or withdrawn from a situation, leaving only the other, ostensibly, as the single communicator. But of course these meta-level indications of unity and these claims of agreement and identity of messages are independent of actual similarity or difference in two messages—*i.e.*, they may be false. Thus, the three-person situation has possibilities for a "victim" to be faced with conflicting messages in ways that the inconsistency is most difficult to observe and comment on that are quite similar to the two-person case.

Although we are here concerned mainly with conceptual analysis of three-party communicational possibilities, still it may be noted that empirical evidence is already accumulating to demonstrate that the possibilities suggested above are actually encountered in families with a schizophrenic member and are relevant to the schizophrenia. For example, although the work of Lidz and his coworkers is oriented and conceptualized quite differently from our own, many of his observations on family interaction fit in with our schema. Typically, the families studied exhibited either "marital skew" or "marital schism" (5). The "skew" situation is one in which the father and mother apparently share some rather peculiar view of marriage and family life: "The distorted ideation of one partner was accepted or shared by the other, creating an atmosphere of *folie à deux*" (5). This agreement, however, is apparent rather than real, and indications of disagreement and conflicting messages to the children are given via more covert messages. "Considerable 'masking' of potential sources of conflict occurred, creating an unreal atmosphere in which what was said and admitted differed from what was actually felt and done" (5). In the S. Family, "a severe schism actually existed despite the peace between the marital couple" (5). " 'Masking' . . . refers to the ability of one or both parents to conceal some very disturbing situation within the family and to act as if it did not exist," yet in a typical case it is also admitted that while the wife was maintaining a myth of successful marriage to a strong father-figure, still "the children could not help but know that it was all fraudulent" (6).

Another case report excerpt makes the pattern of overtly expressed unity and covertly expressed differences especially clear. "In line with his beliefs, the father disapproved of and never expressed any hostility. Everybody was 'happy' in this family. The mother, however, despite her subservience, belittled and criticized the father's disinclination toward fresh air, sports, and physical exercise, all of which she worshipped and considered extremely important for her children" (6). Another point illustrated in this excerpt is worth special notice, even though it is tangential to the main topic of this paper: the mother justifies differing from her husband not in terms of her own individuality and her relationship with him, but in terms of her "benevolent" interest in the welfare of the children; that is, the responsibility for parental differences of opinion is laid on them. In our experience with the families of schizophrenics this is typical (though not confined to the mothers alone), and it is devastating to the children and to the family as a whole (7).

These excerpts make it clear that Lidz's "family skew" involves situations of apparent parental agreement but covert disagreement, situations which, in terms of communication, must involve incongruent messages to the children, but with concealment, denial, and inhibition of comment operating in the ways we have outlined. Indeed, one case description approaches these terms: "Although neither parent overtly discredited the other to the children" yet within the family there were other "obvious" or "apparent" indications about father, mother, and their relationship which resulted in "perplexing discrepancies" and "inconsistent and contradictory images" (8).

When Lidz's discussions of the fathers of schizophrenics (8, 9) are considered together with his discussions of "family skew," it appears that while in these families one parent overtly seems to dominate, the range is exceedingly wide—from a picture of apparent agreement, actually undercut by the subordinate partner, to a picture in which one parent appears a nonentity, where passive withdrawal may still express both agreement and failure to agree. This latter picture, in which "the children are left virtually fatherless," is perhaps intermediate between more active three-person interaction and the two-person interaction we originally examined.

Lidz's "marital schism" category is not so easy to align with our views, because it involves and indeed emphasizes open parental disagreement, "severe chronic disequilibrium and discord" (6). Nevertheless, it seems that these families might, in broad terms, be seen as being in line with our schema. On this point, without having more complete information about Lidz's families or observing them ourselves, we can only suggest several possible lines of explanation arising from our own experience with the families of schizophrenics. Are the parental difficulties and conflicts manifest *to the children*? We find that parents are often willing to express feelings and difficulties to us but very reluctant to repeat what they have said before the patient, their child. There is also a question of timing in this connection. Were parental conflicts once concealed, only to become manifest later, at a time when a child might feel the emerging conflict to be his fault? Are the overt conflicts about the real points at issue? We find the families of schizophrenics adept at involvement in arguments that conceal rather than clarify the main conflicts. Such arguments may be about tangential questions, or even quite unreal ones, as in one example given by Lidz himself: the father in a family pretended to have a mistress but really did not; still "many of the family quarrels centered on this non-existent situation" (6). It is clear that these families must communicate major contradictions and inconsistencies via different levels of communication and inhibit recognition of them, even though this communication is made in a way that is inverted or polar to that discussed earlier. That is, the parents in these families are characterized by open expression of, in fact emphasis on, differences and separateness—yet they are couples who, for many years, have lived together and continue to do so. Clearly, on the level of action they communicate relatedness of some kind. They show dependence on each other, yet are busy denying it.

Bowen's findings (10) in a sense tie together the two polar pictures developed from Lidz's families. He saw parents as struggling with "marked emotional distance" between them by combinations of overt, highly emotional disagreement and formal, controlled agreement. Though some families were at one extreme or the other, most of them "were aware of differences but they consciously avoided the touchy points. They maintained sufficient impersonal distance to keep disagreements at a minimum" (10). Or, in our terms, they must have been giving inconsistent messages, deliberately emphasizing agreement and similarity despite basic disagreement. Our views, of course, consider this as pathogenic in the family, and it is interesting in this connection that Bowen states that, in therapy with these families, increasing self-assertion by the father heralded therapeutic progress, via more overt father-mother conflict at first and then improvement of family relationships generally, and also that the families with the most open disagreements have done the best in family psychotherapy.

Wynne and his colleagues have examined families of schizophrenics in terms of role behavior and over-all family role structure (11), a quite different approach from our own. Nevertheless, Wynne's clinical examples, descriptions of family interaction, and main concepts all give evidence of contradictory injunctions and concealment of the contradictions as prominent in the families he studied. His central concept of "pseudomutuality"— of relationships that are not so close as they purport to be—necessarily implies the existence of some messages claiming closeness while others indicate the reverse. This is made especially clear in a discussion of the ways in which family members co-operate to escape recognition of pseudomutuality: "in characteristically schizophrenic relations, when both of a pair of contradictory expectations are communicated, the shared mechanisms [of interpreting communications] facilitate a *failure* in selection of meaning" (11); *i.e.,* facing the existence of contradiction at all is jointly avoided. Wynne himself states that this view seems to concur with our own group's original double-bind views (11). The concept of the "rubber fence" as a defining line maintained by the family has similar implications. Such a "rubber fence," altering to define all relationships that can be claimed as complementary as being within the family and all that are uncomplementary as being without, agrees with our observations of family behavior, but this fence can only be maintained by much contradiction and its concealment.

A striking example from our own work in conjoint family therapy confirms and summarizes these views. The father and mother insisted for some time both that they were in agreement on all important matters and that everything was all right in their family—except, of course, the concern and worries caused by their son's schizophrenia. At this time he was almost mute, except for mumbling "I dunno" when asked questions. During several months of weekly family interviews, the therapist tried to get the parents to speak up more openly about some matters that were obviously family problems, such as the mother's heavy drinking. Both parents denied at some length that this was any problem. At last the father reversed himself and spoke out with only partially disguised anger, accusing his wife of drinking so much every afternoon with friends that she offered no companionship to him in the evenings. She retaliated rather harshly, accusing him both of dominating and of neglecting her, but in the course of this accusation she expressed some of her own feelings much more openly and also spoke out on differences between them. This session was reviewed and discussed with the participants the next week (and a tape recording of the argument was played back). In the following session, the son began to talk fairly coherently and at some length about his desires to get out of the hospital and get a job, and thereafter he continued to improve markedly.

THE INSTITUTIONAL SITUATION

The three-party institutional situation resembles the three-party family situation closely, with individuals or groups in the institution taking roles that parallel those of parents. Perhaps this connection is especially close for families of schizophrenics, because like purposefully established organizations, they tend to conceive of themselves and to function in terms of strongly defined roles and their relationships rather than in terms of the interaction and development of individuals. This aspect of the family, rather clearly implicit in much of the above descriptive material, is made explicit in a recent paper by Wynne's group (12).

Stanton and Schwartz's widely known original findings on pathological excitement and covert staff disagreement (4) are a good basis for brief analysis of the institutional situation, although their focus of attention is somewhat narrower or less general than the present one and their point of observation different. (Other institutional difficulties have been described at length and analyzed in double-bind terms by Fry [13].)

In summary, Stanton and Schwartz found that "whenever a patient showed manic excitement, he was always the subject of disagreement between two people who were often unaware of their own disagreement" (4) and that "pathologically excited patients were quite regularly the subjects of secret, affectively important staff disagreement and, equally regularly, their excitement terminated, usually abruptly, when the staff members were brought to discuss seriously their points of disagreement with each other" (4). These disagreements involved authority, influence, and decisions:

> In the course of the day-to-day determination of policy regarding any particular patient, small disagreements inevitably arose between [staff members] who had power to decide. If they became antagonistic to each other for any reason, they tended to magnify these small disagreements, and were unable to discuss and resolve them; for instance, one . . . might regularly permit a patient to do something that the other . . . might regularly prohibit. If they could not discuss the problem . . . the one who was more restrictive came increasingly to play the role of policeman or disciplinarian, while the other came to play the role of the indulgent mother. . . .
>
> The patient responded to each in terms of these roles. Inconsistencies arising in the course of the patient's management became systematic and, more important, the whole process in its middle stages was very, very quiet (4).

"Pathological excitement," as used by Stanton and Schwartz, covers a considerable range of symptomatic behavior: "increased tension or confusion," heightened "preoccupation with suicide," "delusional accusation," "overt aggression," "overactivity," "evidence of dissociation." They tend to exclude withdrawal from their picture, but it remains unsettled whether this omission is appropriate. They note that "it is possible that exactly similar phenomena occur widely among schizophrenic patients in which . . . the phenomenon may be complicated by a tendency to withdraw . . . so that a split in the social field remains unrectified, and dissociated processes become chronic." But in their study, "markedly withdrawn patients were only rarely the subject of any disagreement; to form a part of the triangular process apparently required a certain degree of activity by the patient" (4). And in the light of our experience with the family situation and of the writings of others on the family cited above, an alternate interpretation, connecting these views, is suggested: withdrawal may be related to deeper and more continuous covert disagreement, so that both disagreement and disturbed behavior are less apparent than in overt excitement.

At any rate, Stanton and Schwartz give indications that the disagreements involved in cases of pathological excitement were often covert by virtue of being (a) not discussed directly between the two parties immediately involved and (b) not communicated openly to the patient, although perhaps quite evident to others:

> The open recognition of the fact of a disagreement was often evaded by everyone concerned long after it should have been obvious—and recognition had to precede discussion and resolution. Discussion between the persons at odds with each other was also evaded and was often achieved only through the skilled mediation of a third party. . . . The disagreement was always covert during its early stages. . . . The two participants were themselves not clearly aware of its importance, although they might have been discussing it with friends for some weeks and all the staff except themselves were clearly aware of it (4).

Or in other instances, the two parties would "go through the formalities of a discussion of aspects of the patient's treatment which were only peripherally related to their disagreement." Or there might be a silent, withdrawn situation, with "one member of the personnel inconspicuous." And, most striking in view of Wynne's discussion, and various examples above, of family "pseudomutuality," "pseudoagreement is the method *par excellence* for driving a controversy underground and, as such, is particularly dangerous" (4).

This institutional material is fascinating in its manifest parallels with various aspects of the family material presented earlier, and such parallels have not escaped explicit notice, from both professional and patient sides. Lidz's group has mentioned the existence of similarities between family-schism situations and the Stanton-Schwartz situations and has also pointed to a third important possibility—similar conflicts about the patient between family and hospital staff as the two parties (14). They, however, were not concerned with describing such situations generally or formally. From the other side, one of our patients managed to express quite plainly in therapy his fear that his therapist and ward doctor might be in conflict over him, to his detriment and beyond his control, just as his wife and mother were (2). Stanton and Schwartz's material also takes on additional and extended significance in that their remarks on resolution of these situations are highly suggestive of ideas for therapeutic intervention in schizophrenic family situations. To a considerable extent, however, they neglect the role of the "benevolence" stance in concealing inconsistencies and magnifying their effects, though it appears indirectly elsewhere when they discuss hospital finances. (See discussion of this specific point, important at all levels of organization, in ref. 1, p. 263.) Stanton and Schwartz do deal very positively with a related topic—very relevant to family functioning—in discussing organizational functioning and morale (see ref. 4, pp. 398–400). That their observations are thus pertinent is demonstrated by our examples showing that mere exposure of covert parental conflicts, even before they are resolved, is accompanied by patient improvement.

To conclude, however, we must return from such manifest and particular similarities and connections, in spite of their interest and evidential value, to point again to a formal pattern of communication in these institutional situations very like that in the mother-child and family situations already examined. This general and formal level is our central interest, as most significant for developing a general theory of disruptive interaction and thus, ultimately, most significant for practice.

Stanton and Schwartz say rather little directly about their covert disagreement situations as communication viewed from the patient's side; they center on staff communication and interaction on the one hand and patient symptoms on the other. In passing, they do remark on the patient's being presented with two different roles to which to respond; or, in other words, "the two most immediately important persons in his life were, so to speak, pulling him in opposite directions" (4) but not even doing so clearly and openly. These indications, put together with an inverted viewing of their remarks on staff communications (much as our original double-bind description was inverted earlier), result again in the characteristic general picture:

The patient

(a) is faced with inconsistent messages—necessarily, since the other two parties must be conveying their different views to him in some way, and any attempt to avoid this incongruity reinforces the secrecy aspect of the situation; such avoidance also intensifies the extent, probably always appreciable in these situations, to which *each* of these two persons is issuing two incongruent messages, but concealing this—*i.e.*, individually giving double-bind messages, as well as jointly engaging in a larger double-bind message;

(b) from those in authority over him and on whom he is dependent;

(c) so that it is important to see and deal with the contradictory influence of these messages; while

(d) any notice and validation of these contradictions is made difficult by unawareness, concealment, denial, all operating within a frame of the "unity" and "benevolence" of the hospital, and, not least, the illness of the patient and therefore the imputed unreliability of his perceptions.

A communicational approach, then, has helped in discerning and clarifying one basic pattern of significance for the genesis of schizophrenic behavior in three settings differing in the size and kind of social system involved. In conclusion, it can be suggested that developments and extensions of such analysis of communication patterns into investigation of other, related problems of psychiatric interest already appear to follow logically from this work. For example, one could investigate more complex systems, of four or more parties. This would be relevant to many unresolved questions, such as the role of a sibling in a schizophrenic's family, or the nature of the interaction occurring when a potentially schizophrenic adolescent becomes involved in a love relationship outside the family. One could go beyond schizophrenia and investigate whether other patterns of contradictory communication are involved in other forms of psychiatric disorder. To mention a perhaps oversimplified case, might such cyclical disorder as manic-depressive psychosis be related to contradictions that, rather than being closely juxtaposed, are sequential in time, thus forming a pattern of alternation? Or, moving further toward a social psychiatry, one could investigate the existence, handling, and effects of incongruent messages in wider spheres of social and cultural organization. Certainly the great institutions of business, government, and religion can hardly be completely free of these problems, involving inconsistent messages and their concealment, the denial of personal behavior and responsibility, and the assertion of unity and benevolence that we have seen causing such difficulty within the family and mental hospital systems.

References

1.   G. BATESON, D. D. JACKSON, J. HALEY, and J. H. WEAKLAND, Toward a theory of schizophrenia, *Behavioral Sci., 1*: 251–264, 1956.

2.   J. H. WEAKLAND and D. D. JACKSON, Patient and therapist observations on the circumstances of a schizophrenic episode, *A.M.A. Arch. Neurol. & Psychiat.*, *79*: 554–574, 1958.

3.   D. D. JACKSON, A note on the importance of trauma in the genesis of schizophrenia, *Psychiatry, 20*: 181–184, 1957.

4.   A. H. STANTON and M. S. SCHWARTZ, *The Mental Hospital,* New York: Basic Books, 1954, pp. 352–365.

5.   T. LIDZ, A. R. CORNELISON, S. FLECK, and D. TERRY, The intrafamilial environment of schizophrenic patients: II. marital schism and marital skew, *Am. J. Psychiat., 114*: 241–248, 1957.

6.   T. LIDZ, A. R. CORNELISON, D. TERRY, and S. FLECK, The intrafamilial environment of the schizophrenic patient: VI. the transmission of irrationality, *A.M.A. Arch. Neurol. & Psychiat., 79*: 305–316, 1958.

7.   S. FLECK, D. X. FREEDMAN, A. R. CORNELISON, T. LIDZ, and D. TERRY, The intrafamilial environment of the schizophrenic patient: V. the understanding of symptomatology through the study of family interaction. Paper presented at Am. Psychiatric Assoc. meeting, May 15, 1957.

8.   T. LIDZ, A. R. CORNELISON, S. FLECK, and D. TERRY, The intrafamilial environment of the schizophrenic patient: I. the father, *Psychiatry, 20*: 329–342, 1957.

9.   T. LIDZ, B. PARKER, and A. R. CORNELISON, The role of the father in the family environment of the schizophrenic patient, *Am. J. Psychiat., 113*: 126–132, 1956.

10.   M. BOWEN, R. H. DYSINGER, and B. BASAMANIA, The role of the father in families with a schizophrenic patient, *Am. J. Psychiat., 115*: 1017–1020, 1959.

11.   L. C. WYNNE, I. M. RYCKOFF, J. DAY, and S. I. HIRSCH, Pseudo-mutuality in the family relations of schizophrenics, *Psychiatry, 21*: 205–220, 1958.

12.   I. M. RYCKOFF, J. DAY, and L. C. WYNNE, The maintenance of stereotyped roles in the families of schizophrenics. Paper presented at Am. Psychiatric Assoc. meeting, San Francisco, May, 1956.

13.   W. F. FRY, JR., Destructive behavior on hospital wards, *Psychiatric Quart.*, to be published.

14.   S. FLECK, A. R. CORNELISON, N. NORTON, and T. LIDZ, The intrafamilial environment of the schizophrenic patient: II. interaction between hospital staff and families, *Psychiatry, 20*: 343–350, 1957.

14. A CLINICAL STUDY OF
CHILDHOOD SCHIZOPHRENIA

Maleta J. Boatman and S. A. Szurek

Since 1946, the staff of the Children's Service of the Langley Porter Neuropsychiatric Institute * has been engaged in clinical-research efforts to test the hypothesis that the etiology of psychotic disorders of childhood are

Maleta J. Boatman, M.D., is a clinician and Assistant Director of the Children's Service at the Langley Porter Neuropsychiatric Institute, San Francisco. S. A. Szurek, M.D., is Director of the Service, having been trained at the Illinois Neuropsychiatric Institute, the Institute for Juvenile Research, and the Institute for Psychoanalysis in Chicago. Both are on the staff of the University of California School of Medicine, San Francisco.

* The Langley Porter Neuropsychiatric Institute is a 110-bed hospital and associated outpatient department set up by the California State Legislature and opened in San Francisco in 1943. It is under the California State Department of Mental Hygiene, is primarily for training and research, and is affiliated with the University of California Medical Center.

The Children's Service administers a 15-bed ward for children under 12 and an associated outpatient service for approximately 100 children under 18. The staff consists of 35 persons: 2 full-time, 5 half-time, and 6 consulting psychiatrists; 3 full-time psychiatric social workers, and 1 supervisor for students in psychiatric social work (part-time with the service); 1 clinical psychologist and 1 part-time research psychologist; 8 psychiatric nurses; 5 psychiatric technicians; 1 elementary-school teacher; 1 occupational therapist (part-time) and 2 secretaries. There is also a trainee or temporary staff of approximately 25 persons who participate in the work of the service.

Well over 50 persons have participated actively in the work for periods of a year or more; about 30 have participated for over 4 years, including seven of the current staff, who have continued for more than 10.

entirely psychogenic. Our hypothesis that the psychotic disorder is the result, in the form of conflict and its compromise solution, of the postnatal experience of each particular child early in life in interaction with significant adults who were themselves in conflict has been tested primarily by means of psychotherapy carried on concomitantly with each child and at least one, usually both, of his parents. Close investigation and careful evaluation of somatic factors have been part of the clinical study. Additional emphasis has also been placed on the therapeutic aspects of the entire staff's contribution to the experience that each family has with the Institute. With hospitalized children this has included the daily life on the ward and those contacts between parent and child that have relevance to the ward situation.

Inextricably related endeavors have been the development of modes of study, the refinements of methods of psychotherapy, and the continuous exploration of methods of training psychiatrists and other professional workers.

One of the authors * was interested in the testing of this hypothesis as far back as the period before World War II, working with Dr. Adelaide Johnson and other colleagues at the Institute for Juvenile Research in Chicago (1–6). In their outpatient psychotherapeutic work with the families of neurotic and impulsively aggressive children, they were struck by the fact that they found no disturbed child whose parents were not also in conflict. They also found that the nature and extent of each child's emotional integration, *as well as* the form and severity of his particular conflicts and their symptomatic expression, were directly related to and primarily the consequence of the timing, intensity, and duration of his experience with significant adults, primarily his parents. They also attempted similar (but brief and incomplete because interrupted by the war) studies of psychotic children at the Children's Ward of the Illinois Neuropsychiatric Institute. These beginning studies raised the possibility that factors similar to, but more intense than, those found in the work with the neurotic and impulsive children might be found in thorough clinical study of these more severe psychotic disorders.

The question raised by these early studies was: How much of every form of mental *disorder* of childhood and of such physiological disturbances as have not been proved to be the result of impersonal factors producing *disease,* is the result of the child's experience in living with other persons who are themselves in conflict? The clinical assumption then was that psychotic disorder in childhood is the result of "early continuous distortion of biological tendencies of the human organism after birth by anxieties in-

* S. A. Szurek.

duced from anxious parents" (7). In the light of previous psychoanalytic experience (7–15), it seemed logical to hypothesize that if such disorder arose through conflictful living it could be both studied and reversed through intensive psychotherapeutic work with the child and his parents by therapists free, or relatively free, from similar disorder in their own personalities.

This early Chicago work was carried out with an experienced staff, who had had similar training and were accustomed to working together; in San Francisco at the end of the war, such a staff had to be developed and had primary responsibilities to the teaching and training programs. Therefore, it seemed that whatever research was done must be an integral part of these other ongoing endeavors. It was fully appreciated that such an approach might be disadvantageous to both the training and the research program; however, it also seemed possible that such a multi-faceted effort to provide for *all* patients the most theoretically consistent service that was realistically possible at any given time might afford the method and the milieu for both the training and the clinical research.

Because of the obvious inherent difficulties, the staff made no effort to encourage the referral of psychotic children to the Institute, but they did maintain a policy of accepting applications for psychiatric evaluation of *any* type of child, within the limits of staff time, whose behavioral difficulties could possibly be wholly or in part psychogenic in origin. They have, however, seen many more psychotic children than initially anticipated, and much of the work has found a focus in the clinical research efforts to test the hypothesis of the psychogenic etiology of childhood schizophrenia.

The authors hope that the following discussion will be an accurate reflection of the experience of the entire staff. All participants, however, may not subscribe to all statements made, and the authors accept full responsibility for any errors or inaccuracies that may be present.

IDENTIFICATION OF SAMPLE

In the twelve years, 1946–1957, this staff has seen approximately 200 families in which a child was schizophrenic or severely schizoid. In 120 of these, one or more children have shown continuous psychotic maldevelopment or have had psychotic episodes; 20 of these were adolescents. In an additional 30 families, the child was severely schizoid. In another 50 families, the child's disorder appeared to be classifiable as schizophrenic or schizoid but was complicated by known organic disease or strong suggestive evidence thereof. These 200 families represent almost 15 per cent of the total families seen during this time. Our reasons for including all these in our study may be clearer from our subsequent clinical descriptions and from the greater detail furnished in the appendix.

The work has inevitably been influenced by the complexity of the problem itself and the time it has taken us all to gain as much skill as we have and to become as integrated as we are in our endeavors. Training and mutual learning still continue as a progressive refinement of technical thera-peutic procedures, and we all wish we were more skilled. The time such a study inevitably requires, as well as our own and the patients' limitations of time for the work, are factors that contribute to our recognition of how much needs yet to be done. We would have preferred to see more of the families for fairly long periods. With most, we would have preferred to offer a greater frequency of therapeutic sessions than we were able to, par-ticularly with the parents. Our experience has, however, been thorough enough and, in some instances, satisfying enough to convince us of the value of continuing our endeavor. Our hopes for the future will be mentioned in more detail in our concluding discussion.

It is only within the last year that the research psychologist and several experienced members of the staff have been able to undertake a careful review of the records and a more statistical collation of the data than had previously been possible. This careful study of the material is still in prog-ress and is far from completion. Such statistical material as is presented in the following descriptions and discussions is based on this preliminary work and is somewhat more complete than that available in previous presenta-tions of various aspects of our experience (7, 16–19). Subsequent review and study will make possible more precise tabulations and may, possibly, neces-sitate some revision of what is stated here. We would like to add, however, that so far the findings seem to be in accord with our clinical impressions.

The ages of the children at the time of first clinical contact with us have ranged from 18 months to 17 years. Most have been under 12 and, in recent years, an increasing number have been under six. Regardless of the time of first contact with us, almost all have had a history of some degree of disorder extending back to an early (preschool) age.

The sex differential of approximately three boys to two girls has not been explained but there is evidence that this is not unique to this group because it occurs in most children's clinics in the country with all age groups and all types of disorder (20).

The family histories of the psychotic children we have seen show no par-ticular patterns in areas of classifiable social factors. The parents have been from all economic and educational levels. Some have had family backgrounds which were like their own current status in these areas and some have been in the process of class mobility. We have seen families of Protestant, Jewish, and Catholic faith. We have seen a number of Negro and Chinese as well as Caucasian children. The ordinal position of the child in the family has included that of first and last born and all points between. Some have been only children. The parents' marital status has been of every kind. For some, the child was born in a first marriage and, for some, in a marriage subsequent to divorce or death of a first spouse. Many of the children came from an intact family while some came from homes broken by death, divorce, or separation. In some, but not all, of these latter instances the parent or parents had remarried. The only such factor which has seemed, perhaps, to show a significant pattern is that very few of the children have been reared away from both parents.

In most instances both parents have participated in whatever study or therapy was undertaken. A few of these have been adoptive parents. In a very few instances, when one parent was dead or had actually given up all contact with the child, only one parent was seen. In some families, a stepparent has been seen in addition to one or both actual parents. We have had contact with grandparents in several families, and, in one, the maternal grandmother participated in psychotherapy in addition to the mother. In at least four unusual situations, we have not seen either parent but have seen some other interested adult. These were: a maternal grandmother who had pretended to be the mother of an illegitimate child from before his birth; the maternal grandmother of an illegitimate child whose mother left him at one year; the maternal grandparents of a child whose father had killed the mother and himself when the child was one; and the social worker and foster mother of a nine-year-old child who had lived with his parents only between eight months and three-and-one-half years because of the hospitalization for psychosis first of the mother and later of both parents. In about 10 per cent of the families seen in outpatient therapy, the mother participated longer or markedly more regularly than the father. In several families, the reverse was true.

The duration of our clinical contact with these families has ranged from brief periods of three to five weeks of outpatient study (about 20 per cent) to, in one instance, twelve years of study and psychotherapeutic work still in progress. Outpatient study has sometimes been extended by one to three months study on the Children's Ward (about 10 per cent). Most families who have decided with us during the study period to undertake longer and more systematic psychotherapeutic work (60 to 70 per cent) have been seen for periods under three or four years. Some have been seen for five to eight years. Whereas early some children were seen only as inpatients, in recent years all are seen at least briefly as outpatients. The periods of more intensive study or therapeutic work following the outpatient study have been either entirely outpatient, entirely inpatient, or (often) some combination of the two. Outpatient work has usually consisted of weekly interviews with child and each parent. Inpatient work has increasingly often included psychotherapeutic sessions with the child as often as three times a week. The size of the staff has not yet permitted the increase of parents' interviews to more than once a week except in about five instances.

It has never been possible for all individual members of a family to be seen continuously by the same therapists who started work with each of them. Many children and parents have been seen by a series of trainees in child psychiatry who remained on the staff for two years each. Some have been seen by a succession of trainees of various disciplines who remained only six to twelve months each. As the staff has increased, however, some or all members of about ten families have been seen continuously by the same therapists for as long as four to six years (in one family ten to eleven years).

SCHIZOPHRENIC REACTION, CHILDHOOD TYPE

We hesitate to consider at length clinical history, symptomatology, and diagnostic criteria because our experience as to the form of the clinical syndrome that we call Schizophrenic Reaction, Childhood Type, seems to us to be so similar to that of other students who have described childhood schizophrenia, autism, atypical ego development, or psychosis of childhood.*
It may be well for us to do so, however, to identify more precisely the experiences on which our opinions are based. This may be especially necessary because in recent years we have frequently heard the question raised among professional persons from many parts of the country as to whether any two groups of workers are talking about similarly disordered children when they use any one or all of these various nosological terms.

Briefly, it may be said that we consider a child to be psychotic when his disorder is so great that almost all affective expression is distorted and when, in addition, his capacity to experience real satisfaction and to learn at his age level is seriously interfered with. Even this oversimplification of the external manifestations is an overelaboration or fragmentation of what our experience has led us to feel is the unitary nature of the disorder within the

---

* For example, see 11, 12, and 21 through 34. There are, of course, many other references by these authors and others which could be cited.

child. Psychotic symptoms seem to us to be an expression of almost all-pervasive, self-defeating circular conflict about (with repression of) basic sensual drives—conflict which results in distortion of the drives and their frequent breakthrough as sado-masochistic behavior. Those executive skills which have been learned appear as islands of integrated behavior in the midst of the otherwise seemingly chaotic behavior. If the conflict is severe and generalized enough, such islands may be relatively nonexistent or may, for long periods of time, appear to have been lost. They may also be so persistently made use of in the service of the distorted impulses that they bring little attendant satisfaction and may even seem to be symptoms of psychopathology.

More detailed description of the specific symptomatology which the psychotic child may show reveals that for the most part it has a paradoxical quality which is, in itself, a characteristic symptom. He appears stupid and indifferent at one moment and keenly clever the next. He is persistently negative about undertaking any activity and yet accusingly angry, as if cheated of an opportunity, when it is no longer available. He is phobic or clumsy about some things and dangerously foolhardy or amazingly skillful about others. He is withdrawn and frozen at times, violently assaultive or self-destructive at other times, and clinging or cuddly on still other occasions. He may be tenaciously persistent in one type of behavior for great lengths of time and yet may move with lightning-like rapidity from one behavior to the other. He may, as has been indicated, show islands of integrated behavior (that is, learned skills), which, however, he seems able to use only in certain situations with particular people.

The most marked symptom of many of these children is their *apparent* unresponsiveness to other people. On closer observation, it can be seen that they are acutely and minutely aware of all that occurs, particularly on the part of meaningful adults. Each child's struggle, however, seems obviously to be not only with any "mothering" persons in his life, but also and particularly with himself. He may be characteristically quite indifferent or rejecting to his parents, yet, each time they leave him on our ward, he may repetitively ask for them or explode in angry wailing and destructive behavior *after* they are gone. Even the child who clings to his parents, usually does so in a possessively demanding and often physically hurtful way, showing little relaxation or enjoyment in contacts with them. However indifferent or hurtful he is, particularly with his mother, he is clearly intensely "dependent" upon her and experiences panic on separation from her. We have seen even somatic malfunction as indirect manifestations of this struggle and panic—e.g., anorexia or bulemia, constipation or diarrhea, asthma and eczema. For example, one five-year-old boy, who was erroneously considered for many months to be deaf, tenaciously resisted his urges to defecate and developed eczema whenever his mother's regular visits to the ward were interrupted by increase in her alcoholism. This was usually at the time of visits from her own mother who wanted her to place the boy in a custodial institution because of the family's conviction that mother and son were innately unable to be anything but destructive with each other.

Direct responsiveness to peers is even more lacking than to adults. Even "parallel play" is practically nonexistent, other children's activities being ignored except as such activities relate to contact with adults. Jealous outbursts toward another child who is with an adult are not infrequent, but spontaneous interaction with peers seldom occurs until conflict has been reduced in the establishment of some more satisfying relationship with an adult.

The closely related area of physical contact with others is similarly paradoxical. These children seem to crave it insatiably and yet perceive it as a dangerous experience. Even direct eye contact seems frightening. Often indifferent or even cringing at any adult's approach, they will with persistent, precise awkwardness bump into or step on the foot of an adult who is quietly present. If held, they may be limply passive but seldom comfortably cuddly. Again they may hug only to pinch, or kiss only to spit or bite. They are often embarrassingly direct in their curiosity about or attack on adults' breasts or genitalia. Most often after five or six years of age, they may show a startling seductiveness in their body posturing, the sensuousness of their stroking touch, or, more rarely, their verbal requests or invitations for genital contact.

Interference with speech development, which is perhaps the most characteristic single symptom of all, is not exempt from the contradictions. Many children are entirely mute or say only isolated words on occasion. Yet almost all are reported to say meaningful phrases or even sentences at certain times in the presence of certain people. There is also other clinical evidence that at least subvocal speech development often occurs even in a child who is mute. Infant-like vocal play with sounds may precede the appearance or re-establishment of speech, but very few of these children who have "begun to talk" have had to go through the process of learning speech sounds. Speech, when more freely present, seems as often to interfere with communication as to serve it. It is often devoid of inflection, fragmented or like jargon, filled with contradictions and reversals, or seemingly exactly opposed to what is meant. It frequently shows lack of the pronoun "I" or confuses pronouns from moment to moment. It may be parroting or echolalic. Speech often appears to be self-directed only and is full of alternating pseudovoices, animal noises, and self-scolding phrases and threats. When directed to another person, it may be repetitively demanding about some unanswerable question or persistently concerned with something that does not seem to be to the point of the moment. It may be reminiscent of something which occurred years or moments before with someone else, as when the "ABC's" vainly encouraged by the teacher appear with the nurse who is helping the child change clothes. Enough experience with any given child reveals all of these to be extreme forms of condensations or displacements.

Other modes of affective expression are usually distorted as well. Impatiently eager for a planned activity, the child may scream "No" when the time comes. Minor or imagined hurt may lead a child to loud crying, whereas actual hurt is sometimes reacted to with apparent shame. Adult efforts to comfort such a child may bring panic. Sobbing is practically unknown, and disappointment or anger, when expressed, will bring tense, tearless wailing or screeching, or gleeful, hollow laughter. Faces are often impassive, but mask-like scowling, grimacing, or empty smiling may be seen. Simple amusement is rare, but mirthless, angry glee is frequent, particularly at a plight the child has produced for himself or for another. Requests are often subtly or deviously expressed, but their lack of fulfillment, when not divined or correctly understood, may be accusingly protested loudly and sometimes violently. Adults' questions are reacted to as if they were intolerable demands rather than efforts to help the child express his needs or wishes. The proffer of a choice may be ignored or treated as if the adult were too uninterested or uncertain to decide, but a suggestion will be opposed as if it were an arbitrary and inconsiderate order. Story reading and music which require little response are usually tolerated or sought, but some children are so totally overtly unresponsive to all sound that they have been considered deaf.

Related to the above are these youngsters' difficulties in learning and their reluctance to do things for themselves. Even at past four, many of them make little effort to bathe, toilet, dress, or feed themselves. Soiling and wetting are common, and fecal smearing is not infrequent. The inhibition of development of ego skills in hand, mouth, and hand-mouth activities is particularly frequent. Often reluctant to use their hands for any usual activity and sometimes seemingly phobic about offered finger-paint or clay, the same children may play in the toilets, smear food at the table, or cling to saliva-wet string that has begun to smell. Some have never chewed solid food at age three or older. Many children learn to print and draw only with an adult's hand first guiding theirs and then, for many weeks or months, only if the adult still touches the hand however lightly. Many have *never* put their thumbs or things in their mouths. It is frequent to see a child smell a toy and bring it near his mouth, only to stop short in a kind of frenzied shaking. In contrast, some children suck or eat everything they can put in their mouths, including paint, crayons, water from the toilet bowl, and garbage from the street gutter. Some, in addition, lick everything that will not go in their mouths. Strong food preferences or dislikes are common, as well as phobias about eating. Related compulsions and rituals are common. One girl maintained herself on the borderline of malnutrition for years, interrupting her meals with endless compulsive mannerisms and repetitive verbal efforts to define disturbing phrases she had heard used about eating, such as "How much is too much?" For six months, one six-year-old boy would eat only spaghetti cooked in a particular pan.

Efforts to help the child learn self-help, play or school skills appropriate to his age arouse such anxiety that they are resisted with indifference, active protest, or discernibly deliberate failure. In such a situation his attention span is short and his performance scattered. Some children who persist in not learning what the adults around them wish them to, do become avidly interested in pursuits which are seemingly of their own choosing. These are, in actuality, probably exaggerations of some adult's choice. One surgeon's son pursued the collection and dissection of insects. One boy, whose father lived at a considerable distance from our hospital and was a biochemist interested in industrial architecture, avidly pursued the solitary study of geography, interstellar space, and food factories. One girl, whose mother felt fond of her babies only until they could walk, diapered and bathed and spanked her dolls (and sometimes herself) to the exclusion of almost all other activity. One boy, whose father had majored in classical languages before he became a social worker, had playfully learned some of the Greek alphabet at two and one-half, although his use of English was still babyish and largely lacking at five. Seldom can these activities be utilized by parents or therapists to enhance learning in other areas. These are largely solitary pursuits, excluding all else, and the child may be uninterested in or actively unwilling to reveal what he has learned, particularly if such revelation is sought. Many children who are just beginning to have moments of relaxed attentiveness to an activity with an adult will suddenly interrupt themselves with anxious fury, followed by temporarily intensified efforts to conceal what they have learned.

Motor behavior, in general, is likewise varied, although neuromuscular development of motor ability, *per se*, is seldom much retarded. Some children are most often physically as well as emotionally apathetic. Usually the quiet seems a tense, strained frozenness interrupted by various kinds of physical mannerisms such as rocking, head banging, intricate finger play, grimacing, or monotonous, throaty humming. There is frequent clutching or ritualistic twiddling of some particular object, such as string, leaves, specially folded paper, a particular toy, purse, or treasured scrap. These isolated activities also include slow stroking or smelling of objects, such as sheets, blankets, pillows, wool cloth, their own hair or skin, or another child's pajamas, as well as open genital or anal masturbation. All of these acts seem more anxious, and sometimes defiantly gleeful, than pleasurable. Whereas some children are clumsy and unskilled in most voluntary motor activity, some are extremely swift and sure-footed or manually dextrous. One child who was a skillful runner and climber at home seemed unable to stand on his own feet outside the door of his house.

The sudden and often unexpected release of violent affect and motor behavior is characteristic of these children. In a few, we have seen long periods of almost constant vicious self-assaultiveness, such as head banging, face slapping, tongue biting, eye blacking, and skin scratching or chewing. When interfered with, this behavior led to assault on others. More frequent are sudden outbursts of savagery toward the self or others that appear unprovoked because the precipitating event seems so minor or because the reaction is so delayed. Although one girl newly admitted to the ward sat frozen and unresponsive to a nurse's overtures, her eyes often followed the nurse closely. After a few days, she suddenly sprang into action to beat against a concrete wall the head of a small girl who had been sitting contentedly on the nurse's lap a few minutes before. One four-year-old, disappointed when her favorite nurse was unusually busy and a bit impatient, deliberately slammed a door on her own finger and gleefully brought the nearly severed terminal phalanx for the nurse to see. Not so well understood was the incident in which a child leaped from bed in the middle of the night and bit a near-by sleeping child severely on the calf of the leg. Firmly restrained at such moments, a child may finally melt into a clinging, weeping heap in the adult's lap, only to unexpectedly kick, scratch, spit, or bite again some moments later.

It is perhaps this seemingly strange timing and unexpected intensity of each child's shifts from one form of behavior to another that seems so incomprehensible and contributes to the frequent impression that he "lives in a world of his own." The intensity and distortion with which he seems to perceive each situation, as well as the seeming inappropriateness of his response, do indeed have an autistic "own world" quality about them. On close acquaintance with each child, however, it becomes possible to reconstruct the events which surround most shifts in his behavior. As we have already indicated, it has further seemed to us that, when we knew enough about a child and his history, we could understand the probable origins of each specific symptom and of his areas of special competence or special inhibition. Each unusual skill and each fetishistic object appears to be an elaboration of particular experiences of that child with some meaningful adult—experiences which were to some degree more satisfying and integrative than most. The child's effort seems to be both to recapture some modicum of the satisfaction experienced in that area, and yet to incorporate it into his intense struggle with himself and others through the demandingly repetitive re-enactment with its accompanying inevitable disappointment. On the other hand, each describable helplessness, each phobic or compulsive symptom of some patients has become understandable as genetically related to special inhibitions. These inhibitions have arisen in the context of particular anxieties of a parent and the consequent malintegrating experience of the child.

We have put little emphasis on disturbed thinking processes, as such, in the symptomatology of childhood schizophrenia for several reasons. In the first place, the observable and describable symptomatology is largely that of total behavior, since the child's verbal expression or confirmation of what he is or has been experiencing is so often lacking or meager. In the second place, our experiences have, as we have indicated, led us to feel that psychotic symptoms and the timing of their occurrence are usually understandable when we know enough about a child's past history and about the precise details of sequences of current events. We have, therefore, attempted above to describe the symptomatic behavior and the circumstances in which it occurs rather than to indicate much of what may be inferred from it as to disturbances in conscious subjective processes.

The psychotic children we have seen have shown evidence of delusionary thinking which in some respects is similar to, and in others different from, that of adult patients. These children can be said to have delusionary ideas in the sense of intense affective distortion of perception and interpretation of situations. However, we seldom obtain confirmation from their verbal expression as to whether they elaborate such experiences into the form of conscious, discrete delusions in the way adults do. One girl, psychotic from a very early age but known to us first at age twelve, gave fragmented verbal evidence of having ideas of destructive omnipotence, confusion of fecal retention with pregnancy, and fears that food was contaminated with germs. A few other children have stated fears that their food was poisoned. In all of these children, such ideas have been expressed most often at times when they were particularly disappointed and angry in their relationship to some meaningful adult. Apparent diminution or disappearance of the ideas has often occurred when an adult responded with close attention to the child's total behavior and to the precipitating events.

Our clinical experience has likewise never wholly convinced us that any schizophrenic child we have seen had auditory or visual hallucinations. A few children whose period of severe disturbance was extremely acute were reported by their parents to have complained briefly of seeing bugs or snakes. Our own observations soon after did not corroborate this. One very disturbed hospitalized twelve-year-old girl who proved later to have a progressive degenerative brain disease talked vaguely to the nurses of seeing "little men" on the ceiling. Some self-preoccupied, isolated youngsters do stare into space with the appearance of intent listening and with lips moving in a manner similar to adults who hallucinate. These are also, however, the children who give the least verbal expression to any of their experiences. The more senior members of the staff have seldom inferred, on close attention to this behavior, that it was evidence of actual sensory falsification. Prior to referral to us, hallucinations were reported in one six-year-old boy during efforts at psychological testing. He had appeared unable to concentrate on the examiner's test materials because of frightened staring at the corner of the room while mumbling about "a sassy man." Our subsequent experience with him led us to presume that this had probably been his tangential response to the requests being made of him by the examiner rather than an hallucinatory experience.

In our extensive physical and psychological examinations of all children, we have found no signs of any one dysfunction of physiology or maturation—or pattern of dysfunctions—which seems characteristic of those schizophrenic children we have seen.

Our early impression that schizophrenic children probably showed a high proportion of aberrations and irregularities in rate of physical development has not been confirmed by review of the height and weight curves we have been able to compile for many of them. A large number do give the appearance of being younger than their chronological age but this is apparently primarily on the basis of behavior. The weight curves of many have fluctuated, but in direct response to variations in their eating habits. Few, however, have been markedly above or below the normal range. A very few have been in the top percentiles of the normal range as to height. A few have been in the lowest percentiles of normal height and a very few have been below the normal range. Most but not all of these have come from families in which small stature was common. Almost all, however, have shown steady, normal growth curves. We believe we have seen only one psychotic child whose growth in height showed spurts and plateaus not consonant with the expectation for the age. A few have shown some delay in physical maturation as measured by X-ray bone-age studies. This finding has not correlated with that of short stature. Our present preliminary tabulations do not appear to indicate that any or all of these findings are significant in their rate of frequency. In addition, we have seen no delay in the appearance of sexual characteristics as these children approach and reach adolescence except in a very few who have been anorexic.

Neuromuscular and intellectual development also often appears to be retarded or uneven, but probably seldom is in actuality. Age at appearance of motor skills (sitting up, walking) and of first speech sounds and single words, while often late, is seldom outside the normal range. The subsequent selectivities as to the specific skills which are learned and as to the use of these make the usual tests of achieved abilities somewhat inadequate. Many of those schizophrenic children who will participate at all in standardized psychological tests achieve an I.Q. score somewhere in the range of 50 to 70. Characteristic is the unevenness of the performance, with scores on individual items sometimes ranging as much as 20 or more points apart. A very few children who ultimately prove to be of normal intelligence achieve only scores that are uniformly low and indistinguishable from those of a defective child. (See Case C, p. 437.) Although it is impossible to be sure that any child's potential performance capacities are greater than his observable and measurable achievement, we have come to believe that relatively isolated areas of skill, however unstandardized, may give fairly accurate estimates. Fine motor skills used in complex ritualistic twiddling sometimes seem as indicative of neuromuscular development as does shoestring-tying. The speed and accuracy of space-time perception and reasoning used in solving such an unplanned problem as how to get past a complicated row of obstacles before being stopped by a watching adult is, perhaps, an intellectual achievement equivalent to solving the timed test of a picture puzzle. It is furthermore sometimes possible to tell almost as much from what a child does not do as from what he does. Many of these children seem always to stop just short of the correct answer. Many repetitively show a negativism so precisely related to the request made of them that their accurate comprehension of the tasks and their solutions may be inferred. Many also produce all the right answers in the wrong places. In these instances, it seems probable that they are expressing more resistance than lack of ability. One boy who could not count above two in school, glanced at his therapist's watch and asked (correctly) why it had no "8." On the basis of such observations, *we feel we have seen few, if any, schizophrenic children who showed matura-*

tional lags or spurts which were wholly determined by physiological or genetic somatic factors.

Those severely disturbed children who have also shown definite neurological abnormalities referable to the central nervous system have not been counted in our basic group of 120 children with childhood schizophrenia. We would like to mention again, however, that clinical experience has led us to question whether the behavioral symptoms in even these children with diagnosed neurological difficulty were merely the direct result of the organic "disease" of the brain. In the basic group of schizophrenic children, autonomic nervous system instabilities have been observed but have seemed to be no different from what we have seen in other markedly anxious youngsters.

Routine electroencephalographic examination has shown a moderately frequent occurrence of generalized paroxysmal cerebral dysrhythmia of nonspecific type in neurotic and psychotic children alike. In these children, who otherwise show no clinical evidence of epilepsy, such dysrhythmia often disappears or reappears on subsequent tracings. A few of the children have shown shifting or disappearing foci of dysrhythmia. At least three of the schizophrenic or severely schizoid children have had single or several widely spaced grand mal convulsions without other clinical evidence of neurologic abnormality. In these latter instances, there has also been clinical evidence of chronologically related heightened emotional stress (35). In one child, the evidence was also strongly suggestive that the occurrence of three widely separated convulsions was related to the rate of withdrawal of barbiturates and tranquilizers (prescribed periodically by the family's physician in the community).

We are aware that many experienced students of this problem feel that it is necessary clearly to differentiate psychosis from severe neurosis and to make a precise study of each child as to the type and stage of his psychotic disorder. Our experience, however, seems in agreement with that of those workers who feel that clear-cut criteria for one or several diagnostic entities among this group of children are not easily defined. Especially in young children, where speech is minimal or absent and passive negativism is great, it is sometimes difficult to differentiate (prior to prolonged *therapeutic* study) psychotic mental disorder from, on the one hand, mental deficiency or disease of the central nervous or other system, and from, on the other hand, very severe psychoneurosis (obsessional or phobic) or personality disorder. In addition, we have become increasingly convinced that severe mental disorder may possibly be superimposed without organic etiological relationship upon mental deficiency or organic brain disease.

The nature of our research endeavor has made it clinically unnecessary, if not actually undesirable, to differentiate sharply between psychotic and severe psychoneurotic disorder and to attempt to categorize types of psychosis. The prognostic implications that might be gained are not required for our decision to begin therapeutic work with any given child and family. Neither would our therapeutic endeavors during these early years of our work have been altered, except possibly to be impeded, by any differentiation within the psychotic group. Perhaps our reasons for saying this will be clearer from our discussion of therapeutic method. In any event, we can say here that the concept of a gradient of severity of disorder extending along a psychopathological "spectrum" which is not clearly differentiated except at central nodal points is becoming one which seems to fit our experience most closely. We refer here both to the clinical history of the disorder in the various children we have seen and to our therapeutic experience with some of them and their families.

This is not meant to say that we do not believe a more precise differentiation is possible than we have yet been able to formulate. Some clear definition of the meaning of specific symptom complexes may be either necessary for, or the outcome of, the further scientific understanding and exposition of etiological factors, particularly if our hypothesis as to their nature is correct.

FAMILIES

As we have already said, our hypothesis of the psychogenicity of psychosis stemmed from clinical experiences which indicated that experiential factors similar to but more intense than those found to be etiologically related to the development of disorder in neurotic and impulsive children might be found in thorough clinical study of the more severe psychotic disorders. In the past twelve years, such similar factors have usually been found by us in our careful initial review, with all parents, of the chronology and nature of all events in the families of schizophrenic children. The consistent occurrence and the intensity of these factors have seemed to us to be confirmed by our further psychotherapeutic explorations with those families who undertook such work with us.

We would like here merely to describe this clinical data, which we are coming more and more to recognize as being characteristically present in the life histories of schizophrenic children. It may, for the sake of description, be divided thus: the chronology of events in the family in relation to the development of the disorder; what we are able to observe and learn of the parents' personalities; and the nature of the intrafamilial relationships, *i.e.,* the nature of the parents' interactions with each other and with their child.

This division is, of course, somewhat artificial. It has occurred to us that the necessity for such division in the effort to identify more precisely each possible factor in such disorder may be one of the major problems in scientific methodology which actually impedes more precise understanding of the disorder. It would seem probable that the most truly characteristic datum of all is the nearly indescribable longitudinal pattern of total experience that each schizophrenic child has had living in interaction with the complex synthesis of all of these factors, each of which has been in a constant state of mutual modification by and with the others.

Chronology of Events   Consistently present is clinical data which indicate that the onset and any exacerbations of the child's disorder occurred in the context of identifiable events or circumstances constituting a critical strain for the parents. These stresses may have been either transiently severe or more chronic, but they intensified immediately prior to the child's birth or in the early months of his life, prior to any acute onset of symptoms. They have been of two general kinds, "external" or "internal," and usually have occurred in interlocking combination. By "external" we mean those stressful events or circumstances which are primarily external in origin so far as any parental neurosis is concerned. By "internal" we mean those difficult or explosive situations which are primarily a cumulative outgrowth of parental neurosis.

Such primarily external events and circumstances, stressful for the parents, have included serious illness in the family, death of a parent's parent, economic loss, war with threat of the father's enforced absence, and increased job or training responsibilities on the part of the father. The parents' reactions to these stresses—such as sexual apathy or unresponsiveness—often exemplify the internal neurotic component. The reaction of each parent to the situation and to the emotional state of the other often leads to a complexity of events that is difficult to describe without offering detailed case histories. The following additional brief excerpt may, however, serve to point up more clearly the kind of data to which we are referring.

One boy, whose psychotic maldevelopment had begun to be evident in the first year of life, was brought to us at age four because of severe self-slapping, which had started in the brief period between the father's recovery from infectious hepatitis and his leaving for an overseas military assignment. Prior to this boy's birth, the father, after a great number of combat missions during the war in which he carried a heavy responsibility and made an excellent record, decided to give up an assignment which would have meant continued promotion, and take instead another in a climate indicated for the health of one of his two children. His dissatisfaction with this position aggravated pre-existing neurotic difficulties of his wife, who bore another son (this third child, our patient) during this period. This child developed autistically amidst continuing tensions between the parents punctuated by father's developing a peptic ulcer, mother's increasing phobias, and impulses toward marital infidelity on the part of both parents (7, p. 530).

It is true, of course, that some of the more external events stressful to the parents are also directly or *seemingly* primarily stressful to the child. Among these have been painful illness, injury through accident or another's anger, and the witnessing of some violence or pain to another. It is our impression that the single most frequently occurring event is the birth of another child in the family just prior to the onset of acute symptoms during the second through fourth year of the child patient's life. Absences of the father, through war duty or death, are not uncommon. Also frequent are separations of mother and child in the first three years, particularly because of the somatic illness of one of them. In fact, the mother's hospitalization at labor often seems to be an important facet of what the child may experience as traumatic in the events surrounding the birth of a sibling.

This kind of stress is exemplified by a child who experienced painful nursing because of thrush soon after birth and was separated from her mother by the latter's illness when the baby was between nine months and thirteen months old. At this time her psychotic maldevelopment was first apparent. Slightly improved by age eleven, she became violently destructive following a painful and disfiguring injury to a finger.

Another child, already somewhat withdrawn, had, at twenty-two months, become assaultive and self-hurtful in the month following his father's lingering death from a disease discovered while mother was pregnant. Somewhat improved at three after his mother's remarriage, he had an exacerbation of symptoms at five after being in an auto accident which resulted in his mother's abortion of a five-month pregnancy. At age six he became violently and persistently self-assaultive during his mother's brief absence the evening after he witnessed his maternal grandfather's heart attack and continued so for many months.

We have said that such events may be "seemingly" *primarily* stressful to the child because we know of no such series of events that have preceded a psychotic episode unless there was also present considerable attendant internal conflict in one or both parents. There is, for example, fairly clear evidence that in those instances in which the child appears to react so severely to such an event as the birth of a sibling, there is already present a complex sequence of anxious reaction in the child and in his interaction with the parents that is, perhaps, merely heightened by the event itself. We know of no child, for instance, whose psychotic symptoms developed or became worse following the birth of a sibling unambivalently desired and unanxiously enjoyed by the *parents*. In some instances the new baby was more welcome and in others less welcome than the psychotic child had been, but in all instances the time of pregnancy, birth, or neonatal care of the infant sibling was a time of increased stress for the parents. The nature of this stress has included such things as fear of pregnancy or labor, a feeling of burden in caring for an infant, fear of the older child's jealousy before it appeared, and guilt about the pleasure or disappointment in the sex of the infant. In addition, close study of many of these instances has seemed to indicate that the birth of the psychotic child himself had been one of the stressful events in the family which predated his illness. Illustrative of this is the following vignette:

> From work with another young couple, married during the early part of World War II, it was learned that they were both very ambivalently and helplessly dependent on their own parents for many years after their marriage. Father, in an effort to remain out of the service, decided to have children early, and then remained emotionally aloof from the first-born son in order that the child would not be hurt emotionally if he should be drafted. He gave up his remunerative occupation for one more arduous, less remunerative, but more essential to the war effort. Sexual incompatibility between the parents was severe. The mother and son were in a serious neurotic entanglement before a daughter was born when the boy was about 4½. Within a few weeks the boy developed a garbled speech, began tearing at his penis, made efforts to take the baby's place in the crib, and was otherwise so difficult for the parents that within a year he was admitted to a state hospital with a diagnosis of schizophrenia (7, p. 530).

Parents   Among the parents of the schizophrenic or severely schizoid children we have seen, all who have undertaken with us any considerable period of psychotherapeutic work for themselves have been found to be deeply troubled people—troubled not only by their sick child but also by neurotic disorder of their own.

This neurotic disorder of the parents has been either temporarily severe or, though more continuous, heightened in intensity during the months prior to or soon after the birth of the child who is our patient. Our clinical evidence shows that these parents are in conflict about their child and with each other and that, furthermore, these difficulties are but the external evidence of the severe internalized conflicts that each has with himself. In therapy it can be seen that, although these conflicts have usually been intensified by the previously described stressful events or circumstances, they have stemmed from each parent's own earliest life experiences. In some families, particularly when grandparents live near or in the home, it can be seen that the parents' experiences with their own parents not only were but continue to be closely related to the difficulties.

Clear indication of severe internalized conflict has been evident to the senior staff in even the earliest interviews with each parent. However, the degree of parents' integration about some aspects of their lives has varied enough so that the less experienced staff members have sometimes doubted the neurotic nature of the clinical findings until after these parents had become engaged (or been persistently unable to become fully engaged) in therapeutic work for some time. Some parents have achieved and have maintained, with whatever strain, a high degree of professional skill and economic success. Some have, at earlier periods of their lives, achieved a fair degree of integration, however tenuous, in their relationships with certain other people. These may have included their spouse and children born earlier, or even later, in the marriage than our child patient. They have sometimes initially reported a marriage undisturbed by overt dissension, a sincere concern for the welfare of their child, and knowledgeable attentiveness to at least all external aspects of the youngster's care. They have often continued to function with apparent calmness in the face of their child's severe disorder and, not infrequently, in the face of other situations or events wh ch were equally disturbing. These are the parents who often come to us for further neurological study of their child because the referring persons have felt the child's development to be inexplicably erratic and bizarre in view of his "unusually fortunate family environment."

We have found, however, that each experienced psychotherapist who listened attentively and questioned gently but firmly soon heard the indications (often confirmed by the parents) of the effort and strain it had cost each of them to maintain such a level of composure and functioning. Over the years, we have come to recognize the frequency with which this "almost too perfect" initial self-description of the parents gives indication, not only of the actual degree of integration, but also of the severity of the schisis which exists between their internal emotional experience and their affective expression. We have found that, despite their occupational successes, they may be tortured by self-doubts and anxious drivenness. The lack of overt dissension in the marriage is often due to tremendous anxiety about expression of fear, disappointment, or anger. The very lack of any discussion of disagreements has often actually contributed to smoldering resentments and sexual apathy or incompatibility. Sometimes the hovering nature of their concern for the child and the compulsive nature of their attentiveness to the child's external needs are related to great guilt about a lack of spontaneous warmth, a sense of intolerable burden, and anxious surges of murderous rage. Only after many months of therapy have we heard how, in a manner like that of their frozen but sadistically explosive children, some of them had earlier experienced moments of loss of control in which they had physically hurt their infants or, in protection against their anxious fury, had left the child practically unattended for long periods. Likewise it has become evident in therapy that the calmness with which they have faced major external stresses, such as death of an own parent, is often a state of repressed affect in which disappointment, fear, or grief has been replaced by a tense apathy or sense of futility and worthlessness. And again it is in therapy that we often hear how, like their self-defeating, nonlearning child, they have themselves contributed to such stressful occurrences as diminution in financial security, exploitation by others, or disintegration of other family relationships.

As we have seen more families, it is clear that the above-mentioned schisis between affect and expression does not always have the same external form. Many parents are referred to us for hospitalization of their child because it appears that one or both are helplessly at the mercy of his destructiveness and other tyrannical symptomatology. They may present themselves as being nervous, incapable, and overwhelmed by the tasks of their lives. The mother, most often, may tearfully claim for her own and her husband's *actions* the blame for the child's great difficulties. There may be overt disagreement between them and mutual recriminations about their methods of handling the child. Each may doubt his own as well as the other's judgment about all external aspects of child-rearing. That is, they may feel they were too strict, too lenient, too absent, or not often enough engaged in play with the child. What is striking in the accounts from these parents, just as from those who are seemingly more sure and composed, is lack of recognition of the inseparability of affect and behavior. They speak as if they could volitionally control the effect of their interaction with the child by exerting caution as to what is said and what is done with him or in his presence. They often say, for example, that their own specific disappointments, fears, or angers could not possibly have influenced the child since they were very careful never to speak of these things in front of him. The parents often lack recognition also of the apparent discrepancies between different aspects of their overt behavior. Whereas the more controlled parents tend most often to lack recognition of that part of their overt behavior that is not integrated, the more overtly anxious parents tend to lack recognition of what executive capacities they have been able to exercise in various areas of their lives, particularly in relation to their child. They seem unable to notice that some things they have done have brought relief to the problem or, possibly, that they had no such grave self-doubts and uncertainties about the rearing of previously born children. This helpless and discouraged self-picture usually covers conflicts not too dissimilar from those already described. Here, too, are the same repressed griefs, the same anxieties about openly expressed disappointment or anger (especially in the assertion of their own wishes for themselves), and the same guilts about secretly guarded feelings of resentment and rage at the infant.

By this description of two somewhat externally dissimilar presenting pictures, we do not mean to indicate that we have seen clinically identifiable "types" or groups of parents. We mean rather to indicate the essential similarity in the nature of the severe neurotic conflict which we have seen in all parents—conflict which, in its intense form, may have varied in duration and in the degree to which it has resulted in overt disruption of the parents' functioning in some or all aspects of their lives. We have come to recognize earlier the schizoid, obsessional part of each of the parents whom we see. The lack of recognition of the discrepancies in their own behavior and of the relationship between their affective behavior and the youngster's response is closely related to the frequent distortions and discrepancies in their descriptions of the child himself. A child who may appear seriously withdrawn, retarded, or destructive may be described by the parents as not having anything much wrong with him and has been brought to the clinic on someone's urging or because of a school's refusal to accept him. Some parents will describe as unmanageably big, strong, and aggressive a three-year-old child who, with our own staff or other family members, appears rather forlorn and responds quite promptly to a modicum of firmness. Several of the children who have been thought by most of our nursing staff to be appealing in their dainty prettiness, impish liveliness, or quiet wistfulness have been described by their mothers as looking like inhuman monsters. Others have been persistently described by parents as being breath-takingly beautiful, handsome, or sweet who, although fine-featured, have constantly distorted their faces with grimaces, scowls, or maliciously gleeful grinning which made it hard for most people to see them as attractive. Other parents have been convinced of some defect in the child even though they could report moments when his behavior belied this. Mute children who did not respond to speech have been considered deaf even though they sought out music and sometimes hummed tunes. Some parents have been sure their child was stupid no matter how many times he surprised them by accurately remembering the details of situations in which he had behaved as though he did not comprehend.

Another kind of discrepancy is that of attributing to the child emotional reactions which his behavior did not seem to indicate. Just as the parents often do not consider the child's disturbed behavior to be an indication of response to events which they feel they have kept hidden from him, they sometimes describe him, regardless of his behavior, as having been upset by some event which they consider traumatic. For example, one family told us at length of their conviction that their four-year-old son's apathetic withdrawal stemmed indirectly from his having been changed abruptly from breast nursing to special formula at five months of age on the pediatrician's recommendation because of diarrhea. When no data came from them spontaneously as to the child's behavior at that time, inquiry by the psychiatrist revealed that he had accepted it calmly, made no protest about bottle nursing, and had had some relief from the diarrhea. His severe symptoms of apathy had actually appeared two months later, at seven months of age, at the time of the departure of the maternal grandmother. Grandmother had been present to help in the home for about nine months, initially because of mother's severe apathy, fatigue, nausea, and recurrent cramps during the pregnancy. This departure left mother almost entirely alone in the home and with the responsibility for the infant, because, in the same year, father had undertaken an arduous schedule of evening study to obtain an advanced college degree while continuing to hold an already time-consuming position of considerable responsibility.

Although gentle, firm inquiry will often help the parents give a fairly complete account of developmental facts and external events, it does not always do so very easily or quickly. It is sometimes extremely difficult to obtain a clear, concise history of the chronology of the development of the child's symptoms and even harder to obtain any historical sense of the family events preceding and during the child's life. It is often only during the course of therapy that parents recall some of the sequences with vivid inclusion of their own affective states. In some instances, certain facts or details had been consciously omitted because of anxiety about what the psychiatrist would think or because the parents wanted to hear the examiner's conclusions about the child's condition before he became "biased" by the data. More often the gaps and distortions are unconscious and have come to be viewed by us as evidences of repression. As the parents gradually work through their fears about what they have assumed that the therapist would feel toward them, they have less need for the projection of their own experience to the therapist or to the child, and the clinical history slowly unravels.

Many of the parents are phobic about specific things or have frightening fantasies and compulsive thoughts or actions. The mothers who have had impulses to harm their infants are not rare. Suicidal ruminations are fairly common. Many have had recurrent fears during pregnancy that they were carrying a monster. Some are repulsed by physical contact with an infant. Several parents have had phobias about blood. One had nausea whenever he touched velvet. Several have scratched or picked at some portion of their own bodies with such frequency that they maintained small sores. One felt compelled to lift her skirt and touch her knee when tense and experienced panic whenever she heard the word "beautiful." Some are compulsively preoccupied with neatness and cleanliness. Several have been convinced that their child's illness was God's punishment of them for "sinful" thoughts.

Many of the parents have experienced special kinds of helplessness and learning difficulties. Several mothers had had learning blocks, which had developed during their adolescent school years. Many parents, particularly mothers, have felt unable to learn to drive a car and may be unable or reluctant to do their ordinary household tasks. The fathers often complain of their wives' housekeeping and cooking. These mothers, who may initially insist they do as well as any one could with the many tasks they have, usually confirm this inability or reluctance in therapy and express their guilt and self-contempt about it. Likewise, the fathers who initially deny their wives' accusations about their lack of interest in the home or about their failure to earn enough money often confirm in therapy their fear of trying to do as much as they would probably be capable of.

Although few of the parents have had neurotic or psychotic episodes acute enough to have required hospitalization or even to have been considered psychiatric illnesses by their families, many have suffered from acute anxiety states or depressions earlier in their lives. One mother was aware in retrospect that her husband had had very brief psychotic episodes prior to their engagement and that she had been severely depressed in the first weeks of marriage and again during her pregnancy and the child's early weeks of life. Several have had periods as young adults when, for minor, vague somatic illness, they spent most of their time in bed for many weeks or months. A few have been alcoholic. Several whose children were hospitalized have had such feelings of depression and anxiety at certain points during therapy that they have sought hospitalization for themselves. At least three have had overt schizophrenic episodes during the course of therapy.

Other forms of distortion of affective expression are common. Some of the parents are subject to rages when disappointed or frustrated. Even more common is the fear of expression of any strong feeling, leading to long, anxiously sullen silences when they were disappointed or angry. Most of them are afraid and ashamed of weeping. Although some of the mothers cry frequently, it is usually tense and inhibited and lacking in full affect or relief.

Sexual apathy or unresponsiveness is very frequent, particularly in mothers, but also in fathers. Mothers who experience sexual desire are usually extremely fearful and inhibited about acknowledging it with their husbands. The fathers who desire more sexual activity than their wives are often afraid of showing tenderness and tend, rather, to be alternately demanding, obsequious, and sulky with the reluctant spouse. Several parents have expressed guilt over their sexual arousal by the child. Several of the fathers have had compulsive voyeuristic impulses. Sadistic and other distorted sexual fantasies are fairly common, and a very few parents have been overtly sadistic in the sexual act. Some have reported homosexual impulses continuing after marriage.

At present, we also have the clinical impression that a relatively high proportion of the parents of schizophrenic and severely schizoid children have had somatic difficulties of the kind generally believed to be psychosomatic in origin. We have seen obesity, ulcerative colitis, peptic ulcer, asthma, transient rheumatoid arthritis, hypertension, and prolonged convalescence from injury or surgery. Several have been seriously accident prone.

Other serious illnesses, not so frequently considered to be psychosomatic, have occurred in these parents' lives, but the number does not seem unusually high in our preliminary survey. Whether or not some of these might be indicative of adverse hereditary factors has likewise not been determined to our knowledge. Two fathers died of acute leukemia. At least two fathers and one mother died of carcinoma. One father died of coronary disease at age 66. At least one mother and one father had diabetes. One mother had scleroderma. Several parents had recovered from tuberculosis.

Family Interaction   In general, we have already indicated what we have seen to be the nature of the interactions in the families of schizophrenic children. We have also mentioned that this is the most difficult part of the clinical data to describe. There are, however, some further details of this aspect of our clinical experience which we would like to try to indicate.

The discrepancies in the parents' perception of their own behavior and of the child are, of course, also apparent in their way of relating to each other and to the youngster. Those children who are mute or who talk about themselves in the third person are often children whose parents talk about them in their presence as if they were not there. These same parents, when talking *to* the child, often use the pronouns "he" or "we" rather than "you" in regard to the child's wishes or behavior. It is frequent for a parent to answer for a child when the child is spoken to. A parent visiting on the ward sometimes directs most of his attention to a child other than his own and attempts to talk with the nurses about other youngsters as well.

Many parents behave toward the child as if he were stupid or as if he were younger than he is. Hospitalized children who can read and write sometimes receive cards or letters from their parents in which very simple sentences have been carefully printed in large letters. Parents of daughters past eight or nine years of age sometimes clothe them in dresses which are far too short and too childish. Others, who could afford to do otherwise, dress their children in ill-fitting and unattractive hand-me-downs, although they are bewildered at the child's lack of interest in his personal care and appearance.

The parents' interaction with a child often appears to be the manifestation of conflict in both. Between the shifting behavior of each, the two seem never quite to meet. We have already described the child's negativism at length, but at certain moments the parent seems to participate in it. A mother may coax, plead, or order her reluctant child to give her a good-bye kiss only to become distracted just as he finally starts toward her, his kiss falling on a half-turned face now engaged in talk with someone else. If the child bites or spits at this moment, the mother's attention is fully returned, with anger not only about the bite but also about the child's ingratitude. Threats about her wish never to return again may also appear, only to be followed by renewed efforts to get the child to say he loves her. Similar is the parents' urging a child to "be a big boy and walk for mommy and daddy" only to meet each exploratory excursion with admonitions that he not fall and hurt himself. Some parents urge a child to dress or feed himself only to take over once he starts, presumably because he is so slow or so clumsy.

In the initial joint interviews with parents, one or the other often does most of the talking, speaks for his spouse, and appears impatient if the other interrupts or contradicts. The interviewer's close attention to each in turn often results in expressions of disagreement or agreement between them about things which both acknowledge they have never previously discussed. This lack of discussion between parents is very frequent, particularly about feelings. Something which has bothered or worried one of them about the other may go unmentioned for years. Some distressing facts known by both as being known to each have been treated as if they were secrets. In one instance this was the fact of the seven-year-old son's extramarital parentage in a family where the father's inability to conceive a child was a known fact. In one family it was their mutual suspicion that father's failure to repair a heater and mother's lack of caution in its use had been responsible for their older child's burning to death. In another family it was their fear, later confirmed, that their younger three-year-old son's development was that of a defective child. Exchange of tender words, admiration, and approbation is also scanty. In a few families the parents, when disappointed and angry, have not spoken to each other for as long as two weeks at a time. Angry projections, even if unverbalized, are frequent between parents and toward the child.

Neither parent seems able to provide the child with the clarity and firmness that would help him learn to discriminate between safe and dangerous behavior and between "feeling" and "doing." Destructive behavior of the child is often permitted on the assumption that he is just being playful and does not know what he is doing. Sometimes it is allowed because the parent feels unable to stop him or, consciously wishing to break things too, fears that stopping him will harmfully frustrate him. Strong feelings of the child are often felt by the parents as intolerable and are either helplessly snared or rigidly interfered with. Sometimes a mother will weep with an unhappy child, unable to provide him with either the permissive safety of her calmness or the comfort of her consolation. Others immediately urge or order a crying child to stop, with admonitions of how babyish it is or what will happen to him if he keeps on. Some mothers bring their hospitalized children large quantities of food and urge them to eat it, hoard it, or share it without any regard to the child's wishes in the matter. Other mothers allow their children to have any kind or amount of food they desire, however inadequate or strange. One mother bought her son a pound of salt and a great wedge of cheese at his request. If the son in another family refused to eat what was served at a meal, mother or grandmother always left the table to cook whatever the boy asked for. In the same family, the father's own strong food preferences were often ignored and his complaints or requests were called "greedy."

Such complicated situations as are implied in this latter example are frequent. The mother often seems to be involved in an exclusive relationship with the child which anxiously brooks no interference. She is filled with apprehension about his health and welfare, fears to allow him opportunities for exploring the world, and reacts to any protest or greater firmness from the father as if it were cruel or were a derogation of her. In one family the mother, for many weeks after her son's hospitalization, refused intercourse as being too sinful a pleasure to indulge in while her boy was unhappy. In other families it seems that any two members can get along moderately well together so long as the third is not present.

Summary   Such clinical data as the above (obtained, confirmed, and studied during psychotherapy) indicates that in the families of each schizophrenic and severely schizoid child we have seen, each parent is tyrannized by his own internal conflicts about repressed and distorted libidinal impulses. In the face of current frustration and stress, each has experienced intensified unconscious needs for exclusive, all-loving, undemanding, tender care and understanding from the spouse. Already fearful, from early life experiences, that such needs are in themselves dangerous and "bad," their own mounting self-contempt has increased their sense of frustration. The needs have become desperate demands, largely unmet for identical reasons in the spouse, and usually uncompensated for by satisfaction through adequate mastery of the parent's own job, housewifely or other skills. Such frustrations and inadequacies have served only to confirm and to justify the buried self-contempt which, in circular fashion, further inhibits any capacity for spontaneous relationship with another and for more thorough learning of skills. Spontaneous expression of simple "childlike" feelings such as tenderness, longing for closeness, sensuality, disappointment, and anger become frozenly impossible, and the world of adult relationships seems hopelessly dissatisfying or even hostile. Sapped by the conflict and the spouse's reaction, the father often resigns from much overt effort at emotional investment in the family and the mother often turns toward the child for satisfactions. Unconsciously seeking, and yet desperately defending herself against, regressive identifications with the helpless infant, the mother is anxious and unstable in her care of him. Alternately overinvolved and frozenly withdrawn, she can neither unambivalently help her child experience the passive gratifications necessary to the helplessness of his infancy nor yet confidently help him learn each new skill as his advancing age makes it appropriate. Neither can she stand firmly but calmly by to help him through any regressive reactions of panic and anger. When the child's reaction to all of this is apathetic withdrawal, outbursts of rage, and reactive nonlearning, both parents feel an even greater sense of helplessness, failure, guilt, and rage.

METHODS OF CLINICAL STUDY

It has seemed important to us to describe the children and parents we have seen as fully as possible before attempting to describe our current methods of study since the development of these methods has been so intimately related to our actual clinical experience as well as to our hypotheses and to our own historical realities. There will need to be some further references to all these factors, although here our primary intent is to describe our clinical methods as precisely as possible.

As we have said, our primary method of testing our hypothesis of the psychogenicity of childhood schizophrenia has been that of concomitant psychotherapy with each child and at least one, usually both, of his parents. Also important to our study have been the careful evaluation of the child's clinical history and of somatic factors, and the close attention to the nature and significance of all contacts which the family has with the Institute, in addition to psychotherapy.

Application and Intake Interview   Although we accept "self" referrals, most families are referred to us by other medical or social agencies. The first step in our work (beyond conferences with referring persons who have already been engaged in helping the parents with the disturbed child) is to ask that one of the parents write or phone us about the problem as they see it and about their wish for an appointment to discuss this and our available services. Our clinical assumption that both diagnostic and therapeutic work (however brief or long they are to be) begin with the first phone call developed from our repeated discovery that the very act of the family's applying sometimes resulted in a shift in the clinical picture, as well as that problems often developed in subsequent work when we had made any kind of plan directly with the referring person rather than the parents themselves.

Upon such application from a parent by telephone or letter, as early an intake appointment as possible (within a few days or weeks) is arranged for both parents, usually with one of the psychiatric social workers. A psychiatrist may participate in this interview, either because of the nature of the problem or for his own training experience. If the parent who calls insists on coming alone for a first interview, this is agreed to, at which time the possibility of a second interview with both parents is explored. If both of the parents continue to have contact with or legal or financial responsibility for the child even though they are separated or divorced, both are seen if possible, usually together. If one prefers to come alone or they prefer to come separately, this is arranged for a first interview, with the possibility of a second joint meeting being left open for discussion. Stepparents in the child's home are also asked to participate.

The intake interview is used for general exploration, rather than for complete history-taking. The parents are helped to discuss the nature and duration of the problem, the precipitating reasons for seeking help at this time, their own impression as to the cause of the difficulties, and the family's current living and economic situation. With all of the parents who may wish their child to be seen, there is also discussion about the following: the importance of several outpatient study interviews with a psychiatrist before any mutual commitment is made; the various kinds of services that may be available at the Institute; how long any delay may be in the availability of service because of staff time; and the nature and probable availability of alternative sources of help elsewhere. If the parents wish to proceed further with us after this preliminary exploration, a plan is tentatively arrived at with them. It is explained that this will be discussed with the psychiatric staff within a few days, and plans are made for further contact with them after the discussion. If a mutually satisfactory plan cannot be reached in one interview, or if the staff discussion raised further questions, a second (or more) interviews are arranged.

If staff time permitted, a period of immediate outpatient study with a psychiatrist would be offered to all families who wished to continue their application with us. Since staff time in relation to the pressure of applications does not permit this, our decision as to how soon study can be offered is based on consideration of such factors as previous studies, degree of urgency, probable outcome of study, clarity of the presenting clinical picture, and the nature of the parents' request. Most families whose child's disturbance is so profound as to be eventually called schizophrenic are offered outpatient studies within several months, if alternative services such as private referral are not readily available to them. When there is a considerable sense of desperation on the part of the parents, or when there is question of possible serious overt crisis consequent to delay, every possible effort is made to see the child and parents at once.

Whatever its timing in relation to the intake interview, at least a brief period of outpatient study with a psychiatrist is part of every plan for further work with us. This is so even when the parents' request after the intake interview is still clearly for hospital study or for inpatient or outpatient psychotherapy. On a few rare occasions early in our work, when the referral was an urgent request for immediate hospitalization, we admitted the child directly to the ward the day of the intake interview. In several of these very few instances, the parents withdrew the child from the ward the next day, and, in at least one, they terminated all contact with us.

Initial Study and Evaluation   Outpatient study usually consists of three or four weekly visits of the child and parents to the Institute. The parents often find the weekly intervals between visits useful for reflecting on the previous interview, discussing the situation with each other, and observing the child and themselves in a new light. Transient and superficial as it may be if not followed by a period of psychotherapeutic work, improvement is not infrequently noted during the course of the study period, and beginning resolution, of at least the crisis situation, often occurs. (See Case A, p. 435.)

During the study, we attempt as complete a review and examination of the child's life and illness as possible. In a joint interview, the psychiatrist in charge of the study helps the parents to give as clear a chronological account as possible of the development of the disorder, the child's developmental history and medical history, and the family history. In an individual interview, each parent is encouraged to elaborate on these and to explore his own life history in as much detail as he is able. Permission is obtained from the parents for requesting information from other doctors, schools, and agencies who have known the child. The child is seen, usually alone and usually in a playroom, depending on his age and the degree of the parents' anxiety about leaving him if he appears fearful. Complete physical and neurological examination is made and routine laboratory studies are obtained, including complete blood count, blood serology, urinalysis, check for phenylketonuria, chest X-ray, and electroencephalogram. The psychologist sees the child for as thorough psychological study as the child's condition permits. Intelligence testing is almost always attempted, using one, all, or parts of the Wechsler Intelligence Scale for Children, Stanford-Binet, and Arthur Performance Scale. If possible, projective tests are usually given, including the Draw-a-Person and Bender-Gestalt. Rorschach, Thematic Apperception Test, and Blacky may also be used if appropriate. The psychologist may also interview the parents for such studies as the Vineland Social Maturity Scale, and a very few have been seen for projective testing.

Consultation with other medical specialists from the adjacent Medical Center may be arranged during this outpatient study, but usually if serious questions remain as to the possible presence of identifiable somatic disease or anomaly, the parents are encouraged to allow us to admit the child to the Children's Ward for two to four weeks of further and more intensive study and observation. Any uncertain signs or indications of somatic disease or defect are then pursued by every means available to our own or to our consultants' knowledge. Skull films and bone age studies are routine, and with some children we have obtained such additional studies as spinal tap, pneumoencephalogram, angiogram, ventriculogram, visual field studies, and audiometric examination. The ward setting also permits close observation of the child's and, to a considerable extent, the parents' interactions with other persons and with each other in a variety of situations. The latter is possible inasmuch as the parents usually visit freely on the ward. At least weekly individual interviews with the child and each parent are continued by the psychiatrist during such inpatient study.

During the study interviews, each parent is encouraged by the psychiatrist to relate all that he has thought or feared about the nature of the child's disorder and his own experience in relation to the difficulties. As the nature of the child's and family's troubles begins to unfold during these interviews, the psychiatrist also shares his findings and tentative impressions with the parents and encourages their own further exploration of their impressions as to the possible nature, cause, and solution of the problem. As possibilities are touched upon which seem in accord with the findings, the psychiatrist shares with them our clinical data and mentions possible treatment or other resources which might be of help if these possibilities should become more thoroughly confirmed as the study progresses. He explores with the parents their previous experiences with and attitudes toward such things as outpatient psychotherapy, medical intervention, hospitalization, social agency help, foster home placement, school possibilities, and family aid. The probable availability or unavailability of these resources, with us or elsewhere, is made clear, and the steps which can be taken to clarify this more exactly are discussed. For the past eight years our own staff has seldom introduced a recommendation for inpatient rather than outpatient work except in the above-mentioned instances where needed diagnostic procedures or observation seemed to require it. If, however, this possibility has been raised by parents or referring person, the parents are invited to see the ward so that their own impressions of it, however brief, can contribute to the discussions of the advantages and disadvantages of hospitalizing the child for whatever period of time.

Occasionally the family may interrupt their contact with us even before completion of these initial steps. In all other instances the psychiatrist shares with the family our impressions as to what part of the child's difficulties may be inborn or due to disease and what part may rather be the result of the youngster's early experiences in living. There is discussion of what treatment plans are or are not available for whatever deficiency, anomaly, or disease is present. By this time, the child's and family's external troubles and usually some of each family member's own internal troubles have also been talked about. There is clear, direct, noncritical discussion with the parents by the psychiatrist of the possible or probable relation of these to whatever part of the child's behavior may be due to emotional disturbance. The psychiatrist discusses this in terms of the parents' having been unable to experience together with their child the satisfactions they themselves would have preferred. He then shares with the parents our belief that such difficulties might be wholly or in part reversible if the child were seen for regular psychotherapeutic work and if each of them would also be willing to try in psychotherapy to see what he might gain for himself in the way of reduction of his own internal troubles. The parents are told of our own willingness to undertake whatever work might be helpful if we have time.

The psychiatrist tries to be alert to the importance of helping the parents explore the possible real disadvantages as well as advantages of undertaking therapy with us in the light of alternative possibilities. He is, at the same time, clear and firm about the conditions under which we can begin work and is unhesitating and direct in his statement of whatever degree of conviction he has that such work may be helpful. Although he may express his honest concurrence with, regret about, or doubt concerning whatever decision the parents may make, he remains profoundly *noncoercive* about the choice. This attitude extends to the parents' right to choose therapeutic work in the face of what appears to their friends and relatives to be intolerable sacrifice, as well as to choose not to undertake work with us.

Such outpatient, or inpatient plus outpatient, studies may have several possible outcomes for the child whom we consider to be schizophrenic, or probably so, on the basis of this preliminary work. As we have gained more experience in all phases of work with families, we have been more often able to help the parents, in these early contacts with us, experience something of what we are proposing as to the possible resolution available through psychotherapy. Probably as a result of this, we have found more and more parents, fathers as well as mothers, who are willing or even eager to undertake such therapeutic work with us. Some others choose to look further for help elsewhere where more neurological or physiological studies may be done, where the child may receive somatic therapy of some kind, where the emphasis may be more specifically centered on education, or where their own participation may not be considered so important. The staff accepts uncritically whatever the parents' decision may be at this point and offers to do whatever they can to facilitate the plan.

If the parents wish to consider psychotherapeutic work at this point, all possible resources in addition to our own are discussed with them. Until recently, we were usually able to estimate the period before staff time would become available for outpatient work with us as being between six and twelve months. This has gradually increased until, in the last year or so, it has become eighteen months to two years. The names of only a few families whom we anticipate being able to see within one to four months are kept on an outpatient waiting list which implies our commitment to call them when we have time. All families can, however, expect to be seen in the order, for the most part, of their original request for service if, at suggested intervals, they confirm their continuing interest in further work with us. Our staff is also available for consultation around any crisis situation during this interim time. Because of the unavailability of other resources, equal delays in therapy time elsewhere, or their own preferences, many families decide that, despite the delay, they wish to consider work with us when it becomes available.

Psychotherapeutic Work   It can be seen from the foregoing that prolonged psychotherapeutic work is undertaken by mutual decision between parents and staff at a point when the family is already somewhat familiar with our personnel, with our various facilities, including the ward, and with our attitudes as to what kind of mutual endeavor may have the best chance of being helpful.

It is often not possible for all the family members, if any, to begin their therapeutic work with the same staff person or persons whom they saw in the initial phases of the contact. For the most part, initial outpatient-therapy assignments are made to staff or trainees as their time becomes available, with only minimal special consideration being given to their experience or professional discipline. As has been indicated earlier, this practice stemmed first from the fact that twelve years ago we had no other choice because our staff was very small and, for the most part, relatively inexperienced in psychotherapeutics. We found this to be not too discouraging a therapeutic experience for patients and training experience for staff. Furthermore, some of these families were able to continue in therapy and to show clinical progress, however slow, despite the frequent changes of therapists which are an inevitable consequence of this kind of therapist assignment in a training setting. In more recent years we have therefore continued this rather than to take the alternate course of seeing only that small proportion of families whom we could assign to more permanent and more experienced therapists.

None of this is meant to indicate that careful thought is not given to therapy assignments nor that every effort possible is not made to insure as much therapist continuity as our training setting will allow. Neither is it meant to say that such assignments are not a therapeutic handicap. Even with close attention to the trainees' learning about the transference problems attendant upon shifts in therapists, we do see related clinical regressions and plateaus and presumably related terminations of therapy (particularly with fathers). Perhaps further detail about "Case C—Doubtful," illustrates much of the above.

> Eleven therapists participated in the almost five years of work with this family from the time of their application, when the boy was three and one-half, until mother decided things were going so well that she wished to stop when he was eight and one-half. The father was seen for only ten interviews in the three months before his therapist, a psychiatric resident, had to leave the Institute sooner than had been planned. Father was unwilling to start again when another therapist became available. Mother was seen for two 2-year periods by child psychiatry trainees and then for nine months by a member of the permanent social work staff, for a total of one hundred ninety-four interviews. The child was seen for a total of one hundred sixty playroom sessions by: four graduate psychology students for six, three, five, and ten months each; by a trainee in child psychiatry for twenty-three months; and by two psychiatric residents for six and three months each. Although there were some plateaus in the work related to these transfers of therapists, mother and child continued and showed major and seemingly durable progress. (See also p. 437.)

There has been, of course, some opportunity to modify the above method of therapist assignment with some families. If the clinical picture in the early months indicates that crises actually disruptive to continuing work are likely to be inevitable with inexperienced or frequently shifting therapists, special effort is made to have the second assignment, if the family continues, be with a more experienced person who will stay longer. Because of the special problems of the multiple kinds of needed collaboration on the ward, inpatient children and parents are assigned only to senior staff or to two-year full-time trainees in child psychiatry. In addition, specifically for research reasons, each permanent staff member sees one or more members of at least one of these families for as long as therapy continues, whether inpatient or outpatient.

Worthy of mention is another general aspect of our work, which also

developed originally and semi-inadvertently from our historical necessities
and then from subsequent clinical experience. This is our increasing use of
one therapist with more than one member of a family, often with a whole
family. The very initial tentative explorations were made, again by necessity,
by one of the authors * with both parents of a very few children. Despite his
knowledge of the body of contrary opinion and despite his own uncertainties
about this method at that time, he discovered that it was possible for each
of two parents to enter into therapy of a conflict-reductive nature in essentially the same way as if they were seeing separate therapists. When problems of staff time later sometimes made it possible to start work with a
family only if one or another of the staff or trainees were to see two or all
members, this was tried. Although there were difficulties, particularly for
the learning therapists, it was found that the work sometimes progressed
more smoothly than when there were problems of collaboration between
several therapists who had differing degrees of experience or who had not
worked together long enough to be able fully to exchange clinical data,
especially that which involved their own participation in the therapeutic
process. In addition, some patients seem to find this plan for work particularly useful in the resolution of old rivalries and projections. This appears
to be related to the fact that the therapist listens to each family member
attentively with no need for his cross-communicating any information obtained in interviews with one of them to any other. We have become convinced not only that it can be done but also that, in a training setting, it
offers rewarding experiences to trainees and to some or most patients (18).
For these reasons we have continued to have one therapist for all family members with increasing frequency, even when staff time does not necessitate it.

Our few trials at seeing both parents in joint therapeutic interviews has
not been continued, although it does sometimes occur in the course of
therapy at points at which decisions are needed that cannot be made any
other way.

Finally, we wish to mention again the frequency of psychotherapeutic
interviews. In outpatient work each family member has usually been seen
weekly. For inpatient work, in recent years, the child has usually been seen
up to three times a week; we have, to date, been able to see most parents
only weekly. In a few instances, in both inpatient and outpatient work, we
have been able to increase these frequencies. We would do so in all instances if our time and the family's time permitted.

The Psychotherapeutic Research Method   Our psychotherapeutic method

* S. A. Szurek.

of clinical research may be described as a process with five inextricably related but identifiable aspects: (1) attentive study of the dynamics of the psychological functioning (conflicted and integrated) of the child and each of his parents; (2) use by the therapist of the understanding so gained, to respond in a manner which is ever more precisely consistent with facilitating for *each* individual member of the family the resolution of internalized conflicts with the consequent freeing of energies; (3) use by each family member of any such freed energies for more thorough learning of how, when, where, and with whom vital gratifications may be obtained non-destructively to self and others—the possible results for the family being either more mutually satisfying living together, or, occasionally, a clear decision on the part of the parents, such as to place the child or to dissolve the marriage; (4) study of all such clinical experience by the therapist and the staff (through mutual reporting, discussion, and collation of data) in order to facilitate the development of greater knowledge of and skill in psychotherapeutics; (5) the study and synthesis of such data and experience gained in individual work with each family member in the effort both to reconstruct and understand the nature of past and present interactions within each family and to determine in what ways they may be like and unlike those in other families (including both those where the child is and those where the child is not psychotic).

In the application of this psychotherapeutic method of research the therapist needs the kind of self-awareness that permits his close attentiveness to both his own internal motivations and his behavior with others, in the interests of: (1) providing the evenly hovering attentiveness which makes possible his therapeutic contributions to the conflict-reductive process for the patient; (2) achieving a degree of objectivity about the subjective that permits his effective study of intrapersonal and interpersonal processes; and (3) facilitating considerate, full exchange of clinical experience with other clinicians so that the data available for mutual, thoughtful collation and study may be as complete and as accurate as possible.

Such needed capacities for self-awareness on the part of the therapist are ones which are, of course, acquired through training. In a setting such as ours, the need for many of the therapists to acquire this training simultaneously with beginning the therapeutic work necessarily affects the work and its results.

In the part of this process that has the pre-eminent therapeutic goal of conflict-reduction, the therapist needs to hold the expectation from the very beginning that eventually the work with each family member could (and hopefully will) include prompt, full, ever more verbal expression by the patient of all that he experiences in the therapeutic situation. More specifically, this therapeutic process means for the therapist the following: (1) many hours of attentive listening and observation; (2) no interference of any kind with any behavior of the patient which is not destructive; (3) prompt, unhesitating, nonretaliatory, firm response to prevent *only* the destructive aspects of the patient's sado-masochistic behavior; (4) participation in instituting reparative behavior after any destruction which he has failed to help the patient prevent; (5) nonparticipation with the patient in any mutual sexually sensual activity; (6) consistent indication of the ordering of behavior which might afford the patient acceptable (nondestructive, hence nonguilt-producing) means of gratification; and, finally (7) tentative offering of interpretative statements regarding what may not have been expressed by the patient.

Specifically, this process means for each child and parent the opportunity first to experience, then gradually to identify with, and finally to incorporate as his own, such attitudes of the therapist as the following: (1) nonanxious acceptance of the conscious experiencing of all feelings; (2) conviction that conflictful feelings *can* be expressed in a way other than destructive; (3) assurance that such *nondestructive* expression *can* result in relief rather than in the previous schisis-intensifying cycle of guilt about destruction, fear of retaliation, further distortion of already distorted impulses, increased hopelessness about gratification, and withdrawal or further destruction; (4) expectation that conflict-free energies *can* be used to *learn* skills which may lead to the obtaining of needed satisfactions; and (5) lack of assumption that anyone necessarily will (let alone should or must) do or learn to do what another suggests, even though the other may have experience which leads him to believe that so to do would be of value to the person himself.

In those parts of our psychotherapeutic research method which have as their pre-eminent goal the increase in available data, knowledge, and skill, the therapist needs to give especial attention to the means through which he may facilitate his own and others' professional development. It is in this part of the work that a therapist who has not yet achieved even so much self-awareness or skill as have others of his colleagues may become engaged in the mutual, collaborative effort of all of them to learn more. Having become so engaged, he may be able to exercise what skill he does currently have with enough regard for what he may eventually acquire that he is able both to be of considerable therapeutic help even to severely conflicted patients and to make valuable contributions to the total undertaking of the staff.

DISCUSSION

The foregoing pages have attempted to describe the kind of clinical data from (and to indicate something of the twelve-year history of) our efforts to test the psychogenic theory of childhood schizophrenia through providing the most theoretically consistent psychotherapy possible in a training setting. It is our impression that the current progress of this work can perhaps be understood only in the light of a detailed review of the gradual evolution of our psychotherapeutic and training methods. Because, however, each of these is material enough for a chapter in itself, we have tried merely to indicate something of their nature at those points at which it was pertinent to the presentation of our material and impressions.

It is perhaps important here that we restate the hypotheses on which this work has been based. The basic hypothesis has been that the psychotic disorder is the result, in the form of conflict and its compromise solution, of the postnatal experience of each particular child early in life in interaction with significant adults who were themselves in conflict. In other words, the clinical assumption has been that psychotic disorder in childhood is the result of continuous distortion of the biological potentialities of the human organism by anxieties induced, early after birth, from anxious parents. The further hypothesis has been that such disorder resulting from conflictful living could be both studied and reversed through intensive enough psychotherapeutic work and experience of the child *and* his parents with persons free or relatively free from similar disorder in their own personalities.

It goes almost without saying that the scientific validity of such clinical research lies in the uncompromising strict adherence to the formulated hypotheses for methodological purposes, an ever self-critical attitude of the tester, and a readiness to modify the original hypotheses when (but only when) the carefully deduced facts require (17, 37). It is, of course, the very real difficulties of adhering to these scientific needs in clinical practice and of reporting clearly and accurately what has actually occurred that so frequently raise doubts about the meaningfulness of clinical research. Our endeavor to apply such an adequate test to our hypotheses has naturally required the clear identification of other working postulates concerning human behavior and therapeutics; the careful derivation from these of methods of practice; the consistent effort to apply such methods with precision; and the continuous evolution and progressive refinement of both the postulates and the methods in the light of experience. It is also obvious that the translation of any working postulate into its practical test involves the acquirement by each participant of skill in the methods by which, as well as close attention to the conditions under which, the test is being made. We would like to re-emphasize that it is our detailed experience with all these vital factors which has had to be, for the most part, greatly condensed or omitted here.

There are, however, certain implications of the above that have so frequently been misunderstood that it may be well to comment on them further. We refer here to the concurrent use of psychological and somatic methods and agents in the study and therapy of these disorders. There is nothing in our hypotheses that precludes the utilization of any somatic means of exploration available for the identification of diagnosable somatic disease or defect. It is, in fact, our practice to pay close attention to the gathering of all possible information about each child's physical development and medical history and to pursue all indicated lines of investigation of the child's physical status within the scope of the present medical knowledge, skill, and facilities available to us and to our consultants from all the medical specialties. The situation is different, however, once it has been determined to the satisfaction of all concerned that no diagnosis can currently be made of known disease or defect. From that point on in our work with a child and family, it has seemed imperative for our endeavor that—unless subsequent signs of somatic disease arise—our clinical efforts be as precisely as possible theoretically consistent with our hypotheses of psychogenic etiology and of psychotherapeutic reversibility. Where these conditions prevailed, we have therefore confined our use of somatic therapies of any kind to those which were clearly indicated for intercurrent disease or injury.

None of this is meant to deny or ignore the exciting possibilities that have been raised by the progress of somatic studies and therapies in recent years. Should the biochemists, pharmacologists, endocrinologists, or others in our field find the curative drug or somatic procedure, no one could be more convinced of its advantages than those of us who know from long personal experience how arduous and often discouraging is the psychotherapeutic endeavor. We do feel, however, that, while we are awaiting such discovery, it is important to pursue our own line of study in as thorough a manner as possible. Regardless of the nature of the eventual findings by any method, it is only then that either the psychogenic etiology or the psychogenic factors can be elucidated with the greatest possible clarity.

It is furthermore a fact that our experience to date has increased rather than diminished our belief that a more definitive understanding of the etiology of childhood schizophrenia is evolving from psychotherapeutic studies with families. This attitude has come about primarily from observations of our own of the kind we have already reported, and also from our recognition of the similarity of the observations being reported with increasing frequency by others. Although various workers have formulated their experiences within somewhat different frameworks, this essential similarity of clinical data seems to us to be present even in the reports of some workers whose psychotherapeutic study of families has been primarily concerned with schizophrenic reactions in adults (38–43).

It is likewise not discouraging to us that after only twelve years we do not have definitive data to confirm our hypothesis of the reversibility of the schizophrenic disorder in children. In other words we are fully cognizant of how long it has necessarily taken to develop even those methods of work we now have. We know how long it has taken us to acquire that degree of skill that we have, as well as what is required in the way of time and supervision for the development of skill by each new staff participant. In addition, we have only recently had the time and staff available to begin the necessary careful review and more statistical study of the clinical data that we have accumulated.

Therefore, what information we do have in the direction of "results" is, if anything, encouraging. Briefly we can say that of the one hundred preadolescent schizophrenic children we have seen, twenty have shown major improvement in the course of therapeutic work. By this we mean they have become able to function with some fair degree of integrated behavior in their homes, in the community, and in public schools for periods of at least several years. Three of these have had subsequent major difficulties: two in adjusting to the transfer from grammar school; one in maintaining adequate unsupervised care of herself and her two children when her soldier husband proved, following discharge from the service, to be irresponsible in his behavior. An additional thirty-four of the hundred showed seemingly durable improvement in major areas of symptomatology although they were still unable to function without special supervision. These include such children as those who ceased mutilating themselves, began to talk after having been mute, became able to laugh and weep for the first time, or became able to allow themselves to learn in school or to play. An unknown number of these were transferred by their parents to state hospital programs after their age and size prevented their remaining on our children's ward or after the family's situation or wishes precluded further therapeutic work with us. Of the twenty-one children seen for study only, three showed some degree of immediate symptomatic improvement of unknown duration. The other twenty-three children who were seen in therapy for varying periods of time did not, or have not, shown any degree of consistent improvement.

With most of these, however, the therapist or parents reported transient moments or periods of understandable shifts in behavior such as those we have come to view as the precursors of more lasting change. Of the total hundred, approximately thirty are still being seen in therapy with us.

Whether or not such "therapeutic outcomes" prove with further study, time, and experience to have warranted any encouragement remains, of course, to be seen. It is, however, the *total* body of clinical data already described in this chapter—including that from families where therapeutic work was not undertaken—which needs brief summary and further comment at this point.

All too briefly we may summarize these data as follows: (1) Regardless of the age of onset, the symptomatology of the children has been, in most instances, indistinguishable. (2) Where the onset was episodic, there was evidence of prior disturbance which was indistinguishable from neurosis. (3) When we could learn enough about a child and his history, each of his specific symptoms became understandable as condensations or displacements of conflict as elaborations of particular experiences of that child with some meaningful adult. (4) Few, if any, of the children we considered to be schizophrenic showed somatic manifestations (developmental lags, etc.; see pages 401–403) which seemed to be wholly determined by physiological or genetic factors. (5) When the child's psychotic symptomatology did show gradual recession, the disorder merged into a moderate to severe psychoneurotic condition. (6) Consistently present have been clinical data which indicated that the onset and any exacerbations of the child's disorder occurred in the context of identifiable events or circumstances which constituted a critical strain for the parents. (7) These stresses have usually consisted of a combination of "external" events more or less beyond the family's control and of "internal" difficulties which were primarily an outgrowth of each parent's own conflicts. (8) In each instance where the parents have undertaken any durable period of psychotherapeutic work for themselves with us, these internal conflicts have clearly been the expression of lifelong neurotic disorders of their own and not merely the reaction to the illness of their child. It is these facts of our experience with all cases, rather than any therapeutic results, which seem to lend weight to the possibility that psychogenic factors are at least important.

We have then no doubt that in our psychotherapeutic work with the families of schizophrenic children we have found consistently present the same kinds of experiential factors which have come to be considered etiologically related to the development of disorder in neurotic (and impulsive) children. We cannot say that we have found any particular kind of traumatic event, any particular kind of parental neurosis, or any particular kind of parent-child interaction which is *unique* in the families of psychotic children. We doubt then that any of these individual factors we can now *list* can in itself answer the remaining question of why schizophrenia rather than neurosis. It may well be asked if this is not evidence that something inherent in the particular child from birth determined the schizophrenic reaction to the stressful experiences. This latter possibility remains, of course, but it seems to us more likely that such remaining questions may be answered by refinement of the methodology for describing and conceptualizing the findings of the psychotherapeutic test.

As we have mentioned earlier, it seems to us that part of the dilemma in considering the psychogenic theory alone may lie in the need to conceptualize as a unitary process some combination of factors interacting both simultaneously and sequentially. Perhaps the methodological difficulties involved, first, in such conceptualization and, also, in recording and reporting such simultaneity have impeded the thinking about this disorder. It is perhaps to be remembered that when this study was conceived more than fifteen years ago, the same type of question as to the etiological significance of the intrafamilial climate in neurotic and impulsive disorders remained more widespread than it does today. The subsequent confirmation by many workers of the presence of pathological familial factors identifiably related to the child's symptoms has led most of us to feel that their effect is understandable in terms of timing, intensity, and duration. It would seem similarly probable to us that the answers to some of the remaining questions as to "what kind" of stress leads to schizophrenia may come from learning to understand the interrelatedness of "when, how much, and for how long."

Here, too, it seems to us that some of our own experience leaves these questions not quite the mystery they once were. The nature of the stress appears to lie in the anxiety of the parental persons about basic sensual impulses. The timing is in the earliest months and years of life, the period of greatest developmental vulnerability. The duration is more or less constant. The intensity is greatest at periods that coincide closely with the onset and exacerbations of the child's severest symptoms and that almost always follow periods of identifiable increased strain for one or both parents and between them. It is our strong impression that the pathologic moments for the child are ones in which the executive function of the parent has been strained to or near the breaking point. Our therapeutic work with parents has convinced us that these moments have been more intense and more frequent in the early experience of the schizophrenic than of the neurotic children we have seen. It would seem to us that the truly most characteristic data we have found in each family is the longitudinal pattern of total experience which each schizophrenic child has had living in interaction with the complex synthesis of all of these factors, each of which has been in a constant state of mutual modification by and with the others.

It is within this framework that the psychogenic theory seems to us to be consistent with our clinical observations, not only of these children's life histories but also of the nature of their disorder. By this we refer to our earlier discussion of our present conception of the psychopathology of the psychotic and the severely schizoid disorders of childhood. In these children there is an extremely tenacious, generalized motivational conflict. One aspect of this conflict is a severe restriction and distortion of "ego" development or executive capacity. That is, there is not merely failure but also negativistically anxious refusal to learn many skills—refusal which perpetuates the helplessness, the so-called "dependence" or tenuous "ego strength." Another aspect of the conflict is repression of and consequent severe sadomasochistic transformation of sensual impulses of many modalities and zones. The repression is so severe and generalized in many patients that the return of the repressed, a breakthrough into overt action of such distorted impulses, is often a great and an actual danger. This danger is increased paradoxically when "toward" impulses are stimulated or intensified by opportunities for prolonged and intimate contact with another person—as in the therapeutic situation. Among the "toward" impulses we would include those impulses which are expressive of an urge to learn to do things for oneself, to think things out for oneself—particularly in the presence of another (44). It is in this context that we concur in the relevance of concepts and expressions such as: "circular pathologic conflicts"; "the double bind" (41); the loss of "ego-boundaries"; and the endless complications of dilemmas of "independence-isolation" and "dependence-enslavement." Also in this context we have come to understand the general aloofness, withdrawal, and negativistic attitude of these children as an essential defense against the very real dangers of eruptions of distorted wishes for basic sensual satisfactions. We have come to view all of this as being more completely and accurately describable in terms of the degree of integration or schisis within the *total* personality (45). In other words, however relevant and necessary it may be to describe "aspects" of the external manifestations of the psychopathology, we feel that the disorder within the child is unitary in nature.

Many of the parents who have continued in therapeutic work with us for fairly prolonged periods have expressed their own conviction of the correctness of our assumptions. This has been equally true whether the sick child did and did not show major improvement. Many have sharply contrasted their available capacity to be truly "mothering" with the infant who became psychotic as with their babies who developed more normally, particularly those born late in the course of therapeutic work. One mother commented before she placed her adolescent son in a state hospital that her own internal experience and her current, more satisfying and integrated behavior with her younger boy left her no doubt but that our hypotheses were correct. It was only that their work with us, begun when the boy was nine, had been "too little" of what was needed "too late" to effect sufficient resolution of the distressing emotional entanglement between her and the older child.

"Too little, too late" has indeed seemed to us to be our own greatest dissatisfaction with our work to date. Training and mutual learning still continue as a progressive refinement of technical therapeutic procedures, and we all wish we were more skilled. It is only in recent years that schizophrenic children have been referred to us with any frequency while still at preschool age. We have been able to offer very few parents or outpatient children visits at more than weekly frequency. It is also only as our core staff has gradually increased in number that the same therapists have been able to continue work for periods of more than a year or two with a few children and parents. Increasing attention to all of these factors together with the development of better methods of review and collation of data are considered to be important to the future progress of our work. The experience has, however, been thorough enough and satisfying enough in some instances to convince us of the value of continuing our clinical test of the same basic hypotheses with which we started.

APPENDIX

The clinical histories of the approximately 200 psychotic or severely schizoid children we have seen have shown two somewhat differentiated patterns as to the onset of the disorder, episodic or continuous.

Among the approximately 100 preadolescent children whom we considered to be clearly schizophrenic, one-fourth showed the episodic pattern of onset of disorder. The onset of psychotic symptomatology was abrupt after a period of relatively normal maturation, although in most instances there was evidence of some degree of pre-existing neurotic personality maldevelopment. The onset was usually between the ages of 3 and 5 years, but ranged from 18 months to 11 years. In all instances the onset occurred in the chronological context of heightened internal and, usually, external stress for one and usually both parents. We know of no instances of spontaneous remission of the symptomatology, although in a few the disorder lessened markedly following relatively brief therapeutic contact with the family. The duration of the psychotic period ranged from a few weeks or months to an as yet unknown number of years. Where there was gradual recession of the psychotic symptoms, the disorder then merged into a moderate to severe psychoneurotic condition. (See Case A—Episodic Psychosis.)

Similar, of course, as to history of onset are those children who developed psychotic manifestations during early adolescence. That we have seen only about 20 such cases reflects the fact that the Children's Service does not undertake hospitalization of any child already over 12, and many of the patients potentially in this group are referred elsewhere since the initial application is often for inpatient treatment.

In about three-fourths of the 100 preadolescent schizophrenic children, continuous maldevelopment was evident from the first or second year of life. Although in most instances symptomatically indistinguishable from the episodic group, it is this group of about 75 children that we consider to be the "core" group of our research sample. In these the disorder developed insidiously and was chronic and continuous for periods measurable in years. In all instances in which therapeutic work was undertaken, it has seemed to us that clear evidence became available that the disorder developed in the context of a family environment influenced by severe internalized conflict of, usually, both parents. Such conflict had either been fairly constant in degree for most of their lives or, more usually, had been heightened in response to some external stress either prior to or during the early months of the child's life. As in the former episodic group, when the psychotic symptomatology did show gradual recession, the child's disorder merged into a moderate to severe psychoneurotic condition. (See Case B—Continuous Psychosis.)

The 30 severely schizoid children were in most instances similar to this latter "core" or continuous group as to history of onset. Ten have been borderline between psychosis and severe personality disorder of an aggressive or impulsive nature in that there were behavior characteristics of both simultaneously or alternately present. The disorder in 20 was such that it seemed to be in a borderline area where it was difficult or impossible to apply either the term psychosis or neurosis for any length of time since characteristics of both were present.

The remaining 50 children of the total 200 sample are those whose disorder appeared to be classifiable as psychotic or schizoid but in whom there was also known organic disease or defect or strong suggestive evidence thereof. Our "doubtful" group is comprised of more than 20 of these who closely resemble the continuous "core" group both as to history of onset and symptomatology. In these the psychotic symptomatology had been so pervasive at every level of functioning from early months of life that it has proved impossible to date, even in those who are still being seen, to rule either in or out some fairly severe degree of mental deficiency. A few of the present "core" group were in this category of doubtful prior to improvement which permitted determination of at least average intelligence. (See Case C—Doubtful.) It is perhaps of interest that in several of these the first clue to the eventual diagnosis was obtained from our evaluation of the degree of psychopathology in the parents. It is anticipated that with further therapy it will become clear that some of this present group also belong in the "core" group. On the other hand, a few children once in this group proved, on recession of their psychotic symptomatology, to be actually mentally defective. They are now considered to have had "mixed" diagnoses.

Our total group of some 25 children with mixed diagnoses shows both acute and chronic onset of psychotic-like symptoms. In addition to this aspect of the clinical pictures, there has also been diagnosable mental deficiency, central nervous system disease or severe sensory handicap such as blindness. It is our current impression that, whereas the deficiency or disease may be a major contributing stress, the psychosis is probably not an organically inevitable concomitant but rather a genetically separate entity not to be differentiated from psychosis in a child who has no definable "disease."

Although the following brief case examples are no substitute for detailed case histories, they may serve to illustrate somewhat more graphically than the foregoing, the differences we have described as to the clinical histories as well as to indicate the similarities of symptomatology from one group to another.

Case A—Episodic Psychosis   Within one week, a girl of 4½, whose development had seemed normal to her parents, became mute and enuretic and often sat immobilized in one position for long periods. Within a few months more she developed night terrors, lost weight, and showed sudden outbursts of violent destructive behavior, attacking her mother and once throwing her kitten into a burning fire. These symptoms persisted for over a year with only short partial recessions when she was twice hospitalized briefly for somatic illness. In the 16 months prior to this acute onset of symptoms she had been gradually becoming less active and spontaneous.

Her acute symptoms developed in the chronological context of the following family stresses: (1) her father's emergency surgery one year prior for a strangulated hernia, followed by a prolonged period of convalescence; (2) her beloved 86-year-old paternal grandmother's becoming ill and leaving the household for a convalescent home a few months before; (3) the rapid increase, during the preceding year or two, of the secretly guarded sexual conflicts, suicidal preoccupation, and homicidal impulses toward this youngest of two daughters on the part of the mother, who was better educated than and 16 years junior to her husband. The father's anxious and prolonged convalescence from surgery seemed related to his childhood experience of being hospitalized in a cast for 4 years with tuberculosis of the hip, as well as to his own mother's increasing infirmities. The mother's increasing anxieties and preoccupations seemed related to her own mother's 9-year hospitalization for post-alcoholic mental disorder.

The girl's symptoms started to subside after a brief study here, followed by a period in which her mother began to discuss *her own* problems with a minister, a pediatrician, and (by correspondence) the psychiatrist. This was before plans could be worked out for direct outpatient psychotherapy with the child and both parents. Within a year after therapy started, the girl appeared more neurotic than psychotic and was able to function with special help in public school. During the last 4 of the 5 still continuing years of psychotherapy, most of her phobias and compulsions have gradually disappeared. She has become able to do well scholastically and socially in her correct age group in school.

The mother's fear that she herself might do something violent has been resolved as her near-psychotic preoccupations, although still present, have become more centered in the transference relationship with her therapist. Still concerned, both neurotically and realistically, about her husband's age, health, and earning capacity, she has taken correspondence courses which would help her get a teaching credential should she later need or want to.

Father first discontinued therapy after 2 years under circumstances (including serious accident-proneness during his therapist's vacations) that seemed indicative of unresolved transference problems. He resumed therapy a year later when his elder, always-shy, 13-year-old daughter (whom we also began to see at that time) began to have tantrums and perform poorly in school. During the work he became less apprehensive and somewhat more assured. More self-assertive, although still anxiously and ambivalently so, he began to express resentment about the real problem of time and money involved in their long trips to the Institute. The smoldering conflict between the parents became more open and direct and found a focus in disagreement about the degree of their need for therapy. At a time of change of therapists 6 months ago, father angrily decided not to continue. Although mother and both girls continue, the possible alternatives about further work are not yet resolved. If father does not resume visits soon, mother may decide that the older girl or all of them should discontinue, at least for a time.

Although the parents' conflicts still often center around the daughters, particularly the adolescent who is father's favorite, their disagreements are more overt and seem to affect the children's behavior less than formerly. Both parents seem even freer and less ambivalent about a third child, a 4½-year-old son who was conceived after the family's initial contacts with us. This boy has shown no obviously disturbed behavior to the present.

Case B—Continuous Psychosis   One boy, seen by us first at age 6, had worried his educated, successful parents since age 2½ because he did not speak. As an infant they had considered him "model" because he did not fuss although left alone a good deal, even to the extent of mother's propping his bottle for "efficient" nursing. He had been diagnosed as aphasic at 5 when 2 years of speech-therapy exercises had not helped. Although sure-footed to the point of dangerous daring and, like his father, unusual in mechanical skills, he had been slow in early motor development and difficult in toilet training (holding feces as well as soiling). He had not learned to dress himself. He alternately ignored and made whining demands on his parents. Between 5 and 6 he had developed severe temper tantrums and vicious cruelty to his pets. He was put out of a special school because he couldn't learn and didn't play with others. He insisted on bathing each time he was made to use the toilet. When admitted to our Children's Ward he was a silent, handsome, poker-faced 6-year-old, who often screamed loudly but tonelessly. He refused all psychological tests except performance items, on which he scored in the superior range. In the subsequent 4 years of psychotherapy (1 inpatient and 3 outpatient) he became a bright, responsive youngster, who sometimes chattered animatedly with his parents and who spoke appropriately with everyone but his therapist, with whom he remained mute.

During the parents' early therapy, we slowly learned how inaccurate had been their first insistence that they had no troubles but the son. His elder sister was shy and fearful, and his younger sister suffered from enuresis, stuttering, and severe thumb-sucking. The father, a self-driving son of an ambitious mother, was a success in a service career and also in several hobbies and extra money-making ventures. His assignments to overseas posts had necessitated several family moves and one lengthy separation prior to and during most of his son's first 4 years of life. Even when home he had often worked long hours 7 days a week. Despite his successes, he actually felt very unsure of his capabilities. He disliked and ignored all children who were not old enough to *talk*. The mother, a pretty, unusually youthful-appearing woman, felt little closeness to her own "helpless" mother (whom she looked like) and had been "dominated" all her life by her stern father (whom her son looked like). She felt disfigured when pregnant, was repulsed by the thought of breast feeding or cuddling her babies, and felt fearful of and seldom talked to the children as infants. During a visit with her parents prior to her son's birth, she and they had been shocked at the expression of unexpectedly violent feelings by one of her sisters. When the sister's outburst culminated in an overt psychotic episode, her already pervasive fear of how dangerous it was to express strong feelings of any kind had been strengthened. In therapy, this fear was first expressed around her anger at her therapist's expectation that she come for interviews until close to term with her fourth pregnancy. As this was resolved, she also expressed her smoldering rage about her husband's long hours and her son's silences and demands. To her surprise, she became both firmer and more loving with her children. As the work continued, father felt more confident and worked fewer hours away from home. Both parents began to talk with each other, became more responsive to their first 3 children, and thoroughly enjoyed the 2 more babies born during the course of therapy (one of whom was also a boy).

At the time therapy was terminated by the father's transfer to another area, the boy still had trouble playing with peers, had some compulsive behavior, and continued to have learning difficulty. When we last heard from them 4 years later, his improvement had continued during a period of therapy in the new city. He was progressing better in school with near age peers and had learned to enjoy more spontaneous play.

Case C—Doubtful Group   A 3½-year-old boy was referred to us after 6 months of study at a child-guidance nursery school because they were unable to determine whether he was a disturbed mentally defective child or a psychotic. He had been moderately slow in all motor development and toilet training, had said single words sporadically since 2, seemed not to comprehend most of what was said to him, and was tearfully fearful of all strange people and experiences as well as of getting dirty. He had rocked and banged his head from 6 or 9 months, sucked his thumb excessively, and had occasional tantrums in which he bit and scratched. He never chewed, eating only pureed or ground foods. He smelled and listened to objects, but rarely mouthed them. He danced excitedly to rhythmic music. Weaned from the bottle at 1½, he refused milk from a cup. While fascinated with a baby bottle in play, he never got it completely to his lips. In no activity or test did he reveal evidence of having capabilities beyond a 21-month level.

The mother, 21 when this child was born, was 19 years her husband's junior. Her baby had been largely cared for in his first 3 months by her own disliked stepmother, who insisted mother was not capable. Mother's fear and hatred of her stepmother stemmed from the age of 12. Her own mother had been nursed in terminal illness by this woman, who became her stepmother shortly thereafter. Our patient's mother felt very strongly that this stepmother had caused an estrangement between her and her father and had later tried to prevent her marriage. Mother had had dirt phobias and hand-washing compulsions since childhood.

Father was a shy, obese man who had had frequent attacks of chest pain since his mother's death from coronary thrombosis when his son was 1½. Although father felt he was greatly helped in therapy, he refused to start again after his first therapist left. Mother and son continued in weekly outpatient therapy for 5 years.

For the first year or two we were uncertain as to whether this boy was mentally defective or not because of the absolute absence of signs of capacity at his age level. It gradually became apparent that he was displaying a consistent, determined helplessness. As he became more responsive, he gave more overt evidence of the negativism which was operating. His degree of participation in the playroom dispelled his therapist's doubts about his intelligence. His I.Q., as measurable in the testing situation, lagged behind the clinical impression but proceeded from 48 at 3¾ years through 63 at 4½ and 80 at 5, to 91 at 7½. The last examiner had no doubt that the boy had at least average intellectual capacity when mother decided they were getting along well enough to discontinue therapy when he was 8½.

References

1. ADELAIDE M. JOHNSON, E. I. FALSTEIN, S. A. SZUREK, and MARGARET SVENDSEN, School phobia, *Am. J. Orthopsychiat.*, *11*: 702, 1941.

2. S. A. SZUREK, ADELAIDE M. JOHNSON, and E. I. FALSTEIN, Collaborative psychiatric therapy of parent-child problems, *Am. J. Orthopsychiat.*, *12*: 511, 1942.

3. S. A. SZUREK, Notes on the genesis of psychopathic personality trends, *Psychiatry*, *5*: 1, 1942.

4. S. A. SZUREK, Child therapy procedures, *Psychiatry*, *7*: 9, 1944.

5. ADELAIDE M. JOHNSON and S. A. SZUREK, The genesis of antisocial acting out in children and adults, *Psychoanalyt. Quart.*, *21*: 323, 1952.

6. ADELAIDE M. JOHNSON and S. A. SZUREK, Etiology of antisocial behavior in delinquents and psychopaths, *J.A.M.A.*, *154*: 814, 1954.

7. S. A. SZUREK, Childhood schizophrenia: psychotic episodes and psychotic maldevelopment, *Am. J. Orthopsychiat.*, *26*: 519, 1956.

8. H. S. SULLIVAN, The modified psychoanalytic treatment of schizophrenia, *Am. J. Psychiat.*, *10* (o.s. 88): 519, 1931.

9. H. S. SULLIVAN, Therapeutic investigations in schizophrenia, *Psychiatry*, *10*: 121, 1947.

10. A. A. BRILL, Psychotic children: treatment and prophylaxis, *Am. J. Psychiat.*, *82*: 357, 1926.

11. H. W. POTTER, Schizophrenia in children, *Am. J. Psychiat.*, *12*: 1253, 1933.

12. J. LOUISE DESPERT, Schizophrenia in children, *Psychiatric Quart.*, *12*: 366, 1938.

13. ELISABETH R. GELEERD, "A Contribution to the Problem of Psychoses in Childhood," in *The Psychoanalytic Study of the Child*, Vol. II, New York: Internat. Univ. Press, 1946.

14. J. N. ROSEN, The treatment of schizophrenic psychosis by direct analytic therapy, *Psychiatric Quart.*, *21*: 3, 1947.

15. FRIEDA FROMM-REICHMANN, Notes on the development of treatment of schizophrenics by psychoanalytic therapy, *Psychiatry*, *11*: 263, 1948.

16. S. A. SZUREK, Dynamics of staff interaction in hospital psychiatric treatment of children, *Am. J. Orthopsychiat.*, *17*: 652, 1947.

17. S. A. SZUREK, The family and the staff in hospital psychiatric therapy of children, *Am. J. Orthopsychiat.*, *21*: 597, 1951.

18.   S. A. SZUREK, Some lessons from efforts at psychotherapy with parents, *Am. J. Psychiat., 109*: 296, 1952.

19.   S. A. SZUREK and I. N. BERLIN, Elements of psychotherapeutics with the schizophrenic child and his parents, *Psychiatry, 19*: 1, 1956.

20.   J. F. ROBINSON *et al., Psychiatric Inpatient Treatment of Children,* Washington: Am. Psychiatric Assoc., 1957.

21.   C. BRADLEY, *Schizophrenia in Children,* New York: Macmillan, 1941.

22.   LAURETTA BENDER, Childhood schizophrenia, *Nerv. Child, 1*: 138, 1942.

23.   L. KANNER, Early infantile autism, *J. Pediat., 25*: 211, 1944.

24.   MARIAN C. PUTNAM *et al.,* Case study of an atypical two-and-a-half-year-old, round table, *Am. J. Orthopsychiat., 18*: 1, 1948.

25.   MARGARET S. MAHLER, J. R. ROSS, JR., and ZIRA DE FRIES, Clinical studies in benign and malignant cases of childhood psychoses (Schizophrenia-like), *Am. J. Orthopsychiat., 19*: 295, 1949.

26.   BEATA RANK and DOROTHY MACNAUGHTON, "A Clinical Contribution to Early Ego Development," in *The Psychoanalytic Study of the Child,* Vol. V, New York: Internat. Univ. Press, 1950.

27.   E. R. CLARDY, A study of the development and course of schizophrenia in children, *Psychiatric Quart., 25*: 81, 1951.

28.   W. J. HENDRICKSON, Etiology in childhood schizophrenia: an evaluation of current views (see especially "References"), *Nerv. Child, 10,* 1952.

29.   R. L. JENKINS, The schizophrenic sequence: withdrawal, disorganization, psychotic reorganization, *Am. J. Orthopsychiat., 22*: 738, 1952.

30.   A. FABIAN, Some familial considerations in childhood schizophrenia, round table on childhood schizophrenia, *Am. J. Orthopsychiat., 24*: 484, 1954.

31.   S. W. FRIEDMAN, Diagnostic criteria in childhood schizophrenia, *Bull. Menninger Clin., 18*: 41, 1954.

32.   H. H. HERSKOVITZ, Chairman, Childhood schizophrenia, round table, 1953, *Am. J. Orthopsychiat., 24*: 484, 1954.

33.   J. C. HIRSCHBERG and K. N. BRYANT, Problems in the differential diagnosis of childhood schizophrenia, *A. Res. Nerv. & Ment. Dis., Proc., 34*: 454, 1954.

34.   L. EISENBERG, The course of childhood schizophrenia, *A.M.A. Arch. Neurol. & Psychiat., 78*: July, 1957.

35.   I. N. BERLIN and C. L. YEAGER, Correlation of epileptic seizures, electroencephalograms and emotional state: some preliminary observations in several children, *Am. J. Dis. Child., 81*: 664, 1951.

36.   S. A. SZUREK, Remarks on training for psychotherapy, *Am. J. Orthopsychiat., 19*: 36, 1949.

37.   H. MORGENAU, Ethical science, *Scient. Month., 69*: 290, 1949.

38.   TRUDE TIETZE, A study of mothers of schizophrenic patients, *Psychiatry, 12*: 55, 1949.

39.   P. G. S. BECKETT, D. B. ROBINSON, S. H. FRAZIER, R. M. STEINHILBER, G. M. DUNCAN, H. R. ESTES, E. M. LITIN, R. T. GRATTAN, W. L. LORTON, G. E. WILLIAMS, and ADELAIDE M. JOHNSON, Studies in schizophrenia at the Mayo Clinic, I. the significance of exogenous traumata in the genesis of schizophrenia, *Psychiatry, 19*: 137, 1956.

40.   ADELAIDE M. JOHNSON, MARY E. GRIFFIN, JANE WATSON, and P. G. S. BECKETT,

Studies in schizophrenia at the Mayo Clinic, II. observations on ego functions in schizophrenia, *Psychiatry, 19*: 143, 1956.

41.   G. BATESON, D. D. JACKSON, J. HALEY, and J. H. WEAKLAND, Toward a theory of schizophrenia, *Behavioral Sci., 1*: 251, 1956.

42.   R. W. LIDZ and T. LIDZ, The family environment of schizophrenic patients, *Am. J. Psychiat., 106*: 332, 1949 (and subsequent writings).

43.   R. EKSTEIN, K. BRYANT, and S. W. FRIEDMAN, Childhood schizophrenia and allied conditions, a review of the literature. Privately mimeographed, 532 titles, 1946–1956.

44.   S. A. SZUREK, *The Roots of Psychoanalysis and Psychotherapy, A Search for Principles of General Psychotherapeutics*, Springfield, Ill.: Thomas, 1958 (esp. part one, chap. 2).

45.   S. A. SZUREK, Playfulness, creativity, and schisis, *Am. J. Orthopsychiat, 29* (4): 667–682, 1959.

Name Index

Abood, L. G., 91–112, 130
Ackerman, N., 351
Adler, Alfred, 71, 74
Agarwa, P. S., 136
Akerfeldt, S., 32, 130
Alanen, Y. O., 48, 50, 55
Allen, G., 81
Alstroem, C. H., 51
Altschule, M. D., 153
Alzheimer, A., 4, 121
Amin, A. H., 134
Anderson, J. K., 197
Arieti, S., 251, 261, 264, 280
Atkinson, R. L., 230–231, 262
Axelrod, J., 128
Azima, H., 270

Babcock, H., 200
Bailey, P., 92
Baldwin, A. L., 238
Bales, A., 337
Banerjee, S., 136
Barcroft, J., 177
Bard, P., 159
Barron, F., 216
Barry, H., Jr., 55
Bateson, G., 262, 305, 307–308, 358 n., 362, 373 n.
Bayley, N., 365
Beach, A., 275
Becker, W. C., 215, 221
Bell, R. Q., 235, 238, 365 n.
Benda, C. E., 61
Bender, L., 9
Benedek, T., 348 n.
Bercel, N. A., 159–174
Berlyne, D., 252
Bevan, L. W., 192
Bexton, W., 252, 268
Biedl, L. M., 46
Biel, J. H., 103
Binder, A., 203–204, 258
Birren, J. E., 45
Black, J., 237, 258
Bleke, R., 229

Bleuler, M., 6, 15, 28, 37, 42, 45, 48, 50–51, 71, 121, 147–148
Bliss, E. L., 5, 74
Blum, R., 266
Boatman, M. J., 389–448
Boller, M. M., 193
Böök, J. A., 23–33, 37, 41, 43, 55, 137
Boring, E. G., 192
Boszormenyi-Nagy, I., 93
Bowen, M., 38, 56, 305–307, 311, 346–371, 382
Brackbill, G. A., 216
Bracken, H. von, 64
Breese, F. H., 238
Brill, A. A., 69
Brim, O., 258
Brodie, B. B., 102
Bryan, J., 265
Burlingham, D., 66, 68
Buscaino, V. M., 110
Buss, A. H., 229
Byrne, D., 264

Cade, J. F., 37
Callaway, E., 214
Cameron, N., 173, 224, 275–276, 280
Caplan, G., 357 n.
Carstairs, G. M., 26
Cavanaugh, D. K., 223
Chapman, L. J., 224–225, 280–281
Charcot, J. M., 5
Chuang-Tze, 272
Clausen, J. A., 207–208, 237, 295–318
Cleghorn, R. A., 5
Clemes, S., 257
Cofer, C. N., 199
Cohen, B. D., 205, 216, 223, 230, 283
Cornelison, A., 323 n.
Craike, W. H., 40, 75, 77
Cramer-Azima, F., 270
Crammer, J. L., 173
Crawford, B. B., 134
Cronin, H. J., 68, 74
Crookes, K. R. L., 227, 228

441

Davids, A., 236
Davis, R. H., 222
DeBruyn, J. W., 192
Degan, J. W., 194
Dember, W., 270
Deutsch, H., 68–69
Diabler, H. L., 74
Diamond, M. D., 212
Dobson, W. R., 219
Dollard, J., 241
Domarus, E. von, 280
Dunham, H. W., 296–297
Dunn, W. L., Jr., 218
Dysinger, R. H., 359

Earl, R., 270
Eaton, J. W., 49
Eccles, J. C., 106
Edison, C. B., 131
Eisenberg, L., 306
Elkes, J., 137
Elsässer, G., 46, 53, 57
Epstein, S., 224–225
Essen-Möller, E., 40–41, 43, 59, 62, 65, 75

Fabing, H., 100
Fairbairn, W. R., 6
Faris, R. E. L., 296–297
Federn, P., 6
Feldberg, W. S., 103
Fenichel, O., 68, 251, 269
Festinger, L., 254–255, 259, 276
Fine, H. J., 216
Fisher, S., 56
Fitzherbert, J., 205
Flataher, L., 131
Flavell, J. H., 223
Fleck, S., 323–342
Frazee, H. E., 45
Freeman, R. V., 235
Freud, Sigmund, 6, 250, 359
Friedman, H., 215
Fromm-Reichmann, F., 6
Fry, W. F., 373 n., 384
Funk, R., 258
Funkenstein, D. H., 226
Fuster, J., 268

Gaddum, J. H., 100, 134, 137
Galton, F., 40, 80
Gantt, W. H., 232
Gardner, E. J., 74
Garfield, S. L., 203
Garmezy, N., 217–218, 228–229, 237, 241, 262

Gatewood, L. C., 172
Gedda, L., 40, 60
Geiger, R., 102
Gerard, D. L., 236
Gerard, R. W., 91, 107
Gerty, F. J., 91, 93, 125
Gillespie, R. D., 49
Gjessing, R., 5, 17, 126
Goldfarb, W., 266
Goldstein, H., 121, 193, 220–221, 250, 281
Gordon, G. S., 125
Gorham, D. R., 221
Gralnick, A., 55, 68–69
Grayson, H. M., 235, 251
Greenblatt, N., 281
Griffith, R., 267
Grisell, J. L., 207
Guertin, W. H., 194, 202
Gullock, A. H., 122

Hahn, I. N., 211
Haley, J., 262, 373 n.
Hall, F., 176
Hall, K. R., 227–228
Hamister, R. C., 248 n.
Hanhart, E., 47, 56
Hardwick, S. W., 5
Hare, E. H., 26
Harlow, H., 252
Harper, A. E., 194, 199, 202–203
Harris, C. W., 214
Harris, J. G., 218
Harris, M. M., 125
Hausmann, M. F., 193
Heath, D. H., 226
Heath, R. G., 32, 95, 128–130, 146–154
Hebb, D., 252, 257, 263, 268
Henderson, D., 49
Herbart, J., 254
Heron, W., 252, 268
Heuyer, G., 74
Hilgard, J., 50 n.
Hill, L., 56, 305, 307, 316, 348 n., 352
Hillson, J. S., 220
Hirst, H. L., 225
Hoagland, H., 40
Hoch, P., 10, 17, 43
Hoff, D., 258
Hoffer, A., 128
Hoffman, A., 97–98
Hoffman, J., 252
Holland, B., 5, 128
Hollingshead, A. B., 56
Holmberg, C. G., 96, 128–129

Horwitt, M. K., 121–122, 125
Hoskins, R. G., 11
Howe, E. S., 232–233
Hull, C. L., 192
Hunt, D., 259
Hunt, J. McV., 193, 199
Huston, P. E., 28, 205, 207, 209, 216, 223, 227–228, 283
Hyman, M., 280–281

Ingalls, T. H., 176–177

Jackson, D. D., 3–19, 37–81, 137, 237, 262, 305–306, 312, 352, 358, 362, 373 n.
James, William, 252, 272
Jenkins, R. J., 194
Jenkins, R. L., 248 n., 274–275
Johansen, E., 45, 48–51
Johnson, A., 80, 390
Johnson, L., 278
Jones, A., 217
Jung, Carl, 160, 192

Kaila, M., 27
Kalhorn, J., 238
Kallmann, F. J., 28, 37–38, 40–42, 44, 46, 49–52, 55, 58–59, 61, 64–65, 68, 70–71, 73, 75, 77–78, 150, 308
Kanner, L., 37, 42, 48, 266, 306
Kantor, R. E., 215–216, 235–236
Kardiner, A., 313
Kasanin, J., 71
Keller, D., 269
Kelly, G., 254, 259–260, 280
Kelsey, F. E., 122
Kelsey, F. O., 122
Kendig, I., 197–199, 201, 204
Kent, G. H., 192
Kenyon, M., 128
Kety, S. S., 120–138
Keup, W., 121
Kihn, B., 72
King, H. E., 207–208
Klebanoff, L. B., 315
Kleist, K., 71
Kohler, W., 210
Kohn, M. L., 237, 295–318
Kolle, K., 49
Kopin, I., 137
Kosman, M. E., 107
Kraepelin, E., 6, 10, 14, 16, 49, 121, 160, 193
Kramer, M., 309
Kranz, H., 62

Krech, D., 273
Kretschmer, E., 7, 41, 44

LaBrosse, E. H., 127
Landau, D., 208
Lange, J., 63
Langfeldt, G., 17
Laurell, C. B., 96, 128–129
Lawrence, P., 296 n.
Leach, B. E., 32, 128–129
Lecky, P., 254–255
Leonhard, K., 45, 48, 71
Levin, H., 238
Ley, A., 40
Liddell, H. S., 165
Lidz, R. W., 55, 312, 348 n.
Lidz, T., 38, 55–56, 70–71, 74, 305–307, 310, 312, 323–342, 348, 358 n., 380–382, 385
Lilly, J., 252, 269
Limentani, D., 348 n.
Lindsley, O. R., 233
Leviton, R., 251
Lombroso, C., 6, 41
Lorr, M., 194
Lovinger, E., 212–213
Lowe, I. P., 132
Lubin, A., 51
Luidens, H., 74
Lundby, P., 48
Luria, A. R., 209
Luxenberger, H., 40, 43, 58–59, 61, 69–70, 72

Maas, H. S., 15
Maccoby, E. E., 238
McBride, K. B., 199 n.
McCullough, W. S., 17
McDonald, R. K., 5, 128, 130
McDougall, W., 252
McFarland, R. A., 121
McGaughran, L. S., 221, 280, 282
McGeer, P. L., 110
Mackavey, W. R., 207
McReynolds, P., 248–287,
Magruder, W. W., 71, 74
Mahler, M., 348 n.
Maier, N. R. F., 231, 269–271
Mainord, W. A., 205
Malmo, R. B., 209, 232, 240
Malzberg, B., 50
Mann, J. D., 127
Mark, J. C., 235, 305
Marrazzi, A. S., 100
Mason, A. A., 197
Masterson, J. F., 47

Maudsley, H., 8
Maxwell, J. P., 176
Meadow, A., 226, 281
Mednick, S. A., 241
Meduna, L. J., 17, 125
Melander, R., 95
Mendell, D., 56
Meyerson, P. G., 208
Miller, N. E., 241
Milton, G. A., 238
Miner, J. B., 197
Mittelmann, B., 351
Moffit, J., 258
Monashkin, I., 235
Montgomery, K., 252
Moore, T. V., 193–194
Moran, L. J., 221, 280, 282
Morel, B., 3
Morris, D. P., 44
Mott, F. W., 4
Moya, F., 125
Mueller, H. J., 56
Munson, P. L., 178
Murphy, T. W., 74
Mussen, P. H., 238

Neel, J., 46, 57, 61–62, 80
Nelson, M. M., 176
Newman, H. H., 58, 64, 76
Nissen, H., 252
Nolting, J. de S., 80

Oatman, J. G., 71–72
Oberndorf, C., 69
O'Connor, J. P., 194
Odegaard, O., 47
Olds, J., 136
Olds, M. E., 136
Oltean, M., 235
Ormiston, D., 253
Osgood, C., 273
Ovesey, L., 313

Pacht, A. R., 213
Papez, J. W., 159
Parsons, T., 337–338
Pasamanick, B., 26, 57, 61
Pascal, G. R., 229–230
Pastore, N., 81
Patterson, V., 237
Pauling, L., 38
Pavlov, I., 159, 265
Payne, R. W., 225

Peak, H., 254, 259
Penrose, L. S., 11, 43, 46, 50, 61, 65, 67
Perkins, C., 296 n.
Perlin, S., 128
Peters, H. N., 161, 209, 227–228, 231–232, 280
Pfeiffer, C. C., 104
Philip, B. R., 211
Phillips, L., 218
Piaget, J., 255
Plant, J. S., 313
Polatin, P., 17
Pollack, H. M., 50, 55
Preyer, W., 177
Price, B., 61
Prout, C. T., 30, 236

Rabin, A. I., 202, 219
Rado, S., 147–148, 150–151
Rapaport, D., 202
Raush, H. L., 212–214, 217
Redlich, F. C., 56
Rees, W. L., 42
Regensburg, J., 352
Reichard, S., 306, 348 n., 360 n.
Rennie, T. A. C., 45
Richmond, W. L., 40, 197–199, 201, 204
Richter, D., 121, 125
Riegelhaupt, L. M., 110
Robins, E., 132–133
Robinson, N. L., 230–231, 262
Rodnick, E. H., 27, 206, 218, 237, 241, 262
Roe, A., 197–201
Rogers, C., 250, 254, 259–260
Rorschach, H., 193, 213
Rosanoff, A. J., 40, 59, 61, 65
Rosenbaum, G., 207
Ross, E. L., 110
Roth, M., 49
Roumajon, Y., 49
Rubins, H. E., 73
Rudin, E., 41, 45–46, 53, 57
Rush, Benjamin, 58

Sanders, R., 213
Sano, I., 110
Saucer, R., 266
Schaefer, E. S., 235, 238, 365 n.
Schafer, S., 323 n.
Schein, E., 267
Scheinberg, P., 125
Schiene, J. F., 125
Schofield, W., 202
Schroder, H., 179, 259

Schull, W. J., 61–62, 80
Schultz, B., 28, 45–56, 48, 53, 57, 71
Schwartz, M. S., 379, 384–386
Sclare, B. A., 37
Scott, T., 252, 268
Sears, R. R., 236, 238
Senf, R., 205, 216, 223, 283
Sewell, W. H., 238
Shagass, C., 232
Shakow, D., 194, 197–201, 204, 206–209, 227–228
Shannon, D., 276
Sharpless, S., 268
Shaw, E., 134, 137
Shea, J. E., 37, 73
Sheldon, W. H., 7, 51
Sherif, M., 212
Sherwood, W. L., 110
Shipley, W. C., 200
Shoben, E. J., 235
Siegel, E. L., 215–236
Siemens, H. W., 72
Simmins, C., 200
Sivadon, P., 56
Skinner, B. F., 233
Slater, E., 28, 40–43, 50, 52, 58, 60–61, 63–66, 68, 71, 73, 75–76
Smith, A. A., 232
Smith, K., 132
Smock, C., 258–259
Sokoloff, L., 125
Soloman, H., 281
Solomon, R., 74
Sontag, L. W., 175–186
Spence, K. W., 232
Spiegel, J. P., 352
Spinley, B. M., 313
Stagner, H., 258
Stanton, A. H., 379, 384–386
Starer, E., 217
Statsky, B. A., 208
Stephens, F. E., 74
Stokes, A. B., 5
Stolze, H., 69, 72
Storch, A., 75
Strassman, H., 267
Straus, E., 267
Suinn, R., 258
Sulkowitch, H., 153
Sullivan, H. S., 6, 216, 250, 264
Swensen, C., 229–230
Szara, S., 128
Szurek, S. A., 383–448

Tannenbaum, P., 273
Taylor, J. A., 224, 232, 280–281
Terrill, J., 264
Terry, D., 323 n.
Thaler, M., 267
Thomas, J., 258
Thompson, W. R., 184–185, 214
Thudichum, J. W. L., 120–121
Tillman, C., 306, 348 n., 360 n.
Tizard, J., 206
Trendelenburg, U., 103
Troland, L., 252
Tyler, L., 255

Ullmann, L., 248, 276
Umbreit, W., 269
Urse, V. G., 125

Venable, P. H., 206
Vernon, J., 252
Vigotsky, L. S., 193
von Bracken, *see* Bracken, H. von
von Domarus, *see* Domarus, E. von
Voth, A. C., 211

Wallace, R. F., 179, 219
Wallach, H., 210
Wallner, J. M., 215
Walther-Büel, H., 75
Weakland, J., 38, 56, 262, 373–387
Weatherly, J., 74
Webb, W. W., 225, 283
Wechsler, D., 202
Weckowicz, T. C., 214
Weil, R. S., 49
Weinberg, S. K., 49, 52
Weisenburg, T., 199
Wentworth, M. M., 193
Wertheimer, M., 210
White, M. A., 30, 236
White, R., 252, 266
Whiteman, M., 222–223
Wigers, F., 72–73
Wilson, W. P., 69, 125
Winder, C. L., 191–242
Windle, W. F., 177
Winter, C. A., 131
Witt, P. N., 161, 162, 170
Wittenborn, J. R., 194
Wittman, M. P., 227
Woodworth, R., 251
Wooley, D. W., 102, 134, 137
Worchel, P., 220

Wright, H. V., 176
Wulfeck, W. H., 209
Wynne, L. C., 73, 307, 335, 358 n., 382, 384–385

Zehnder, M., 46, 50, 67
Zeller, E. A., 136
Zilboorg, G., 6, 17
Zuckerman, M., 235

Subject Index

abnormalities, congenital, 176
abstract-concrete hypothesis, 220
abstraction, 217, 278, 281
acetic acid indole, 110
acetylcholine, 101, 103–106
acetylcholinesterase, 105
ACTH (adrenocorticotrophic hormone), 16, 94–95
adaptation, symbolism in, 326
adaptive levels, 13
Addison's Disease, 9
adenosinetriphosphate, 93, 102
adolescence, 13; mother-child relationships in, 366–367; schizophrenia and, 47, 331
adrenal cortex, 5; stress and, 94, 123
adrenal glands, 5
adrenalin, 96, 99, 100, 103, 105; behavior effects of, 107–108
adrenalin oxidation, 32
adrenalin studies, 32
adrenochrome, 19, 98–100, 108, 128–129
adrenocortex, see adrenal cortex
adrenolutin, 99, 108, 128–129
affection, lack of, 39
affective expression, 397
age, male-female difference in, 50
age-level tests, 201, 215–216, 236
aggression, overt, 384
Akerfeldt test, 130
akinetic seizures, 103
albumin, 153
alcohol, 9
alcoholism, 132, 196, 383; schizophrenia and, 41, 50, 74; in twin studies, 76
amebiasis, 122
amentia, 43, 46
American Psychiatric Association, 16–17, 70
amine metabolism, 109, 126–127, 153, 160; stress and, 146–147
amphetamine, 137
amytal, 205
animal experiments, 160
anorexia, 395
anoxia, 102
antibiotics, 178

anti-insulin mechanism, 125
antimetabolites, 176
anxiety, 9, 240–241, 248–287; in childhood schizophrenia, 427; in concept formation, 225–226; described, 256, 259; exaggerated, 123; fear and, 260; incongruency and, 259; in mother-child symbiosis, 368; percept assimilation and, 255–257; as principal etiological factor, 248–249
apathy, 267–268; sexual, 405, 409, 413
arecoline, 104–105
armed forces, intelligence tests in, 196
Army Alpha subtest, 204
arthritis, 413
Arthur Performance Scale, 419
ascorbic acid, 128, 130, 153, 160
assimilation, 270, 278–279, 282–283; anxiety and, 255–261; avoidance or withdrawal and, 263–268
association, 201, 281; in identical-twin psychoses, 71
Association of Psychoanalytic Medicine, 146 n.
asthma, 395, 413
ataractic drugs, 123–124, 134
ataxia, 177
ATP, see adenosinetriphosphate
atropine, 104
auditory hallucinations, 131
autism, 133; infantile, 266
autistic thinking, 150
autointoxication theory (Kraepelin), 160
autokinetic phenomena, 211–212
autonomic nervous system, 161
avoidance, selective, 263–264, 285; withdrawal and, 263–268

β-hydroxy-pseudotryptophane, 110
basal metabolism, decrease in, 124–126; see also metabolic dysfunction
basal state, 123
bedwetting, 397
behavior analysis, 191–192
behavior theory, 241

beliefs, incongruencies and, 273–274; unreality and, 277
Bender-Gestalt test, 193, 209, 419
benzyl analogue, of serotonin, 135
beriberi, 44
Berlin, expectancy figures for, 47, 51
Binet test, 177; *see also* Stanford-Binet test
biochemistry, 91–112, 120–138, 146–154; genetics and, 31–33
biological data, 151–154
biological psychiatry, 129
Blacky test, 419
blindness, congenital, 176
blocking, 133, 269
blood, ascorbic acid level in, 128–129; serum copper levels in, 129–131
blood-brain barrier, 32, 134
blood-sugar level, in pregnancy, 183
bodily estrangement, 133
body build, 51
body chemistry, 160
body fluids, toxic substances in, 160
body image alteration, 269
body type, 41; "schizoid personality" and, 4
body weight, resistance to schizophrenia and, 42
borderline schizophrenia, 26, 44
boredom, 267
brain, amines in, 134–136; biochemical constitution of, 94; capacity of, 10; "computer model" of, 18, 138; reserpine level in, 136; serotonin level in, 135
brain cells, fetal environment and, 185; formation of, 178
brain disease, degenerative, 401
brain functions, acetylcholine in, 101; rationality and, 329
brain lesions, 325
broken home, 49–50, 55
brom-LSD, 101
bufotenine, 32, 99, 134
bulemia, 395

carbohydrate metabolism, 124–126
carbonic anhydrase, 92
carcinoma, 95
castration complex, 336
catatonia, 13, 28, 49, 96, 104, 126, 131, 160, 168, 173, 196, 199, 211, 228, 297; "acute periodic," 17; periodic, 5
catatonic stupor, 267
catechol amines, 96, 109, 131
categorizing, 281–282
cats, akinetic seizure in, 103

causation, theory of, 5
cell studies, 33
central nervous system, 179; serotonin in, 136
cerebral cortex, *see* cortex
ceruloplasmin, 32, 95–96, 129–134, 153, 160
child, inborn needs of, 324; sex-linked roles and, 329–338
child development, 327–328
childhood experiences, 295 *ff.*
childhood schizophrenia, 17, 389–433; application and intake interviews in, 417–418; cause of, 427; clinical data in, 404–417; clinical study of, 389–433; destructive behavior in, 399, 415; external-internal stresses in, 405; family dynamics and, 404–417; family histories in, 392–393; family interaction and, 414–417; motor behavior in, 398–399; outpatient study of, 419; parental relations and, 407–413; physical contact in, 396; physical development and, 401–402; psychotherapeutic work in, 422; therapeutic outcomes in, 429–430; *see also* Schizophrenic Reaction, Childhood Type
child-parent relations, *see* parent-child relationships
child rearing, 236, 238–239
children, parental love of, 314–315
Chi-Square value, 170
chlorpromazine, 101, 136
cholinergic responses, 105
cholinesterase activity, 92, 98
chromatographic analysis, of urine, 110, 127
cigarette smoking, fetal heart rate and, 179
clarification, sudden, 274–275
clinical study, methods of, 417–426
closure, 275
CNS, 103–104, 107
cognitive dissonance, 254
colitis, 413
communication, 17, 326–327; in family network, 308–309, 312
communicational approach, 387
compulsive symptoms, in childhood schizophrenia, 399–400
compulsive thoughts, 412
computer analogy, 18, 138
concealment, in double-bind, 377
concept formation, 193, 200, 220–226
concept implementation, 224–225
conceptual disorganization, 195
conceptual schemata, 253–254, 272–274, 277

conceptual thinking, 204
conditioning, 231–234
conflict-reduction, 425–426
consanguinity studies, 46, 52
constancy, 212–214
constipation, 395
constitutional factors, 9, 48, 51
copper, serum, 129–130
copper-oxidizing enzymes, 154
cortex, 132; nerve cells of, 4
cortical atrophy, progressive, 94
cortical cells, degeneration of, 41, 51
cortisone, 95
cousin marriages, 56
creatine, 123
criminality, 7, 41–42
CSF, 16
cultural anthropology, 12
culture, family and, 327
curiosity drive, 252
Cushing Syndrome, 95
cyclothymic blood, 173

deficit(s), 217–218; correlates of, 227–228; differential, 200–204; intellectual, 195–205; in psychological functioning, 240
"degeneracy," theory of, 7, 41
dclusions, 276–278, 400; anxiety and, 275; shared, 71
dementia praecox, 3, 5, 192, 199; definition of, 6; *see also* schizophrenia
denial, 377–378
depersonalization, 269
destructive behavior, 398–399, 415
deterioration, 325; concept of, 196; defined, 204–205
dexterity, 208–209
DFP, 98, 103–105
diagnosis, "interactional," 17; problem of, 17
diarrhea, 395, 411
differential deficit, 200–204
Digit Symbol, 202
diisopropylfluorophosphate (DFP), 98, 103–105
disorders, clusters of, 13–14
disorientation, 277
disturbed homes, 330–331; *see also* broken homes
dizygotic twins, 54
D.N.A., 14
double-bind, 262, 305, 432; hypothesis of, 373–387
Draw-a-Person test, 419

drug therapy, 53, 126
dysrhythmia, 403

ecdysis, 166
ecological studies, 297
eczema, 395
ego, "weak," 16
ego boundaries, loss of, 432
ego development, 328
ego distortion, 432
ego fission, 66–68
ego fusion, 66–68
ego integration, 324
ego strength, 432
Ehrlich's reagent, 110
electrical abnormality, 152
electric shock, as motivation, 230
electroencephalographic changes, 131
electroencephalographic examination, 403
electron transfer, 93
electroshock comas, 123
electroshock therapy, 9, 95, 111, 207
Elgin Prognosis Scale, 215, 221
emotional distance, 382
"emotional divorce," 354
emotional stress, 123
endocrine dysfunction, 15, 32, 94; in pregnancy, 177–178
endogenous inborn defect, 152
energetics, 124–126
England, first admissions in, 43
environmental factors, 9, 13–14
enzymatic activity, impairment of, 146
enzymatic changes, 92–97
enzyme poisons, 179
enzyme system, genetic factors and, 137–138
epidemiology, genetical, 24–25
epilepsy, 81, 152
epinephrine, clinical response to, 153; excretion of, 123, 153
epinephrine hypothesis, 127–129
Epstein test, 225
errors, in diagnosis and etiology, 121–124
erythrocyte, metabolism of, 125
escape-shock procedure, 232
eserine, 104–105
EST, *see* electroshock therapy
etiological agents, 12; *see also* schizophrenia, etiology of
eugenics, "natural," 56
excitement, pathological, 384
executive skills, in childhood, 395, 432
expectancy data, 47; in co-twins of schizophrenics, 60; evaluation of, 51–54

exploratory drive, 252
extroverts, 45

family, in child studies, 428–429; deficiencies in, 336–337; "family concept of schizophrenia" and, 346–371; formal structure of, 337; multiple psychoses in, 50; role of, 323–342; schizophrenia development in, 352–370; as single organism, 351; sociocultural matrix of, 313–316; "three-generation" concept in, 352–353
family dynamics, 346–371, 373–433
family history, 10
family interaction, in childhood schizophrenia, 414–417
family network, 306–308
family psychotherapy, 349
family quarrels, 354–356
family relationships, pathological, 149–150; *see also* interfamily relationships
family roles, analysis of, 338
family skew, 381
family studies, 7, 29, 40, 46, 48, 52, 55–56, 59, 66, 80, 149, 304–309, 332; Bowen's, 346–371; methodological critique of, 309–317
family unit, 350–351
father, occupation of, 299–302; schizophrenogenic, 306, 331–335; in three-party interaction, 379–383
father-child relationships, 363–364
father-mother-child relationships, 373 ff.
fear, anxiety and, 260
fecal smearing, 397
feeblemindedness, 42
Fels Research Institute, 175 n., 184
fetal heart rate, smoking and, 179; stimulation of, 180–181
fetal learning, 182–183
fetal-maternal endocrine system, 178
fetus, increased activity of, 184; oxygen supply to, 176–177
figure reversal, 211
Finland, schizophrenia in, 50
first admissions, 43, 296, 302
First International Congress of Genetics, 47
5-hydroxyindole acetic acid, 136
5-hydroxytryptamine, 134
5-hydroxytryptophan, 135
folic acid, 170
folie à deux, 55, 58, 64–65, 68–71, 73, 75, 77, 380
freemartins, 178

frontal lobotomy, 162
fruitfly, 167–172

gamma-amino-butyric acid, 137
gargoylism, 93
general paralysis of the insane (paresis), 7–8
genes, mutilated, 25
genetical diseases, identification of, 24
genetical evidence, etiology and, 28–29
genetical prerequisite, 31
genetical research, objectives of, 24–25
genetical-statistical methods, 28
genetic factors, enzymes and, 137–138; vs. experimental, 317
genetics, biochemistry and, 31–33; critique of literature on, 37–81; medical, 24; penetrance in, 29–30
genetic studies, 7, 55–56
German psychiatry, 41
gliosis, 4
globus pallidus, 92
glucose tolerance, 16
glutathione, 125, 132
glyoxylic test, 110
goiter, 15
Goldstein-Gelb-Weigl test, 221
"goodness of fit," 282–283
grandiosity, 195
group dynamics, 12
guilt feelings, in sisters, 67–68

Hagerstown (Md.) study, 298–304, 311
hallucination (s), 5; in childhood schizophrenia, 401; experimental, 269; problem of, 269–272
hallucinogenic agents and drugs, 96–97, 108, 126, 128, 131, 134, 269; chemical structure of, 99
hand-mouth activities, 397
hebephrenia, 78, 196, 199, 201, 211, 228, 277
hereditary "vulnerability," 80
heredity, 7; mental illness and, 24; "poor," 41–42; social, 7, 9
heterozygotes, 29
histamine, 99, 102–103, 105, 147
homeostasis, physiological, 325
homosexual fears, 67, 69, 73
homosexual impulses, 326, 333, 336, 340, 413
homosexuality, in twins, 73
homozygotes, 29
Hospital Adjustment Scale, 194
hospitalization, duration of, 302–304; as selective avoidance, 285

hostile-dependent attachment, 68
Hullian tradition, 260
human integration, 323–342
humoral agents, in pregnancy, 183
Huntington's chorea, 43, 94
Hutterites, studies of, 49
hydrocephalus, 175
hyperglycemic activity, 92, 125
hypertension, 95, 413
hypnotic drugs, 123
hypochondriacal delusions, 104–105
hypoglyccmia, 178
hypophyseal-adrenocortical axis, 94
hypothalamus, 102, 107, 214
hysteria, 5

identical twins, 58, 61–62, 71–80
identification, 69
Illinois Neuropsychiatric Institute, 390
Illinois State Mental Health Fund, 91
imidazoles, in urine, 126
inadequacy feelings, 360
inbreeding, 24
incest, 326, 339, 341
incongruency, 253, 262, 264, 283, 387; percepts and, 257
Indo-China, studies in, 49
indoles, 101, 110, 126, 137
infant care, 338
information, utilization of, by brain, 18
inheritance factors, 29–31; single- and double-, 46; *see also* genetics
inhibition, 264–267, 377-378
inkblot test, 193, 214–217, 236, 282
Institute for Juvenile Research, 390
insulin, tolerance to, 92
insuline coma, 95, 123
insulin shock, 111
insulin shock therapy, 9, 12
intake interview, 418
intellectual deficit, 195–205
intellectual deterioration, 204–205
intelligence quotient, *see* IQ
intelligence tests, 192, 196, 203–204, 224–225; childhood schizophrenia and, 419
interfamily relations, 301; impaired, 149
internal-external discrimination, 270–271
interpersonal relationships, 301–302, 333; history of, 234–239; maladjustment and, 38
interviewing, therapeutic, 332
iproniazid, 136

IQ (intelligence quotient), 14, 16, 202–203; in twin studies, 76
isolation, social, 300–301, 325

jealousy, 69–70

kinesthetic images, 210
Korsakov's psychosis, 94

labeling, fiction of, 11, 18
Laboratory of Clinical Science, 124
Langley Porter Neuropsychiatric Institute, 383 n.
learning deficit, 228
learning studies, 226–234
learning theory, 12
leprosy, 42
leptosomic build, 7, 15
lipid metabolism, 93
Lissajou figures, 211
liver disease, 95, 122
lobotomy, frontal, 162
logic, development of, 328–329
Los Angeles Mental Health Association, 159
love, parental, 314–315, 338
LSD, 18, 32, 97–100, 106, 108, 134–135, 138, 159, 161; pleasant experience with, 6; schizophrenia and, 5
LSD psychoses, experimental, 32
lysergic acid diethylamide, 128, 134–135, 161

manic-depressive psychosis, 10–11, 43, 57, 71, 104, 196, 299, 387
marijuana, 98
marriage, 13; disturbed, 332–333; marital schism in, 381; schizophrenia and, 315–317
maternal emotions, 356–358; during pregnancy, 183–185
mathematical techniques, 80
maturity, family and, 327; vs. immaturity, in family schizophrenia, 353–354
meanings, development of, 329
Mecholyl test, 15
Mendelian genetics, 25, 29, 41
mental defect, in Negroes, 57, 61; schizophrenia and, 41–42
mental disease, chemical approach to, 91–112; as public-health problem, 23
Mental Disorders in Urban Areas, 296
mental hospitals, first admissions to, 43, 296, 302

mental illness, democratic ideas and, 3; heredity of, 24; public interest in, 3; time factor in, 39
mental retardation, 132
mepharsan, 178
mescaline, 97–99, 161
mesodermal resistance, 41
"mesodermal weakness," 53–54
metabolic dysfunction, 25, 32–33, 54, 123–126, 160, 210; inborn, 93, 147
metabolites, 110, 127, 160–161; relation of, to psychoses, 106–112
methemoglobinemia, 93
methodological critique, in family studies, 309–317
mislabeling, 18
mitochondria, 109–110
"model psychosis," concept of, 97, 112
Mongolism, 61, 176
monoamine oxidase, 101
monosynaptic reflexes, 102
monozygotic twins, 30, 33, 54, 57, 61
morbid risk, table of, 27
morbidity studies, 53, 298
Morgnani's Syndrome, 42
mother, emotional demand of, 367–368; emotional stabilization of, 364–365; emotions during pregnancy, 183–185; as "magnetic field," 367; as primary love object, 334; sexual inhibition in, 413; sharing of, 73; symbiotic attachment to, 348, 365–366; "threats" of, 366; in three-party interaction, 379–383; *see also* schizophrenogenic mother
mother-child equilibrium, 357, 364
mother-child relationship, 50, 150, 218, 234–239, 298, 305–306, 333–334, 348, 359; projection in, 360–362
mother-infant symbiosis, 348, 365–366
motherhood, physical gratification and, 316
motor behavior, in childhood schizophrenia, 298–399
Multidimensional Rating Scale, 194
multiple-choice learning task, 231
multiple-level analysis, 226 ff.
murderous impulses, 341
mushroom, hallucinogenic, 98
mutation, 25; language and, 326–327; *see also* genetics
myelinization, 178

n, n-diethyltryptamine, 32
n, n-dimethyltryptamine, 32
nail bed, 125

National Institute of Mental Health, 130
nature-nurture problem, 72, 81
Negroes, mental defect in, 57, 61; schizophrenia in, 72
neobehaviorism, 191
neostigmin, 105
nerve cells, alteration in, 4
neuramic acid, 93
neuroanatomy, 12
neurochemistry, 111
neurohumoral amines, 91, 97–106, 111; disturbance of, 107
neurohumoral transmission, central, 103
neuromuscular development, childhood schizophrenia and, 402
neuron, cerebral, 102; depolarization of, 106–107
neuropharmacology, 111
neurophysiology, 12
neurosis, distinguished from schizophrenia, 284; stress in, 151
neurotics, 213, 220; in armed forces, 197
neurotropic agents, 106
newborn, mature, 182
New York, schizophrenia expectancy figures for, 47
Niemann-Pick's disease, 93
nitrogen balance, 5
nitrogen metabolism, 126
N-methyl-3-piperidyl, 96
noradrenalin, 107
norepinephrine, 123, 135
Norway, schizophrenia incidence in, 48
nosology, problem of, 17, 44
nucleotides, 105
nutrition, 5; prenatal, 175–176; *see also* metabolic dysfunction; vitamin deficiency

obesity, 413
object relationships, 326; intrafamilial, 330
occupational groups, 299, 301–302
Oedipal phases, 331, 338
oligodendroglia, 102
"Oneirophrenia," 17
operant conditioning, 233–234
organic factors, 12
outpatient studies, 419–421
overadequacy, maternal, 354, 359–360, 363
overinclusiveness, 224–225, 280
overpossessiveness, 315–316
overprotection, 359–360
oxindolyalamine, 110
oxygen metabolism, 124–126
oxygen supply, to fetus, 176–177

pain, anxiety and, 260
panic, 151, 326, 395
paradoxical reaction time, 206
parallel play, 396
paralogical thinking, 333
paranoia, 13, 49, 202, 312; chronic, 9
paranoid delusions, 104, 220
paranoid disorders, 49
paranoid projection, 195
paranoid schizophrenia, 199
paraphrenia, 17
parent (s), 304, 308–309; disturbed, 333; in evaluation of childhood-schizophrenia patient, 420–421; interactions with child, 414–417 (*see also* parent-child relationships); interdependency of, 337; in joint therapeutic interviews, 424; love of children in, 314–315; phobias of, 412; quarreling between, 354–356; sexual apathy in, 413; *see also* schizophrenogenic mother
parental conflict, 325
parental maturity, 354
parental relationships, childhood schizophrenia and, 407–413; discrepancies in, 410–411; *see also* parent-child relationships
parent-attitude scale, 235
parent-child relationships, 312–315, 324, 335; three-party interaction in, 379–383
parenthood, 13
paresis, 7–8
"patient-as-a-whole" concept, 11–12
Pavlov, Ivan, 232
penetrance, concept of, in genetics, 29–30
percept(s), assimilation of, 253–255, 270, 272; defined, 250; influx of, 251–253, 257
perception, 18, 248–287
perception theory, 12
perceptual disorder, 195
perceptualization, 250–255; rate of, 286; withdrawal and, 277
personality development, 308
personality disorder, 403
personality disorganization, 324
personality inventories, 193
personality theory, 12
phenogenetics, 25
phenolic acids, in urine, 127
phenotypes, 147
phenotypical defect, 43
phenylamine metabolism, 93
phenylenediamine, 129
phenylketonuria, 93, 110, 419
phenylpyruvic amentia, 43, 46

Phillips scale, 218
Phlogetan, 53
phobias, parental, 412
phosphorylation oxidative, 125
phthisic constitution, 7
physical contact, among schizophrenic children, 396
physical development, in childhood schizophrenia, 401, 428
"physical" diseases, 44
physiological abnormalities, 14
physiology, 159–186; schizophrenia and, 5
Picture Completion Test, 202
piperidyl benzilates, 105
polypeptides, 105
population density, 56
population studies, 80
porphyria, 93
placental barrier, 178–179
plasma oxidase, 154
pre-eclamptic toxemia, 177
pregnancy, childhood schizophrenia and, 406–407; husband-wife relationships in, 356–357; nutritional deficiency in, 176; toxemia of, 177
premorbid adjustment, 217–218, 239
premorbid intellectual efficiency, 197–198
premorbid personality, 8, 237–238
prenatal environment, 175–186
prenatal nutrition, 175–176
prepsychotic personality, 45
presenile psychoses, 94
problem solving, 220–226
process features, 14, 16
projection, 360–362
propositi, in genetic studies, 30–31
proprioceptive defect, 151
proprioceptive diathesis, 148
"protoplasmic inferiority," 6–7
proverbs, interpretation of, 221
pseudocholinesterase, 92
pseudohermaphrodism, 178
pseudomutuality, 307, 382, 385
pseudoneurotic schizophrenia, 17
Psilocybe Mexicana, 98
psiloscibine, 99, 100
psychiatrist, custodial role of, 6
psychic development, assimilation in, 255
psychoanalytical theories, 6
psychodynamics, 12, 66–67; factors in, 147; stress and, 150
psychoendocrine stimulation, 183
psychogenic trauma, 39–40
psychological causation, 15

psychological functioning, deficits in, 240
psychological studies, 14
psychological tests, 12, 16–17; *see also* intelligence tests
psychology, 191–242, 248–287
psychomotor functioning, 205–210
psychoneurology, 18
psychoneurosis, 11, 403; *see also* neurosis; neurotics
psychosis, by association, 69; metabolites and, 106–112; period of, 198–200
psychosomatic illness, 413
Psychotherapeutic Intervention in Schizophrenia, 352 n.
psychotherapeutic interview, 423–425
psychotherapeutic studies, family and, 428–429
psychotherapy, 148, 151; in childhood schizophrenia, 422–423; major purpose of, 285; outcomes of, 429–430
psychotic behavior, 152
psychotic children, 450 *ff.*
psychotic reorganization, 224
psychotomimetic agents, 98–100, 129, 137, 160–161
punishment, as motivation, 262; reward and, 228–230, 240
putamen, 92

quarreling, family, 354–356
quinine, 178

racial superiority, 6
rapport, 230, 278
rating scales, 194
rationality, development of, 328–329
reaction-sensitivities (Cameron), 276
reaction time, 205–207
reactive features, 14, 16
reality, limiting of, 264; perception of, 329; structure of, 272–277
reality distortion, 272
recessivity, vs. dominance, 46
regression, 196, 327
rejection, maternal, 369
"religious insanity," 49
remembering, 192
reserpine, 32, 102, 105–106, 134
response system, 210
restructuring, 253, 255, 286
reward and punishment, 228–231, 240
riboflavin deficiency, 94
rickets, fetal, 176

Rorschach test, 16, 193, 214–217, 236, 282, 419
"rubber fence," concept of, 383

sado-masochistic behavior, 395, 432
Sanovitan, 53
scapegoat role, 337
schisis, degree of, 409, 432
schizo-affective form, 17
schizoform psychoses, 52
schizoid personality, 9; described, 44
schizophrenia, "acute," 122; adolescent, 47; age-level of, 215; ambulatory, 17; anticipation of, as entity, 33; anxiety and, 240–241, 248–287; in armed forces, 196; assumptions in, 14–15; avoidance and withdrawal in, 263–268; beliefs in, 273–274; biochemical concept of, 38; biochemistry of, 91–112; biological data on, 151–154; biological theory of, 58; "blindness" about, 347–348; body type and, 4; borderline (*see* borderline schizophrenia); catatonic (*see* catatonia); "cause" of, 261; childhood (*see* childhood schizophrenia); concept formation and problem solving in, 220–226; conditioning in, 231–233; "cortical degeneration" and, 41; cyclic, 45; defined, 193–195, 325; deteriorating and nondeteriorating, 54; diagnosis and data in, 10–13; as "disease" or "disorder," 4, 6–10; distinguished from neurosis, 284; dominance vs. recessivity in, 46; double-bind hypothesis of, 373–387; drug therapy in, 53; early and late development periods in, 331; educational-level percentages in, 197; enzymatic changes in, 92–97; etiological agent of, 5; etiological dichotomy in, 4; etiology of, 4, 6, 26; expectancy figures (Kallmann), 47; family concept of, 346–371; family role in, 323–342; fiction in labeling of, 11; *folie à deux* and, 69–70; Freud's and Kraepelin's etiological theories of, 6; "fundamental symptoms" of, 147; future diagnosis and treatment in, 13–19; hebephrenic, 28, 49, 196, 199, 201, 211, 228, 277; human integration and, 323–342; hysteria and, 5; general considerations regarding, 261–263, 347–348; genetically determined, 79–80, 146; genetic studies in, 40 *ff.*; genetic transmission of, 11, 29–31, 46; as genotype, 44; goiter and, 15; incidence and chronicity of, 3, 296–297; "inheritance" of, 11, 29–31; interpersonal-rela-

tionship history in, 234–239; "key" to, 10; Kraepelinian categories of, 16; learning in, 226–234; as major medical problem, 3; methodological critique of family studies in, 309–317; morbidity figures, 53; morbid risk of, 26–28; multiple causation of, 14; as "neurosis," 151; nondeteriorating, 62; nosological labels in, 17; as organic disease or disorder, 12–13; paranoid type, 28; parents' role in, 234–239 (*see also* parent); perception in, 210–220, 248–287; perceptualization process in, 250–255; persistence of, 284–285; physiology of, 159–186; prenatal environment and, 175–186; prognosis in, 8–9; pseudoneurotic, 17; psychoanalytical approach to, 6; psychodynamic thesis in, 66–67; as psychogenic disorder, 13, 38; psychological studies of, 191–242; psychology of, 191–287; psychomotor functioning in, 205–210; "reactive, atypical" (Leonhard), 45; recent biochemical theories of, 120–138; relation to other diseases, 50–51; religion and, 49; research in, 11–12; "resistance" to, 53; same-sexedness and concordance for, in twins, 64; vs. schizoform psychoses, 52; shock therapy in, 9; simple type, 9, 211; single-factor inheritance in, 38; social isolation and, 300–301, 325; sociology of, 295–318; as somatopsychic disease, 186; sources of error in, 121–124; subtypes of, 199; symptom determinants in, 283–284; syphilis and, 7–8; thought disturbances in, 277–283; treatment implications of, 285–286; tuberculosis and, 7, 42, 50–51, 53, 76, 413; twin studies in (*see* twin studies); unique features of, 8–9; *see also* dementia praecox; schizophrenic patient; schizophrenic psychoses, etc.

schizophrenic patient, families of, 304–309 (*see also* family; family studies); identity problem of, 66; laboratory tests on, 32; spinal fluid from, 111; stress in, 150–151

schizophrenic psychoses, epidemiology of, 26–28; genetic aspects of, 23–33; occurrence of, 26

Schizophrenic Reaction, Childhood Type, 394–404

schizophrenic urine, 32–33, 43, 110–111, 123, 125, 162

schizophrenogenic father, 306, 334–335

schizophrenogenic mother, 150, 234–235, 238, 298, 305–306, 314–317, 334

schizotype, 147–148

Scottish Rite Mason's Grant, 91

security, need for, 329

self-awareness, therapist's, 425

self-concept, 219–220

self-esteem, 325

sensory threshold, 192

sensual drives, 395, 431

"separation protection" (Luxenburger), 70

serotonin, 32, 98–102, 105, 134–137, 160

serum copper, increase in, 129

17-ketosteroid, 16, 95

sex-role identification, 301–302

sexual apathy, 405, 409, 413

sexual equilibrium, 70

sexual identity, 334, 340

sexual organs, degeneration of, 51

sexual relations, parental, 338

shoestring-tying, 402

siblings, normal, 340, 349

sibling studies, 30, 45–46, 48, 52, 58, 67, 73

simple schizophrenia, 9, 211

"sinful" thoughts, 412

sisters, "closeness" in, 67

slum life, 297

smooth muscle, serotonin action on, 134

social factors, 14; vs. biological, 39

social heredity, *see* heredity, social

social isolation, 300–301, 325

social mobility, 299

social organization, 26

social-psychological theory, 295

social status, 296

Society of Biological Psychiatry, 146 n.

socio-economic factors, 42, 48, 57, 61, 299, 332

sociology, 12, 295–318

sodium salicylate, 178

somatotyping, 4

speech development, in childhood schizophrenia, 396–397

spider, schizophrenic serum effect on, 159–174

spinal fluid, studies of, 33; substances in, 111

spinal tap, 420

Stanford-Binet tests, 193, 200–201, 204, 419

startle reflex, in fetus, 179

starvation, 39

statistical studies, 80

stimulation, fetal response to, 179

stimulus, vs. deficit, 240

stimulus content, 217, 221–224

stimulus needs, 251–253

stimulus-response formulations, 192, 250, 266
stress, development of, 150–151
stroking, in childhood schizophrenia, 398–399
subgroup differences, 227
subjective bias, 123
subtypes, 199; Kraepelinian, 193
sucking, 397–398
suicide tendencies, 326, 384
Sulfoan, 53
sulfonamides, 178
Sweden, schizophrenic data in, 43, 47; twin studies in, 59
Switzerland, schizophrenic studies in, 80
symbolic distortions, 328–330
symbolic functioning, in adaptation, 326
symbolism, 217
symptomatology, classic, 147; clinical, 12
symptom formation, 148
synaptic transmission, 99
syndromes, schizophrenic, 30–31
syphilis, paresis and, 7–8

tachycardia, 133
tapping, speed of, 207–208
taraxein, 18, 32, 96, 129–134, 146; brain activity and, 154; isolation of, 152
Tay-Sachs disease, 93
10⁻⁶ M, 109
Terman Vocabulary Test, 200
Thematic Apperception Test (TAT), 193, 218–219, 419
therapist, in childhood schizophrenia, 425–426
thiamine, 94
thinking, "reasonable," 328–329; *see also* thought disorders
thought disorders, 277–283
threat and anxiety, in concept formation, 225–226
"three generation" concept, 352–353
three-party interaction, 373–387
Thurstone test, 203–204
thyroid function, 12, 123
thyrotoxicosis, 95
time concepts, 219
time factor, in mental illness, 15, 39
toxic psychoses, 135
toxin-X (Jung), 160
tranquilizers, 100–102, 286
transcallosal region, 107
trauma, childhood, 30, 39–40, 231; in childhood schizophrenia, 430–431

tryptophan load, 136–137
tuberculosis, schizophrenia and, 7, 42, 50–51, 53, 76, 413
Tulane University group, 128, 130–132, 150
"twin psychosis," 74; *see also folie à deux*
twin studies, 28, 30, 33, 38, 40, 42, 44, 47, 49–50, 52–54; concordant twins in, 61–62, 64–65, 71; homosexuality and, 73; identical twin cases, 58, 71–80; like-sexed and opposite-sexed, 60–61, 64–65, 67–68; literature on, 57–80; photographs in, 64; reservations about, 61–66; third party in, 74; uniovular and biovular, 63
2-brom-LSD, 135
two-person interaction, 374–379

ulcer, 413
United States, expectancy figures for, 51–52
unreality feelings, 277
urine, amine substances in, 153; aromatic compounds in, 126; laboratory studies of, 32–33, 43, 125, 162; organic substances in, 109–111; volume and concentration of, 123
uroporphyrin, 93

venous distention, 133
verbalization, 105, 326, 359; association and, 281
Veterans Administration, 197, 373 n.
Vineland Social Maturity Scale, 419
Virchowian pathology, 7
vitamin deficiency, 94, 122, 126, 175–176
vocabulary scores, 200, 222–223

ward living, in family studies, 349–350
web formation, in *Zilla-x-notata* spider, 160–162, 166–167
Wechsler Intelligence Scale, 419
Wechsler-Bellevue Verbal Scale, 202, 204–205, 222–223
white superiority, 6
"William Wilson," 66
Wilson's disease, 95
withdrawal, 195, 330, 410
word association, 192
World Health Organization (WHO), 26

Xenopus levis, 131

Yale Psychiatric Institute, 323 n., 331

Zilla-x-notata, 159–174

616.8982
J13